Physics

E orse CE Physics A

Heinemann is an imprint of Pearson Education Limited, a company incorporated in England and Wales, having its registered office at Edinburgh Gate, Harlow, Essex CM20 2JE. Registered company number: 872828

www.heinemann.co.uk

Heinemann is a registered trademark of Pearson Education Limited

First published 2008

12 11 10 09 08
10 9 8 7 6 5 4 3 2 1

British Library Cataloguing in Publication Data
A catalogue record for this book is available from the British Library

ISBN 978 0 435691 95 0

Edited by Emma Hoyle
Index compiled by Wendy Simpson
Glossary and module summaries compiled by Graham Bone
Designed by Kamae Design
Project managed and typeset by Wearset Ltd, Boldon, Tyne and Wear
Original illustrations © Pearson Education Limited 2008
Illustrated by Wearset Ltd, Boldon, Tyne and Wear
Picture research by Wearset Ltd, Boldon, Tyne and Wear
Cover photo from the Hubble Space Telescope of a dust shell around the star v838 Monocerotis
© Science Photo Library/NASA/ESA/STSCI/H. Bond
Printed in China (SWTC/01)

Acknowledgements
We would like to thank the following for their invaluable help in the development and trialling of this course: Graham Bone, Amanda Hawkins, Dave Keble, Maggie Perry, Gareth Price, Simon Smith and Carol Tear.

The authors and publisher would like to thank the following for permission to reproduce photographs:

p3 Bernhard Edmaier/Science Photo Library; **p14 M** Edward Kinsman/Science Photo Library; **p14 B** TRL Ltd./Science Photo Library; **p17** CERN/Science Photo Library; **p23** NASA/Science Photo Library; **p29** Mark Thomas/Science Photo Library; **p30 MR** AJ Photo/ Science Photo Library; **p30 BL** Horst Reinhelt; **p32** Mark Simons/ California Institute Of Technology, 1997/Science Photo Library; **p36** NASA/Science Photo Library; **p37** NASA/Science Photo Library; **p38** Detlev Van Ravenswaay/Science Photo Library; **p40** David Ducros/ Science Photo Library; **p41 M** NOAA/Science Photo Library; **p41 B** Worldsat International/Science Photo Library; **p50** Robert Hutchings; **p51** Science Photo Library; **p53** Alfred Pasieka/Science Photo Library; **p59** Geospace/Science Photo Library; **p72** Bernhard Edmaier/Science Photo Library; **p73** Martin Dohrn/ Science Photo Library; **p74** Andrew Lambert Photography/Science Photo Library; **p75** Patricia Lu; **p79** Clive Freeman/Biosym Technologies/Science Photo Library; **p89** Jack Finch/Science Photo Library; **p96** Roger Harris/Science Photo Library; **p98** David Taylor /Science Photo Library; **p99 TL** Maximilian Stock Ltd./Science Photo Library; **p99 TR** James King-Holmes/Science Photo Library; **p99 MR** Spencer Grant/ Science Photo Library; **p104** James Holmes/Oxford Centre For Molecular Sciences/Science Photo Library; **p105** TEK Image/Science Photo Library; **p106** Andrew Lambert Photography/Science Photo Library; **p113** Maximilian Stock Ltd./Science Photo Library; **p115 R** Chris B. Stock/Science Photo Library; **p115 L** Andrew Lambert Photography/Science Photo Library; **p125** Ton Kinsbergen/Science Photo Library; **p126** Andrew Lambert Photography/Science Photo Library; **p134** Sandia National Labatory; **p135** Andrew Lambert Photography/ Science Photo Library; **p143** CERN/Science Photo Library; **p144** Adam Hart-Davis/Science Photo Library; **p151 T** Science Photo Library; **p151 B** Brookhaven National Laboratory/ Science Photo Library; **p156** N. Feather/Science Photo Library; **p157 T** Andrew Lambert Photography/Science Photo Library; **p157 M** C. Powell, P. Fowler & D. Perkins/Science Photo Library; **p157 B** Goronwy Tudor Jones, University Of Birmingham/ Science Photo Library; **p164 T** James King-Holmes /Science Photo Library; **p164 B** James King-Holmes/Science Photo Library; **p165 T** Cordelia Molloy/ Science Photo Library; **p165 M** Martin Bond/Science Photo Library; **p171 T** SKYSCAN/Science Photo Library; **p171 B** Steve Allen/ Science Photo Library; **p173** ITER/Science Photo Library; **p183** Alfred Pasieka/Science Photo Library; **p184** Science Photo Library; **p189 T** Antonia Reeve/Science Photo Library; **p189 B** Science Photo Library; **p190 L** Zephyr/ Science Photo Library; **p190 M** Living Art Enterprises, LLC./Science Photo Library; **p190 R** Living Art Enterprises,LLC./ Science Photo Library; **p192 T** Bob Sciarrino/Star Ledger/Corbis; **p192 B** Prof. J. Leveille/Science Photo Library; **p193 TR** Pascal Goetgheluck/Science Photo Library; **p193 M** Dr John Mazziota et al/ NEUROLOGY/Science Photo Library; **p194** Colin Cuthbert/Science Photo Library; **p196** Spencer Grant/Science Photo Library; **p197** Sovereign, ISM/Science Photo Library; **p197** Simon Fraser/Science Photo Library; **p200** Saturn Stills/Science Photo Library; **p202** Sovereign, ISM/Science Photo Library; **p205 M** Susan Leavines/ Science Photo Library; **p205 TR** Dr Najeeb Layyous/Science Photo Library; **p211** European Southern Observatory/Science Photo Library; **p212 ML** Robert Gendler/Science Photo Library; **p212 BL** Canada-France-Hawaii Telescope/Jean-Charles Cuillandre/Science Photo Library; **p213 TR** John Chumack/Science Photo Library; **p213 MR** Eckhard Slawik/Science Photo Library; **p213 BR** David Nunuk/ Science Photo Library; **p214 TL** NASA/Science Photo Library; **p214 M** Davide De Martin/Science Photo Library; **p216 ML** Jerry Lodriguss/ Science Photo Library; **p216 BL** Dr. Fred Espenek/Science Photo Library; **p216 MR** NASA/ESA/STSCI/M.Karovska, Harvard CFA/ Science Photo Library; **p216 BR** NOAO/Science Photo Library; **p217** NASA/Science Photo Library; **p224** Mark Garlick/Science Photo Library; **p225** Detlev Van Ravenswaay/Science Photo Library

Every effort has been made to contact copyright holders of material reproduced in this book. Any omissions will be rectified in subsequent printings if notice is given to the publisher.

Websites
There are links to websites relevant to this book. In order to ensure that the links are up-to-date, that the links work, and that links are not inadvertently made to sites that could be considered offensive, we have made the links available on the Heinemann website at www. heinemann.co.uk/hotlinks. When you access the site, the express code is 1950P.

Exam Café student CD-ROM

Original illustrations, screen designs and animation by Michael Heald
Photographs © iStock Ltd
Developed by Elektra Media Ltd

Technical problems
If you encounter technical problems whilst running this software, please contact the Customer Support team on 01865 888108 or email software.enquiries@heinemann.co.uk

OCR

Physics

Exclusively endorsed by OCR for GCE Physics A

Roger Hackett and Robert Hutchings

www.heinemann.co.uk

✓ Free online support
✓ Useful weblinks
✓ 24 hour online ordering

01865 888080

In Exclusive Partnership

Contents

Introduction

How to use this book

In this book you will find a number of features planned to help you.

- **Module opener pages** – these carry an introductory paragraph to set the context for the topics covered in the module. They also have a short set of questions that you should already be able to answer from your AS course or from your general knowledge.
- **Double-page spreads** filled with information about each topic together with some questions you should be able to answer when you have worked through the spread. The final question may be more challenging.
- **End-of-module summary pages** to help you link all the topics within each module together.
- **End-of-module examination questions** selected to show you the types of question that may appear in your examination.

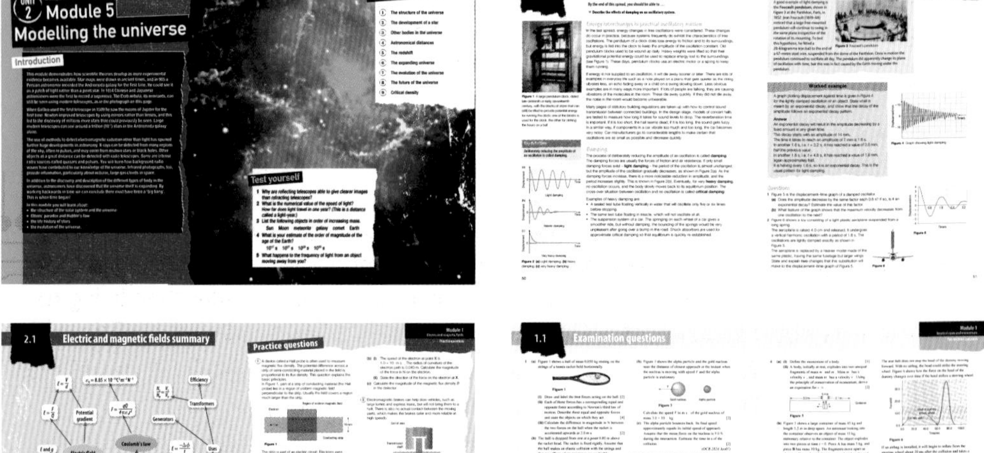

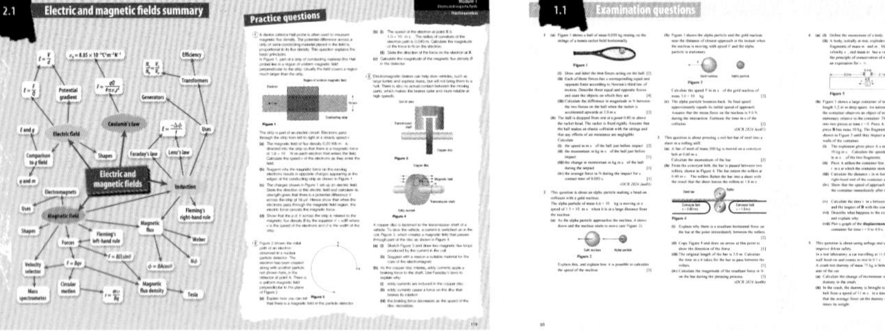

Within each double-page spread you will find other features to highlight important points.

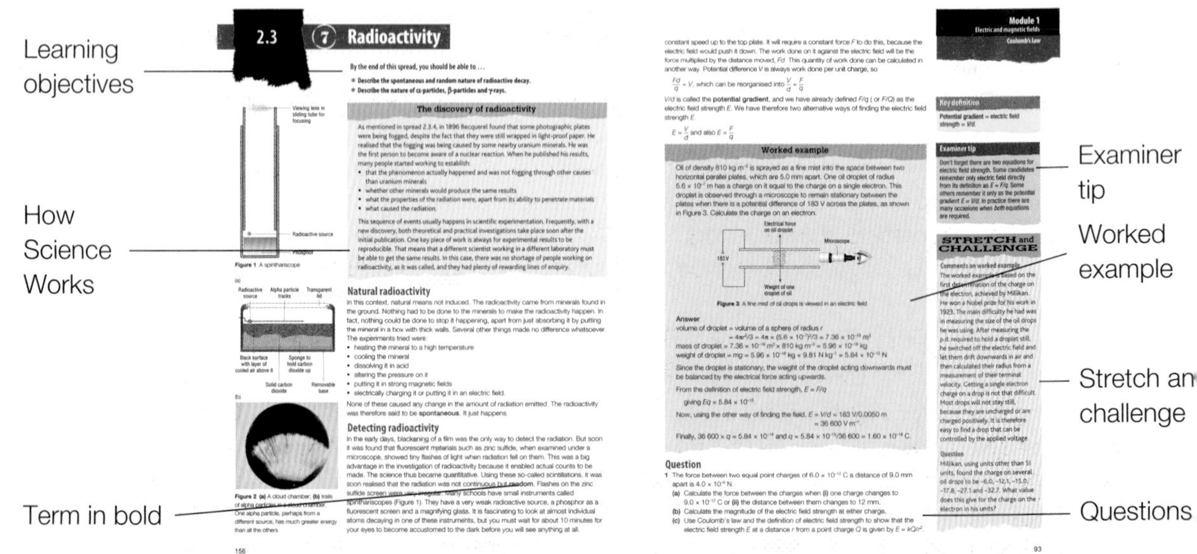

- **Learning objectives** – these are taken from the Physics A2 specification to highlight what you need to know and to understand.
- **Key definitions** – these terms appear in the specification. You must know the definitions and how to use them.
- **Terms in bold** – these draw attention to terms that you are expected to know. These are important terms with specific meanings used by physicists. Each term in bold is listed in the glossary at the end of the book.
- **Examiner tips** – these will help you avoid making common errors in the examination.
- **Worked examples** – these show you how calculations should be set out.
- **How Science Works** – this book has been written in a style that reflects the way that scientists work. Certain sections have been highlighted as good examples of How Science Works.
- **Stretch and Challenge** – these boxes will help you to develop the skills you need to tackle Stretch and Challenge questions on your final examination. You do not have to learn extra information, but you will need to make links across work you've met at AS and A2 and to be able to apply your existing knowledge in unfamiliar contexts.

The examination

It is useful to know some of the language used by examiners. Often this means just looking closely at the wording used in each question on the paper. When you first read a question, do so carefully. Once you have read something incorrectly, it is very difficult to get the incorrect wording out of your head.

- Look at the number of **marks allocated** to a part question – ensure you write enough points down to gain these marks. Do not repeat yourself. Different marks are for different ideas. The number of marks is a guide to the depth of treatment required for the answer.
- Look for words in **bold**. These are meant to draw your attention.
- Look for words in *italics*. These are often used for emphasis.
- **Diagrams, tables and equations** often communicate an idea better than trying to explain everything in sentences. Diagrams can usually be drawn freehand. For example, some candidates waste valuable time drawing electrical circuit diagrams in which every tiny line is drawn with a ruler.
- Write legibly. You cannot be given any marks for something that is illegible.

Look for the **action word**. Make sure you know what each word means, and answer what it asks. The meanings of some action words are listed below.

- *Define:* only a formal statement of a definition is required.
- *Explain:* a supporting argument is required using your knowledge of physics. The depth of the answer should be judged from the mark allocated.
- *State:* a concise answer is expected, with little or no supporting argument.
- *List:* give a number of points with no elaboration. If you are asked for *two* points then only give two!
- *Describe:* state in words, using diagrams where appropriate, the main points of the topic.
- *Discuss:* give a detailed account of the points involved in the topic.
- *Deduce/Predict:* make a logical connection between pieces of information given.
- *Outline:* restrict the answer to essential detail only.
- *Suggest:* you are expected to apply your knowledge and understanding to a 'novel' situation that you may not have covered in the specification.
- *Calculate:* a numerical answer is required. Working should be shown.
- *Determine:* the quantity cannot be obtained directly. A sequence of calculations may be required.
- *Sketch:* a diagram is required. A graph need only be qualitatively correct, but important points on the graph may require numerical values.

Checking your work all the time is essential. Check each line in your working. Check that an answer is realistic; check that its units are possible; check that it answers the question. If you wait until the end of the examination you may not have time and you will have forgotten the detail of a numerical question. If you do have time at the end of the examination, read through your descriptive answers to ensure that what you wrote is what you intended to write.

UNIT 1

Module 1 Newton's laws and momentum

Introduction

You are familiar with many ideas concerning motion from your AS course. In this module we will study Newton's laws further and look at momentum. Momentum is particularly important, because it is always conserved. Many aspects of Newton's work have been modified since Einstein's theory of relativity and quantum theory for atomic structure were developed, but the law of conservation of momentum remains.

Conservation of momentum enables astronomers to make calculations about collisions taking place between large bodies in space. We can also calculate the probable effects of the collision of a large meteorite with the Earth. The photograph is an aerial view of the Wolf Creek meteorite crater on the edge of the Great Sandy Desert, Western Australia. The crater was formed when a meteorite weighing thousands of tonnes collided with the Earth 1–2 million years ago. It had as much kinetic energy as an atomic bomb and produced a crater with a diameter of 853 metres. The meteorite's momentum would have been added to the Earth's momentum, causing a small percentage change. Collisions of large meteorites with the Earth are very rare events, and if a meteorite collided with the Earth today it would probably land in the sea or in a barren place, since these regions occupy a large fraction of the Earth's surface. If it landed in the sea it would do surprisingly little damage. Atom bombs have been exploded under the sea and the resulting wave is far smaller than the tsunami of Boxing Day 2004. However, there is a tiny but finite possibility that one could land on London.

Conservation of momentum is also important for nuclear physicists. By observing the collisions between nuclear particles they can establish the mass of the particles.

Module contents

Test yourself

1. Can you still define acceleration?
2. What unit is used for each of the following quantities: displacement, velocity, acceleration, force, work, energy, power?
3. What is the difference between mass and weight?
4. Kinetic energy is the energy stored in a moving body that gives it the ability to do work. Put the correct symbols into the equation

   kinetic energy = work done.

1.1 (1) Newton's first law

By the end of this spread, you should be able to ...

- **State and use Newton's first law of motion.**

Introduction

If you look at the rim of a £2 coin you will see the inscription 'Standing on the shoulders of giants'. This is Newton's acknowledgement of the benefit he received from such people as Copernicus, Brahe, Kepler and Galileo. Copernicus is recognised as the first person to challenge the view that the Sun rotated around the Earth. There were many inside and outside the Church who objected to his theory that the Sun was the centre of the solar system and that the Earth rotated around the Sun. Brahe and Kepler produced laws about the movement of the planets in their orbit around the Sun, and Galileo used their ideas to lay the foundation for Newton's first law.

In mechanics Newton achieved more than producing three laws of motion. He brought together motion on a terrestrial scale and motion on an astronomical scale. In other words, he showed that the same rules apply to our own world (the small scale) and to distant planets (the large scale). He knew that acceleration on the surface of the Moon is (approximately) 1/3600 of the acceleration of free fall on the surface of the Earth, and that the moon is 60 times further from the centre of the Earth than an object dropped on the Earth's surface is. He noticed that $60^2 = 3600$, hence an inverse square law. You will find out more about gravitation in section 1.2 (Circular motion and oscillations).

Newton's first law

The law gives a definition of force.

A force is necessary to change the state of rest or of uniform motion in a straight line of a body.

For instance:

- if you are stationary, you will remain stationary unless a resultant (net) force acts on you
- if you want to change your direction of travel, a resultant force must act on you
- if you want to speed up or slow down, a resultant force must act on you.

But there is one idea which is sometimes overlooked. It is that

- if you are moving with constant velocity, there is zero resultant force acting on you.

The law says that force is needed for a *change* in uniform motion. If the motion is not changing, then zero force is required. People sometimes think that an object travelling with constant velocity does have a resultant force acting on it – just a little force, just to make sure it keeps going. But this is not so. A good illustration of the first law in action is provided by space vehicles sent out of the solar system. They have been accelerated to high speed by rocket motors. Once a vehicle is travelling fast, the motors are switched off for good. It continues to travel through space at constant velocity for billions of kilometres. No force acts on it; no change in velocity takes place.

As another example, imagine yourself getting into a lift that is going up. To start with, the force the lift exerts on your feet is greater than your weight and so you accelerate upwards. Once the lift reaches a constant upward velocity, the upward force on your feet equals your weight exactly. The resultant force is zero, and your motion stays unchanged. On the way down, you accelerate downwards to begin with, when the force upwards on your feet is less than your weight; then at constant downward velocity again your weight exactly equals the upward force. For the middle, constant part of the motion, whether the lift is going up or going down, the upward force on your feet equals your

Key definition

Newton's first law states that a force is necessary to change the state of rest or of uniform motion in a straight line of a body.

weight exactly. The two situations are illustrated in Figure 1. Note that at the bottom (Figure 1(a)), an acceleration going up must have the same forces acting as a deceleration going down, and that at the top (Figure 1(b)) a deceleration going up requires the same forces as an acceleration going down.

All of this can be summarised by the following double statement.

Force causes acceleration: zero resultant force, zero acceleration.

Worked example

(a) A person of mass 80 kg is sitting in a bullet train travelling on a straight level track at 80 m s^{-1}. What vertical support force and what forward force does the train provide for the person?

(b) The train now moves at the same speed onto a track that is still straight but has an upward gradient of 0.25%. What vertical support force and what forward force does the train now provide for the person?

(c) Explain why pouring a drink on a train might be difficult when changing direction, but not when travelling with constant velocity.

Answer

(a) The weight of the person is $mg = 80 \times 9.8 = 784$ N, so the support force = 784 N upwards (resultant force zero).
Zero forward force because velocity is constant.

(b) The vertical support force must still be = 784 N (resultant force zero). Zero horizontal force because velocity is constant. (If you take components along the slope and at right angles to the slope then you get 1.96 N and 783.998 N respectively. Using Pythagoras' theorem on these values gives the upward force 784 N with zero overall resultant, since this is equal and opposite to the weight.)

(c) When changing direction there will be an acceleration as the velocity is changing. The cup into which the drink is being poured is accelerating, but the drink in mid-air has nothing to provide a horizontal force, so the drink might well slop over the side of the glass. (For this reason, stewards on planes and boats never fill cups more than about half full.)

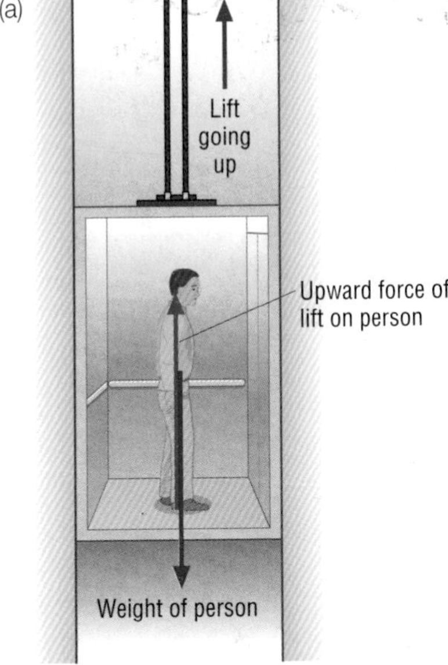

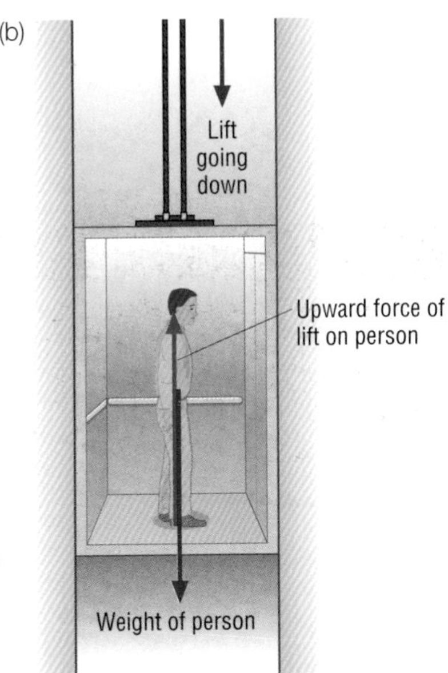

Figure 1 Forces on a person in a lift going: **(a)** up; **(b)** down; note that the two diagrams are identical

Questions

1 Imagine you are holding a newtonmeter (a spring balance calibrated in newtons). A mass of 1.0 kg hangs from the meter, causing it to register 9.8 N.
   (a) What forces are acting on the mass? What are their values and directions?
   (b) You accelerate your hand upwards. What forces are acting on the mass during the acceleration? Are their values equal in magnitude? Explain.
   (c) You lower your hand steadily. What forces are acting on the mass during this action? Are their values equal in magnitude? Explain.
   (d) Does the mass or its weight change in **(b)** and **(c)** above? Justify your answer.

2 In a nightmare you find yourself standing at rest on a perfectly frictionless hard surface, the middle of a sheet of ice.
   (a) Explain why the slightest movement of your body sideways causes you to fall flat to the surface.
   (b) Suggest how you might produce a force to move you to the edge of the ice. You are unable to scratch or otherwise dig into the surface.

3 Why cannot a wheel roll on a frictionless surface?

1.1 (2) Momentum

By the end of this spread, you should be able to …

* **Define linear momentum and appreciate its vector nature.**

Key definition

Linear momentum is defined as the mass of an object multiplied by its velocity. It is a vector. The symbol used for momentum is usually p.

$p = mv$

Examiner tip

You will not meet angular momentum in A2, so you can safely assume that when you see the term momentum, by itself, it means linear momentum, that is momentum in a straight line.

Linear momentum

Linear momentum is defined as the mass of an object multiplied by its velocity.

Linear momentum is a vector, since it is a scalar (mass) multiplied by a vector (velocity).

The symbol used for momentum is usually p. This gives the equation for momentum as

$p = mv$

The reason for using the term *linear* momentum is that there is another term, *angular* momentum, for objects rotating.

In your AS course (Unit 1 Module 3: Work and energy) you met the scalar quantity kinetic energy, which was shown to be equal to $\frac{1}{2}mv^2$. Linear momentum also relates the mass and velocity of an object, but is a vector. In order to show that there is a significant difference between these two terms, work through the following example, which is done in tabular form so that the contrast between the two terms shows up.

Worked example

A truck going north along a motorway has a mass of 4000 kg and a velocity of 18 m s^{-1}. A car, also going north along the motorway, has a mass of 1400 kg and a velocity of 35 m s^{-1}. Calculate

(a) the kinetic energy of each vehicle
(b) the momentum of each vehicle
(c) the distance each vehicle takes to stop against a retarding force of 7000 N
(d) the time each vehicle takes to stop against the same retarding force as in **(c)**.

Answer

	Truck	Car
mass/kg	4000	1400
speed/m s^{-1}	18	35
kinetic energy/J	$\frac{1}{2} \times 4000 \times 18^2$ = 648 000	$\frac{1}{2} \times 1400 \times 35^2$ = 857 500
momentum/kg m s^{-1}	4000×18 = 72 000 due north	1400×35 = 49 000 due north
deceleration/m s^{-2}	$= F/m = 7000/4000 = 1.75$	$7000/1400 = 5.00$
distance to stop/m	$= v^2/2a = 18^2/(2 \times 1.75) = 92.6$	$35^2/(2 \times 5.0) = 122.5$
time to stop/s	$= v/a = 18/1.75 = 10.3$	$35/5 = 7.0$

There is no point in having lots of different terms unless there is a good reason for it, so now examine the results of these calculations. The first point to notice is that although the car has a greater kinetic energy than the truck, it has a smaller momentum. Next, notice that the car takes a greater distance to stop, but the truck takes a longer time. Now remember that energy is force × distance. Using this enables the distance to stop to be obtained directly from 648 000 J/7000 N = 92.6 m for the truck and 857 500 J/7000 N = 122.5 m for the car. Finally, notice that momentum/force gives the time for stopping, 72 000 kg m s^{-1}/7000 N = 10.3 s for the truck and 49 000/7000 = 7.0 s for the car.

The conclusion from this is that momentum is always force × time in the same way that kinetic energy is force × distance. Indeed, the unit of momentum is often quoted as N s. This unit does not have a name, unlike the name joule for the N m. The following table sums up the contrast between momentum and kinetic energy. If you want distances, use kinetic energy; if you want times, use momentum.

kinetic energy	force × distance = change in kinetic energy	$Fd = \frac{1}{2}mv^2 - \frac{1}{2}mu^2$	unit: N m = J	scalar
momentum	force × time = change in momentum	$Ft = mv - mu$	unit: N s	vector

Questions

1 Prove the equation $Ft = mv - mu$ for a body of mass m being accelerated by a force F from velocity u to velocity v in time t.

2 The unit of momentum is either kg m s^{-1} or N s. Show that these two units are equivalent.

3 A player serves a ball in a game of tennis with a racket of mass 0.40 kg. The racket is moving at 20 m s^{-1} as it hits the stationary ball.

(a) Calculate the momentum of the racket.

(b) In a typical serve 25% of the momentum of the racket is transferred to the ball of mass 0.050 kg. Calculate the velocity of the ball as it leaves the racket.

(c) Calculate the percentage of the kinetic energy of the racket which is transferred to the ball.

4 A tennis ball of mass 0.050 kg travelling at 15 m s^{-1} hits a wall head on and bounces back along the same path at 10 m s^{-1}.

(a) Calculate the change in velocity of the ball.

(b) Calculate the change in momentum of the ball.

5 A toy car of mass 0.080 kg moves across a horizontal floor until it collides with a toy brick. Just before it hits the brick, its speed is 3.0 m s^{-1}. It rebounds at two thirds of its speed.

The contact time is 0.2 s.

(a) Calculate the change of momentum of the car in the impact.

(b) Calculate the average force in N on the brick during the impact.

1.1 (3) Newton's second law

By the end of this spread, you should be able to ...

- **State and use Newton's second law, and explain that $F = ma$ is a special case.**
- **Define net force on a body, and select and apply the equation $F = \Delta p/\Delta t$ to solve problems.**

Key definition

Newton's second law states that the rate of change of the momentum of an object is directly proportional to the net force acting upon it.

Newton's second law of motion

Now that momentum has been defined, **Newton's second law** can be quoted.

The rate of change of the momentum of an object is directly proportional to the resultant (net) force acting upon it.

In equation form, this can be written $\frac{\Delta p}{\Delta t} \propto F$, where Δp is the change in the momentum and Δt is the time interval. Note that this second law includes the first law, because if the resultant force on the object is zero, then it will not change its momentum, i.e. it will 'continue in its state of rest or of uniform motion in a straight line'.

The second law in mathematical terms

Consider an object of mass m being accelerated by a resultant, or net, force F. The object accelerates uniformly in time t from velocity u to velocity v in a straight line. These are related as follows:

$$\frac{mv - mu}{t} \propto F$$

This gives $\frac{m(v-u)}{t} \propto F$ and hence

$$ma \propto F$$

Note the proportionality sign. In order to make this an equation, a constant of proportionality k must be introduced. This gives Newton's second law as

$$ma = kF$$

This looks somewhat different from the way you may have seen it before. The reason for this is that the equation makes no mention of the units in which mass, acceleration and force are measured. Provided k is included, any system of units could be used. If we use just SI units, it is necessary to determine the value of k. This can be done after defining the SI unit of force.

The SI unit of force, the newton (N)

Key definition

One **newton** is the force that gives a mass of one kilogram an acceleration of one metre per second each second.

One **newton** is the force that will give a mass of one kilogram an acceleration of one metre per second each second.

When this particular set of conditions is put into the basic second law equation, we get 1 kg × 1 m s^{-2} = k × 1 N. This tells us that the numerical value of k is 1 and that the newton has base units kg m s^{-2}. Because the constant of proportionality is equal to 1, we now get the familiar equation

$$F = ma$$

or the equivalent momentum equation

$$F = \frac{\Delta p}{\Delta t}$$

Provided the force is measured in newtons, the mass must be in kilograms, the acceleration in m s^{-2} and the momentum in kg m s^{-1}.

Weight and mass

We've looked at these two terms previously, in AS Unit 1:

- **Mass** is the inertia of an object, or how difficult it is to accelerate the object. In other words, something with a large mass is difficult to accelerate; something with a small mass is easy to accelerate. Mass is measured in kilograms using the SI system of units.
- **Weight** is the gravitational force the Earth exerts on an object, pulling it towards the ground.

Figure 1 shows an object of mass *M* in free fall near the Earth's surface. Its weight *W* causes it to accelerate at 9.81 m s^{-2}. Weight is a force, so it will be measured in newtons. The second law equation therefore enables the relationship between weight and mass to be determined:

$W = M \times 9.81 \text{ m s}^{-2}$

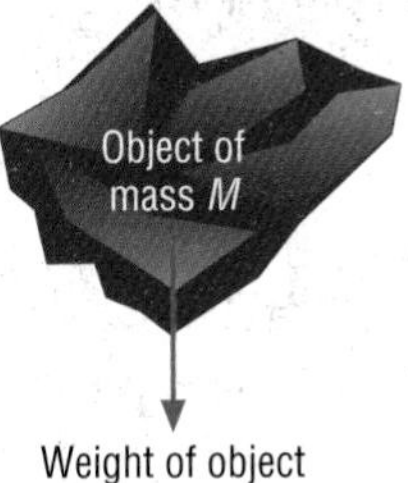

Figure 1 An object of mass *M* in free fall near the Earth's surface. Its weight causes it to accelerate

Worked example

In an experiment to measure the charge on an electron, an electrical force of 2.8×10^{-8} N is exerted upwards on a charged oil drop of mass 3.0 μg. What is the acceleration of the oil drop?

Answer

This straightforward question can be full of pitfalls if enough care is not taken. It is mainly a problem of getting the units correct at all stages – so start with a sketch diagram, as shown in Figure 2.

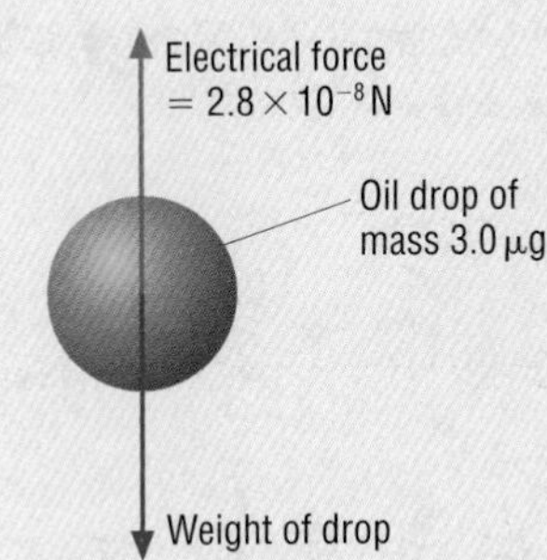

Figure 2 The forces acting on the oil drop

The mass needs to be in kg, not just grams.
$3.0 \text{ μg} = 3.0 \times 10^{-6} \text{ g} = 3.0 \times 10^{-9} \text{ kg}$.

The weight *W* of the drop is
$3.0 \times 10^{-9} \text{ kg} \times 9.81 \text{ m s}^{-2} = 2.943 \times 10^{-8}$ N.

This gives the resultant downward force on the drop as
$2.943 \times 10^{-8} \text{ N} - 2.8 \times 10^{-8} \text{ N} = 0.143 \times 10^{-8}$ N.

Now all the units are correct, we can use $F_{down} = m \times a_{down}$ to get

$0.143 \times 10^{-8} \text{ N} = 3.0 \times 10^{-9} \text{ kg} \times a_{down}$

and hence $a_{down} = 0.143 \times 10^{-8} \text{ N}/3.0 \times 10^{-9} = 0.477 \text{ m s}^{-2}$.

Note that you should not keep rounding up numerical values when doing a multi-stage problem. The only definite figure here is the first, since two nearly equal numbers have been subtracted. It is therefore sensible to give the answer as $a = 0.48 \text{ m s}^{-2}$ downwards. Deal with significant figures at the end of the problem.

STRETCH and CHALLENGE

Another way of writing the second law equation is

$$\frac{\Delta mv}{\Delta t} = kF$$

For a constant mass this becomes

$$\frac{m\Delta v}{\Delta t} = ma = kF$$

as before.

Question

Derive the equation if the mass is not constant, such as when a rocket takes off, uses up fuel and hence steadily reduces its mass.

Questions

1 On take-off an air-powered rocket ejects 8.0×10^{-3} kg of air at a velocity of 250 m s^{-1}.
   (a) Calculate the momentum of the air leaving the rocket.
   (b) The air is ejected over a period of 0.20 s. Calculate the average thrust on the rocket.

2 The upward force *F* on a high-altitude meteorological balloon at the Earth's surface is 1.4×10^5 N. The initial acceleration of the balloon as it is released is 25 m s^{-2}. The total mass of the filled balloon and its load is *M*.
   (a) Copy Figure 3. Draw and label suitable arrows to represent the forces acting on the balloon immediately after lift-off.
   (b) Calculate the value of *M* in kg.

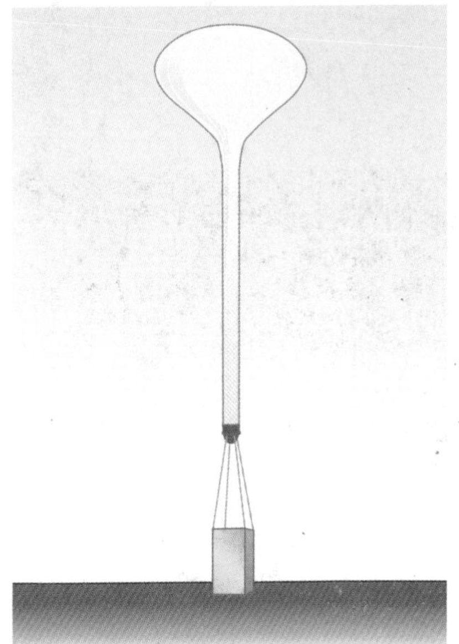

Figure 3

Newton's third law

By the end of this spread, you should be able to ...

- **State and use Newton's third law.**

Key definition

Newton's third law states that when body A exerts a force on body B, then body B exerts on body A a force that is equal, opposite in direction and of the same type.

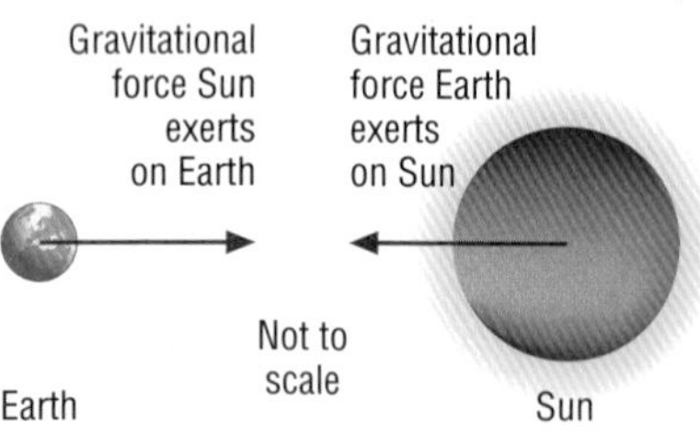

Figure 1 The gravitational force that the Sun exerts on the Earth is exactly equal and opposite to the gravitational force that the Earth exerts on the Sun

Newton's third law of motion

When body A exerts a force on body B, then body B exerts on body A a force that is:

- equal
- opposite in direction
- of the same type.

This can be written as a single statement, but it is laid out here to show the three conditions for the two forces. They must be equal in magnitude, they must be in opposite directions and they must be the same type of force. For instance, if one of the forces is an electrical force, then the other must also be electrical, or if one is gravitational, the other must be gravitational. Figure 1 shows one pair of equal and opposite gravitational forces. One force acts on body A, the Sun; the other force acts on body B, the Earth. Force X is the gravitational force the Sun exerts on the Earth; force Y is the gravitational force the Earth exerts on the Sun: equal, opposite and both gravitational. The magnitude of both of these forces is 3.55×10^{22} N. A force of this huge size makes the Earth, of mass 6×10^{24} kg, go around the Sun once per year. The effect of the force on the Sun, of mass 2×10^{30} kg, is minimal.

Probing the universe

The force that the Earth exerts on the Sun is minimal, but it does cause a small wobble of the Sun. If a distant star is seen to wobble in its position in the sky, then we know that the star has a planet to cause the wobble. By measuring the timescale of the wobble, the length of the planet's year can be determined, and hence how far it is from its star. This can give an indication of its temperature and therefore whether life forms like us are possible on it. Until recently, sufficient wobble was noticed only for giant planets, of the size of Jupiter. With extremely accurate measurements, it is now possible to detect the influence on stars of planets more similar in size to the Earth and hence more likely to support life.

Free-body force diagrams

To determine the acceleration of any object, all the forces on the object need to be known. Force diagrams therefore need to be drawn for one object at a time. For example, if a ladder is resting on the ground and leaning against a wall, it is not the force on the ground or the force on the wall that is wanted, but the force on the ladder. So draw a diagram as in Figure 2(a) rather than the one in Figure 2(b). A diagram like Figure 2(a) is called a **free-body diagram**. Figure 2(b) is too confusing, and if you draw a diagram like this, you may end up determining forces in exactly the opposite directions to those you need.

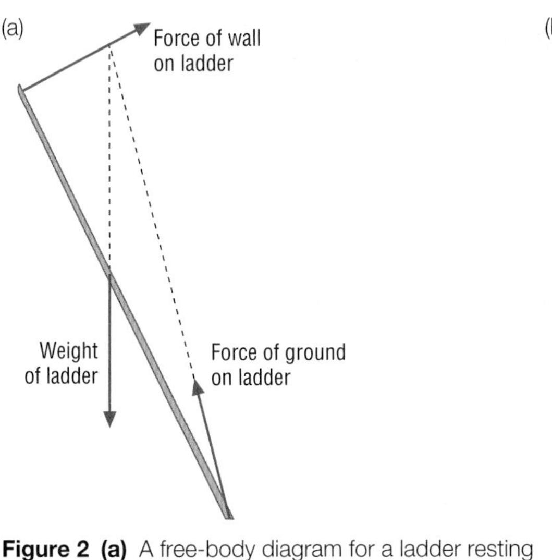

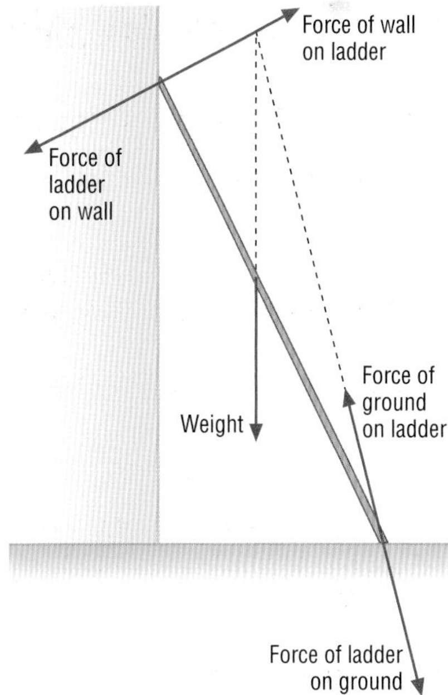

Figure 2 **(a)** A free-body diagram for a ladder resting on the ground and leaning against a wall;
(b) a confusing diagram trying to put across too much information about forces on different objects

Questions

1 State the force that is 'equal and opposite' to the one given, and state the type of force involved. (Type of force will be gravitational, magnetic, electrical or contact. In fact, all contact forces are electrical, since all solids are held together by electrical attraction between atoms.)
- **(a)** The force the Earth exerts on you.
- **(b)** The force a car exerts on a caravan it is towing.
- **(c)** The force a magnet exerts on a piece of iron.
- **(d)** The force a car exerts on a road.
- **(e)** The force a football exerts on a football boot kicking it.
- **(f)** The force a tug-of-war team exerts on the rope.
- **(g)** The force the Sun exerts on the Earth.
- **(h)** The force a negative ion exerts on a positive ion.

2 Draw free-body diagrams for the following items. For each force labelled, state the type of the force shown.
- **(a)** A person standing still and carrying a suitcase.
- **(b)** The suitcase in **(a)**.
- **(c)** An egg in free fall.
- **(d)** The egg in **(c)** as it hits the floor.

3 A circus clown fires a large water pistol that ejects water horizontally at a speed of 7.1 m s^{-1}. The water leaves the gun at a rate of 2.8 kg s^{-1}.
- **(a)** Show that the rate of change of momentum of the water on leaving the pistol is about 20 kg m s^{-2}.
- **(b)** Explain why the clown holding the pistol experiences a backward force of about 20 N.
- **(c)** The water strikes a second clown at the same velocity as it left the pistol. The water bounces off the clown. Explain why this clown could experience a force greater than 20 N from the water jet.

Figure 3

4 An ejector seat to enable a pilot to escape from a fighter plane is tested with the plane at rest on the runway. The combined mass, 270 kg, of the seat and pilot is fired vertically at a velocity of 50 m s^{-1}.
- **(a)** Calculate the change in momentum of the seat and pilot.
- **(b)** Calculate the average force needed to give this change in momentum in 0.25 s.
- **(c)** In which direction will the body of the plane move during the firing of the ejector seat? Explain your answer.

Figure 4

1.1 (5) Conservation of momentum

By the end of this spread, you should be able to …

* **State the principle of conservation of momentum.**
* **Apply the principle to solve problems.**

The deduction of the principle of conservation of momentum

The principle of conservation of momentum can be proved directly from Newton's third law of motion in the following way.

Consider any two objects colliding with one another. The objects can be massive, like colliding stars, or very tiny like colliding molecules, or one object can be big, for example the Earth, and the other small, such as a tennis ball. According to Newton's third law, when the two objects collide, the force object A exerts on object B is equal and opposite to the force that object B exerts on object A. In its simplest form the two forces are shown in Figure 1. They are equal forces in opposite directions. That is why the force that B exerts on A is shown as negative. Both forces must last for the same length of time, because this is an interaction between the two objects.

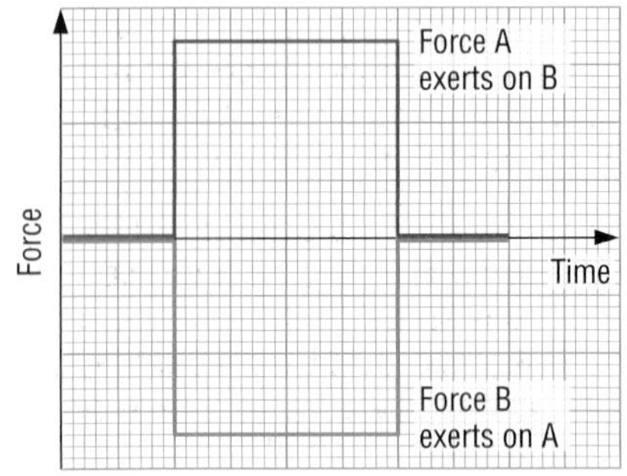

Force
Time
Force A exerts on B
Force B exerts on A

Figure 1 A force–time graph showing that the force A exerts on B is always equal and opposite to the force B exerts on A

The areas enclosed by each graph and the time axis are identical and represent force × time. In spread 1.1.2 it was shown that

force × time = change in momentum

$Ft = mv - mu$ where v is the final velocity and u is the starting velocity.

This means that the gain in momentum of B, in a particular direction, is exactly equal to the loss in momentum of object A in that direction. That is, the total momentum before the collision is the same as the total momentum after the collision.

The principle of conservation of momentum

In any direction, in the absence of external forces, the total momentum of a system remains constant.

This is one of the fundamental laws of physics. Although quantum theory and relativity have replaced some of Newton's laws when high velocities are involved, the law of conservation of momentum is unchanged. The part about 'external forces' simply means that, if some other object is involved in the collision, it too will exert a force on one or both of the objects and so will gain or lose some momentum. The law means that momentum is never created or destroyed. Every time one object gains some momentum, another object must lose the same amount.

Key definition

The principle of conservation of momentum states that, in any direction, in the absence of external forces, the total momentum of a system remains constant.

Worked example

A railway engine of mass 80 tonnes and travelling at 5.3 m s^{-1} collides with, and becomes attached to, a truck of mass 20 tonnes travelling at 1.8 m s^{-1} in the opposite direction. Look at Figure 2.

(a) Calculate the speed of truck and engine immediately after the collision.

(b) Calculate the loss of kinetic energy in the collision.

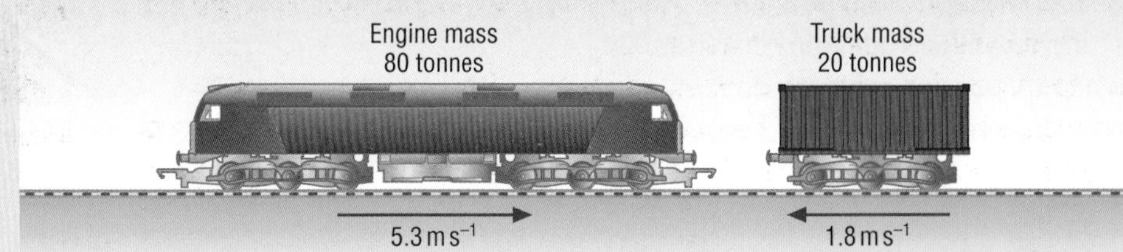

Figure 2 An engine colliding with a truck

Answer

(a) Mass of engine = 80 000 kg (1 tonne = 1000 kg)
Momentum of engine before collision = 80 000 × +5.3 = +424 000 N s
Momentum of truck before collision = 20 000 × (–1.8) = –36 000 N s
Total momentum before collision = 424 000 – 36 000 = 388 000 N s
Using the principle of conservation of momentum

total momentum before collision = total momentum after collision
388 000 N s = (80 000 + 20 000) v

where v is the speed of engine and truck after the collision
v = 388 000/100 000 = 3.88 m s^{-1}
= 3.9 m s^{-1} to 2 significant figures (sig. figs) as the data is given only to two sig. figs.

(b) Kinetic energy of engine before collision = ½ × 80 000 × 5.3^2 = 11.2 × 10^5 J
Kinetic energy of truck before collision = ½ × 20 000 × (–1.8)^2
= +0.324 × 10^5 J
Total kinetic energy before collision = 11.5 × 10^5 J
Kinetic energy of both together after collision = ½ × 100 000 × 3.88^2
= 7.53 × 10^5 J
Loss of kinetic energy = (11.5 – 7.53) × 10^5 = 4.0 × 10^5 J.

Examiner tip

As a general rule, keep figures in a calculation while you are doing it rather than chopping off excess figures. Then, at the end of the calculation reduce the answer to no more than three significant figures.

Note in the worked example how the number of significant figures varies. Several features of a calculation can cause problems:

(i) When a constant such as π is introduced, a calculator will work to 10 sig. figs.
(ii) When squaring or square-rooting a number, you usually get more sig. figs, e.g. 36^2 = 1296.
(iii) When you add two numbers, the number of sig. figs may change, e.g. 64 + 78 = 142.
(iv) Even worse, when you subtract, the number of sig. figs may drop badly, e.g. 8.406 – 8.397 = 0.009 is to only 1 sig. fig.
(v) Multiplying or dividing may change the number of sig. figs, e.g. 24 × 6 = 144.

Questions

1 Two students sit at opposite ends of a stationary boat floating in a river. They throw a heavy ball backwards and forwards between them without moving their positions in the boat. Other students observe the experiment from the river bank. Describe and explain the motion of the boat that they see.

2 A basic air rifle fires slugs of mass 0.50 g at a velocity of 160 m s^{-1}.
(a) Suppose the air rifle of mass 0.80 kg is free to move when a slug is fired. Calculate the speed with which it recoils.
(b) Normally the rifle is held. What mean force does the person experience to prevent the rifle recoiling more than 0.50 mm when he fires it?
(c) The recoil of rifles used in the First World War was in excess of 100 N. The military now use recoil-less rifles. Expanding gas within the barrel chamber pushes the bullet forwards, and some of the gas escapes from the chamber. Suggest how this gas can 'absorb' the recoil.

3 An astronaut can propel himself during a space walk by emitting pulsed jets of gas backwards from his backpack.
(a) Explain why the astronaut, initially at rest, moves forward when a jet of gas is emitted from the backpack.
(b) The backpack expels 0.04 kg of gas in one pulse at an average velocity of 400 m s^{-1}. Calculate the momentum of the pulse of gas.
(c) The mass of the astronaut and his equipment is 120 kg. Calculate the increase in velocity of the astronaut.

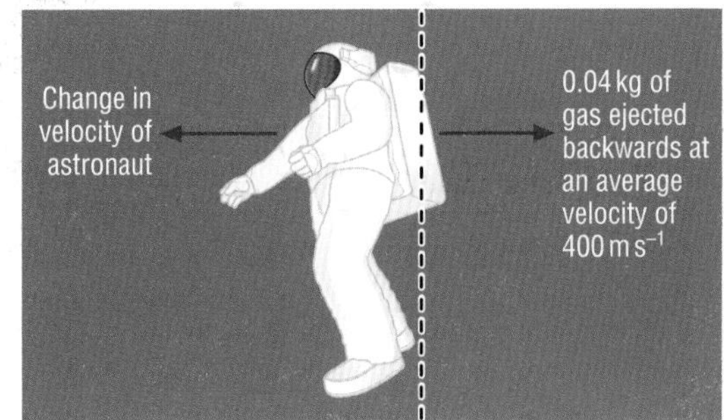

Figure 3

4 Two identical air pucks are connected by an open-wound spring which can expand or compress. The pucks move without friction on a horizontal surface. Describe and explain the subsequent motion when the pucks are pulled apart and
(a) are released together
(b) puck A is held still when puck B is released. Puck A is then released at the instant the spring is reduced to its natural length.

1.1 (6) Impulse

By the end of this spread, you should be able to ...

* **Define the impulse of a force.**
* **Determine impulse from a force–time graph.**
* **Recall and use the equation impulse = change in momentum.**

Introduction

A situation often arises when the force on an object is, for a short time, large and variable. For example, the sudden force acting on a tennis ball when hit by a racket, a nail hit by a hammer, an object dropped onto the floor or a car colliding with a gatepost.

Typical force–time diagrams of such impacts are shown in Figures 1 and 2. In Figure 1 the impact force rises smoothly to a maximum and then decreases smoothly to zero. This type of impact occurs with a tennis ball and racket, where the force might rise to several hundred newtons during the few milliseconds of contact. The photo in Figure 3 shows the distortion that takes place during impact. Immediately after impact, the tennis ball is distorted, and the distortion rapidly rises to a maximum before decreasing back to zero as contact is lost. The overall effect is to change the velocity of the ball considerably. The photo of the car-testing collision, Figure 4, is more complex. Different parts of the car hit the obstacle at slightly different times, so the force–time graph for this collision will be more like the one shown in Figure 2.

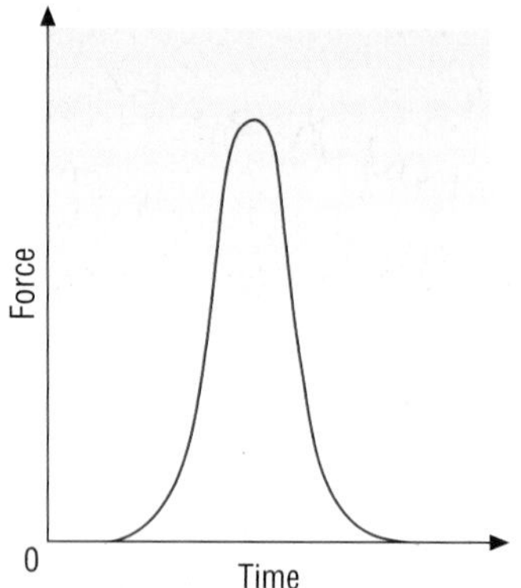

Figure 1 Force–time graph for smooth impact

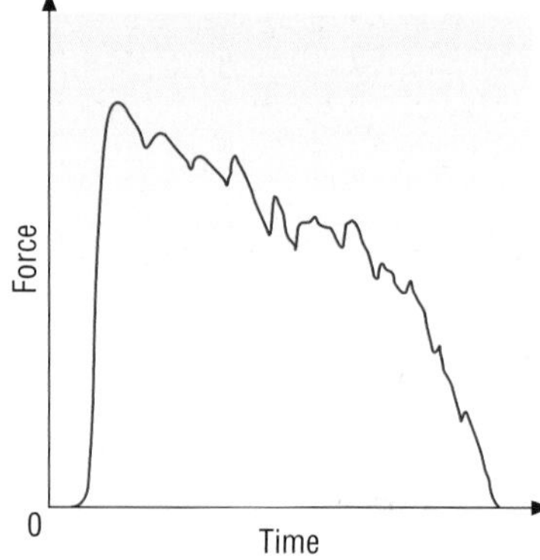

Figure 2 Force–time graph for complex impact

Figure 3 A tennis ball hit by a racket

Figure 4 A car test crash

Impulse

In most cases, the duration of the impact and the maximum force of impact are relatively unimportant. What is important is what happens to the object. The momentum of the object should change. Using the equation from spread 1.1.5, we get

$$\Delta p = F\Delta t$$

where Δp is the change in momentum.

$F\Delta t$ is the assumed constant force multiplied by the time interval. The value of $F\Delta t$ is called the **impulse**.

Key definition

Impulse is defined by the expression $F\Delta t$. It equals the change in momentum of a body. It is equal to the area beneath a force–time graph.

Worked example

1 To see how this works, consider first a theoretical situation in which a steel ball of mass 0.10 kg is acted on by a force of 500 N for a time of 4.0 ms. A force–time graph for this is shown in Figure 5. The area beneath the graph, the impulse given to the ball, is 500 N × 0.0040 s = 2.0 N s. The change in the momentum of the ball is therefore 2.0 N s. Assuming the ball started from rest, this means that $mv = 2.0$, where v is its final speed. $v = 2.0/0.10 = 20$ m s^{-1}.

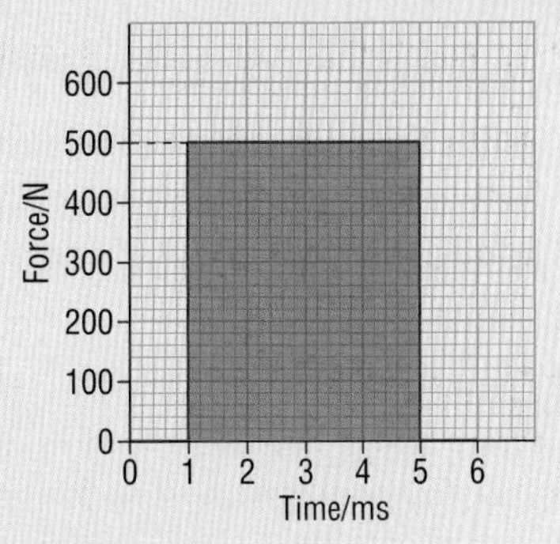

Figure 5 The force on the steel ball is constant for 4.0 ms

2 A ship of mass 8.0×10^6 kg (8000 tonnes) travelling slowly towards a jetty collides with a wooden protection post. The braking force provided by the post varies with time in the way shown in Figure 6. How fast was the ship travelling before it hit the post?

Answer

The area beneath the graph is the first thing to determine. Figures 6(a), 6(b) and 6(c) show three ways of doing this.

Method (a) involves counting squares.

The total number of small squares = 25 + 29 + 10 + 63 + 100 = 227
1 small square represents 10 000 N × 0.5 s = 5000 N s
so 227 small squares represent 1.14×10^6 N s.

Method (b) uses a rectangle judged to have the same area as the graph.

This has area = 130 000 N × 9.5 s = 1.23×10^6 N s.

Method (c) uses two triangles and a rectangle judged to have the same area as the graph.

The area here is (½ × 3.5 × 130 000) + (5 × 130 000) + (½ × 4 × 130 000) = 1.14×10^6 N s.

You can see that all the values obtained are of the same order of magnitude. Counting small squares is the most accurate of the methods, so we will proceed using the value it gives.

The area beneath the graph represents the impulse, which is equal to the change in momentum.

Therefore, $1.14 \times 10^6 = mv = 8.0 \times 10^6 \times v$, giving $v = 1.14 \times 10^6/8.0 \times 10^6 = 0.12$ m s^{-1}.

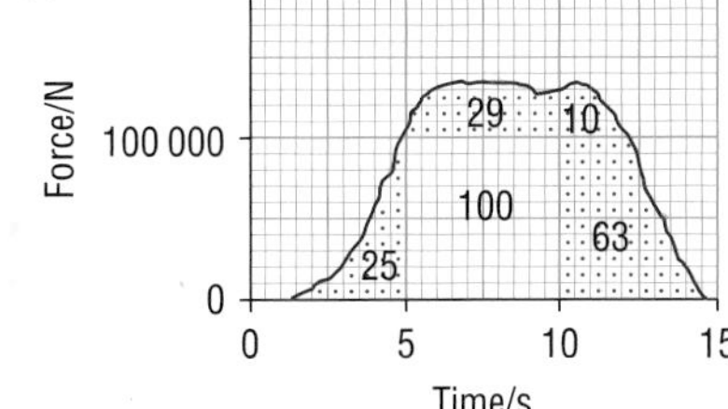

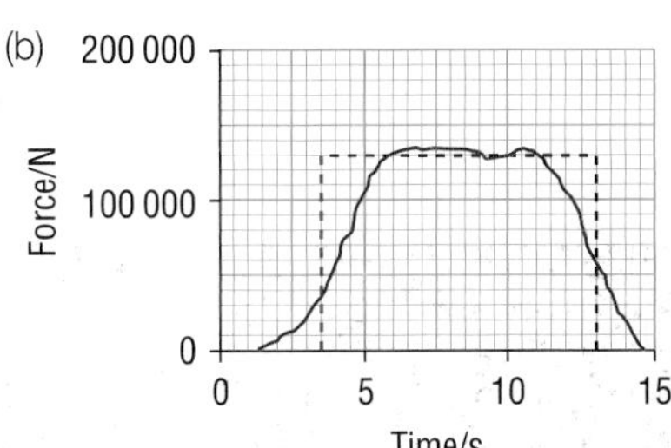

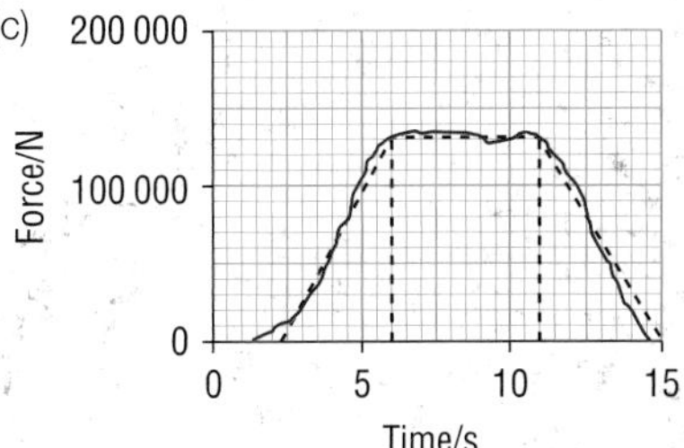

Figure 6 Three ways of measuring the area beneath a graph

Questions

1 Figure 7 shows how the force exerted by a golf club on a ball varies during the time of contact.

(a) Show that the impulse given to the ball is about 2 N s.

(b) Calculate the speed of the ball of mass 0.045 kg, initially at rest, at the instant it leaves the club.

(c) What is the mean accelerating force?

(d) Imagine a horizontal line drawn on Figure 7 at the value of the force of part **(c)** to the maximum time of contact. Does the area within the curve above the line equal the area above the curve but below the line? Explain.

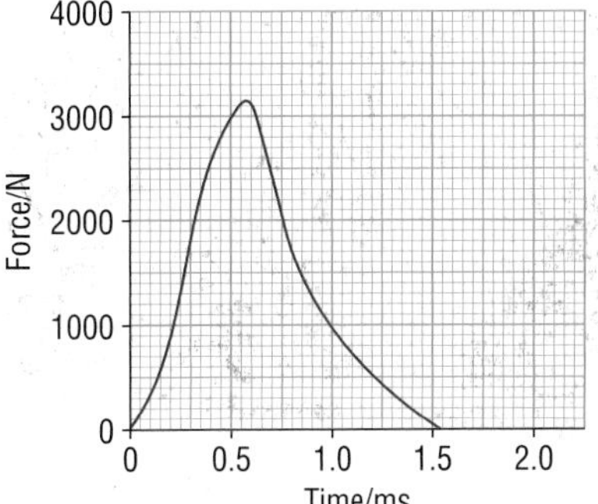

Figure 7

Elastic and inelastic collisions

By the end of this spread, you should be able to …

- **Define a perfectly elastic collision and an inelastic collision.**
- **Explain that, while the momentum of a system is always conserved, some change in kinetic energy usually occurs.**

Elastic and inelastic collisions

In spread 1.1.5, a worked example showed that when a railway engine collided with a truck, kinetic energy was lost. This shows that momentum can be conserved even though kinetic energy is not conserved. But this does not mean that the law of conservation of energy has been broken, just that some of the original kinetic energy was lost producing sound and heating the colliding objects.

In some collisions all the original kinetic energy remains as kinetic energy. These collisions are called **perfectly elastic collisions**. They will be totally silent because no kinetic energy is converted to sound energy. An example of a perfectly elastic collision is one molecule colliding with another molecule. Some everyday collisions are sometimes treated as if they were perfectly elastic collisions, for example a snooker ball colliding with the rubber on the table edge, or a glider on a linear air track bouncing silently off another glider if magnets are attached to them so that one north pole repels another.

Collisions that are not perfectly elastic are called **inelastic collisions**.

Key definitions

A **perfectly elastic collision** is one in which no momentum or kinetic energy is lost.

In an **inelastic collision**, momentum is conserved, but kinetic energy is not.

Examiner tip

Be careful with the terms 'perfectly elastic' and 'inelastic'.

Sometimes the word 'elastic' on its own means 'perfectly elastic'.

Sometimes the term 'perfectly inelastic' is used, to indicate that the two objects have stuck together, but they might still be moving.

Another term you may see is 'superelastic', meaning there is more kinetic energy after the collision than before. This can happen only when some extra energy is given to the two objects involved, perhaps in an explosion.

It is usually clear from the rest of the question exactly what is intended.

Worked example

A 60 kg mass travels at 12 m s^{-1} to make a head-on elastic collision with a 40 kg mass travelling in the same direction at 7 m s^{-1} (Figure 1). Show that after the collision the 60 kg mass travels forward at 8 m s^{-1} and the 40 kg mass forward at 13 m s^{-1}, and that there is no loss of kinetic energy.

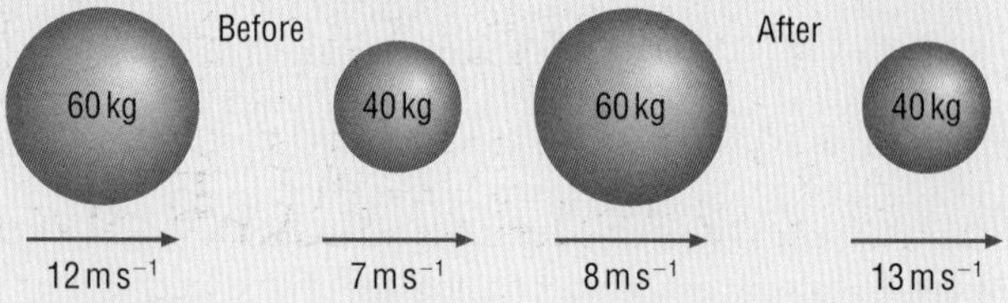

Before: 60 kg at 12 m s^{-1}; 40 kg at 7 m s^{-1}. After: 60 kg at 8 m s^{-1}; 40 kg at 13 m s^{-1}.

Figure 1 A collision between two masses

Answer

As with all collision questions, start with conservation of momentum.

Momentum before collision = momentum after collision.
(60 × 12) + (40 × 7) = (60 × 8) + (40 × 13) (each term is a mass in kg multiplied by a velocity in m s^{-1})
giving 720 + 280 = 480 + 520, and both sides of the equation come to 1000 N s.

For an elastic collision the total kinetic energy is the same before and after the collision.

Kinetic energy before collision = kinetic energy after the collision
$(\frac{1}{2} \times 60 \times 12^2) + (\frac{1}{2} \times 40 \times 7^2) = (\frac{1}{2} \times 60 \times 8^2) + (\frac{1}{2} \times 40 \times 13^2)$
(each term in joules)
giving 4320 + 980 = 1920 + 3380, with both sides equal to 5300 J.

Notice what has happened to the velocities. The large mass was catching up on the small mass at a rate of 12 m s^{-1} −7 m s^{-1} = 5 m s^{-1} before the masses collided. After the collision, the small mass moved away from the large mass at a rate of 13 m s^{-1} − 8 m s^{-1} = 5 m s^{-1}. This is always the case for a perfectly elastic head-on collision: the velocity at which the objects approach one another equals the velocity with which they separate. A simple, familiar illustration is when a ball falls and hits the Earth – it bounces back at the same speed, provided it is a 'perfect' ball.

Examiner tip

It often makes calculations easier if you use the following fact. In an elastic collision between two objects, no kinetic energy is lost, and the velocity of approach always equals the velocity of separation.

Using conservation of momentum in nuclear physics

Conservation of momentum can be applied to nuclear particles. Figure 2 shows what happened when a high-energy oxygen ion collided with a nucleus of lead in a CERN particle accelerator. A large number of particles were produced, and each left a track showing its path. The paths are curved because the collision took place in a strong magnetic field. The particle that spirals inwards as it loses energy is an electron. The mathematics of the conservation of momentum of a collision such as this is far more complex than the question answered above, but the principles involved are identical.

Figure 2 A streamer chamber photograph of an oxygen-ion collision with a lead nucleus (left) producing a spray of particles that shoot out to the right; one particle is a low-energy electron that spirals inwards in the chamber's magnetic field

Questions

1 Uranium fission within a nuclear reactor produces (amongst other things) high-speed neutrons. These must be slowed down for them to trigger a chain reaction within the uranium. In a heavy-water reactor the neutrons of mass m make multiple elastic collisions with deuterium nuclei of mass $2m$, losing speed at each collision. To appreciate this process, consider the following simple model.

(a) Suppose a fast-moving neutron of speed v makes a head-on elastic collision with a stationary deuterium nucleus. Show that its speed is reduced to $v/3$.

(b) For the neutron to be absorbed by a uranium nucleus its speed must be about 10^{-4} v. Estimate how many collisions the neutron must make to reduce its speed to this value.

2 A nuclear fusion reaction occurs when a deuterium nucleus, mass $2m$, and a tritium nucleus, mass $3m$, combine. Most of the energy released in the fusion is carried away in the kinetic energy of the product neutron, mass m. The other product is a helium nucleus, mass $4m$. Figure 3 shows the nuclei approaching before the fusion and the products separating after the fusion, with their relative speeds given in terms of v.

(a) Show in terms of m and v that momentum is conserved in the process.

(b) Calculate the kinetic energy released in the fusion in terms of m and v.

(c) Estimate the value of v given that $m = 1.7 \times 10^{-27}$ kg and the energy released is 2.8×10^{-12} J.

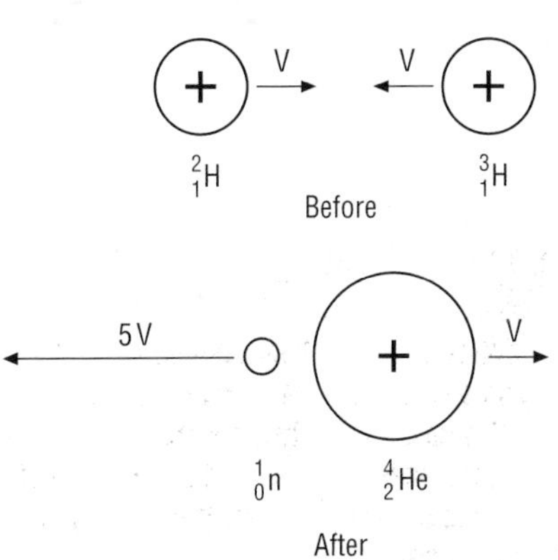

Figure 3

1.1 Newton's laws and momentum summary

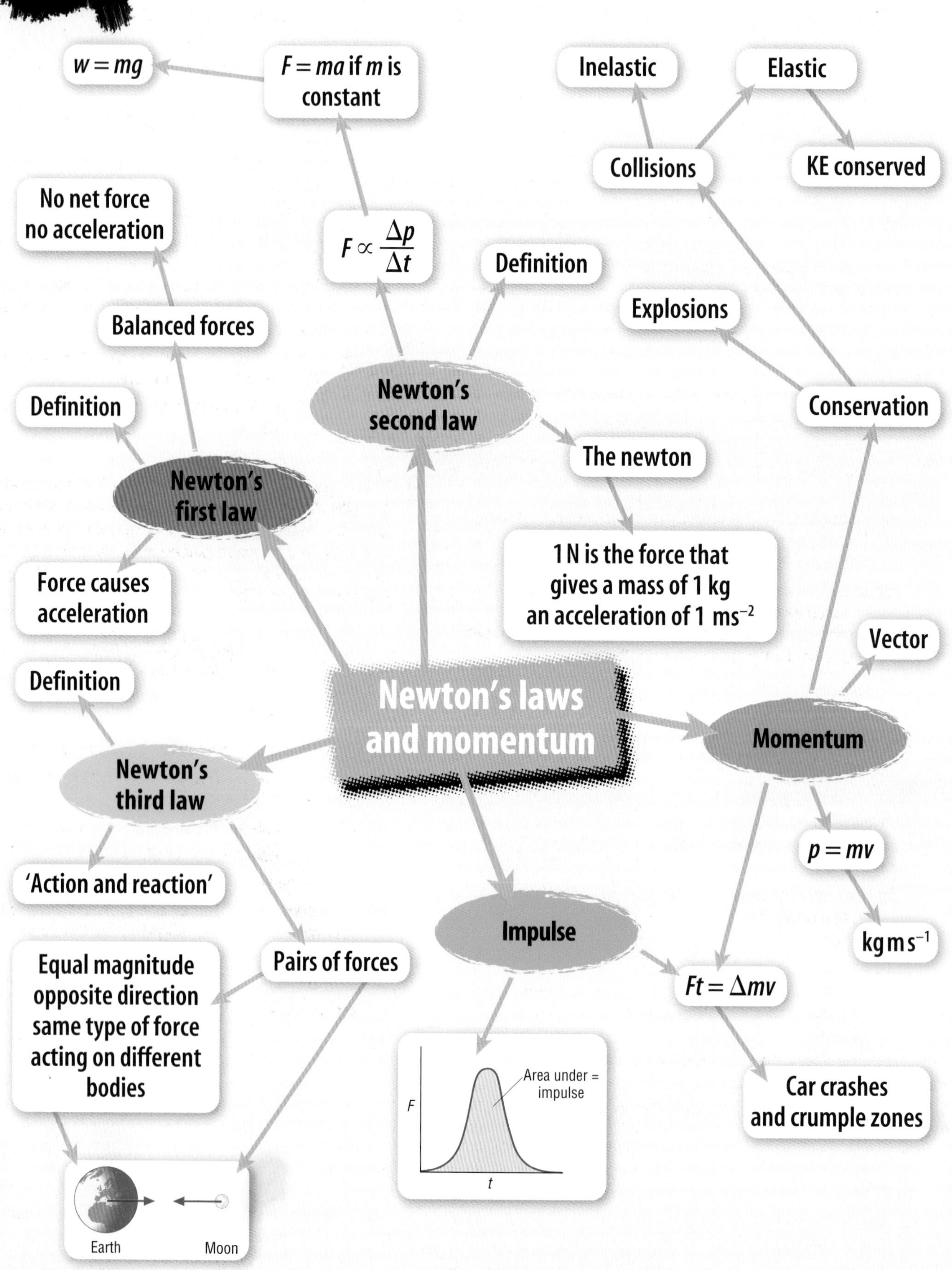

Practice questions

1. The touch paper of a firework rocket is lit and the rocket rises vertically from the ground. The velocity–time graph of the first part of its flight is shown in Figure 1.

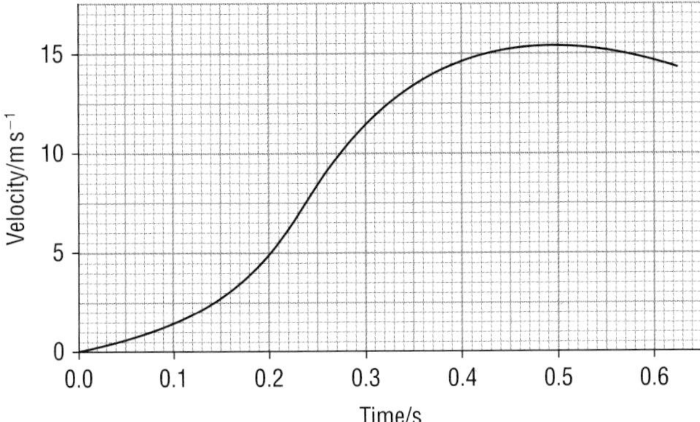

Figure 1

(a) Find the acceleration of the rocket at 0.25 s.

(b) Assuming that the escaping gases and chemicals provide a constant thrust up to a time of 0.25 s, explain why the acceleration is greater at 0.25 s than at 0.15 s.

(c) At about 0.5 s the velocity of the rocket is constant. Explain in terms of basic physical principles how this happens. Assume that air resistance is negligible.

(d) Later, after the fuel has been used up, the rocket reaches its highest point above the ground. The velocity–time graph is now a straight line. Explain why this is so. State the gradient of the line.

2. A cricketer throws a cricket ball. How the force on the ball from the cricketer's hand varies with time is shown in Figure 2. The ball starts from rest and is thrown horizontally.

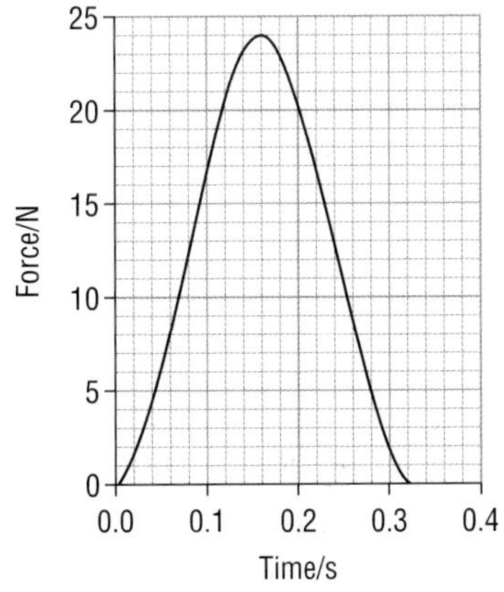

Force/N: 0, 5, 10, 15, 20, 25
Time/s: 0.0, 0.1, 0.2, 0.3, 0.4

Figure 2

(a) Estimate the area in N s under the graph.

(b) What physical quantity is equal to the area under the graph?

(c) The mass of the ball is 0.16 kg. Calculate its speed in m s^{-1} when it is released.

(d) Calculate the maximum horizontal acceleration in m s^{-2} of the ball.

3. **(a)** An isolated nucleus of mass 4.0×10^{-25} kg is initially at rest. It decays, emitting an alpha particle of mass 6.7×10^{-27} kg with kinetic energy of 1.2×10^{-14} J.

(i) Show that the speed of the alpha particle is about 2×10^6 m s^{-1}.

(ii) Calculate the momentum in kg m s^{-1} of the alpha particle.

(iii) Hence find the speed in m s^{-1} of the recoiling nucleus.

(b) Before the decay the nucleus is at a point P. Mark point P in the middle of the next line on your answer sheet.

(i) Place a small cross at a possible position, to full scale, of the alpha particle 8.0×10^{-9} s after the emission.

(ii) Indicate with an arrow, starting at P, the direction of movement of the nucleus.

(iii) Estimate in mm how far the nucleus has moved in 8.0×10^{-9} s.

4. This question is about the use of Newton's second and third laws to determine the forces between five identical, perfectly elastic solid cubes. Figure 3 shows five numbered cubes each of mass m placed in contact on a frictionless horizontal surface. A steady horizontal force P is applied to the end surface of block 1.

Figure 3

(a) Show that the acceleration of block 5 is $P/5m$.

(b) Hence state an expression for the resultant force F_5 on block 5.

(c) Similarly, state expressions in terms of P for

(i) the acceleration a_3 of block 3

(ii) the resultant force F_3 on block 3.

(d) Now consider the forces acting on block 3. Write down an expression for the magnitude of the force and state its direction applied by

(i) block 2 on block 3, F_{23}

(ii) block 4 on block 3, F_{43}.

1.1 Examination questions

1 **(a)** Figure 1 shows a ball of mass 0.050 kg resting on the strings of a tennis racket held horizontally.

Figure 1

(i) Draw and label the **two** forces acting on the ball. [2]

(ii) Each of these forces has a corresponding equal and opposite force according to Newton's third law of motion. Describe these equal and opposite forces and state the objects on which they act. [4]

(iii) Calculate the difference in magnitude in N between the two forces on the ball when the racket is accelerated upwards at 2.0 m s^{-2}. [2]

(b) The ball is dropped from rest at a point 0.80 m above the racket head. The racket is fixed rigidly. Assume that the ball makes an elastic collision with the strings and that any effects of air resistance are negligible. Calculate

(i) the speed in m s^{-1} of the ball just before impact [2]

(ii) the momentum in kg m s^{-1} of the ball just before impact [1]

(iii) the change in momentum in kg m s^{-1} of the ball during the impact [1]

(iv) the average force in N during the impact for a contact time of 0.050 s. [1]

(OCR 2824 Jan03)

2 This question is about an alpha particle making a head-on collision with a gold nucleus.
The alpha particle of mass 6.6×10^{-27} kg is moving at a speed of 1.5×10^{7} m s^{-1} when it is at a large distance from the nucleus.

(a) As the alpha particle approaches the nucleus, it slows down and the nucleus starts to move (see Figure 2).

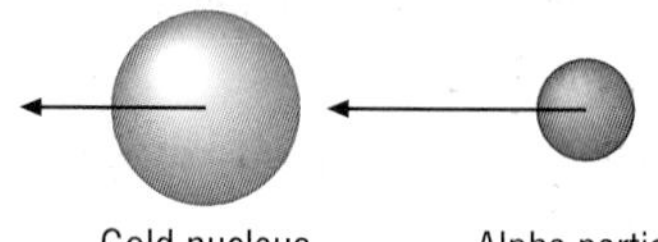

Figure 2

Explain this, and explain how it is possible to calculate the speed of the nucleus. [3]

(b) Figure 3 shows the alpha particle and the gold nucleus near the distance of closest approach at the instant when the nucleus is moving with speed V and the alpha particle is stationary.

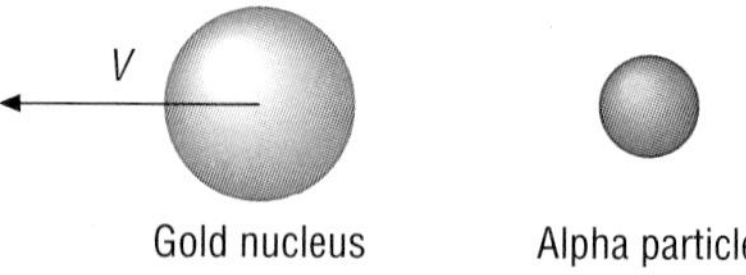

Figure 3

Calculate the speed V in m s^{-1} of the gold nucleus of mass 3.0×10^{-25} kg. [2]

(c) The alpha particle bounces back. Its final speed approximately equals its initial speed of approach. Assume that the mean force on the nucleus is 9.0 N during the interaction. Estimate the time in s of the collision. [2]

(OCR 2824 Jan07)

3 This question is about pressing a red-hot bar of steel into a sheet in a rolling mill.

(a) A bar of steel of mass 500 kg is moved on a conveyor belt at 0.60 m s^{-1}.
Calculate the momentum of the bar. [2]

(b) From the conveyor belt, the bar is passed between two rollers, shown in Figure 4. The bar enters the rollers at 0.60 m s^{-1}. The rollers flatten the bar into a sheet with the result that the sheet leaves the rollers at 1.8 m s^{-1}.

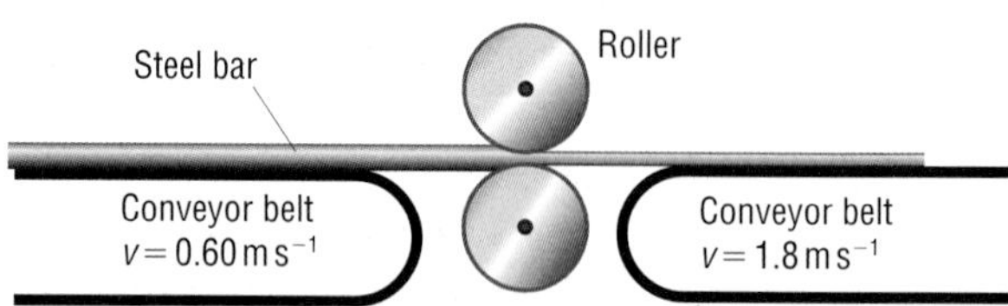

Figure 4

(i) Explain why there is a resultant horizontal force on the bar at the point immediately between the rollers. [2]

(ii) Copy Figure 4 and draw an arrow at this point to show the direction of the force. [1]

(iii) The original length of the bar is 3.0 m. Calculate the time in s it takes for the bar to pass between the rollers. [1]

(iv) Calculate the magnitude of the resultant force in N on the bar during the pressing process. [3]

(OCR 2824 Jun06)

4 **(a)** **(i)** Define the *momentum* of a body. [1]

(ii) A body, initially at rest, explodes into two unequal fragments of mass m_A and m_B. Mass m_A has a velocity v_A, and mass m_B has a velocity v_B. Using the principle of conservation of momentum, derive an expression for v_A/v_B. [2]

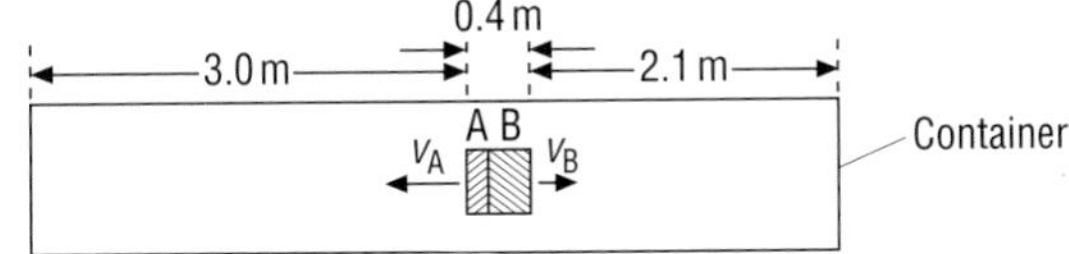

Figure 5

(b) Figure 5 shows a large container of mass 45 kg and length 5.5 m in deep space. An astronaut looking into the container observes an object of mass 15 kg, stationary relative to the container. The object explodes into two pieces at time $t = 0$. Piece **A** has mass 5 kg, and piece **B** has mass 10 kg. The fragments move apart as shown in Figure 5 until they impact and stick to the end walls of the container.

(i) The explosion gives piece **A** a momentum of 10 kg m s^{-1}. Calculate the speeds v_A and v_B, in m s^{-1}, of the two fragments. [1]

(ii) Piece **A** strikes the container first. Calculate the time t_1 in s at which the container starts to move. [1]

(iii) Calculate the distance x in m between **B** and the right-hand end of the container at time t_1. [1]

(iv) Show that the speed of approach between **B** and the container immediately after time t_1 is 1.2 m s^{-1}. [1]

(v) Calculate the time t_2 in s between the explosion and the impact of **B** with the container. [1]

(vi) Describe what happens to the container at time t_2 and explain why. [2]

(vii) Plot a graph of the **displacement** in m of the container for time $t = 0$ to 4.0 s. [3]

(OCR 2824 Jun07)

5 This question is about using airbags and seat belts to improve driver safety.

In a test laboratory, a car travelling at 11.0 m s^{-1} strikes a wall head-on and comes to rest in 0.1 s.

A crash test dummy of mass 75 kg is belted into the driver's seat of the car.

(a) Calculate the change of momentum in kg m s^{-1} of the dummy in the crash. [2]

(b) In the crash, the dummy is brought to rest by the seat belt from a speed of 11 m s^{-1} in a time of 0.14 s. Show that the average force on the dummy is about eight times its weight. [2]

The seat belt does not stop the head of the dummy moving forward. With no airbag, the head could strike the steering wheel. Figure 6 shows how the force on the head of the dummy changes over time if the head strikes a steering wheel.

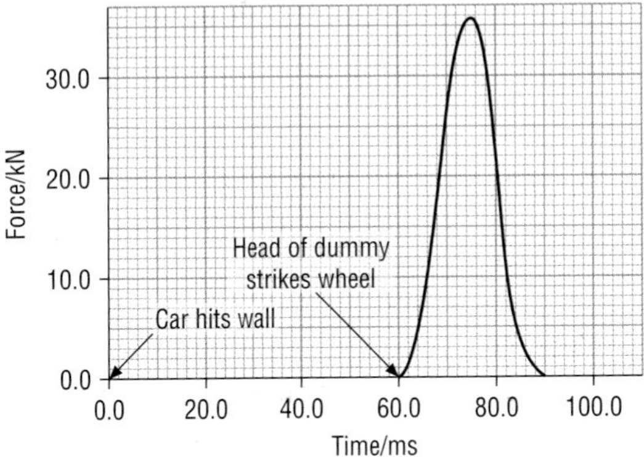

Figure 6

If an airbag is installed, it will begin to inflate from the steering wheel about 20 ms after the collision and takes a further 20 ms to inflate fully. 40 ms after the collision the bag begins to deflate.

(c) Suggest why airbags are most helpful if they are already deflating when the head strikes them. [2]

(d) Copy Figure 6 and draw a second graph on it to show how the force on the head changes if an airbag is present. Explain how your graph shows

(i) that the average force on the head is lower with an airbag

(ii) that the change of momentum of the head is the same in both cases. [4]

(OCR 2863 Jan02)

6 **(a)** Define the momentum of a particle. State the principles of the conservation of linear momentum and the conservation of energy as applied to head-on collisions between particles. Explain the conditions under which linear momentum and kinetic energy are conserved. [6]

(b) Use one or both of the principles in (a) to explain why in elastic collisions a small particle bounces back from a massive stationary particle (Figure 7(a)), whereas a large massive particle incident on a small particle does not bounce back (Figure 7(b)). [6]

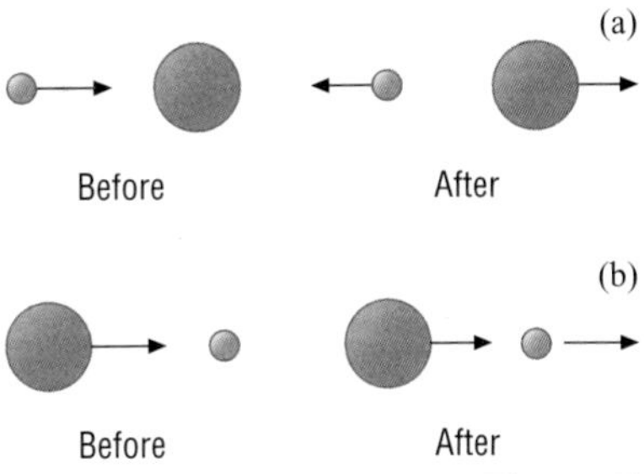

(a) Before After

(b) Before After

Figure 7

(OCR 2824 Jun04)

UNIT 1 Module 2 Circular motion and oscillations

Introduction

So far in your advanced physics course we have mostly considered travelling in a straight line. Circular motion is important too, because it is so common in the Universe and in all sorts of machinery.

The photograph on these pages is a computer-enhanced photograph of the planet Saturn taken from the Voyager 2 satellite at a distance of 43 million kilometres on 12th July 1981. One of Saturn's moons is seen at upper left. Saturn is a gas giant planet composed mainly of hydrogen and helium. Traces of other gases, such as ammonia and methane, are also present. It is the second largest planet in the solar system; it has a diameter of about 120 000 kilometres and is around 95 times more massive than the Earth. Its ring system is mostly made up of millions of orbiting chunks of ice. Each chunk of ice is being pulled by Saturn's gravity, and it is this gravitational force that keeps the ice in orbit for millions of years. In the same way, Saturn is being pulled by the gravitational force between itself and the Sun. It travels once around the Sun in one Saturn year of 29.5 Earth years.

The theory of oscillations has many similarities with circular motion. Both have a frequency, for example. As with circular motion, oscillations have many practical applications. All sound involves oscillations. All vibrations involve oscillations. In fact, any pattern of oscillation, no matter how complex it is, can be considered as a collection of plain, smooth oscillations. Once you have learnt how to deal with regular oscillations you can effectively deal with complex vibrations.

Test yourself

1 Can you name the planets of the Solar System?
2 Which way does the Earth rotate – east to west or west to east?
3 How long does it take for
- the Earth to spin once on its axis
- the Earth to go once round the Sun
- the Moon to go once round the Earth?

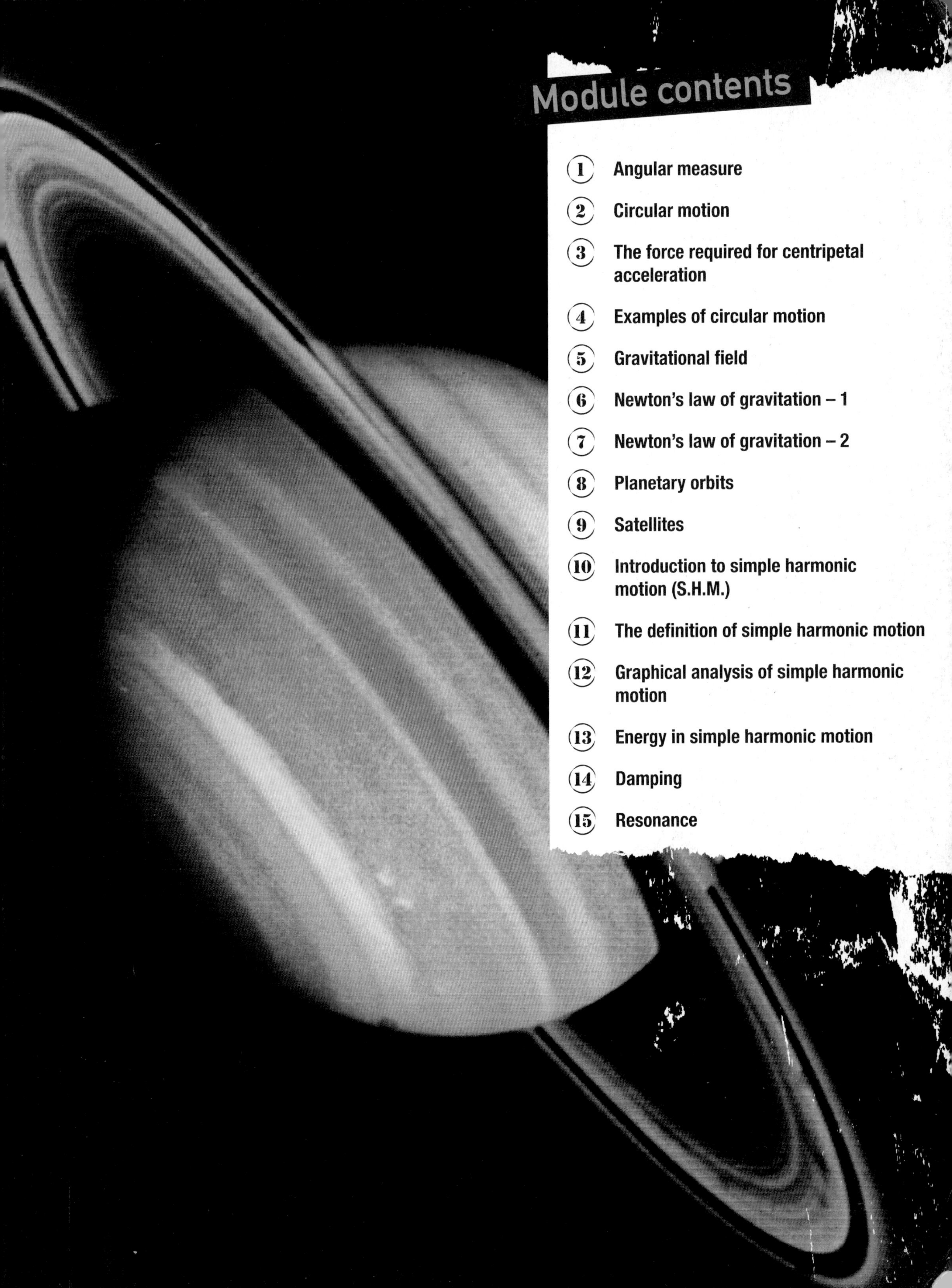

Module contents

1.2 (1) Angular measure

By the end of this spread, you should be able to ...

* **Define the radian and relate it to the degree.**
* **Convert angles from degrees into radians and vice versa.**

Angular measure

By now you know how to measure angles in degrees, with 90° in a right angle and 360° in one complete revolution. During your AS course, when we considered waves, we looked at another unit for angular measure, the **radian**. The radian is the SI unit of angle and is defined in a different way from degrees.

Key definition

One **radian** is the angle subtended at the centre of a circle by an arc of length equal to the circle's radius.

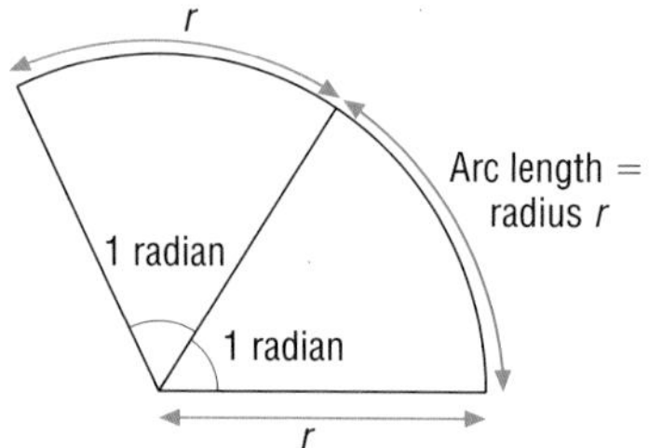

Figure 1 Each radian corresponds to an arc length equal to the radius of the circle

The radian

Imagine you are using a compass to draw a circle. Any radius will do. You put the point of the compass into the paper and start to draw the circle. The arc of the circle you draw has a length. If you stop when the length along the arc equals the circle's radius, then you have rotated the compass through an angle of 1 radian. If you carry on until the arc length is twice the radius of the circle, then the angle will be double that, namely 2 radians. The diagram you will have drawn will look like Figure 1.

Any angle θ, measured in radians, is given by dividing the curved distance along the arc of a circle c by the radius r of the circle.

$$\theta = \frac{c}{r}$$

This is shown in Figure 2.

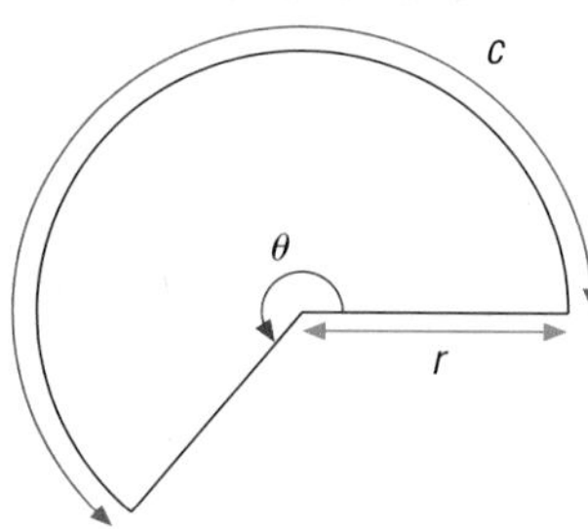

Figure 2 An angle θ in radians, given by $\theta = \frac{c}{r}$

The angle, in radians, for one complete revolution is shown in Figure 3 and will give

$$\text{one revolution} = \frac{\text{circumference of circle}}{\text{radius of circle}}$$

$$= \frac{2\pi r}{r} = 2\pi \text{ radians } (2\pi \text{ rad})$$

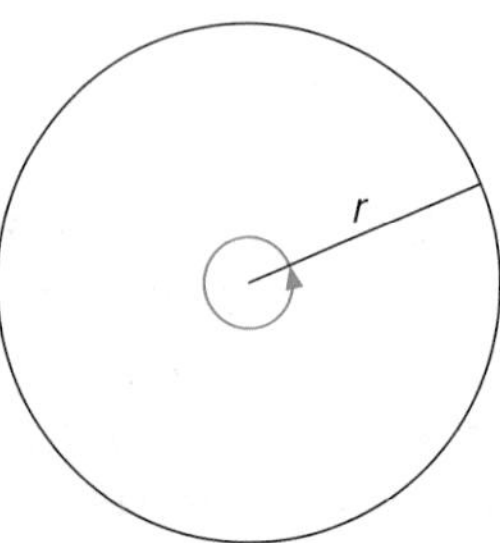

Radius = r
Circumference = $2\pi r$
$\therefore$ Angle = $\frac{2\pi r}{r} = 2\pi$ rad

Figure 3 The angle for one revolution is 2π rad

Conversion of degrees to radians and vice versa

Since one revolution is 2π radians, it is easy to construct a table to convert degrees to radians or vice versa. It is worthwhile making sure that you can use your calculator in both degrees and radians and that you know how to convert one to the other.

Radians	Degrees	Right angles	Revolutions
$2\pi = 6.283$ rad	360	4	1
π	180	2	½
$\pi/2$	90	1	¼
$\pi/3$	60	⅔	1/6
$\pi/4$	45	½	1/8
$\pi/6$	30	⅓	1/12
$\pi/180$	1	1/90	1/360
1	$360/2\pi = 57.3°$	$2/\pi$	$1/2\pi$

Table 1 Converting degrees to radians and vice versa

Rather than using a table for this conversion, you can apply just one conversion that you are familiar with, such as

2π radians = 360°

The reasons for using radians

The radian was chosen as the fundamental measurement of angle in the SI system for several good reasons. One is that the unit itself is a distance divided by a distance and so does not have dimensions. For instance, 6 rad = 6 metres/metres is not necessary. In an equation, the radian figure is applied just as a number, although the unit 'rad' is usually put in just to make it clear that it is an angle.

Another reason for the radian is that the factor of 90 in degrees, while familiar, is a strange number to use when everything else is decimal, that is, measured in tens, hundreds, etc. However, the main reason for using the radian is to do with rotation. A measurement of the rate of rotation of an engine is sometimes quoted in revolutions per minute, but scientists measure the rate of rotation, or angular velocity, in radians per second.

Questions

1 A car windscreen-wiper moves back and forth through an angle of 2.0 radians. Assume that the wiper blade changes direction instantly at the end of its motion.
- **(a)** What is this angle in degrees?
- **(b)** It takes 1.0 s to move from one end of its motion to the other. Plot a graph of its angular displacement in radians starting from the rest position against time for a period of 4.0 s.
- **(c)** Plot a graph of its angular velocity against time for the same time period.
- **(d)** How are the two graphs related?

2 Passengers on a fairground roundabout are 4.0 m from its rotation axis. It rotates once every 12 s.
- **(a)** Write down the angular displacement in degrees and radians of a passenger after a time of 2 s, 6 s, 9 s and 12 s. Is it easier to work in degrees or in radians expressed as a number, or in radians expressed in units of π?
- **(b)** How long does it take for a passenger to move through an angle of $\pi/2$ radians?
- **(c)** The ticket collector walks radially towards a passenger from the centre of the roundabout at 1.5 m s^{-1}. Through what angle, in degrees and in radians, has the roundabout turned when she reaches the passenger? Sketch her path relative to the ground viewed from above.

1.2 ② Circular motion

By the end of this spread, you should be able to ...

- **Explain that a force acting perpendicular to the velocity of an object will make the object describe a circular path.**
- **Explain what is meant by centripetal acceleration.**
- **Use the equations for speed and centripetal acceleration.**

Key definition

The **period** T of an object in circular motion is the time taken to complete one revolution. It is related to the speed v and the radius r by the equation

$$v = \frac{2\pi r}{T}$$

The period *T* for an object in circular motion

When an object travels with constant speed in a circular orbit, the time it takes to complete one complete revolution is called the **period *T*** of rotation. The period will be related to the radius r of the orbit and its speed v, since

$$\text{speed} = \frac{\text{distance}}{\text{time}} = \frac{\text{circumference of circle}}{\text{period}}$$

In symbols this is $v = \dfrac{2\pi r}{T}$

Change in velocity at constant speed

There is a difference between the speed and the velocity of an object, so this heading does make sense. A car going round a corner at a constant speed is changing velocity because the *direction* of the velocity is changing, although its *magnitude* remains constant. The challenge is to calculate a numerical value for the change in velocity – and this can be achieved only when velocities are considered as vectors.

Calculating change in velocity

Consider a simple subtraction problem in monetary terms. You had £18 in your purse last week and now you have £25. What change in the amount of money in your purse has taken place? The answer is obviously £25 – £18 = £7. You could just as easily have worked it out by calculating what must be added to the original amount to get the final amount, with the answer still £7.

Working out a change in velocity, which is a vector, can be done more easily this second way. The addition of vectors can be used in the usual way, but the answers are often quite surprising when using vectors.

In Figure 1 a vector representing the original velocity of a car is shown together with the final velocity after it has gone round a bend. The change in velocity that has taken place is the velocity that has had to be added to the original velocity to get the final velocity.

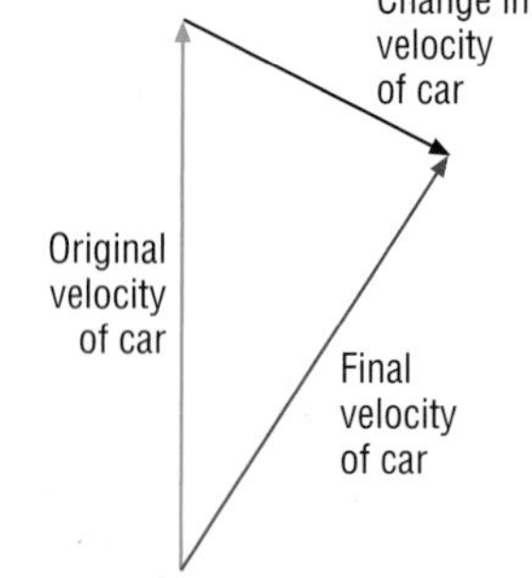

Figure 1 The original velocity plus the change in velocity gives the final velocity

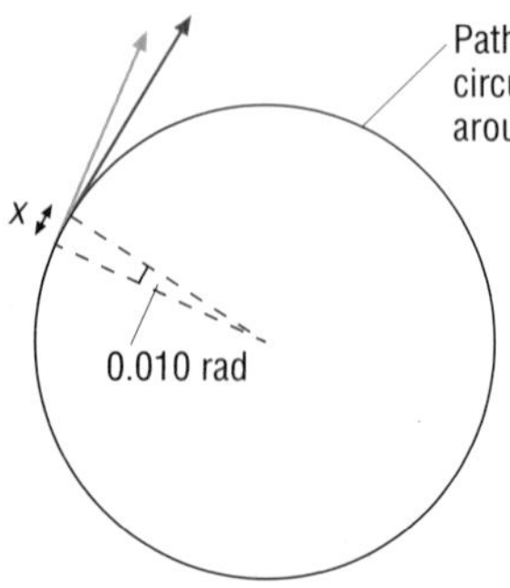

Figure 2 Path of the Moon in orbit around the Earth

Motion in a circle

Now consider how this applies to an object going round in a circle. This could be the Moon going round the Earth, for example. The Moon travels with a constant speed. In one hour it moves through an angle of about 0.01 radians. This is shown in Figure 2. The size of the angle has been exaggerated for clarity. In order to find the change in velocity, the method of Figure 1 needs to be used. This is drawn in Figure 3. The original velocity is on the left-hand side of the figure (blue) and the black change in velocity has been added to it to find the final velocity (pink). Note that the change in velocity is almost at right angles to both the original velocity and the final velocity and it is directed towards the centre of the circular orbit, that is, towards the Earth.

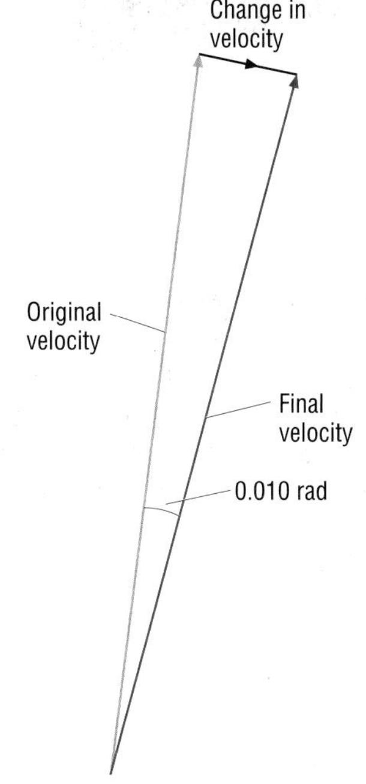

Figure 3 Change in velocity shown by the black arrow

Centripetal acceleration

The change in velocity of something travelling round in a circle with constant speed was shown in the previous paragraph to be in the direction towards the centre of the circular path. Since acceleration is defined by the equation

$$\text{acceleration} = \frac{\text{change in velocity}}{\text{time}},$$

it follows that the acceleration also must be towards the centre of the circular path. The acceleration of a body moving in a circle with a constant speed is called **centripetal acceleration.**

Figures 2 and 3 enable the value of the acceleration to be calculated.

Using the angle moved through as 0.01 rad, and taking the velocity to be v, we get from Figure 3

$$0.01 = \frac{\text{change in velocity}}{v}$$

or change in velocity = $0.01v$.

From Figure 2 the distance x that the Moon moves in time t is velocity × time = vt, and using the angle of 0.01 rad again, this distance x is $0.01r$. So

$$x = vt = 0.01r \quad \text{giving} \quad t = \frac{0.01r}{v}.$$

Finally, we get

$$\text{centripetal acceleration} = \frac{\text{change in velocity}}{\text{time}} = \frac{0.01v}{\left(\frac{0.01r}{v}\right)} = \frac{v^2}{r}.$$

Key definition

The **centripetal acceleration** a of an object travelling in a circle of radius r with constant speed v is given by $a = \frac{v^2}{r}$ in a direction towards the centre of the circle.

Questions

1 For a passenger in Question 2 of spread 1.2.1, what is his
   (a) angular speed?
   (b) linear speed?
   (c) acceleration?

2 The radius of the Moon's orbit is 3.84×10^8 m. It takes 2.36×10^6 s to rotate around the Earth. Calculate
   (a) the speed of the Moon in its orbit
   (b) the acceleration of the Moon towards the Earth.

3 All astronauts undergo training inside a rotating test rig to simulate, among other things, the large g-forces experienced at take-off. An astronaut moves in a circle of radius 9.0 m at a rotational frequency of 0.50 Hz.
   Calculate her
   (a) speed
   (b) centripetal acceleration in m s^{-2} and in units of g.

4 In a particle accelerator, electrons travel very close to the speed of light, 3.0×10^8 m s^{-1}. The LEP (large electron–positron collider) accelerator at CERN has a length of 27 km. Calculate the centripetal acceleration of the electrons and positrons in this machine.

1.2 3 The force required for centripetal acceleration

By the end of this spread, you should be able to ...

* **Apply the equation for centripetal force.**

Force diagrams for circular motion

When an object is travelling round in a circle, it is subject to Newton's laws in exactly the same way as any object travelling in a straight line. Newton's laws apply to all objects at all times unless they are travelling near the speed of light.

As we saw in spread 1.1.4, all forces outside the nuclei of atoms are electrical, magnetic, gravitational or contact forces (and contact forces between objects are in fact electrical forces between atoms). Any free-body force diagram you draw should include only these forces. The first one drawn here, in Figure 1, shows the Moon in its orbit around the Earth. (The effect of the Sun on the Moon and the Earth has not been included, because it has almost no effect on the relationship between the Moon and the Earth.)

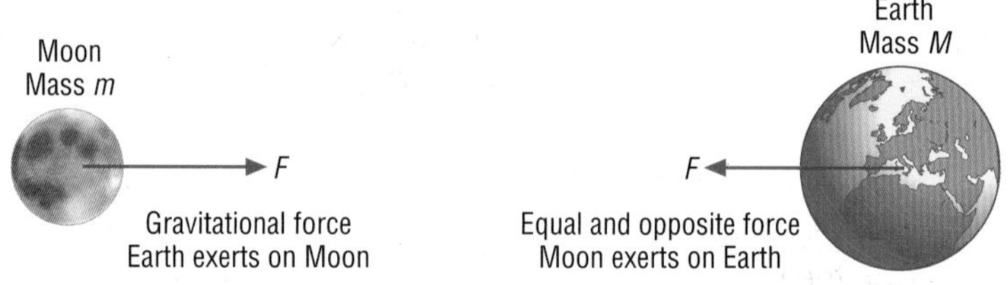

Figure 1 The gravitational forces on the Moon and the Earth

Newton's laws applied to circular motion

In the same way that the Earth exerts a gravitational force on you, pulling you towards the Earth, so the Earth exerts a gravitational force on the Moon, and the Moon exerts a gravitational force on the Earth. These two forces are equal and opposite, and both are gravitational. In other words Newton's third law applies to them. If Newton's second law is applied to the Moon, we get

$$F = m \times a$$

where F is the gravitational force the Earth exerts on the Moon, m is the mass of the Moon and a is the acceleration of the Moon in its orbit around the Earth. In spread 1.2.2 this was shown to be v^2/r in a direction towards the Earth. Note that the direction of the force is the same as the direction of the acceleration. This is always the case. The law, when applied to the Moon, therefore becomes

$$F = m \times \frac{v^2}{r}$$

This is an equation you need to be familiar with, as it occurs in all circular motion problems. In this case it makes it possible to calculate the gravitational force the Earth exerts on the Moon. The mass of the Moon is 7.35×10^{22} kg. From spread 1.2.2 the speed of the Moon in its orbit is 1020 m s^{-1}, giving

$$F = 7.35 \times 10^{22} \times \frac{1020^2}{3.84 \times 10^8} = 1.99 \times 10^{20}\ \text{N}$$

The equal and opposite force that the Moon exerts on the Earth causes tides, but otherwise has a comparatively small wobble effect on the Earth since the Earth has about 80 times greater mass than the Moon.

Examiner tip

Many mistakes are made when dealing with circular motion as a result of candidates drawing correct free-body diagrams showing all the electrical, magnetic and gravitational forces but then adding in an additional force called a centripetal force. Centripetal force is not a separate force from all the others. The example of the Moon shows that the gravitational pull of the Earth on the Moon *is* the centripetal force. There is thus one force on the Moon, not two.

The net force causing the centripetal acceleration is often called the **centripetal force**. Here, the centripetal force *is* the gravitational pull of the Earth on the Moon.

Worked example

A person riding on the London Eye, Figure 2(a), has a mass of 65.0 kg. The radius of the vertical circle travelled through at constant speed is 60.0 m, and one revolution takes 30 minutes.

(a) Calculate:

(i) the speed of the person

(ii) the acceleration of the person

(iii) the resultant (net) force on the person.

(b) Draw force diagrams for the person when:

(i) at the top of the circle

(ii) at the bottom of the circle

(iii) at the side of the circle.

Figure 2 (a) The London Eye. Each observation pod takes 30 minutes to complete one revolution of a circle of radius 60 m

Answer

(a) (i) Speed = distance travelled/time = $2\pi r/t = 2\pi \times 60.0/(30 \times 60) = 0.209\ \text{m s}^{-1}$

(ii) Acceleration = $v^2/r = 0.209^2/60 = 7.31 \times 10^{-4}\ \text{m s}^{-2}$

(iii) Resultant force on person = $m \times a = 65.0 \times 7.31 \times 10^{-4} = 0.048$ N (to 2 sig. figs). The direction of the resultant force is always towards the centre of the circle. It has a very small value because the speed of rotation is slow – unlike the kind of high-speed ride you would expect at an amusement park!

(b) In Figure 2(b), the difference between the forces is exaggerated. The weight of a person of mass 65.0 kg is 65.0 × 9.81 = 637.65 N. To just 1 significant figure, the resultant force is only 0.05 N.

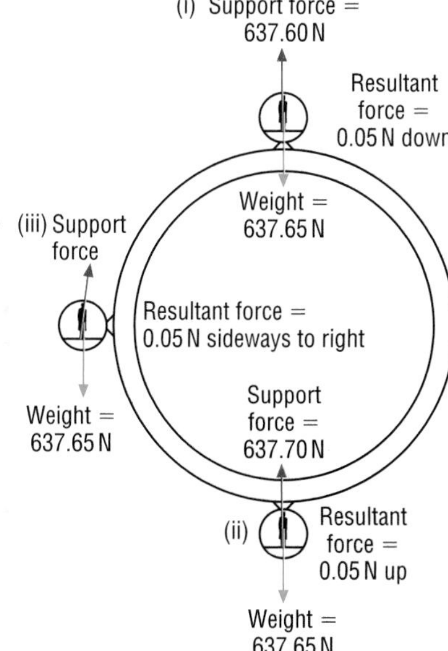

Figure 2 (b) Free-body force diagrams for the person at (i) the top, (ii) the bottom and (iii) the side of the London Eye

Questions

1 Figure 3 shows a child of mass 29 kg sitting on a playground roundabout. Her speed is 1.7 m s^{-1}.

(a) Calculate the centripetal force on her.

(b) What provides this centripetal force? Draw a free-body diagram of the girl, and label with values the three forces acting on the girl.

2 The weight of a person at the Equator is different from his weight at the North or South Pole. One of the reasons for the difference is the rotation of the Earth.

(a) Calculate the change in measured weight caused by the rotation. Take the radius of the Earth to be 6.4×10^6 m and the mass of the person to be 70 kg. One day is 8.64×10^4 s.

(b) Is the person's measured weight greater at the Equator or at the North Pole? Explain.

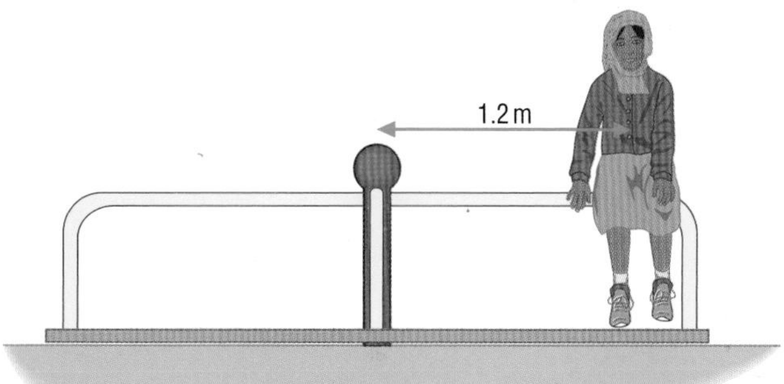

Figure 3

3 A cyclist pedals around a corner in a circular arc of radius 7.0 m at a constant speed of 4.0 m s^{-1}.

(a) What is the resultant force on her and her bicycle of total mass 85 kg?

(b) When going round the corner the cyclist leans inwards towards the centre of the curve. Why is this? Draw a free-body diagram of the cyclist and bicycle, showing the forces acting on them, to illustrate your answer.

1.2 (4) Examples of circular motion

By the end of this spread, you should be able to ...

*** Explain many different features of circular motion.**

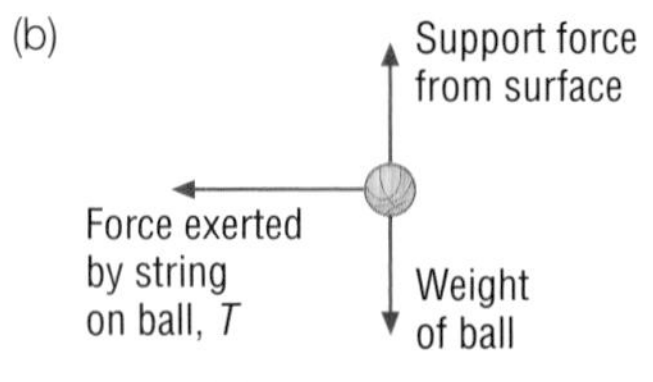

Figure 1 (a) A ball rotating on a flat frictionless circle; **(b)** a free-body force diagram of the ball showing the three forces acting on it. Two of the forces are contact forces; the third is its weight, a gravitational force

Different patterns of circular motion

1 A ball on a string

Figure 1(a) shows the simplest example of this situation, in which the ball is travelling on a friction-free surface. The surface is supporting the ball, and the support force it supplies is equal and opposite to the weight of the ball. The force causing the ball to have acceleration v^2/r towards the central peg is provided by the tension T in the string. r is the radius of the circle. The free-body force diagram for the ball is shown in Figure 1(b).

Newton's second law equation for this situation gives $T = m \times \frac{v^2}{r}$, where m is the mass of the ball.

2 A conical pendulum

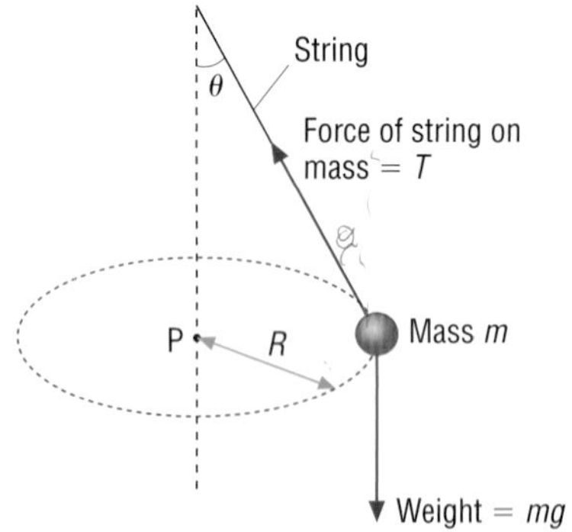

Figure 2 The two forces on a conical pendulum (a mass rotating in a horizontal circle)

Figure 2 shows a so-called conical pendulum. It is basically the same situation as for the ball on the string, but this time without the friction-free surface. The ball rotates in a horizontal circle of radius R, and the resultant (net) force on the ball must be directed towards point P. The force the string exerts on the ball needs to do two things. Its vertical component must be equal and opposite to the weight of the ball, and its horizontal component must accelerate it towards P. This gives

$$T \cos \theta = m \times g \quad \text{and}$$

$$T \sin \theta = m \times \frac{v^2}{R} \quad \text{where } v \text{ is the speed of the ball.}$$

Dividing the second equation by the first cancels out both T and m to give

$$\frac{\sin \theta}{\cos \theta} = \frac{v^2}{Rg} = \tan \theta$$

A conical pendulum is simply demonstrated by swinging a conker round on a string, or hitting a tennis ball when it is attached by a cord to a vertical pole. The effect is also clearly shown on the fairground ride in Figure 3.

Figure 3 A ride at a theme park illustrates a conical pendulum

Figure 4 A theme park ride in which people are rotated so fast that they sit upside down at the top of the circular motion

STRETCH and CHALLENGE

3 A theme park ride

Figure 4 shows a ride in a theme park in which many cabs can be swung in a vertical circle. The occupants of the cab are vertically upwards at the bottom of the ride and vertically downwards at the top. Figure 5 is a diagram of a person of mass 50 kg sitting in one of the cabs when at the top and at the bottom of the circle. The centre of gravity of the person is at a distance of 6.2 m from the centre of rotation, and the cabs rotate once every 3.2 s.

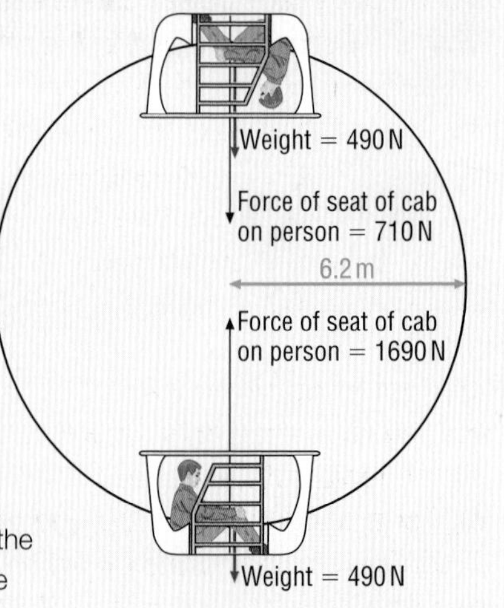

Figure 5 Free-body force diagrams of the person at the top and bottom of the ride

In the free-body force diagram, Figure 5, the first forces to include are the weight of the person in each position shown. The weight is 50 kg × 9.8 m s^{-2} = 490 N. The force that the seat exerts on the person at the top is different from that at the bottom, but the resultant force has the same magnitude at both positions because the acceleration has a fixed magnitude. So now the value of the magnitude of the acceleration needs to be found.

Circumference of circle = $2\pi r = 2\pi \times 6.2$ m = 39.0 m
Speed = 39.0 m/3.2 s = 12.2 m s^{-1}

Acceleration towards the centre = $a = \frac{v^2}{r} = \frac{12.2^2}{6.2} = 23.9$ m s^{-2}

This gives the resultant force towards the centre in both positions as $ma = 50 \times 23.9 = 1200$ N.

At the top there is already a downward force acting on the person, the person's 490 N weight. This is not enough for the acceleration taking place. An additional force is provided by the seat of the cab. This has to be 710 N, making the total correct value of 1200 N.

At the bottom the weight of the person acts in the opposite direction to the acceleration. To get a resultant force of 1200 N acting upwards on the person, there must be a large upwards force exerted by the seat. Its value will need to be 1690 N, so that the resultant force is 1690 N – 490 N = 1200 N. These forces are shown in Figure 5.

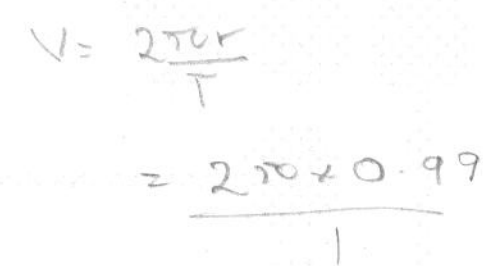

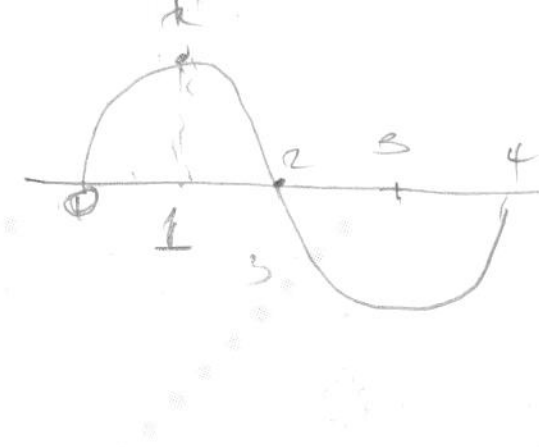

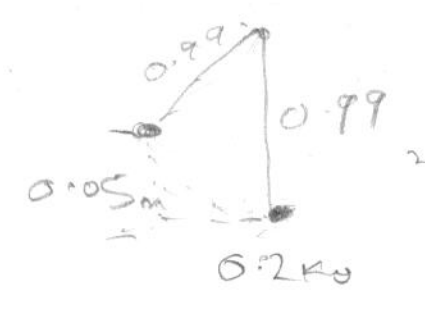

Questions

1 A mass of 200 g is tied to the end of a string of length 0.99 m so that one pass of its swing is almost exactly 1.0 s. The mass is pulled sideways until it is at a vertical height of 5.0 cm above its rest position. The mass is released. Calculate for the instant that the mass is at the lowest point of its swing:

(a) its speed
(b) its acceleration
(c) the tension in the string.

2 The hammer thrown in athletic events consists of a 7.3 kg metal ball at one end of 1.2 m of strong wire cable. The other end of the cable is a handle. To increase the speed of the ball before release, the athlete whirls it around his body on the end of the wire, as shown in Figure 6.
The radius of the swing is approximately 2.0 m. A good hammer-thrower can release the ball at 25 m s^{-1}. Estimate the pull in the athlete's arms just before releasing the hammer.

Figure 6

3 The curved banking of the cycle racing track in a velodrome is carefully designed. Figure 7 shows the front view of a cyclist travelling in a horizontal circle on a banked section of track at angle θ. The combined weight of cycle and rider is W. The force at right angles to the track that the track exerts on the cycle is R. The dotted line shows the line of action of the resultant force.

(a) Show that $W = R \cos\theta$.
(b) Use (a) to show that $\tan \theta = v^2/gr$, where v is the cyclist's speed and r is the radius of the curve.
(c) For a velodrome with banked track of radius 35 m, calculate the angle θ of the banking for the cyclist riding at 15 m s^{-1}.
(d) For a value of W equal to 785 N, calculate R.

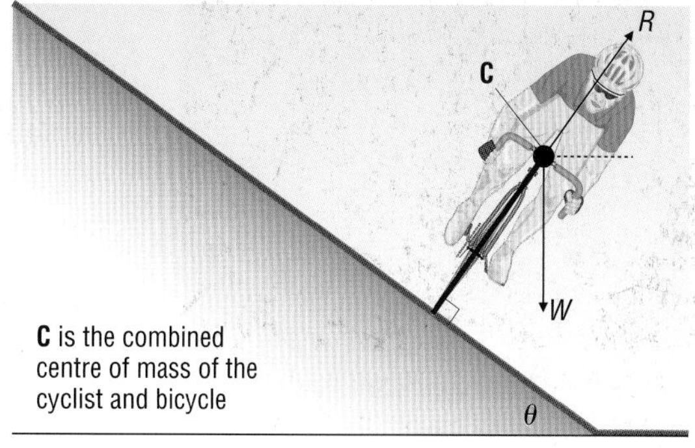

C is the combined centre of mass of the cyclist and bicycle

Figure 7

1.2 (5) Gravitational field

By the end of this spread, you should be able to ...

* **Describe how a mass creates a gravitational field in the space around it.**
* **Define gravitational field strength.**
* **Use gravitational field lines to represent a gravitational field.**
* **Explain the uniformity of the gravitational field strength close to the Earth's surface.**

Key definition

A **field** is the region in which a force operates.

Introduction

We will deal with several types of fields during your A2 course. **Gravitational field** is the first one we will look at here, but you will probably have heard of magnetic fields earlier in your science courses. Electric field is another type of field you will need to understand. Obviously, the use of the word 'field' in these expressions has nothing to do with fields in the countryside. For instance, an electric field is a region where a force is caused on an electric charge.

The special feature of all fields is that the forces are caused at a distance. There is no need for there to be anything connecting or in between the system producing the field and the system on which a force is caused, though of course Newton's third law still applies. In many cases there is a vacuum between the two systems, such as that between the Earth and the Moon.

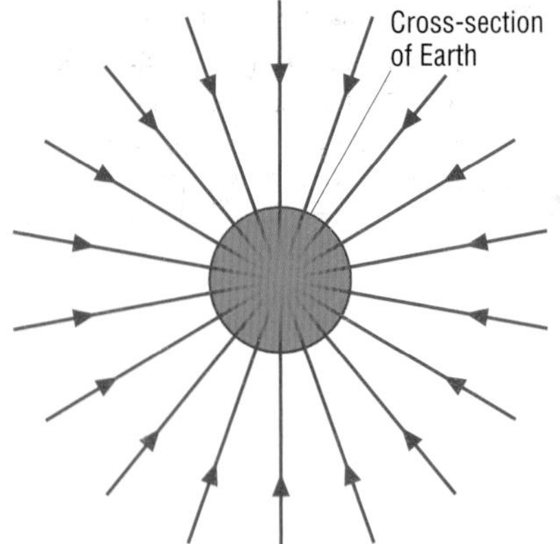

Figure 1 The Earth's gravitational field, shown in two dimensions

Gravitational field

Here, we will look in particular at the gravitational field. In spread 1.2.3, we dealt with the gravitational force that the Earth exerts on the Moon. It is therefore correct to say that the Moon is in the Earth's gravitational field. There is a force pulling the Moon in the direction of the Earth, so the direction of the Earth's gravitational field is directly towards the Earth.

One fundamental difference between gravity fields and electric or magnetic fields is that, in the case of electric fields, unlike charges attract and like charges repel. But masses only ever attract. For this reason, gravity fields always start at infinity and end on matter; electric fields start on positive charges and end on negative charges.

The Earth's gravitational field

A two-dimensional representation of the Earth's gravitational field is given in Figure 1. There are several points to note about the diagram.

- It represents the field. The field covers the whole of the space around the Earth, not just where a line happens to be drawn.
- The field is always directed towards the Earth.
- As field lines meet mass inside the Earth, they fade away. By the time the centre of the Earth is reached, the field is zero.
- The diagram is two-dimensional. Therefore, if you compare the strength of the field at one point with another point twice as far away from the centre, the lines will be twice as far apart. In three dimensions, this will mean that the area covered is four times greater. At twice the distance the field has a quarter the strength. This is an example of an inverse square law. For instance, ten times the distance will result in a hundredth of the field strength.

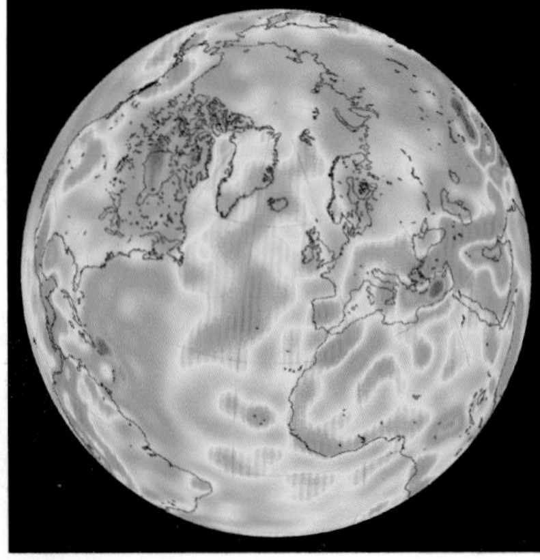
Figure 2 Variations in the Earth's gravitational field at its surface; blue indicates a low field and red a high field

The gravitational field of the Earth varies at the surface of the Earth because matter is not uniformly distributed across the Earth. Water is less dense than rock, for example, and mountains are further away from the centre of the Earth than the sea is. Also, some of the land mass that contains denser mineral deposits has the effect of increasing the value of the gravitational field in that region. Figure 2 shows this variation in false colour.

Definition of gravitational field strength

Gravitational field strength at any point is the force acting per unit mass at that point. Note that this definition makes gravitational field strength a vector since force is a vector, and therefore it determines the direction of the field in the direction of the force.

In equation form this gives

$$\text{gravitational field strength} = \frac{\text{force}}{\text{mass}}$$

The SI unit of gravitational field strength is therefore newtons per kilogram, N kg^{-1}.

Key definition

The **gravitational field strength** at any point is the force acting per unit mass at that point.

The relationship between the acceleration due to gravity and the gravitational field strength

The numerical value of the gravitational field strength at the surface of the Earth now needs to be determined. Figure 3 shows a 1 kg mass near the Earth's surface. The gravitational field strength is therefore given by

$$\text{gravitational field strength} = \frac{\text{weight of a 1 kilogram mass}}{\text{1 kilogram}}$$

However, we also know that in free fall the acceleration of a 1 kg mass when acted on by its weight has the value 9.81 m s^{-2}.

So the weight of a 1 kg mass = $1.00 \times 9.81 = 9.81$ N

This gives the gravitational field strength of the Earth at its surface $= \dfrac{9.81\text{ N}}{1.00\text{ kg}} = 9.81\text{ N kg}^{-1}$.

Because the numerical value of the gravitational field strength of the Earth and the acceleration of free fall due to gravity are the same, there is a tendency to regard them as one and the same thing. However, the acceleration of free fall uses the units of acceleration, whereas gravitational field strength uses different units. In effect, we are using the idea of gravitational field strength when we write or say 'a mass of 10 kg has a weight of 98.1 N'.

Examiner tip

The fact that these two quantities have the same numerical value has a deeper significance. This is that the gravitational pull of one body on another depends on its gravitational mass. The inertia of the same body, that is, its reluctance to accelerate, depends on its inertial mass. The equality of the two values in effect states that

inertial mass = gravitational mass

That is, one quantity, mass, determines how reluctant the body is to accelerate under the influence of a force *and* determines how much it is attracted to another body by the gravitational force.

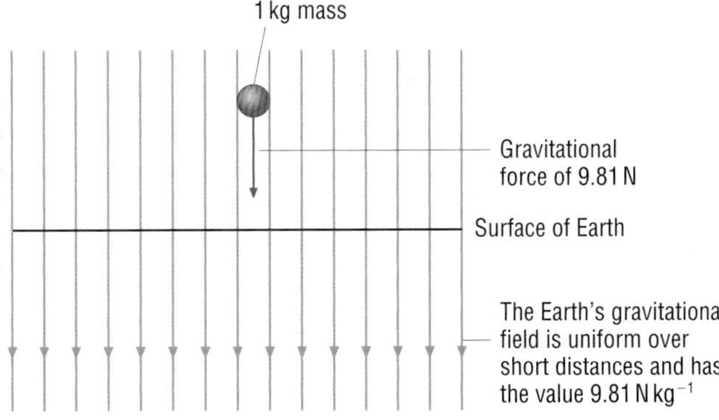

Figure 3 A 1 kilogram mass near the surface of the Earth

Questions

1 Imagine a universe where the stars are flat discs instead of spheres. Imagine a binary star system consisting of two stars of equal mass orbiting around each other with their faces parallel on opposite ends of the diameter of the orbit. Draw gravitational field lines between the disc surfaces using the rules given above, taking the diameter of the orbit to be four times the diameter of the discs.

2 Why can gravitational field lines never cross?

3 An astronaut of mass 120 kg in his spacesuit would weigh 3.2 kN at the surface of Jupiter if he could get there. What is the gravitational field strength at the surface of Jupiter?

4 How far above the surface of the Earth is the gravitational field strength **(a)** half and **(b)** one quarter of its value at the surface? The radius of the Earth is 6.4×10^6 m.

1.2 (6) Newton's law of gravitation – 1

By the end of this spread, you should be able to …

- **State and use Newton's law of gravitation.**
- **Analyse circular orbits relating gravitational force to centripetal acceleration.**
- **Use $g = -\frac{GMm}{r^2}$ to determine the mass of the Earth or a similar object.**

Newton's law of gravitation

When looking at gravitational fields in the last spread, 1.2.5, we saw that gravitational field sketches imply that if you move 10 times further away from a body, the field would be only one hundredth of the value. This was given as an example of an inverse square law. Newton took this idea further when he analysed the motion of planets around a sun. Since distances between planets and a sun are much larger than the sizes of the objects themselves, we will consider the system shown in Figure 1 in which two point masses M and m are separated by a distance r.

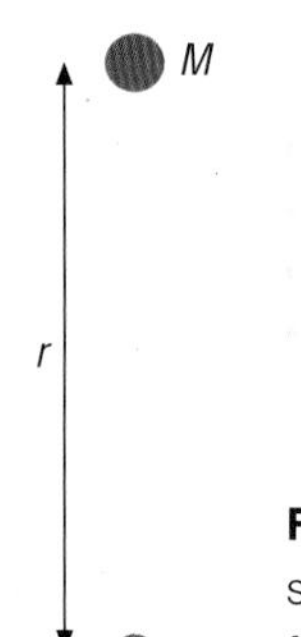

Figure 1 Point mass M separated by a distance r from another point mass m

Key definition

The **gravitational force** of attraction between two bodies is directly proportional to the product of their masses and inversely proportional to the square of the distance between them.

Newton's law states:

> **The gravitational force of attraction between two bodies is directly proportional to the product of their masses and inversely proportional to the square of the distance between them.**

Put into symbols the law becomes

$F \propto \frac{Mm}{r^2}$ or by putting in a constant of proportionality

$$F = -\frac{GMm}{r^2}$$

where G is called the gravitational constant. The reason for including the minus sign in the equation is to indicate that the force is an *attractive* force. (When we later deal with the same sort of equation for electric charges, there will be no minus sign, because two positive charges *repel* one another.)

The numerical value of G was first determined in 1740 by making an accurate measurement of how far from the vertical was a mass suspended on a string when it was being pulled a small amount sideways by a mountain. Some guesswork was needed to know the mass of the mountain. Big G (as it is often called to distinguish it from little g, the acceleration of free fall) is still not known as accurately as most other fundamental constants. The Institute of Physics gives its value as

$$G = 6.673 \times 10^{-11}\ \text{m}^3\ \text{kg}^{-1}\ \text{s}^{-2}$$

(a)

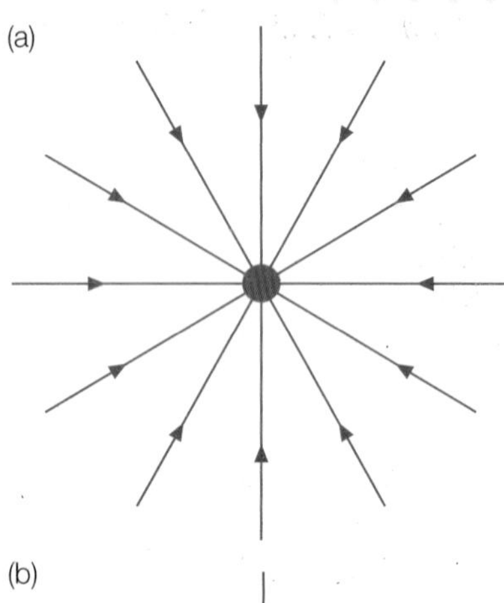

(b)

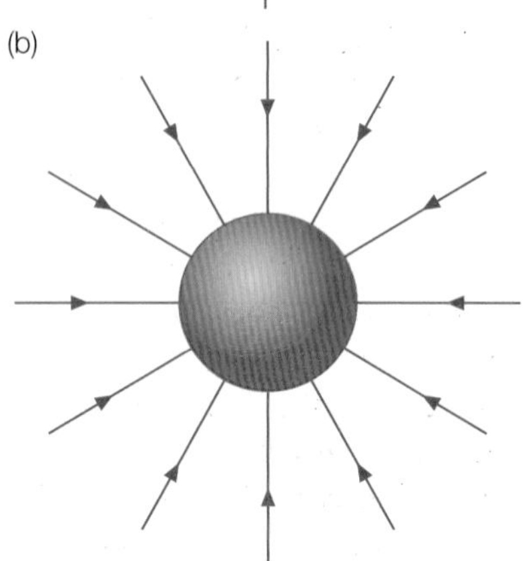

Figure 2 (a) A point object of mass M; **(b)** a sphere of mass M

Calculating the mass of the Sun

When applying Newton's law of gravitation to real objects rather than point objects, the size of the objects involved needs to be considered. Consider two objects, shown in Figure 2. In Figure 2(a) there is a point object of mass M, and in Figure 2(b) there is a sphere of the

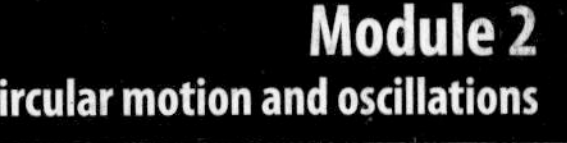

same mass M. The field inside the sphere decreases to zero at its centre, but outside the sphere the field is identical to that of the point mass. This actually makes calculations very straightforward. Most planets and suns are almost spherical, so they can be considered to be point objects at their centres provided the field is needed outside their surfaces.

If the law of gravitation is applied to the motion of the Earth around the Sun, we have the situation shown in Figure 3. The Earth takes a year to travel in its orbit around the Sun, and the orbit is very nearly circular, with radius 1.50×10^{11} m.

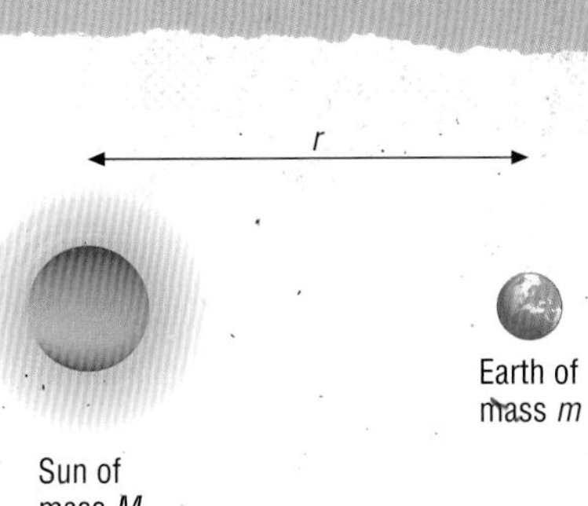

Figure 3 The law of gravitation applied to the motion of the Earth around the Sun

The gravitational force acting on the Earth, F, is

$$\frac{GMm}{r^2} = \frac{6.67 \times 10^{-11}\, mM}{(1.50 \times 10^{11})^2} = 2.96 \times 10^{-33}\, mM$$

The velocity of the Earth in its orbit, v, is

$$\frac{\text{circumference}}{\text{time of 1 year}} = \frac{2\pi \times 1.50 \times 10^{11}}{365 \times 24 \times 3600} = 2.99 \times 10^{4}\ \text{m s}^{-1}$$

The force causes the centripetal acceleration a of the Earth to equal v^2/r, so using $F = ma$ we get

$$2.96 \times 10^{-33}\, mM = m\frac{(2.99 \times 10^{4})^2}{1.50 \times 10^{11}}$$

Note that m cancels from both sides of the equation, giving

$$M = \frac{(2.00 \times 10^{4})^2}{1.50 \times 10^{11} \times 2.96 \times 10^{33}} = 2.01 \times 10^{30}\ \text{kg}$$

Various approximations have been made in doing this calculation:

- The Earth's orbit is not quite circular.
- It has been assumed that the Sun is stationary. The movement of the Sun due to the Earth going round it is very small because of the Sun's very large mass compared with that of the Earth.
- A year is not 365 days exactly.

As we should not quote this answer to more than two significant figures, we get 2.0×10^{30} kg. More accurate determination actually gives the mass as 1.99×10^{30} kg.

If a similar calculation is done for the Moon going round the Earth, then the mass of the Earth can also be found.

Questions

1 Two identical spheres are placed with their centres 1.5 m apart, as shown in Figure 4.

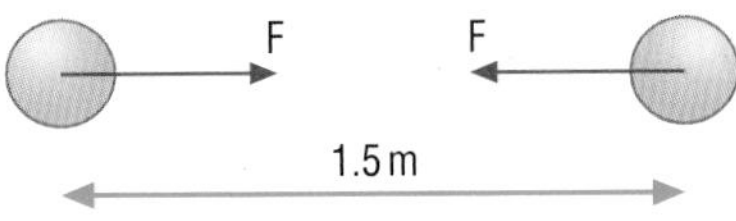

Figure 4

The mass of each sphere is 4.5 kg. Calculate the force of gravitational attraction between the two spheres.

2 The gravitational field strength at the surface of Jupiter is 27 N kg^{-1}. The radius of Jupiter is 11 times that of the Earth. Calculate the mass of Jupiter, taking the radius of the Earth to be 6.4×10^{6} m.

3 The moon Io orbits Jupiter in 43 hours at an orbital radius of 4.2×10^{8} m. Use these data to calculate the mass of Jupiter.

4 Inside the Earth it is only the mass in the sphere beneath you that contributes to the gravitational pull on you. Assume that the Earth is a sphere of uniform density. What is the gravitational field strength halfway to the centre of the Earth? And three-quarters of the way to the centre of the Earth? Write down the general rule for the variation of g with distance from the centre of the Earth to its surface.

STRETCH and CHALLENGE

A hole through the centre of the Earth would be impossible for many reasons. Not only would the digging pose insurmountable problems in the high temperatures but also the outer part of the Earth's core is liquid. Nevertheless, it is often assumed that a body falling freely and directly towards the ground would, if there was a hole large enough, fall right down to the centre of the Earth. There are two main reasons why this is not true. Question 4 should give you an idea for one of these reasons, when you bear in mind that the Earth is not a perfect sphere and that the UK is neither at a pole nor on the Equator. Expand on this reason and suggest the other main reason for a falling body not falling through the Earth's centre.

1.2 (7) Newton's law of gravitation – 2

By the end of this spread, you should be able to …

- **Select and apply the equation for gravitational field strength.**
- **Explain the nature of the gravitational field strength close to the Earth's surface.**

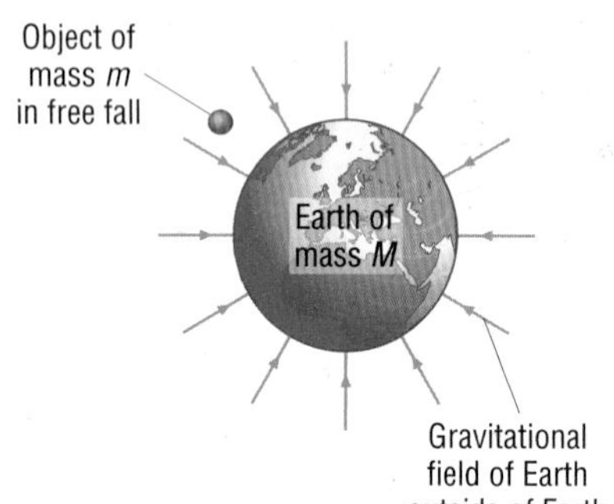

Figure 1 An object in free fall

The relationship between G and g

The value of the attractive force between an object near the Earth's surface and the Earth itself obviously determines g, the acceleration of free fall. To find g in terms of G we therefore need to consider the situation shown in Figure 1.

Remembering that, as it can be considered a sphere, the entire mass of the Earth may be thought of as a point mass at its centre, and applying the law of gravitation together with the $F = ma$ equation, we get

$\frac{GMm}{r^2} = m \times g$, where r is the radius of the Earth.

And m cancels to give $g = \frac{GM}{r^2}$

When accurate numerical values are put into this equation, it gives

$$g = \frac{6.673 \times 10^{-11} \times 5.977 \times 10^{24}}{(6.371 \times 10^{6})^2} = 9.83\ \text{m s}^{-2}$$

Simplifying measurements – assuming ideal conditions

This value of 9.83 m s^{-2} is slightly different from the value of 9.81 m s^{-2} that you are more familiar with. This is because the Earth is rotating, and so when you measure the acceleration of free fall in the laboratory, you are measuring it in relation to the floor. You ignore the fact that the floor itself is accelerating, because it is travelling round in a circle once per day. If you measured the acceleration at the North Pole, you would get a value nearer to 9.83 m s^{-2}. Even then it would not be exact, because the Earth is not quite a sphere. It has a larger equatorial radius than polar radius. Science often develops in this way. A theory is used assuming ideal conditions. In practice, when conditions are not ideal, minor changes are made. Better measurements require further modification, as with the value of g.

The variation of g with altitude

A simple extension of the equation $g = GM/r^2$ enables the value of g to be obtained at any height above the Earth's surface. This is important for satellite positioning, as the worked example on the following page shows.

Satellites

There are literally hundreds of unmanned satellites in orbit around the Earth. But there is one satellite, the International Space Station (ISS), that is permanently manned.

Figure 2 The International Space Station seen over the Earth from the approaching space shuttle Discovery

The ISS has a mass of 280 tonnes, a pressurised volume of 400 m^3 and overall dimensions of 78 m × 45 m. Its power is supplied by photocells that face the Sun. Its distance from the Earth can be varied between about 300 and 450 km, using rocket motors. Contrary to popular opinion, at this distance the gravitational force on it is large. But astronauts appear to be weightless here, because the gravitational force on them is necessary to give them an acceleration.

Astronauts are in free fall, accelerating towards the Earth all the time. This is shown in Figure 3. Consider an object when it is dropped (a). It accelerates towards the centre of the Earth. If it is thrown sideways, then while it is falling it continues to move sideways, landing some distance from where it was thrown (b). The faster it is thrown sideways, the further it travels before landing, (c) and (d). If it is thrown sideways fast enough, it will fall continuously but never hit the Earth. This is what is happening with any satellite. At its distance from the Earth, the atmosphere is so thin that there is very little air resistance, so it keeps on travelling around the Earth.

Another popular misconception is that gravity ceases once you are out of the atmosphere. There is no connection between gravity and air density at all. An object in a vacuum on the Earth's surface has exactly the same gravitational force on it as it would when in air.

Figure 4 shows two astronauts who appear to be weightless. Their weight is accelerating them, and the weight of the space station is accelerating it at the same rate. Therefore, no force is provided by the space station on the astronauts. Normally, a person on the Earth has a support force provided by the floor. But this is not needed in the space station. An astronaut is in the same situation as a person who is in a lift when the lift cable breaks, namely free fall.

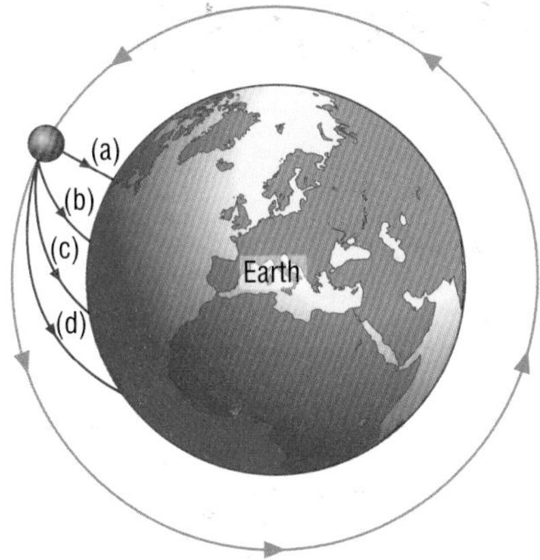

Figure 3 Falling objects near the Earth. If given sufficient sideways velocity, the object falls continuously around the Earth and becomes a satellite

Figure 4 Two astronauts in the International Space Station

Worked example

A communications satellite is to be placed in a polar orbit at a height of 500 km above the ground. What is

(a) the value of g at this height?

(b) the speed at which the satellite needs to be travelling?

Answer

(a) The radius of the orbit = radius of Earth + 500 km = $6.37 \times 10^6 + 5.00 \times 10^5$
$= 6.87 \times 10^6$ km

Value of $g = GM/r^2 = 6.67 \times 10^{-11} \times 5.98 \times 10^{24}/(6.87 \times 10^6)^2$
$= 8.45$ m s^{-2} to 3 sig. figs.

Note: this could have been done using the inverse square law, giving

$$g' = \left(\frac{6.37 \times 10^6}{6.87 \times 10^6}\right) \times 9.83 = 8.45 \text{ m s}^{-2}$$

(b) The acceleration of the satellite is its centripetal acceleration, v^2/r, so

$$8.45 \text{ m s}^{-2} = \frac{v^2}{6.87 \times 10^6 \text{ m s}^{-1}} \text{ giving } v = \sqrt{8.45 \times 6.87 \times 10^6} = 7620 \text{ m s}^{-1}$$

Questions

Take the mass of the Earth to be 6.0×10^{24} kg and its radius to be 6.4×10^6 m.

1 A satellite orbiting in a circular orbit at a height of 36 000 km above the surface of the Earth with an orbital period of 24 hours (86 400 s) is said to be geosynchronous. Explain what this means. Use the data to prove that the statement is true by calculating g at this height and by calculating v^2/r $(= 4\pi^2r/T^2)$.

2 Estimate the orbital period in minutes of a satellite that is only 100 km above the Earth's surface.

3 The space shuttle orbits the Earth at a height of 4.0×10^5 m above the surface. The kinetic energy of the shuttle in this orbit is 2.8×10^{12} J. Calculate:

(a) the force of gravity on the shuttle

(b) the gravitational field strength at this height

(c) the mass of the space shuttle.

4 Look for an algebraic expression for the period T of a satellite of mass m orbiting the Earth, mass M, at a distance r from its centre in spread 1.2.8. Does your expression include the mass m? How does the answer to this question enable you to explain that all objects in the same orbit can move together without touching? Use this to complete the explanation as to why an astronaut appears weightless in a spacecraft with the rocket motors off. What happens when the rocket motors are fired?

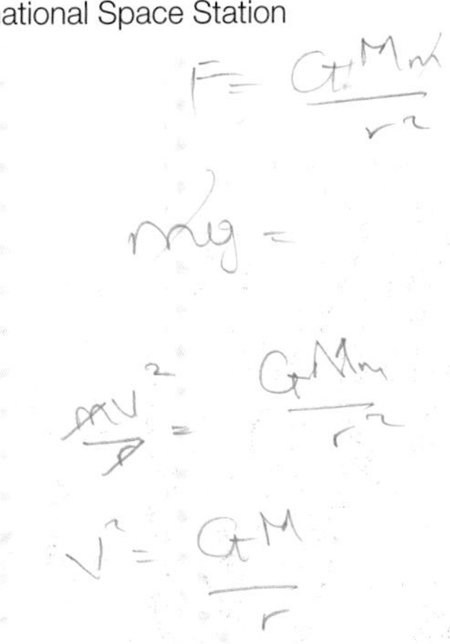

1.2 (8) Planetary orbits

By the end of this spread, you should be able to ...

- ✻ **Define and use the period of an object describing an orbital radius.**
- ✻ **Select and apply Kepler's third law to solve problems.**
- ✻ **Derive the equation $T^2 = (4\pi^2/GM)r^3$ from first principles.**

Introduction

After Copernicus introduced the idea of the Sun being at the centre of all the known planets, an experimental physicist named Brahe spent 20 years or so plotting the positions of all the planets. He did this with no telescope, just a three-dimensional protractor, called an astrolabe. Once all this information had been collected, other people tried to form it into a pattern that made sense.

Kepler did manage to relate the time it took for a planet to complete one orbit around the Sun to the average distance it was from the Sun. He also established that the paths of the planets around the Sun are ellipses rather than circles and that the speed of the planets varies over the course of one revolution. These are Kepler's first two laws. However, since the ellipses are very close to being circles, we will assume that they are circles and that the planets move at a constant speed. Figure 1 shows the Sun and eight planets. The planets' sizes are shown to scale, but they are not the correct distances apart.

Figure 1 The eight planets of the Solar System from left to right in their order from the Sun. The four small rocky planets of the inner Solar System are Mercury, Venus, Earth and Mars. The four gas giant planets of the outer Solar System are Jupiter, Saturn, Uranus and Neptune. In August 2006, Pluto (not shown) lost its status as a planet. Planetary rings and moons, a solar flare and the asteroid belt between Mars and Jupiter are also shown. The size of the Sun and planets are to scale. The distances between the planets are not to scale

Kepler's third law

The previous paragraph summarised Kepler's first two laws. The third law relates two quantities:

- the average distance of a planet from the centre of the Sun, r
- the length of time it takes for the planet to complete one orbit of the Sun, its **period** T.

Kepler found, by analysing the data from Brahe, that

the period squared is proportional to the mean radius cubed.

In mathematical terms this is

$$T^2 \propto r^3$$

Key definitions

The **period** of a planet is the time it takes to complete one orbit around the Sun. For the Earth, it is one year.

Keplar's third law states that the period of a planet squared equals the mean radius of its orbit cubed.

The values of T and r for eight planets are given in the table, using SI units to 3 sig. figs.

Note that one year is 3.16×10^7 seconds.

	Period T/s	Mean radius r/m
Mercury	7.60×10^6	5.79×10^{10}
Venus	1.94×10^7	1.08×10^{11}
Earth	3.16×10^7	1.50×10^{11}
Mars	5.94×10^7	2.28×10^{11}
Jupiter	3.75×10^8	7.78×10^{11}
Saturn	9.30×10^8	1.43×10^{12}
Uranus	2.65×10^9	2.87×10^{12}
Neptune	5.20×10^9	4.50×10^{12}

Table 1 Values of orbital period and radius for eight planets

Newton's explanation of Kepler's third law

Kepler had no idea why his third law was correct. A law like this, made to fit available figures without a theoretical basis, is called an empirical law. It was the application of Newton's law of gravitation and his second law of motion that, when taken together, gave an explanation of Kepler's third law and strong confirmation of Newton's laws themselves. You need to be able to derive Newton's reasoning for yourself. When deriving an expression such as this, start with a sketch diagram on which important details can be drawn. See Figure 2.

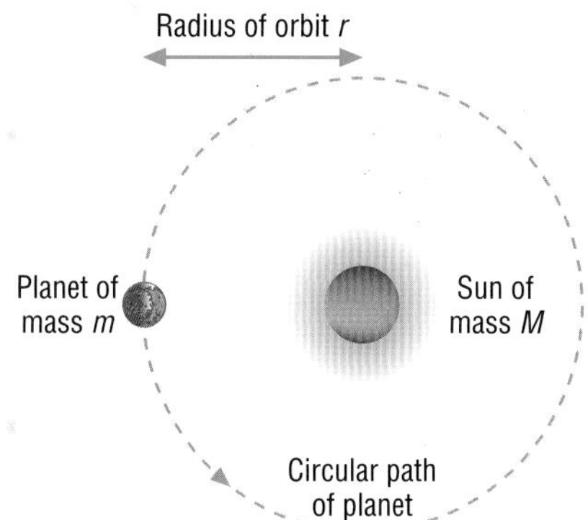

Figure 2 A planet of mass m rotating in a circle of radius r around the Sun of mass M

The gravitational force F that the Sun exerts on the planet is given by the law of gravitation:

$$F = \frac{GMm}{r^2}$$

The mass of the Sun is very much larger than the mass of any planet; therefore, the Sun is assumed to remain stationary, with the planet moving in a circle of radius r. The force F causes the centripetal acceleration of the planet:

$$F = \frac{mv^2}{r}, \text{ where } v = \frac{\text{circumference of circle}}{\text{period}} = \frac{2\pi r}{T}$$

Combining these equations together gives

$$F = \frac{m\,4\pi^2 r^2}{T^2 r} = \frac{GMm}{r^2} \text{ and finally } T^2 = \left(\frac{4\pi^2}{GM}\right)r^3$$

Since $4\pi^2/GM$ is constant, T^2 is proportional to r^3.

Questions

Take the mass of the Sun to be 2.0×10^{30} kg.

1 Answer Question 2 from spread 1.2.7 using the formula above.

2 Use Kepler's third law and the data in Table 1 to calculate:

(a) the orbital period (a year) of Neptune.

(b) the mean radius of the orbit of Venus. (One year on Venus is 225 days.)

3 Use the data for Saturn from the table above to calculate the mass of the Sun.

4 The Sun loses mass at a rate of 6.2×10^{11} kg s^{-1}.

(a) How long will it take for the mass of the Sun to decrease by 1%?

(b) What effect will this change have on the orbits of the planets?

1.2 (9) Satellites

By the end of this spread, you should be able to ...

* **Define the geostationary orbit of a satellite and state the uses of such satellites.**
* **Calculate the radius of a geostationary orbit.**

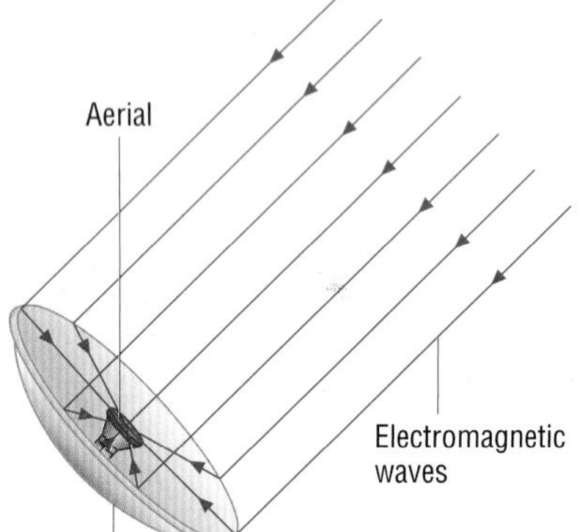

Figure 1 A dish aerial focuses electromagnetic waves from a geostationary satellite onto an aerial

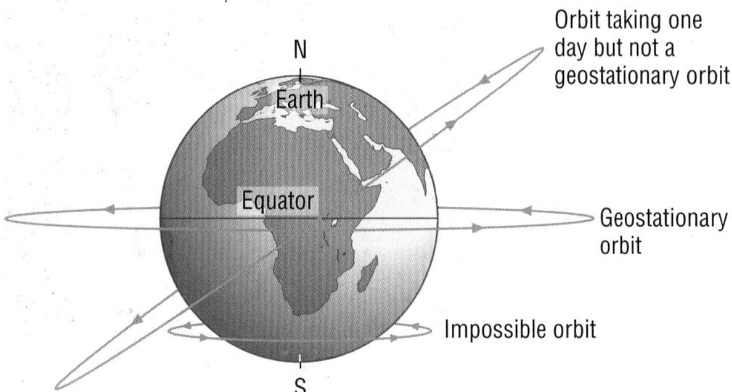

Figure 2 Orbits around the Earth

Figure 3 An Intelsat (international telecommunications satellite) geostationary satellite with photocells to provide power and dish aerials for reception and transmission of signals

Geostationary orbits

In 2004 there were over 130 satellites in a geostationary orbit around the Earth. Most were used for telecommunication, particularly television broadcasting. The dishes you see on houses focus electromagnetic waves carrying a television signal onto an aerial. The dishes must point to a satellite that appears to stay still (see Figure 1).

In order to appear stationary, a geostationary satellite must orbit the Earth at the same rate as the Earth rotates on its axis. Therefore, the satellite must orbit once per day. It must also travel in the same direction as the Earth, from west to east. (Note: the Sun appears to rise in the east and set in the west *because* the Earth itself is travelling from west to east). The satellite accelerates towards the centre of the Earth because the force on it is in that direction. Its orbit must therefore be centred on the centre of the Earth.

Figure 2 shows an orbit that is impossible, as the centre of the orbit is not at the centre of the Earth. It also shows an orbit that is possible but is not geostationary. When this satellite is viewed from the Earth, it would be in the northern sky at the same time each day and then 12 hours later would be in the southern sky (it is geosynchronous). In order to be geostationary a satellite must be directly over the equator. In summary, a geostationary satellite must:

- have its orbit centred on the centre of the Earth
- be travelling from west to east
- be over the equator
- have a period of 24 hours.

The distance a geostationary satellite is from the Earth

At the end of spread 1.2.8 an equation was given for the period T of a planet in an orbit of radius r around the Sun. It was

$$T^2 = \left(\frac{4\pi^2}{GM}\right)r^3$$

A geostationary satellite is effectively a planet of the Earth, so if M is the mass of the Earth, we can use this equation to find the radius of a geostationary satellite's orbit. T needs to be 24 hours = 86 400 s. This gives

$$86\,400^2 = \left(\frac{4\pi^2 r^3}{6.67 \times 10^{-11} \times 5.98 \times 10^{24}}\right)$$

and hence

$$r = \sqrt[3]{\left(\frac{86\,400^2 \times 6.67 \times 10^{-11} \times 5.98 \times 10^{24}}{4\pi^2}\right)} = 4.23 \times 10^7\,\text{m} = 42\,300\,\text{km}$$

This is the radius of the required orbit. The height above the Earth will be

(42 300 km – radius of Earth) = 42 300 km – 6400 km = 35 900 km

The uses of satellites

Geostationary satellites

As stated earlier, geostationary satellites are used for telecommunications. An Intelsat satellite is shown in Figure 3. To get a satellite such as this into its geostationary orbit requires a large gain in its kinetic energy and gravitational potential energy. Figure 4 shows how the potential energy of any object increases as it moves away from the Earth. g decreases as the distance from the Earth increases, so the graph of potential energy against distance from the Earth is not a straight line. This figure is drawn in three dimensions to show what is called the 'gravity well' of the Earth. The high gain in potential energy makes for high costs in putting a satellite into a geostationary orbit.

Cost is not the only problem with geostationary orbits. Because they are a long way from the Earth, they need to transmit at high power. The footprint covered by any satellite can be very large, as shown in Figure 5. This large area is an advantage in that many houses can receive the signal, but there is a limit to how much a signal can be amplified when the power received by a dish can be as little as a few picowatts (10^{-12} W). With international telephone calls, this is less of a problem, as both transmitting and receiving dishes can be shaped to give more nearly parallel beams of radiation.

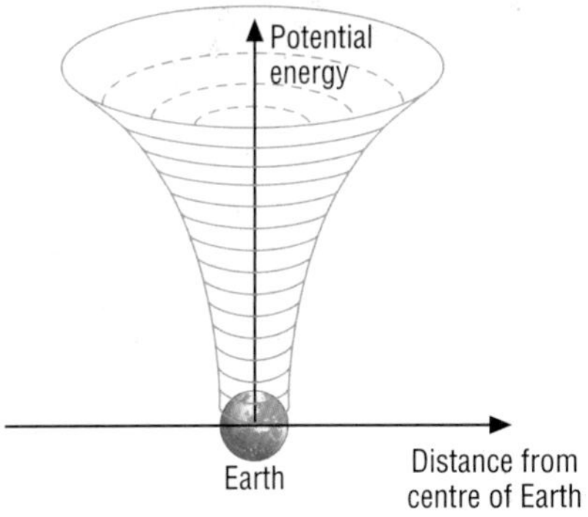

Potential energy
Earth
Distance from centre of Earth

Figure 4 The gravity well of the Earth

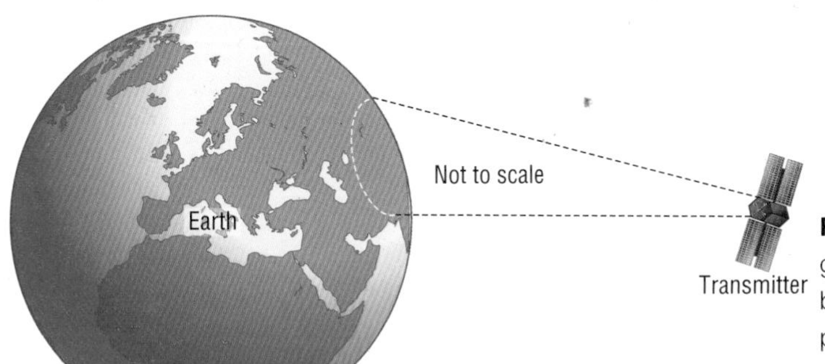

Figure 5 The 'footprint' of a geostationary satellite broadcasting television programmes may be as much as four million square kilometres

Low-level satellites

These satellites are not geostationary. They are usually at heights up to about 500 km. Their transmissions can be received only by using a tracking receiver. Because they are always moving, many of them are necessary for complete coverage of the Earth at all times. The advantages they have are:

- Less expense is required to put them into orbit.
- Greater detail about the Earth can be seen on any photos they take.
- A higher intensity (power per unit area) can be achieved on the Earth's surface.

For these reasons, low-level satellites are used as weather satellites, spy satellites, mapping and global positioning satellites. Some examples are:

- The movement of individual people can be monitored when they are out of doors.
- The positioning system of the Galileo satellites can locate a car to the nearest metre.
- The European Meteosat provides weather detail far greater than just pictures of the clouds. It detects temperature, pressure, humidity and wind speed on the ground.
- The effects of humans on the environment can be seen. Now that a library of photos is available, it is possible to see such effects as deforestation, the shrinking of ice caps, the drying up of inland seas and the effect of urban expansion, among others.

Sample photos taken from space are shown in Figures 6 and 7.

Figure 6 Hurricane Dean on 20 Aug 07 approaching Central America. Cuba is in the top right-hand corner

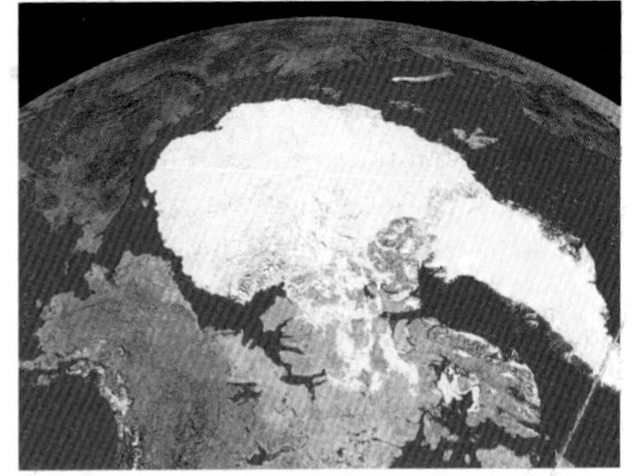

Figure 7 The Arctic ice-cap

Question

1 A geostationary satellite can broadcast digital television signals at the microwave frequency of 30 GHz.

(a) Show that the wavelength λ of this radiation is 10 mm.

(b) The beam of radiation from the dish of diameter d on the satellite spreads out to an angle θ from the forward direction given by the diffraction formula $\sin\theta = 1.22\,\lambda/d$. The satellite is 36 000 km above the Earth's surface. Show that the area of the beam on the ground is about $6 \times 10^{11}\,\text{m}^2$ for a transmitting dish of diameter 1.0 m.

(c) The power of the beam from the satellite transmitting dish of diameter 1.0 m is 100 W. Calculate the intensity (energy per second per unit area) of the signal arriving at the Earth's surface.

(d) Show that the receiving aerial at the focus of the dish on the roof of your house must be able to detect a signal of about 10^{-10} W.

Introduction to simple harmonic motion (S.H.M.)

By the end of this spread, you should be able to ...

* **Describe simple examples of free oscillation.**
* **Define and use the terms used to describe simple harmonic motion (S.H.M.).**
* **Select and use the equation period = 1/frequency.**
* **Explain that in S.H.M., period is independent of amplitude.**

Introduction

The expression 'simple harmonic motion' refers to motion involving a body that oscillates. The reason for the word 'harmonic' is that originally musical instruments sounded in harmony and the strings producing these sounds were seen to be vibrating. 'Simple' is used here to mean a lack of complication. Oscillations taking place in simple harmonic motion are smooth oscillations with no variation in amplitude. In simple harmonic motion, the period is independent of the amplitude. In a musical instrument, these are the oscillations that produce pure notes, such as that from an oboe playing quietly and with no variation in volume.

Free oscillations

Oscillations are much more common than you might realise. The reasons for this are:

- Many of the oscillations that do occur happen for only a short time, and so they are not thought of as involving an oscillation at all.
- Many oscillations that occur are so fast that our senses do not react to them as oscillations.
- Many oscillations take place in ways that we simply cannot sense.

Examples of oscillations that take only a short time are banging a drum, hitting a nail with a hammer and knocking on a door. In these three examples something will vibrate; it will oscillate. Examples of oscillations taking place too fast for us to sense them as oscillations are light and the warming effect of the Sun. Oscillations we cannot sense ourselves are radio waves, X-rays, and microwaves from a mobile phone.

One of the simplest oscillations that we are readily aware of is the swinging of a clock pendulum. Such a pendulum is connected to a driving mechanism so that it will oscillate to and fro for a long time. A graph of displacement against time for such an oscillation is shown in Figure 1. If the pendulum is not connected to a driving mechanism, the effect of friction will gradually reduce the extent of the swing until it stops. The displacement–time then changes to the pattern shown in Figure 2.

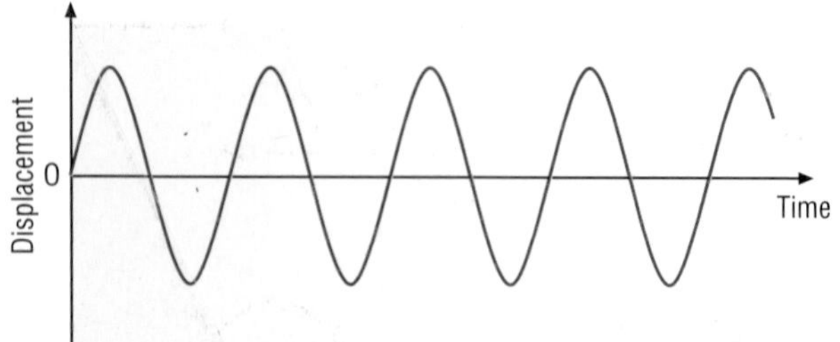

Figure 1 A displacement–time graph for a pendulum

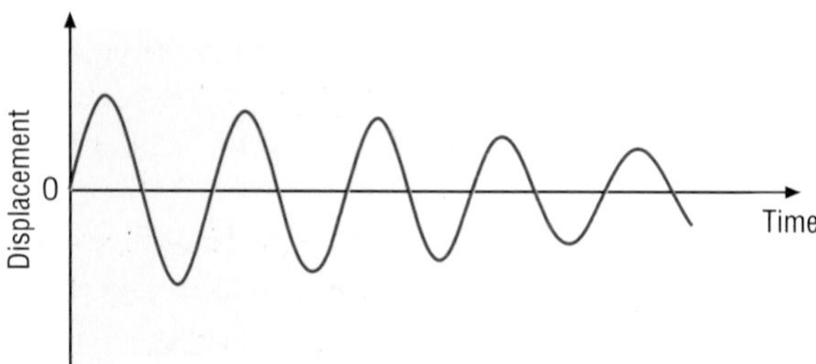

Figure 2 A displacement–time graph for a pendulum with no driving mechanism

A free oscillation has no driving mechanism and zero friction. Once started, it would oscillate for ever, and hence the pattern of oscillation would look like Figure 1. In practice, of course, no oscillation is ever completely 'free'.

The terms used to describe oscillations

Many of the terms used to describe oscillations are similar to those used for waves. The reason for this is that waves are usually set up by oscillations. In an obvious example, it is the oscillation of a guitar string that produces a sound wave. The frequency of the oscillation of the string is the same as the frequency of the sound wave. For the sake of completeness, some quantities defined earlier are repeated here.

- **Displacement** x (in metre units (m)), the distance an object moves from its mean (or rest) position; may be positive or negative.
- **Amplitude** x_0 (in metre units (m)) is the maximum displacement and will always be positive.
- **Frequency** f (in Hertz (Hz)) is the number of oscillations per unit time at any point.
- The **period** T (in seconds (s)) is the time for one complete pattern of oscillation to take place at any point.

It therefore follows that the period = 1/frequency, $T = 1/f$.

Key definition

Displacement is the distance an object has moved from its mean (or rest) position.

Amplitude is the maximum displacement.

Frequency is the number of oscillations per unit time at any point.

The **period** is the time for one complete pattern of oscillation to take place at any point.

Angular frequency $2\pi f$, in units of radians per second (rad s^{-1})

As we saw when dealing with waves, there is a strong connection between oscillations and circular motion. One complete cycle of oscillation can be compared with one rotation. Imagine pedalling a bicycle. A front view of the pedals and the cog-wheel of a bicycle is shown in Figure 3. From in front, the position of a pedal oscillates up and down. Its displacement varies with time as shown in the graph beside the wheel. One oscillation corresponds to one rotation. Using angular measure, this is an angle of 2π radians. If there are f oscillations per unit time, there will be a corresponding angle of $2\pi f$ radians per unit time.

The angular frequency is $2\pi f$. You may see this quantity given the symbol ω, the Greek character omega.

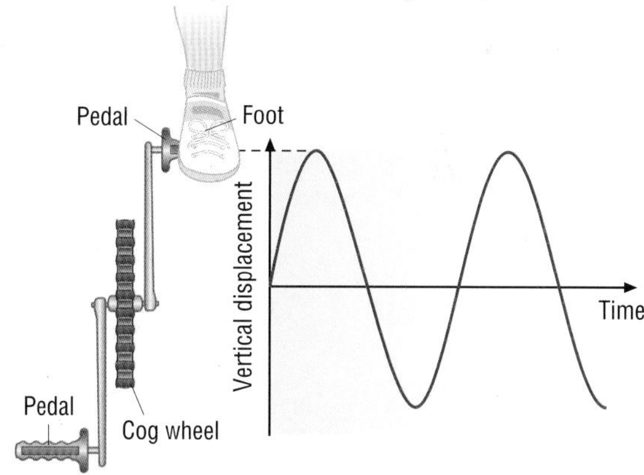

Figure 3 As you cycle, the vertical displacement of your foot is plotted against time

Phase difference ϕ, in units of rad

As with waves, this term concerns the relationship between the pattern of vibration at two points. Two points that have exactly the same pattern of oscillation are said to be in phase, that is, there is zero phase difference between them. If the patterns of movement at the two points are exactly opposite to one another, then the waves are said to be in antiphase. The two pedals on a bicycle are in antiphase with one another. Phase difference is the angle in radians between two oscillations.

Questions

1 What are the differences between a wave and an oscillation?

2 Figure 4 shows a complex wave on a string travelling from left to right at 4.0 m s^{-1}. The wave has just reached point P on the string.
  (a) Draw a graph of the displacement of the string at point P against time for the next second.
  (b) Compare the graph of (a) with Figure 4, which in effect is the graph of displacement against position of the string at time $t = 0$. How are the two graphs related?

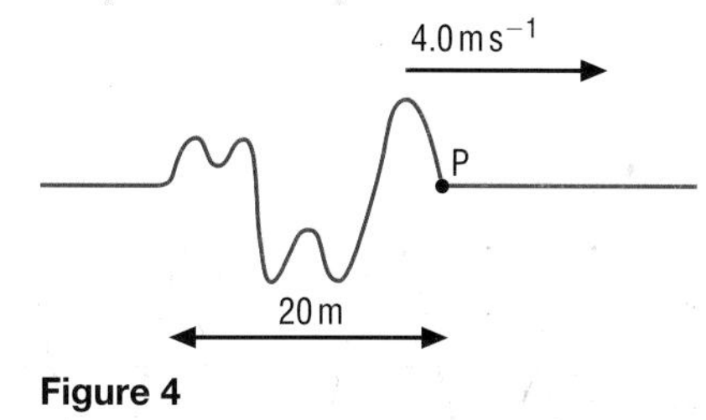

Figure 4

3 Figure 5 shows the displacement–time graph of an object oscillating in simple harmonic motion. Several points on the graph have been labelled.
  (a) Which point(s) are **(i)** at the amplitude of the oscillation, **(ii)** one period apart, **(iii)** in phase, **(iv)** in antiphase?
  (b) What is **(i)** the frequency and **(ii)** the angular frequency of the oscillation?
  (c) What is the phase difference between points **(i)** V and Y, **(ii)** Y and Z?

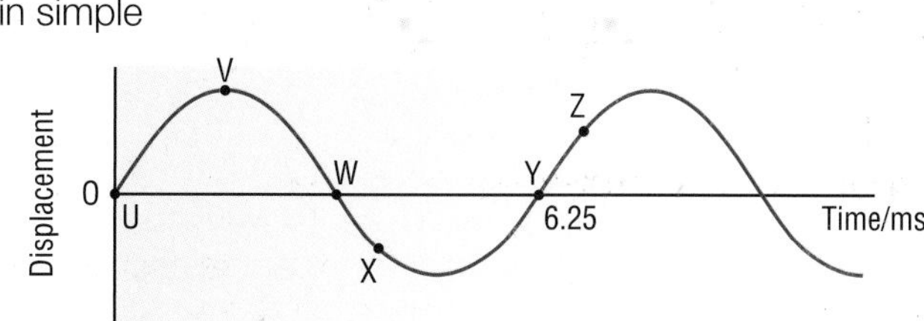

Figure 5

The definition of simple harmonic motion

By the end of this spread, you should be able to …

* **Define simple harmonic motion.**
* **Select and apply the defining equation for simple harmonic motion.**
* **Use solutions to the equation.**

The motion of a mass when oscillating on a spring

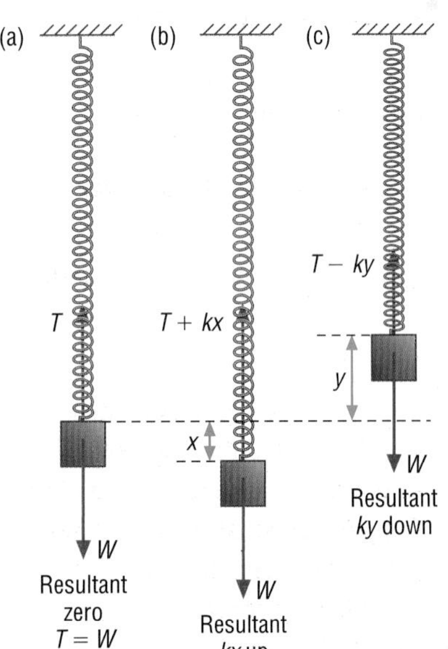

Figure 1 A spring on which a mass is oscillating

Figure 1(a) shows a mass supported by a long spring that has spring constant k. This means that the force per unit extension is k. (See spread 1.3.7 in the AS book.) When the mass is in equilibrium the tension in the spring T equals the weight W of the mass. Now consider the situation when the mass is oscillating up and down from its equilibrium position. In position 1(b) the spring is stretched by a distance x, so the upward force the spring exerts on the mass is $T + kx$. The resultant (net) force on the mass is therefore

$(T + kx) - W = kx$ upwards, since $T = W$.

In position 1(c), the spring is shorter by a distance y. The tension in the spring is therefore $T - ky$, and the resultant force on the mass upwards is therefore

$(T - ky) - W = -ky$ upwards, which is ky downwards.

Summarising this shows that the resultant force on the mass is directly proportional to the displacement but in the opposite direction to the displacement. When the mass goes up, the resultant force is downwards; when the mass goes down, the resultant force is upwards. This pattern of applied force, and hence of acceleration, is used as a definition of simple harmonic motion.

The definition of simple harmonic motion

Two statements *define* simple harmonic motion. An object undergoing simple harmonic motion:

- has an acceleration a proportional to its displacement x from a fixed point
- accelerates in the opposite direction to the displacement.

Put in equation form this becomes

$a = -cx$, where c is a constant

This constant must be positive in order to preserve the opposite signs of a and x. In order to ensure that this is so, the constant is put in as a squared value. It is convenient to put the constant c in as $(2\pi f)^2$, where f is the frequency. So, the defining equation for simple harmonic motion becomes

$$a = -(2\pi f)^2 x$$

Examiner tip

You will not be asked to solve the equation for simple harmonic motion, but you must be able to recognise the solutions shown here.

Solutions to the defining equation

If you are familiar with calculus, you can understand how to solve this equation. A check for the solution is given in the Stretch and Challenge box. If you're not familiar with calculus, you need to be able to choose the appropriate solution from your list of equations and to be able to use the solution.

Two of the solutions to the equation are

$x = A \sin(2\pi ft)$ and $x = A \cos(2\pi ft)$

where t is the time and A is a constant.

The maximum value of the sine of any angle is 1. Therefore the maximum value of x is A. In other words, A is the amplitude of the oscillation.

Worked example

The bob of a simple pendulum undergoes simple harmonic motion with a period of 2.00 seconds. The amplitude of its movement is 15.0 cm. What is

(a) its frequency?

(b) its maximum acceleration?

(c) its displacement **(i)** 0.50 s and **(ii)** 0.25 s after passing through the vertical position?
State the position of the bob for maximum acceleration.

Answer

(a) Frequency $f = 1/\text{period} = 1/2.00 = 0.500$ Hz.

(b) Acceleration $a = -(2\pi f)^2 x$. This will have maximum value in the positive direction when x is maximum value negative, i.e. -0.150 m.
The maximum value of acceleration is therefore $-(2\pi \times 0.500)^2 \times (-0.150) = 1.48\ \text{m s}^{-2}$. Maximum acceleration always takes place for maximum displacement.

(c) (i) At a time of 0.50 s the bob has travelled through a quarter of a cycle. It has therefore reached its maximum displacement, namely 15 cm = 0.15 m.

(ii) At a time of 0.25 s, after an eighth of a cycle it will *not* be at half this value. The equation that should be used is $x = A\sin(2\pi ft)$

$$x = 0.15 \sin(2\pi \times 0.500 \times 0.25)$$
$$x = 0.15 \sin(0.785)$$

Be particularly careful at this point. The angle 0.785 is *not* an angle in degrees but in radians. You *must* either change the angle into degrees or change your calculator into working in radians. (The latter is the easier; you can usually press 'mode' or a similar button to change to degrees or radians.)
This gives $x = 0.106$ m = 10.6 cm.

Questions

1 An object oscillates vertically in simple harmonic motion along the line between points A and B shown in Figure 2.
At which point(s) is it when **(a)** it is stationary, **(b)** it has maximum velocity upwards, **(c)** it has zero acceleration, **(d)** it has maximum kinetic energy and **(e)** it has maximum acceleration downwards?

2 The defining equation of S.H.M. above is $a = -cx$.
(a) What are the units of c?
(b) Two simple harmonic motions are given by $a = -25x$ and $a = -100x$. How do these motions differ?

3 A mass is suspended by a spring. The mass is pulled down and released at $t = 0$. The equation for its displacement x in m from the equilibrium position is $x = 0.050 \cos \pi t$.
(a) What is **(i)** the amplitude, **(ii)** the frequency and **(iii)** the period of the oscillation?
(b) What is **(i)** the displacement and **(ii)** the acceleration of the mass at $t = 0.50$ s, 0.75 s, 1.5 s, 1.8 s?
(c) What is the velocity of the mass at $t = 0.50$ s, 1.0 s?

STRETCH and CHALLENGE

If you can use calculus, you can check that the solutions given for the simple harmonic equation $a = -(2\pi f)^2 x$ are correct. The acceleration a is d^2x/dt^2, and a solution was given as $x = A \sin(2\pi ft)$

Differentiating x twice gives

$$\frac{dx}{dt} = v = A \times 2\pi f (\cos 2\pi ft)$$

and $$a = \frac{dv}{dt} = A \times -(2\pi f)^2 (\sin 2\pi ft)$$

which is $a = -(2\pi f)^2 x$

This is not solving the equation, just showing that the given solution does satisfy the equation. The general equation is $x = A \sin(2\pi ft + \phi)$, where both A and ϕ are unknown constants.
A second-order differential equation such as this will contain two unknown constants.

Question

Differentiate twice, with respect to t, the equation $x = A \cos(2\pi ft)$; hence show that this is a solution to the simple harmonic equation. What is the ratio of the acceleration to the displacement?

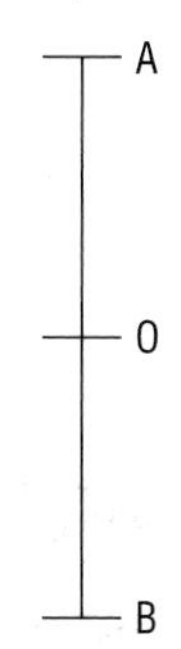

Figure 2

1.2 

Graphical analysis of simple harmonic motion

By the end of this spread, you should be able to …

- **Plot graphs showing how displacement and acceleration vary with time during simple harmonic motion.**
- **Select and apply the equation for the maximum speed of a simple harmonic oscillator.**

The displacement–time graph and the acceleration–time graph

Now that a solution to the S.H.M.-defining equation is known as $x = A \sin(2\pi ft)$, a graph of x against t can be plotted. Since the frequency f is the reciprocal of the period T, we can write this equation as $x = A \sin(2\pi t/T)$.

The following table can be used to plot the graph with a period T. This is shown in Figure 1(a).

The graph $x = A \sin\left(2\pi\frac{t}{T}\right)$ is a sine wave that repeats itself after a time $t = T$.

t	$2\pi t/T$	$\sin(2\pi t/T)$	x
0	0	0	0
$T/8$	$\pi/4$	0.707	$0.707A$
$T/4$	$\pi/2$	1	A
$3T/8$	$3\pi/4$	0.707	$0.707\,A$
$T/2$	π	0	0
$5T/8$	$5\pi/4$	−0.707	$-0.707\,A$
$3T/4$	$3\pi/2$	−1	$-A$
$7T/8$	$7\pi/4$	−0.707	$-0.707\,A$
T	2π	0	0
$2T$	4π	0	0
$3T$	6π	0	0

Table 1

(a)
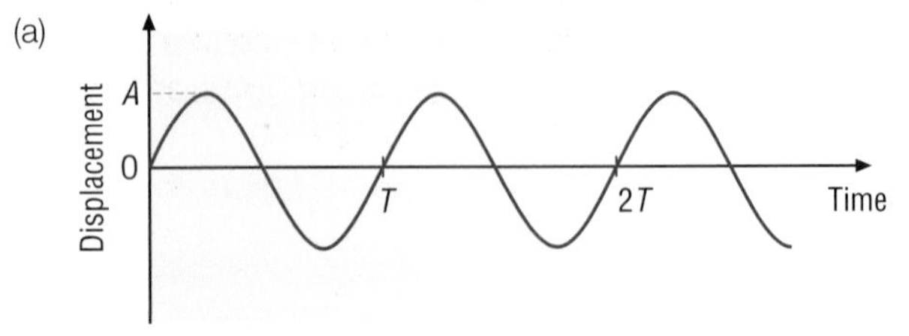

(b)
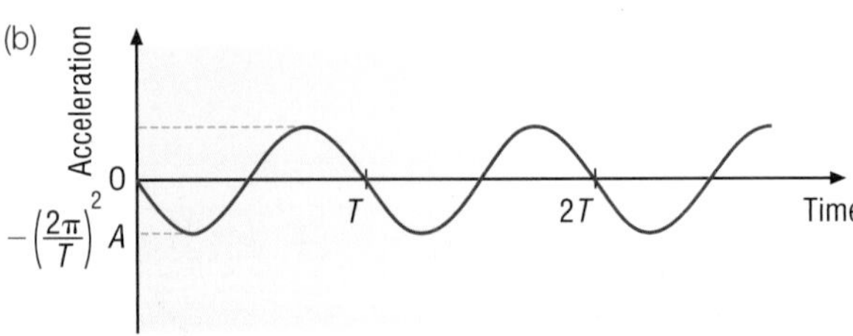

(c)
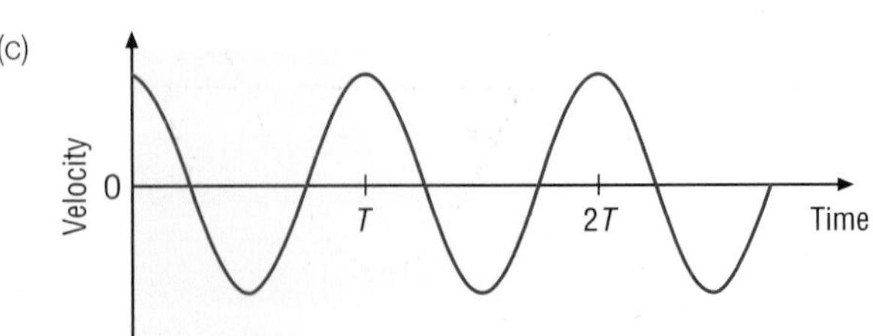

Figure 1 **(a)** Graph of displacement x against time t; **(b)** Graph of acceleration a against time t; **(c)** Graph of velocity against time t

Now that the graph of displacement against time has been plotted, it is straightforward to plot the corresponding graph of acceleration a against time, since by definition $a = -(2\pi f)^2 \times x$. As with the displacement–time graph, $1/T$ will be used instead of f. The acceleration–time graph plotted in Figure 1(b) is the displacement–time graph multiplied at every point by $-(2\pi/T)^2$. The effect of the minus sign is to make all the positive values on the displacement–time graph into negative values on the acceleration–time graph.

The velocity–time graph

Having found how displacement and acceleration vary with time we now need to obtain a velocity–time graph. Since velocity is the gradient of a displacement–time graph, this is the approach to use. Clearly the velocity is zero at maximum displacement and maximum at zero displacement. (Think of a pendulum swinging.) Maximum velocity v_{max}, when calculated, is given by

$$v_{max} = 2\pi fA$$

or in terms of T it is $2\pi A/T$. This graph is plotted as Figure 1(c).

At this stage you should try Question 1 on this spread to check that you have correctly followed this analysis.

Graphs plotted against displacement rather than time

These graphs look very different from graphs plotted against time. To begin with, they cannot lie outside the range from $-A$ to $+A$, because in any oscillation the amplitude A is the maximum displacement. Secondly, for the velocity–displacement graph, there are two possible values of velocity for each value of displacement; an object might have a velocity of +3.2 m s^{-1} on the way out and a velocity of −3.2 m s^{-1} at the same place on the way back. Figure 2 shows two graphs on the same displacement axis. The acceleration–displacement graph, drawn in green, is a straight line of negative gradient because for S.H.M. the acceleration is always proportional to the (negative) displacement. The shape of the velocity–displacement graph, drawn in red, is quite surprising. (For some maths practice, take the velocity equation and the displacement equation, both in terms of t, and eliminate t using $\sin^2\theta + \cos^2\theta = 1$ to find out why this is.)

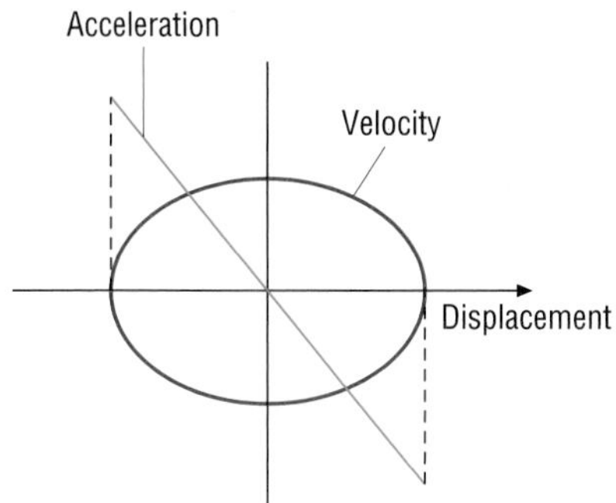

Figure 2 An acceleration–displacement graph, drawn in green, and a velocity–displacement graph, shown in red, for the same S.H.M.

Questions

1 Figure 3 shows a displacement–time graph for a simple harmonic oscillator with four points labelled on the curve.

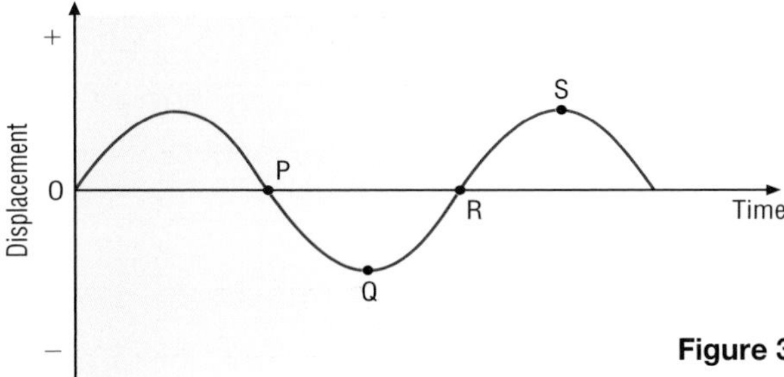

Figure 3

(a) At which point does the oscillator have the greatest negative acceleration?

(b) At which point does the oscillator have the greatest positive velocity?

2 (a) Use the displacement–time graph, Figure 4, to find for this oscillation:

(i) the amplitude A **(ii)** the frequency f

(iii) the maximum velocity v_{max}.

(b) Show that the maximum velocity v_{max} equals $2\pi fA$.

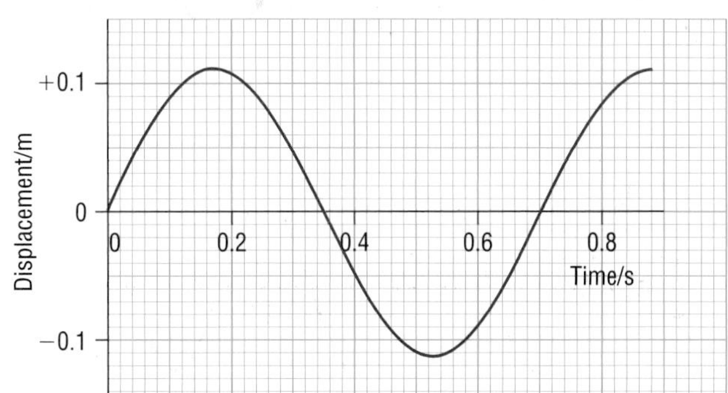

Figure 4

3 The variation in depth of the water in a harbour is approximately simple harmonic. Figure 5 shows this variation for a 24-hour period.

(a) Use the graph to find:

(i) the amplitude of the tide

(ii) the minimum depth of water in the harbour

(iii) the frequency of the tide in tides per hour.

(b) For how many hours in a day is the harbour inaccessible to a boat with a draft (the depth of a vessel's keel below the water line) of 4.0 m?

(c) Justify that *depth* = 5.0 + 2.5 sin 0.5t is the mathematical equation for the tidal motion, where t is measured in hours and *depth* in metres.

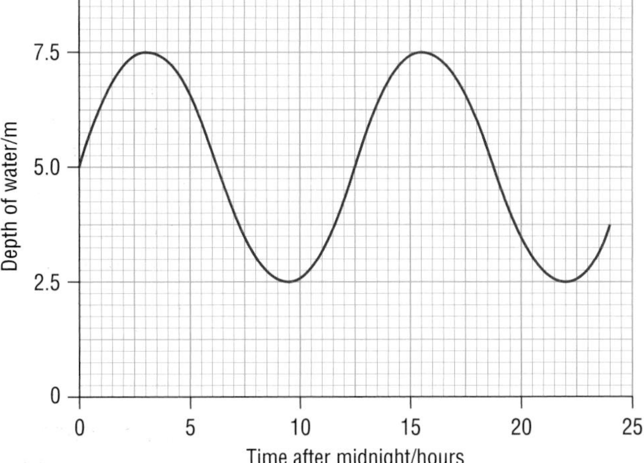

Figure 5

Energy in simple harmonic motion

By the end of this spread, you should be able to ...

* **Describe the energy changes taking place during simple harmonic motion.**

Energy interchanges in simple harmonic motion

In this spread we look at energy changes when the oscillatory motion is not affected by any energy losses to the surroundings. In spread 1.2.10 the term used to describe such oscillations was 'free oscillations'. Free oscillations follow the sine wave pattern of movement without any variation in amplitude.

Nevertheless, although there is no loss of energy to the surroundings, there is clearly some energy change taking place. Just watching a pendulum bob moving makes it obvious that sometimes the bob stops, and therefore has zero kinetic energy, and sometimes it moves fast, when it does have kinetic energy. When the bob loses kinetic energy, it rises and gains gravitational potential energy. Since no energy is lost to the surroundings, any gain in kinetic energy is lost from potential energy and vice versa. This is shown in Figure 1. Note that the period T must be the time for two rises and falls of kinetic energy; the bob will be going fast one way and then the other before it gets back to its starting point.

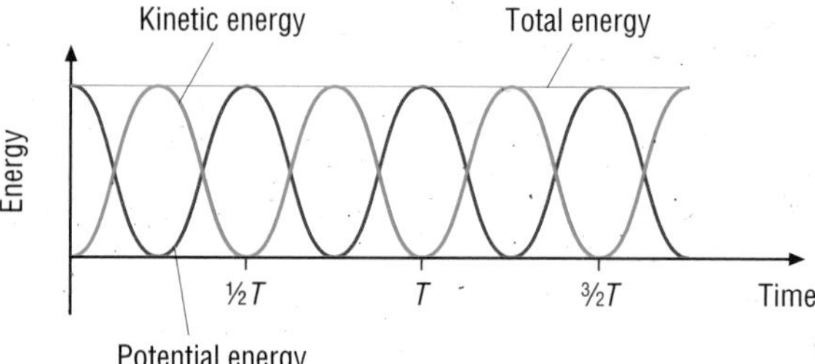

Figure 1 The interchange of kinetic and potential energies with time as a pendulum bob swings. A gain in kinetic energy results in a corresponding loss in potential energy. The total energy of the oscillating system remains constant

Energy changes for a mass on a spring

In this case also the total energy remains constant while the mass oscillates up and down. Again, any gain in kinetic energy is balanced by a loss in potential energy. Here, however, there are two types of potential energy. The spring gains elastic potential energy when the mass goes down, and the mass gains gravitational potential energy when it rises. The elastic potential energy stored by a spring when stretched by a distance x is given by $\frac{1}{2}kx^2$ (see spread 1.3.7 in the AS book). The gravitational potential energy stored when an object rises a distance x is given by mgx. A graph showing how these quantities vary with the position of the mass is shown in Figure 2.

A problem with sketching this graph is what to regard as the zero of the energies. On this figure, they are all taken to be zero at the equilibrium position. That is why some of the energies are shown to be negative and why the graph for kinetic energy is always negative. At the centre the kinetic energy is maximum, and it decreases as the mass moves away from the centre, either up or down.

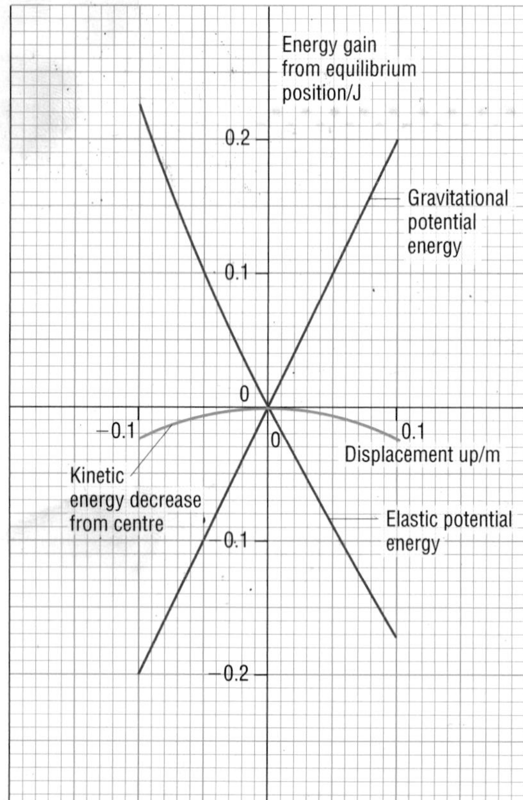

Figure 2 Three superimposed graphs showing how gravitational potential energy, elastic potential energy and kinetic energy change with displacement for a mass oscillating up and down on a spring

The three separate graphs are drawn to scale for a mass of 0.20 kg oscillating on a spring of spring constant k equal to 5.0 N m^{-1}. The amplitude of the oscillation can be seen from the graph to be 0.10 m. Since all three graphs are zero at the centre, the total energy of the system is taken as zero at the centre. If you take any other displacement and add all three energies together, you will find the total to be zero. In other words, the total energy of the system is constant. It is interesting to note that the predominant feature of the graph is the way gravitational potential energy transfers mostly to elastic potential energy as the mass falls, and vice versa. The change in the kinetic energy of the system, that is the noticeable feature from watching the oscillation, is relatively small.

Questions

1 Figure 3 shows how the total energy E of an undamped oscillator of mass m varies with displacement x. The graph also shows how the potential energy $\frac{1}{2}kx^2$ varies with displacement x.

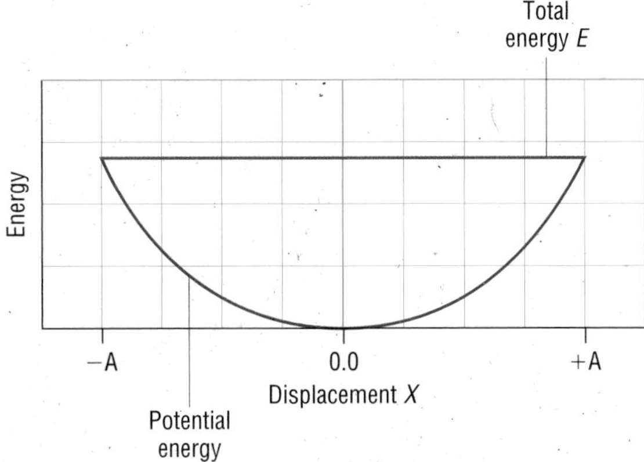

Figure 3

(a) Copy the figure and add to it a curve showing how the kinetic energy of the oscillator varies with displacement.

(b) **(i)** Find an equation for the kinetic energy at any displacement x in terms of the algebraic symbols given above.

(ii) Find an algebraic expression for the maximum speed of the oscillator.

2 A mass rests on a smooth surface. It is attached by an open-wound spring that can be stretched or compressed to a fixed support. See Figure 4.

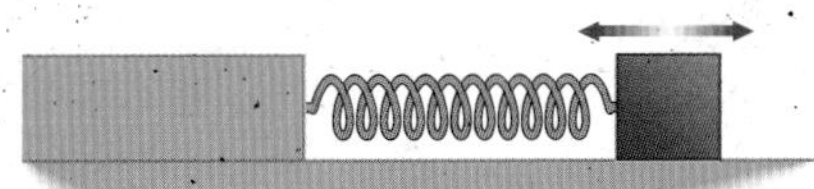

Figure 4

The mass is pulled to the right and released at $t = 0$. The equation for its displacement x in m from the equilibrium position is $x = 0.050 \cos \pi t$ as in Question 3 of spread 1.2.11. The spring constant of the spring is 10 N m^{-1}.
Calculate **(a)** the potential and **(b)** the kinetic energy in mJ of the system at $t = 0$, 0.50 s, 0.75 s, 1.25 s.

3 The amplitude of the motion of the mass in Question 2 is halved. By what factor are your answers to Question 2 changed?

4 A pendulum of period 2.0 s has a bob of mass 400 g. Its total energy when swinging is 50 mJ. Calculate:

(a) its maximum speed

(b) its amplitude.

1.2 (14) Damping

By the end of this spread, you should be able to …

* **Describe the effects of damping on an oscillatory system.**

Figure 1 A large pendulum clock, dated late-sixteenth or early-seventeenth century, with the blocks of stone that can (still) be lifted to provide potential energy for running the clock: one of the blocks is used for the clock, the other for striking the hours on a bell

Energy interchanges in practical oscillatory motion

In the last spread, energy changes in free oscillations were considered. These changes do occur in practice, because systems frequently do exhibit the characteristics of free oscillations. The pendulum of a clock does lose energy to friction and to its surroundings, but energy is fed into the clock to keep the amplitude of the oscillation constant. Old pendulum clocks used to be wound up daily. Heavy weights were lifted so that their gravitational potential energy could be used to replace energy lost to the surroundings (see Figure 1). These days, pendulum clocks use an electric motor or a spring to keep them running.

If energy is not supplied to an oscillation, it will die away sooner or later. There are lots of examples in everyday life such as a note played on a piano that gets quieter as the string vibrates less, an echo fading away or a child on a swing slowing down. Less obvious examples are in many ways more important. If lots of people are talking, they are causing vibrations of the molecules in the room. These die away quickly. If they did not die away, the noise in the room would become unbearable.

Many pages of statutory building regulations are taken up with how to control sound transmission between connected buildings. In the design stage, models of concert halls are tested to measure how long it takes for sound levels to drop. The reverberation time is important. If it is too short, the hall seems dead; if it is too long, the sound gets fuzzy. In a similar way, if components in a car vibrate too much and too long, the car becomes very noisy. Car manufacturers go to considerable lengths to make certain that oscillations are as small as possible and decrease quickly.

Key definition

Deliberately reducing the amplitude of an oscillation is called **damping**.

Damping

The process of deliberately reducing the amplitude of an oscillation is called **damping**. The damping forces are usually the forces of friction and air resistance. If only small damping forces exist – **light damping** – the period of the oscillation is almost unchanged, but the amplitude of the oscillation gradually decreases, as shown in Figure 2(a). As the damping forces increase, there is a more noticeable reduction in amplitude, and the period increases slightly. This is shown in Figure 2(b). Eventually, for very **heavy damping**, no oscillation occurs, and the body slowly moves back to its equilibrium position. The cross-over situation between oscillation and no oscillation is called **critical damping**.

Examples of heavy damping are:

- A sealed test tube floating vertically in water that will oscillate only five or six times before stopping.
- The same test tube floating in treacle, which will not oscillate at all.
- The suspension system of a car. The springing on each wheel of a car gives a smoother ride, but without damping, the bouncing of the springs would be very unpleasant after going over a bump in the road. Shock absorbers are used for approximate critical damping so that equilibrium is quickly re-established.

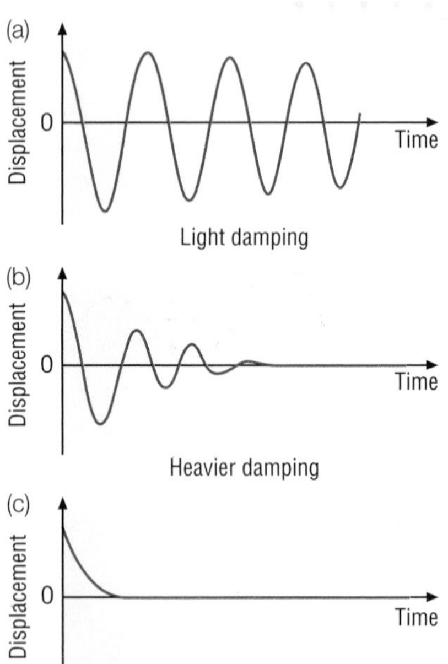

Figure 2 **(a)** Light damping; **(b)** heavy damping; **(c)** very heavy damping

Foucault's pendulum

A good example of light damping is the **Foucault pendulum**, shown in Figure 3 at the Panthéon, Paris, in 1852. Jean Foucault (1819–68) noticed that a large free-mounted pendulum will continue to swing in the same plane irrespective of the rotation of its mounting. To test this hypothesis, he fitted a 28-kilogramme iron ball to the end of a 67-metre steel wire, suspended from the dome of the Panthéon. Once in motion the pendulum continued to oscillate all day. The pendulum did apparently change its plane of oscillation with time, but this was in fact caused by the Earth moving under the pendulum.

Figure 3 Foucault's pendulum

Worked example

A graph plotting displacement against time is given in Figure 4 for the lightly damped oscillation of an object. State what is meant by an exponential decay, and show that the decay of the amplitude follows an exponential decay pattern.

Answer

An exponential decay will result in the amplitude decreasing by a fixed amount in any given time.
This decay starts with an amplitude of 14 mm.
The time it takes to reach an amplitude of 7 mm is 1.6 s.
In another 1.6 s, i.e. t = 3.2 s, it has reached a value of 3.5 mm, half the previous value.
In another 1.6 s, i.e. t = 4.8 s, it has reached a value of 1.8 mm, again approximately half.
It is halving every 1.6 s, so it is an exponential decay. This is the usual pattern for light damping.

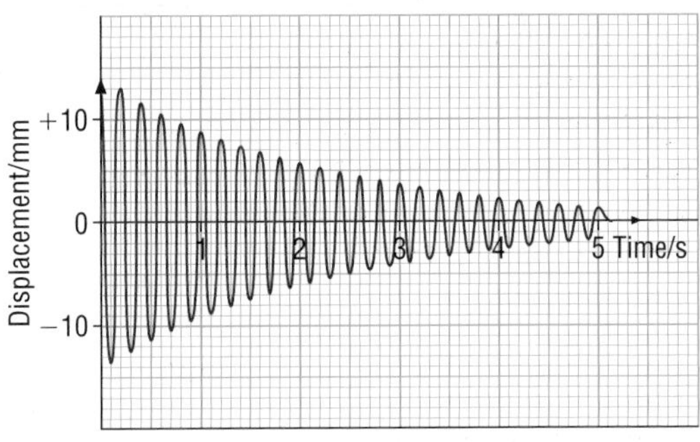

Figure 4 Graph showing light damping

Questions

1 Figure 5 is the displacement–time graph of a damped oscillator.
 (a) Does the amplitude decrease by the same factor each 0.8 s? If so, is it an exponential decay? Estimate the value of this factor.
 (b) What feature of the graph shows that the maximum velocity decreases from one oscillation to the next?

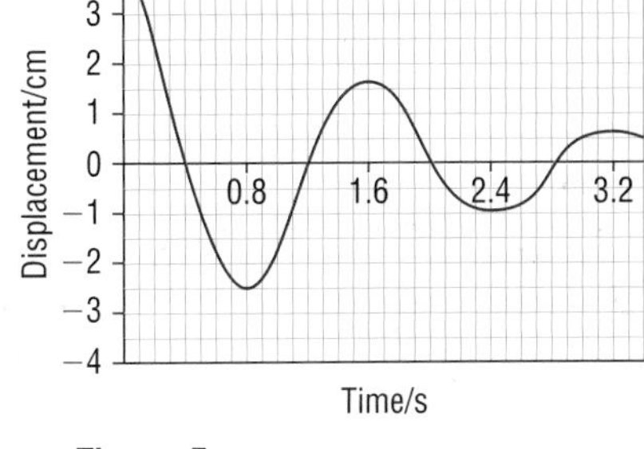

Figure 5

2 Figure 6 shows a toy consisting of a light plastic aeroplane suspended from a long spring.
The aeroplane is raised 4.0 cm and released. It undergoes a vertical harmonic oscillation with a period of 1.6 s. The oscillations are lightly damped exactly as shown in Figure 5.
The aeroplane is replaced by a heavier model made of the same plastic, having the same fuselage but larger wings. State and explain **two** changes that this substitution will make to the displacement–time graph of Figure 5.

Figure 6

15 Resonance

By the end of this spread, you should be able to …

- ✱ **Describe practical examples of forced oscillations and resonance.**
- ✱ **Describe how the amplitude of forced oscillations depends on the driver frequency.**
- ✱ **Describe examples where resonance is useful or where resonance should be avoided.**

Terms used with forced oscillations

There are many occasions when one vibrating object causes another object to vibrate. The classic example is the singer who shatters a wine glass singing at just the right frequency to match a natural frequency of the wine glass. More ordinary examples of this are:

- A rattle in the bodywork of a car when the car is running at a particular speed.
- A radio or public address system that suddenly makes a very loud squeal.
- A bridge like the one over the Tacoma Narrows in the USA, which collapsed on 1st July 1940 as a result of winds causing vibrations that built up over several hours.

In all these cases, there are at least two vibrating objects. There is the object causing the effect. Its frequency is called the **driver frequency**. There is also the driven object, which has a **natural frequency** of vibration. A large-amplitude oscillation is built up when the two frequencies are the same. The effect is called **resonance**.

Key definition

Resonance is the build-up of a large-amplitude oscillation when the frequencies of vibrating objects match.

A useful visual example representation of resonance can be shown with Barton's pendulums (Figure 1), a large mass oscillating on a string and acting as a driver pendulum for all the small masses attached at intervals to the same supporting string. The small mass on a string of the same length as the driver mass has a natural frequency equal to that of the driver pendulum, and it oscillates with a much larger amplitude than any of the other small masses.

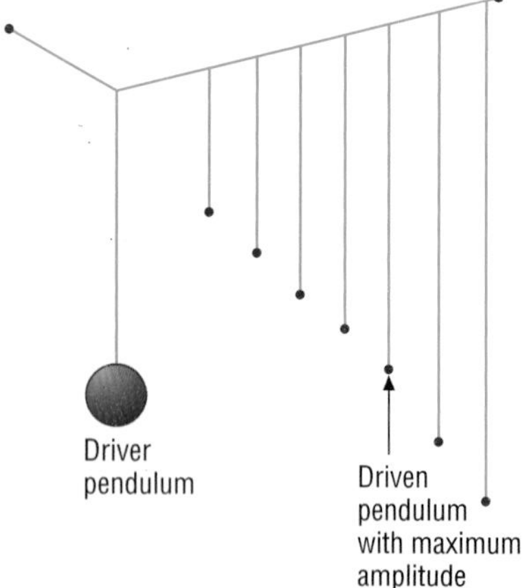

Figure 1 Barton's pendulums

Graphs showing resonance

The basic graph

A graph of amplitude of the oscillation of a driven object against the driver frequency of constant amplitude is shown in Figure 2. A graph such as this can be obtained by using a mechanical vibrator of varying frequency causing a pendulum to oscillate. Notice that the amplitude of the driven object may be many times that of the driver.

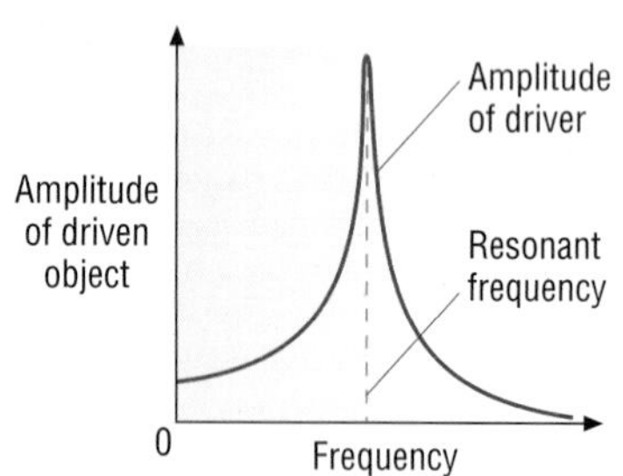

Figure 2 A graph showing how the amplitude of a driven object varies with the frequency of the driver

The effect of damping on the amplitude of the resonant oscillation

When the amount of damping applied to a resonating object is varied it has two effects:

- Increasing the amount of damping reduces the amplitude of the driven oscillation.
- Increasing the damping also slightly reduces the frequency of the driven oscillation.

The graph in Figure 3 shows these two effects.

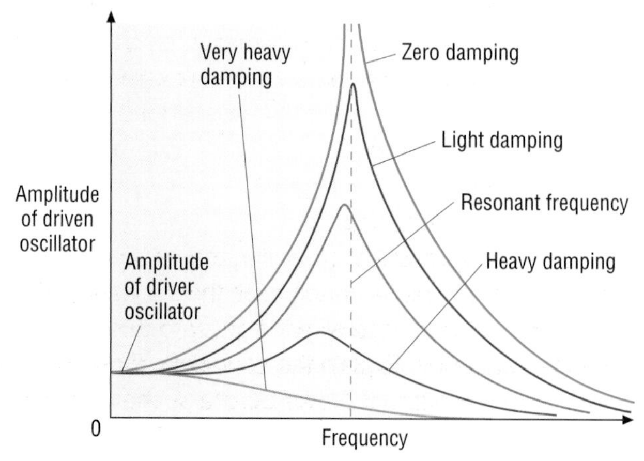

Figure 3 The effect of damping on the resonant response of an oscillator

Practical uses of resonance

Some features of resonance make it very useful. Although not dealt with at A level, electrical circuits can be made to resonate. When you tune in a radio or television programme, you are adjusting the resonant frequency of the radio or television receiver to the frequency of the transmitted signal.

Nuclei of atoms resonate when they are in a field of suitable magnetic oscillations. This principle is used in magnetic resonance imaging to obtain very clear images of body structure. Figure 4 shows one such scan of a person's head (see spread 2.4.7).

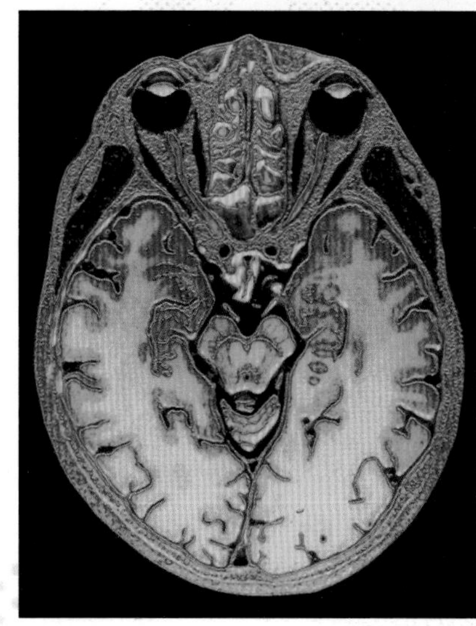

Figure 4 A false-colour magnetic resonance image (MRI) scan of a human head

Microwave ovens use resonance in a cavity in a device called a reflex klystron. Electrons travel past the cavity and create the microwaves at a frequency dependent on the dimension of the cavity just as an organ pipe produces a sound note by resonance when air blows across it. Manufacturers go to great lengths to prevent microwaves leaking from a microwave cooker, since they could make water molecules in people resonate – they could cook you!

The uses of resonance are balanced by its annoying effects. Some of these are listed in the first paragraph of this spread. Engineering designers spend a great deal of time trying to eliminate vibrations. One severe problem they have is that in practice most structures have several natural frequencies of oscillation. Making sure that unwanted oscillations do not build up for these frequencies is very difficult. Usually a combination of damping and careful choice of the dimensions of an object is used. Some of the industries that have to be careful about unwanted oscillations are:

- The construction industry. Tall buildings do vibrate, even in a steady wind. The top of the Toronto CN tower is designed to be able to vibrate with an amplitude of over a metre. The Millennium Bridge over the Thames is an example of a construction where too much vibration occurred. More damping needed to be added to it.
- The car industry. Designers try to eliminate as much resonance (rattling and bouncing) as possible.
- The aircraft industry. Wings of planes bounce on take off and landing. A large plane's wings often have a node two-thirds of the way along the wing and antinodes one-third of the way along and at the tip. The design of the wing must allow for this, and any vibration be quickly damped out.
- The electronics industry. Good-quality sound reproduction requires good-quality microphones and loudspeakers. In a bad loudspeaker one or more frequencies will be particularly loud, because the loudspeaker is resonating at those frequencies.

Questions

1 The external wing mirror of a large coach is often connected to the body of the vehicle by a long arm. The wing mirror assembly sometimes behaves like a mass on a spring, with the mirror oscillating in simple harmonic motion about its equilibrium position.

  (a) With the engine of the coach idling at a particular number of revolutions per second, the wing mirror can oscillate significantly, whereas at other engine speeds the mirror hardly moves. Explain how this phenomenon is an example of resonance.

  (b) Suggest, giving a reason, what happens when

    (i) the mirror has a greater mass or

    (ii) it is mounted on an arm of greater stiffness.

2 The top end of the spring in Figure 6 of spread 1.2.14 is vibrated vertically with a small constant amplitude. The motion of the aeroplane changes as the frequency of oscillation of the top end of the spring is increased slowly from zero through resonance to twice the resonance frequency. Explain the conditions for resonance to occur, and describe the changes in the motion of the aeroplane as the frequency changes.

Circular motion and oscillations summary

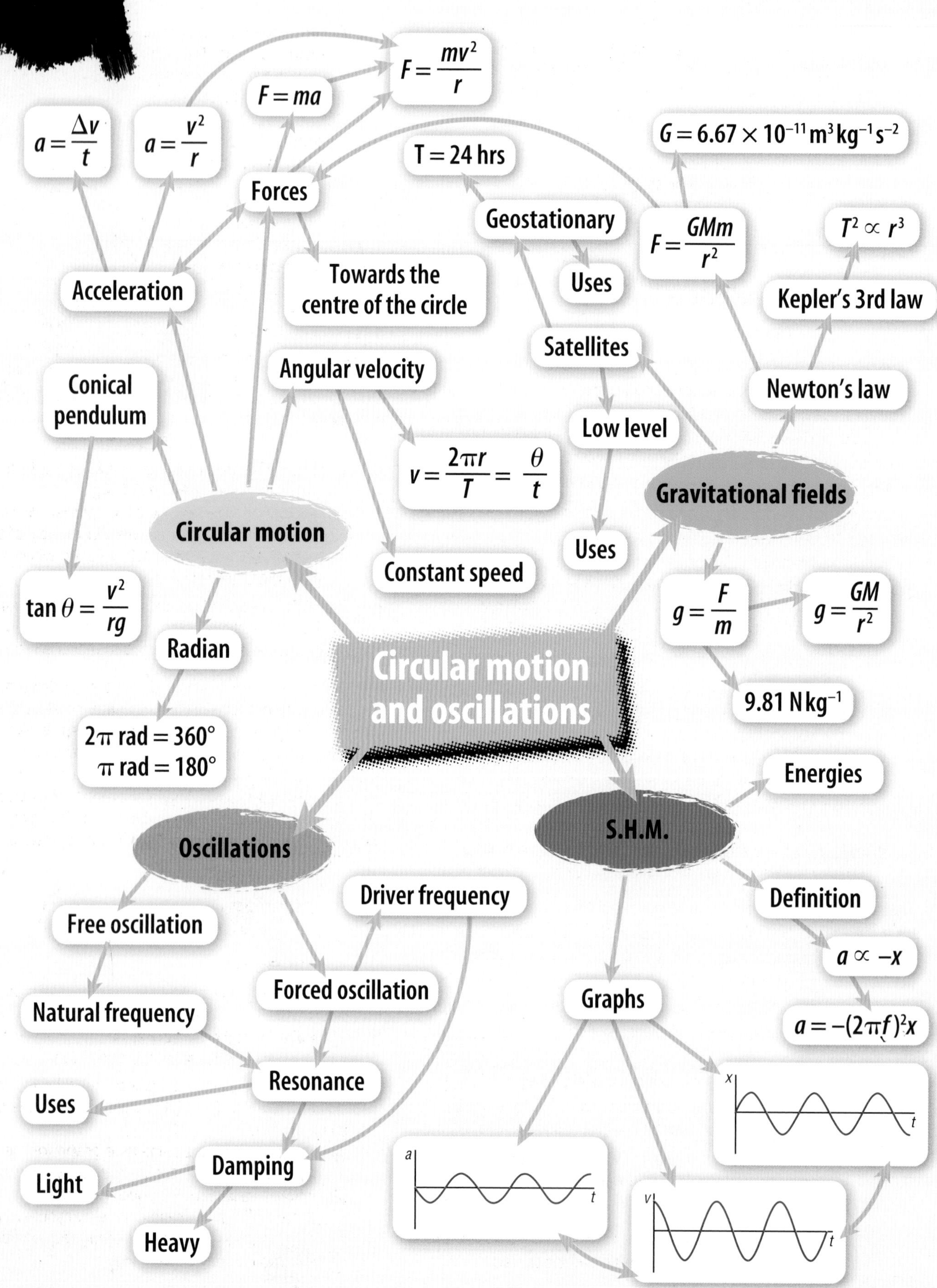

Practice questions

1 The electric motor in a washing machine rotates the drum containing the clothes by means of a rubber belt stretched around two pulleys, one on the motor shaft and the other on the drum shaft, as shown in Figure 1.

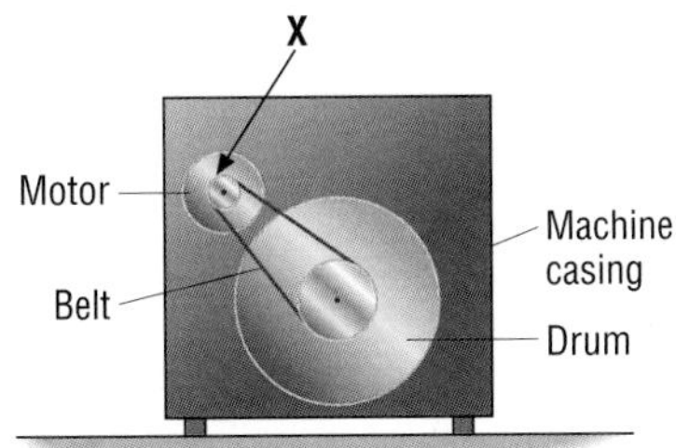

Figure 1

(a) The motor pulley of radius 15 mm rotates at 50 revolutions per second. Calculate:
- **(i)** the speed in m s^{-1} of the belt
- **(ii)** the centripetal acceleration in m s^{-2} of the belt at point **X**.

(b) When the drum is rotated at one particular speed, a metal side panel of the machine casing vibrates loudly. Explain why this happens.

2 **(a)** The gravitational field strength at the surface of a planet of uniform density is 40 N kg^{-1}. A satellite of mass 1500 kg is launched from the surface into a circular orbit around the planet at a height of 1.5×10^5 m with an orbital period of 4.5×10^3 s. The radius of the planet is 2.0×10^7 m.
- **(i)** Estimate the increase in potential energy in J of the satellite.
- **(ii)** Suggest with a reason whether your estimate in **(i)** is likely to be larger or smaller than the true value.
- **(iii)** Calculate the kinetic energy in J of the satellite in orbit.

(b) Figure 2 shows how the gravitational field strength g varies with distance r from the centre of the planet of radius 2.0×10^7 m.

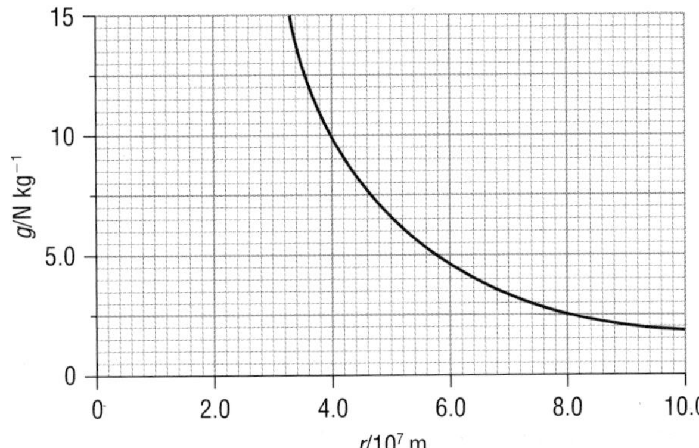

Figure 2

- **(i)** Use Figure 2 to write down the value of g in N kg^{-1} at a height of 4.0×10^7 m above the surface.
- **(ii)** Write down an algebraic expression for g at a distance r from the centre of the planet. The planet can be treated as a point mass of magnitude M situated at its centre.
- **(iii)** The value of g at the surface is 40 N kg^{-1}. Use this information and your answer to **(ii)** to check, by a suitable calculation, your answer to **(i)**.

3 The planet in Question 2 is orbited by two small moons, labelled **O** and **P** in Figure 3. The distances of the moons from the centre of the planet are $4R$ and $5R$, where R is the radius of the planet. The gravitational field strength g at its surface is 40 N kg^{-1}.

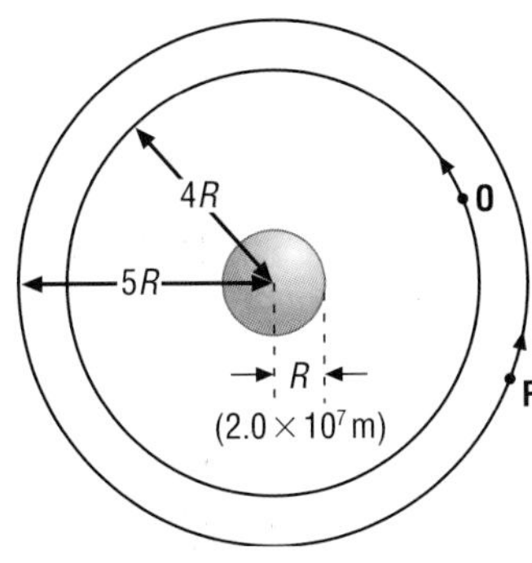

Figure 3

(a)
- **(i)** Show that the gravitational field strength at **O** is 2.5 N kg^{-1} and at **P** is 1.6 N kg^{-1}.
- **(ii)** Using an average value of g, estimate the increase in J of the gravitational potential energy of a small space vehicle of mass 4.0×10^3 kg when it moves from the orbit of **O** to the orbit of **P**.

(b) Calculate the orbital period in s of **P**. Assume that the gravitational effects of the two moons on each other are negligible in comparison to that of the planet.

4 This question is about a simple model of hydrogen iodide. Two ions ${}^{1}_{1}H^{+}$ and ${}^{127}_{53}I^{-}$, are held together by electric forces. The electrical attraction is balanced by a repulsive force so that the two ions are in equilibrium. When disturbed, the ions oscillate in simple harmonic motion. Figure 4 shows a simple mechanical model, consisting of two unequal masses connected by a spring of negligible mass. The mass of the iodide ion is 127 times the mass of the hydrogen ion.

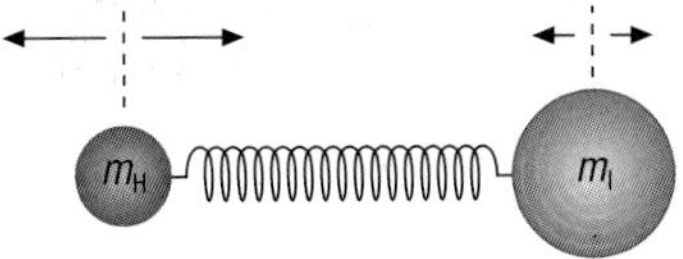

Figure 4

(a) Use Newton's laws of motion and the definition of simple harmonic motion to explain why the amplitude of oscillation of the hydrogen ion is 127 times the amplitude of oscillation of the iodide ion.

(b) The natural frequency of oscillation of the hydrogen ion is 6.7×10^{13} Hz. Take the amplitude of oscillation to be 8.0×10^{-12} m.
- **(i)** Sketch a displacement–time graph for the hydrogen ion over the period 3.0×10^{-14} s.
- **(ii)** Infrared radiation of frequency close to 6.7×10^{13} Hz, incident on the molecules, can cause this oscillation, but other frequencies of infrared do not. Explain why.

1.2 Examination questions

1 Figure 1(a) shows a ball at rest, hanging on a vertical thread from a fixed support, S.

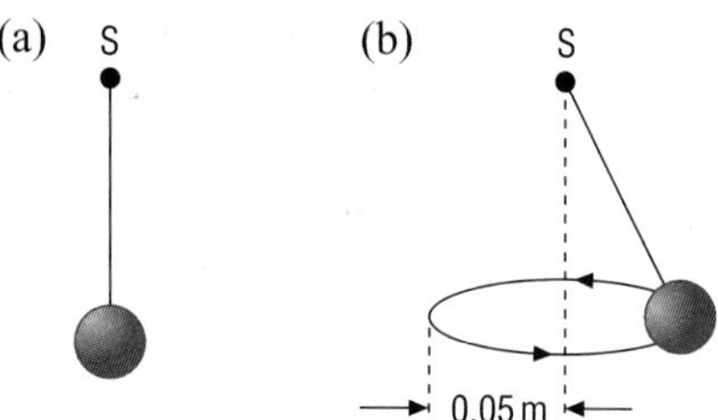

Figure 1

(a) Copy Figure 1(a) and draw and label arrows on it to represent the two forces acting on the ball. [2]

(b) Figure 1(b) represents the ball moving in a circle about a vertical axis through S. Copy Figure 1(b) and draw and label arrows on it to represent the two forces acting on the ball. Explain how they provide the force to make the ball move in a circular path. [3]

(c) The ball has a mass of 0.020 kg and moves in a circle of radius 0.050 m at 1.2 revolutions per second. Assume that the thread supporting the ball has negligible mass.
Calculate:

(i) the speed in m s^{-1} of the ball [2]

(ii) the magnitude in N of the force which keeps the ball moving in a circular path. [3]

(d) Predict and explain the difference in the path of the ball when it is rotating at a higher speed. [3]

(OCR 2824 Jan02)

2 Figure 2 shows a graph of the variation of the gravitational field strength g of the Earth with distance r from its centre.

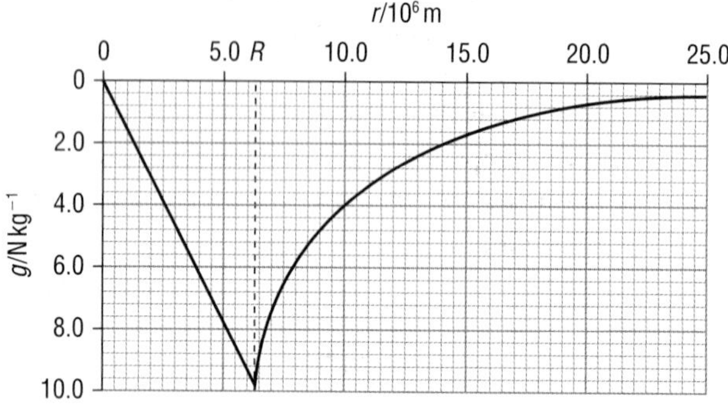

Figure 2

(a) (i) Define the gravitational field strength at a point. [1]

(ii) Write down an algebraic expression for the gravitational field strength g at the surface of the Earth in terms of its mass M, its radius R and the universal gravitational constant G. [1]

(iii) Use data from Figure 2 and the value of G to show that the mass of the Earth is 6.0×10^{24} kg. [2]

(iv) State which feature of the graph in Figure 2 indicates that the gravitational field strength at a point below the surface of the Earth, assumed to be of uniform density, is proportional to the distance from the centre of the Earth. [1]

(v) Calculate the two distances from the centre of the Earth at which $g = 0.098$ N kg^{-1}. Explain how you arrived at your answers. [4]

(b) A spacecraft on a journey from the Earth to the Moon feels no resultant gravitational pull from the Earth and the Moon when it has travelled to a point 0.9 of the distance between their centres. Calculate the mass in kg of the Moon, using the value for the mass of the Earth in **(a) (iii)**. [3]

(OCR 2824 Jun06)

3 Figure 3 shows an airtrack glider of mass 0.40 kg held by two stretched springs. When the glider is pulled 0.050 m to the left and released, it oscillates freely without friction.

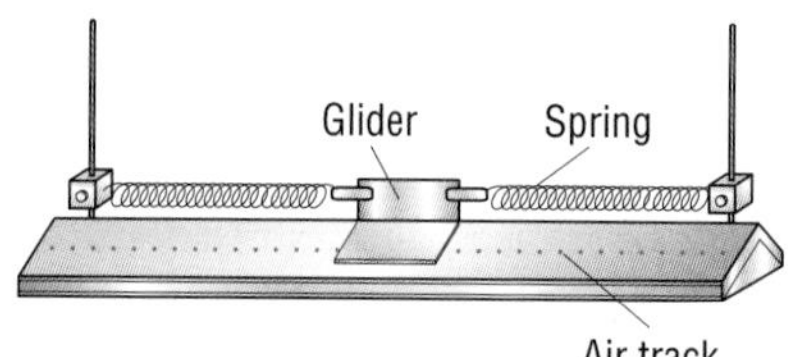

Figure 3

Figure 4 shows the variation of the elastic strain energy stored in the springs with the displacement x from the equilibrium position. Note that the strain energy is 70 mJ when the glider is not oscillating.

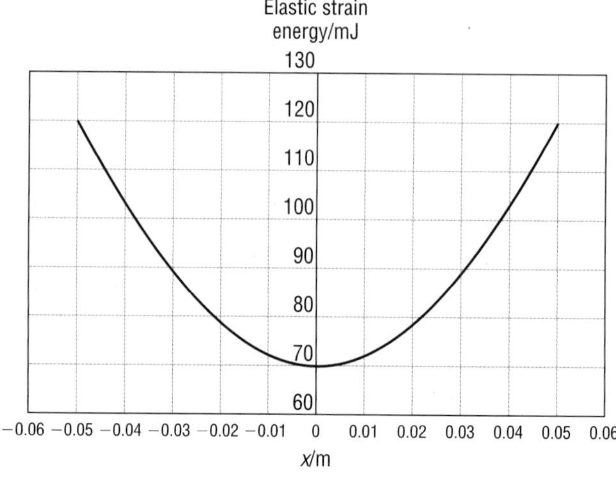

Figure 4

(a) Write down:

(i) the total energy in mJ stored in the system when oscillating [1]

(ii) the maximum kinetic energy in mJ of the glider. [2]

(b) (i) Show that the maximum speed of the glider is $0.50\ m\ s^{-1}$. [2]

(ii) Using Figure 4, or otherwise, find the amplitude in m of oscillation required to halve the maximum speed of the glider. Show your reasoning. [2]

(c) The equation of motion of the glider relating its acceleration a in $m\ s^{-2}$ to its displacement x in m is

$$a = -110\,x$$

(i) Use this equation to show that the period of oscillation is 0.60 s. [2]

(ii) Use the data from **(b) (i)** and **(c) (i)** to sketch the velocity–time graph for the glider. It is released at $x = 0.050$ m at $t = 0$. [3]

(OCR 2824 Jan03)

4 The faulty suspension system of a car is tested. The body of the stationary car is pushed down and released. Figure 5 shows how the vertical displacement of the car varies with time after it has been released.

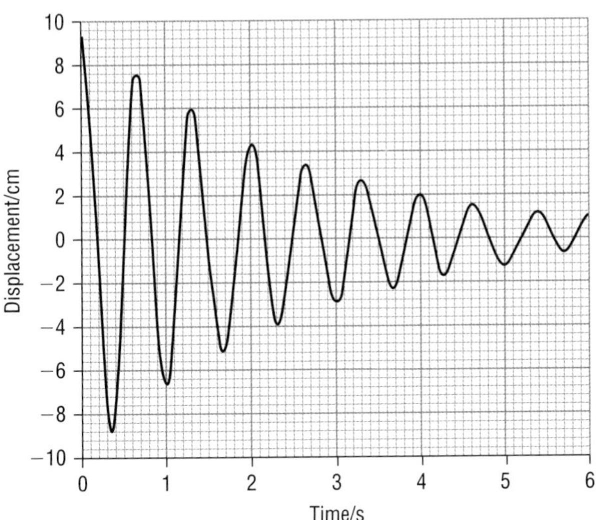

Figure 5

(a) (i) Define simple harmonic motion. [2]

(ii) State **two** features of Figure 5 which indicate that the car body is oscillating in damped harmonic motion. [2]

(b) Use data from Figure 5 to calculate the frequency in Hz of oscillation of the car body. [2]

(c) To simulate the car being driven along a ridged road at different speeds, the floor under the stationary car is oscillated up and down in simple harmonic motion by a mechanical oscillator. The mechanical oscillator provides a movement of variable frequency and constant amplitude. Figure 6 shows the graph of the vertical motion of the car body obtained from the test.

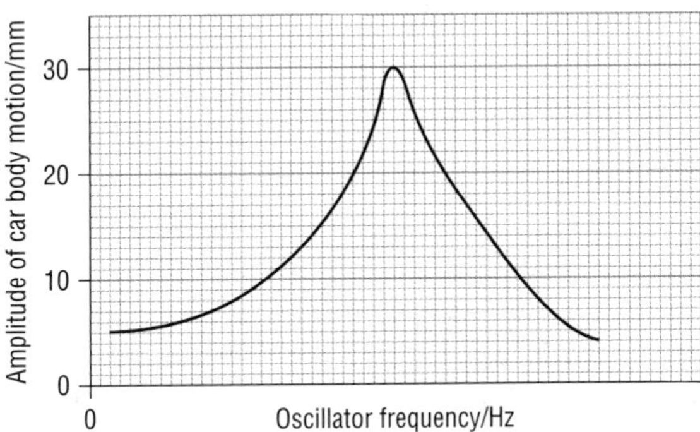

Figure 6

(i) Use information from Figure 6 to write down the amplitude in mm of the motion of the mechanical oscillator. [1]

(ii) Copy Figure 6 and, using your answer to **(b),** add the scale to the frequency axis. [1]

(iii) New dampers are fitted to increase the damping of the car body. On your copy of Figure 6 sketch the graph you would expect for greater damping. [3]

(OCR 2824 Jun03)

5 **(a)** Explain the meaning of the term *resonance*. State **two** examples of oscillating systems in which resonance occurs: one being useful or beneficial, and the other being a nuisance or harmful. Explain their practical significance. You may use diagrams in your answer. State how the oscillation is driven in each case. [7]

(b) Describe how damping in vibrating systems affects their resonant properties. Give an example of a practical resonant system where **two** of the damping effects that you describe could be observed. [5]

(OCR 2824 Jan04)

UNIT 1 Module 3 Thermal physics

Introduction

Almost every day in any newspaper there will be some comment about global warming. Global warming is *very* difficult to measure, so many different values are quoted. It is even more difficult to estimate what will happen in the years to come. However, two things are certain:

- the temperature of the Earth has gone up and down many times during its existence
- over a period of a few years, temperature variations due to weather variability are considerably greater than those due to global warming.

The latter masking effect is probably why global warming was not noticed earlier.

The average surface temperature of each of the planets in the Solar System is largely determined by their distance from the Sun. Neptune is very cold; Mercury is very hot. The mean temperature of each planet is constant because of an energy balance. Energy arriving at the planet's surface from the Sun and from the interior of the planet is balanced out by energy that the planet radiates out into space.

This photograph is a colour-coded infrared view of the Earth taken by a Meteosat weather satellite at 03.30 hrs GMT over the Greenwich meridian, so the side of the Earth visible here is in darkness. The radiation used to make the image is a fraction of the infrared radiation the Earth loses every night. The colours represent temperature, from blue (coldest) to red (warmest). Blue features are the tops of large cloud banks. Lower, and thus warmer, clouds are shown in yellow, particularly across the centre of the frame. Red areas are generally seas and oceans seen through breaks in the cloud. Land areas, such as the Sahara Desert and North Africa (yellow and green above centre), are often cooler than surrounding seas during the night because of large infrared radiation loss.

In this module you will learn about large-scale heating effects and also about the consequent effects on the molecules within the objects being heated or cooled.

Test yourself

1. What is body temperature in °C?
2. What happens to the boiling point of water **(a)** in a pressure cooker, **(b)** at Everest base camp?
3. Why does a liquid evaporating from your hands feel cold?
4. Are you heating ice when you change it into water?

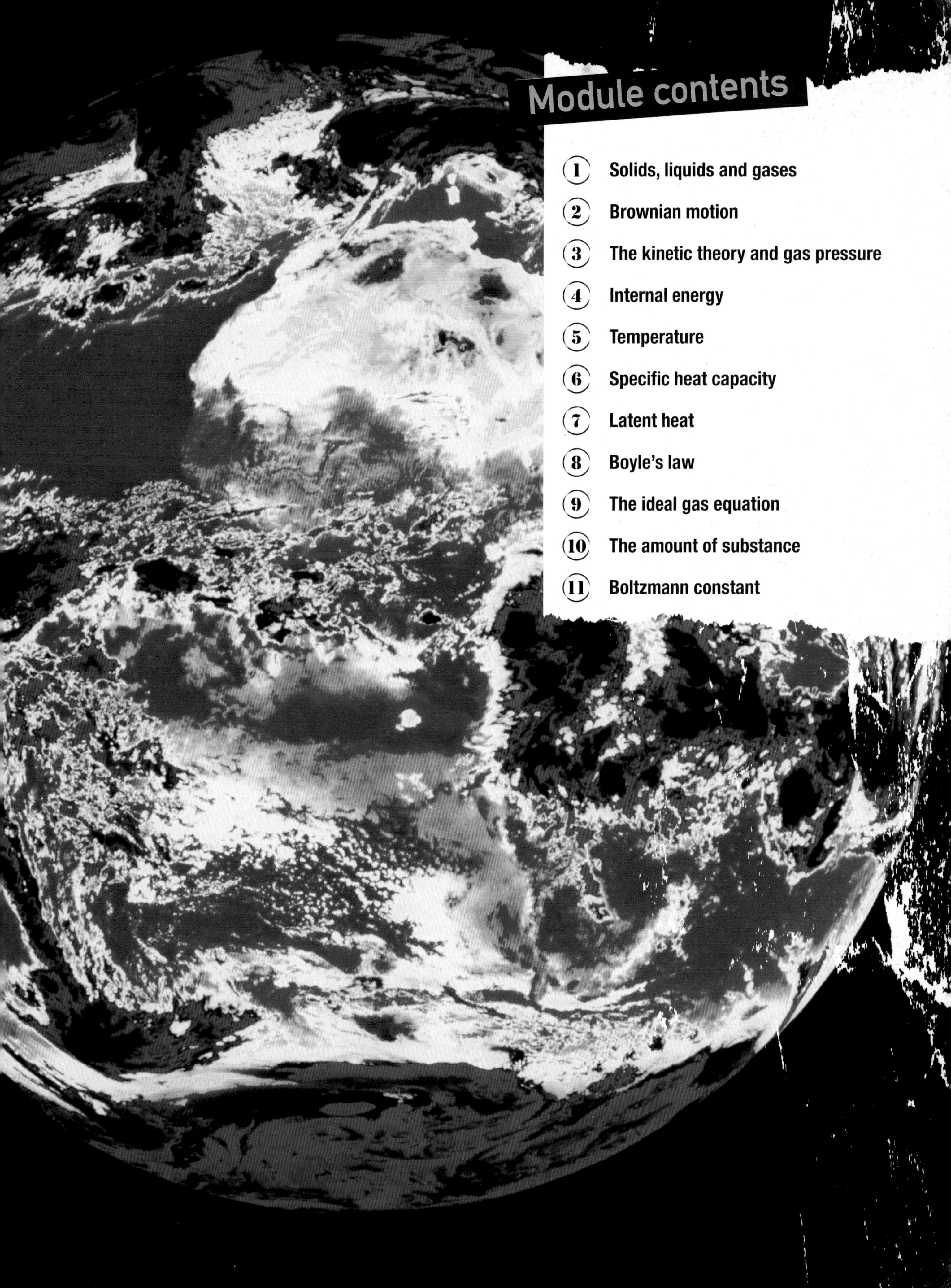

Module contents

1.3 (1) Solids, liquids and gases

By the end of this spread, you should be able to:

* **Describe the differences in the spacing of molecules in solids, liquids and gases.**
* **Describe the differences in the ordering of molecules in solids, liquids and gases.**

Density

Density is defined as the mass per unit volume. The table lists data for the densities of a few substances in the solid, the liquid and the gaseous phases. Not many substances are often encountered in all three **phases** outside laboratory conditions. Carbon dioxide, for example, changes directly from a solid to a gas at room temperature. It would not be easy to measure the density of aluminium gas at 2800 K, so the gas densities of metals are calculated rather than measured and are therefore shown in brackets.

Substance	Solid density/kg m^{-3}	Liquid density/kg m^{-3}	Gas density/kg m^{-3}
oxygen	1300	1100	1.43 at STP
carbon dioxide	1600		1.98 at STP
water	920	1000	0.59 at boiling point
sodium	970	930	(0.24) at boiling point
aluminium	2700	2400	(0.12) at boiling point

STP means standard temperature and pressure, that is, 273 K and 100 kPa (atmospheric) pressure.

Key definition

Phase means whether a substance is a solid, a liquid or a gas.

At this stage the individual values are not important, but there are some striking points to note.

- Solids and liquids are of the order of 1000 times denser than gases.
- Solids are usually a little denser than the corresponding liquid, but this is not always the case. Liquid water, for example, is denser than ice.
- The conditions used for measuring the densities of solids and liquids are not stated; the conditions for gases are quoted (either STP or atmospheric pressure at the boiling point). The reason for this is that pressure and temperature do not alter the density of solids and liquids very much. Since the figures for solids and liquids are only given to 2 sig. figs a change in pressure or temperature will not affect the quoted value. For gases, on the other hand, a change in pressure or temperature has a marked effect on the density.

Atomic or molecular spacing

We will consider water as an example, so we will refer to water molecules. The analysis also applies when atoms are the particles to consider.

The density of any substance in kilograms per cubic metre is given by the following equation:

density = mass of one molecule in kilograms × number of molecules in a cubic metre.

The mass of one molecule is the same for all three phases of water (ice, liquid water and steam), so the density is directly proportional to the number of molecules in a cubic metre. The mass of one water molecule = 3.0×10^{-26} kg. Putting some numerical values into the equation gives

$$\text{1 cubic metre of ice contains } \frac{920\text{ kg}}{3.0 \times 10^{-26}\text{ kg}} = 3.1 \times 10^{28} \text{ molecules}$$

$$\text{1 cubic metre of water contains } \frac{1000\text{ kg}}{3.0 \times 10^{-26}\text{ kg}} = 3.3 \times 10^{28} \text{ molecules}$$

$$\text{1 cubic metre of steam at 100°C contains } \frac{0.59\text{ kg}}{3.0 \times 10^{-26}\text{ kg}} = 2.0 \times 10^{25} \text{ molecules}$$

Assume that the molecules behave like small spheres. Now imagine putting them neatly inside a box that is 1 m long, 1 m wide and 1 metre high. If the distance between one molecule and the next is x, the number along an edge of the box = $1/x$ and so

$$\left(\frac{1}{x}\right)^3 = \text{total number of molecules}$$

The values for x become for ice: 3.2×10^{-10} m
for water: 3.1×10^{-10} m
and for steam at 100°C: 3.7×10^{-9} m.

This illustrates the idea that molecules in a gas are of the order of ten times further apart than they are in a solid or a liquid. Note that ten times further apart means that the density of the gas is a thousandth that of the corresponding solid or liquid (see Figure 1).

Atomic or molecular ordering

Solids

In Figure 1(b) the molecules were shown packed tidily to make a cube. This happens for many substances, phosphorus being one of them. It is the neat arrangement of molecules or ions in solids that gives rise to crystal shapes. A more common packing arrangement in solids gives rise to a pyramid shape, as in Figure 2. This packing arrangement is called close-packing because more spheres can be packed into a given volume than for cubic packing. The molecules or ions packed in a solid are fixed in position. The ions in a piece of rock that emerged molten from a volcano many millions of years ago and soon solidified are still in the same position in the rock now.

Liquids

Like solids, liquids usually contain many molecules packed close together. In water, unusually, they are more closely packed than they are in ice crystals. The difference between a solid and a liquid is that the pattern in a liquid is not so regular and varies from moment to moment. The molecules do not have much space to move about in, but they can slide over one another. For example, a sheet of molecules can move relative to the sheet next to it, such as when water is flowing without turbulence along a pipe. The molecules near the metal of the pipe are almost stationary, but adjacent layers travel faster and faster towards the centre of the pipe. This is illustrated in Figure 3.

Gases

Apart from the vastly increased spacing, the major difference between the arrangement of molecules in gases and those in solids and liquids is that in gases there is no arrangement at all. One word sums up the pattern in gases. It is 'chaotic'.

(a)

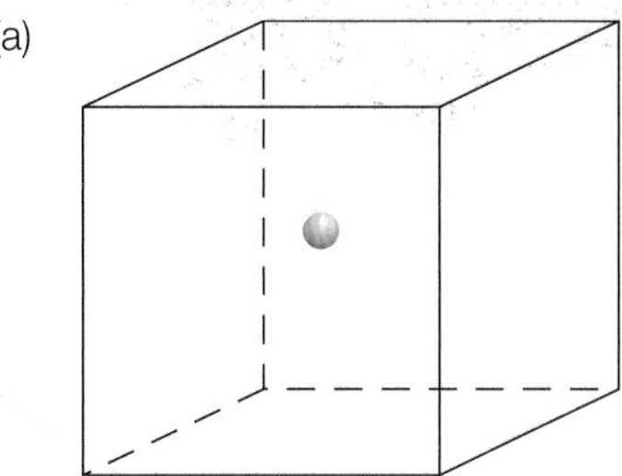

(b)

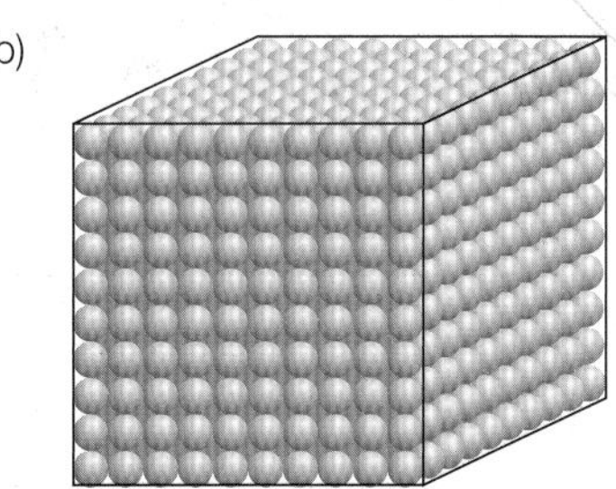

Figure 1 **(a)** A box that is small enough to contain just one molecule of a gas would be able to contain 1000 molecules in the solid or liquid phase, **(b)**

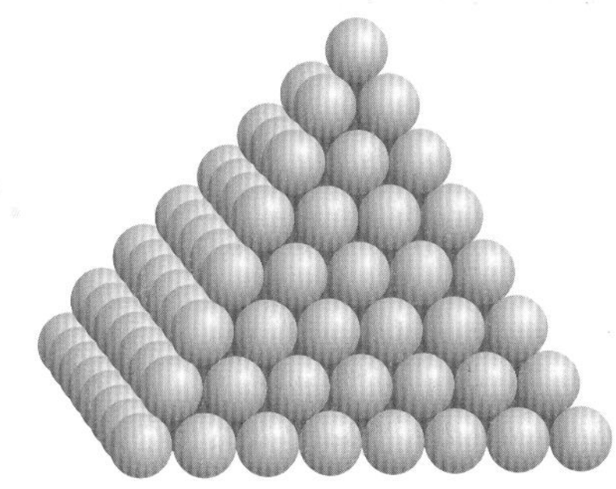

Figure 2 Close packing of molecules in a solid

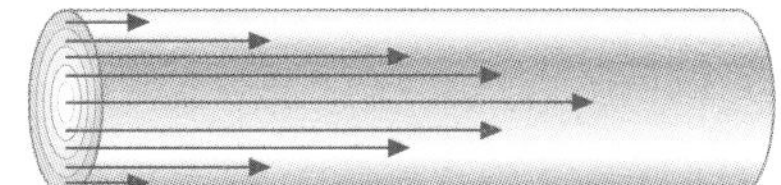

Figure 3 Layers of liquid molecules flowing through a pipe with different velocities

Questions

1 In spread 1.3.10 the mole, the unit of amount of substance, is defined. The mole is a convenient unit for measuring the quantity of matter, rather than using mass, when considering atomic or molecular properties. By definition, one mole of any substance contains 6.022×10^{23} particles. We use this quantity to estimate the size of a copper atom.

(a) The molar mass of copper is 0.064 kg mol^{-1}, that is, 64 g of copper contain 6.022×10^{23} atoms of copper. How many atoms are there in 1.0 kg of copper?

(b) The density of copper is 8900 kg m^{-3}. How many atoms are there in 1.0 m^3 of copper?

(c) Suppose each atom sits in a little box of side equal to its diameter. Find the volume of one box and hence the diameter of an atom.

(d) X-ray crystallography shows that copper atoms have a diameter of 2.55×10^{-10} m. What is the percentage error in your estimate?

2 Again in spread 1.3.10 it is shown that one mole of any gas at atmospheric pressure occupies 22.43×10^{-3} m^3 (22.43 dm^3). We will use this statement to estimate the average distance between gas atoms in the air. Imagine that each atom of the gas is at rest in the middle of an identical box.

(a) What is the volume of one box?

(b) What is the side of one box?

(c) What is the average distance between the centres of atoms in a gas at standard temperature and pressure?

1.3 ② Brownian motion

By the end of this spread, you should be able to …

* **Describe the differences in the motion of molecules in solids, liquids and gases.**
* **Describe a simple kinetic model for solids, liquids and gases.**
* **Describe an experiment that demonstrates Brownian motion.**

(a)

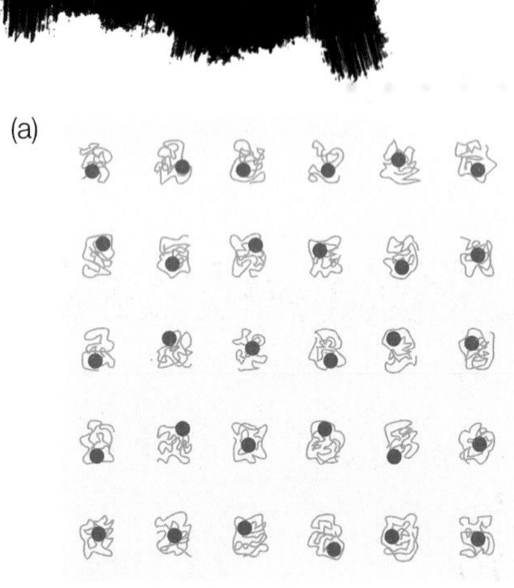

(b)

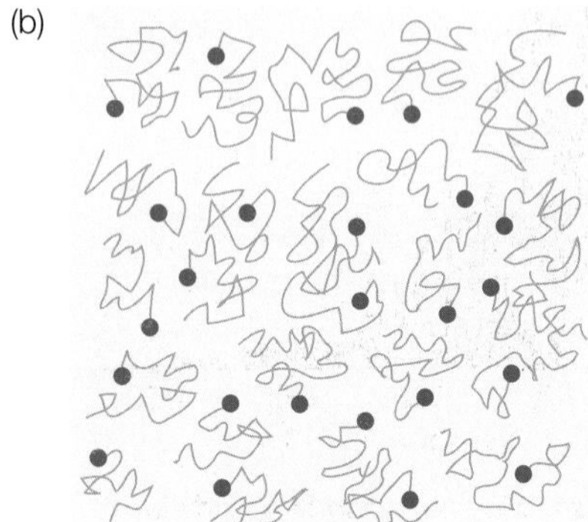

(c)

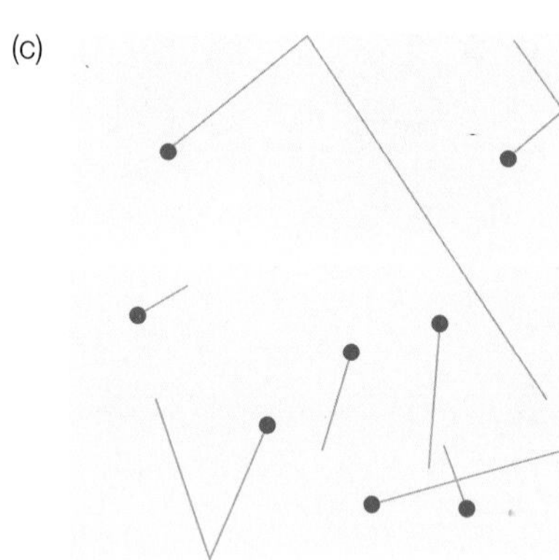

Figure 1 The structure and pattern of movement for molecules in **(a)** a solid; **(b)** a liquid; **(c)** a gas. Though there are far fewer gas atoms in any given volume compared to volumes of liquid or solid, gas atoms do still collide with one another

The speed of molecules

Whenever you describe any phenomenon about the speed of molecules, you must remember that the law of conservation of energy is also involved. If some molecules have an average kinetic energy higher than some other molecules, then when they collide, those with the higher kinetic energy will lose kinetic energy, and the others will gain an equal amount of kinetic energy. The process will stop when the average kinetic energy of both sets of molecules are the same. This is a common occurrence. If you pour cold milk into hot tea the temperature of the milk rises and the temperature of the tea falls. If losses to the surroundings are not taken into account, the kinetic energy that the molecules in the milk gain will equal the kinetic energy the molecules in the tea lose, and all the molecules in both the milk and tea will eventually have the same average kinetic energy.

The temperature of the molecules is directly proportional to their kinetic energy. This will be explored further in later spreads, but at this stage it is crucial to understand that molecules in ice at 0 °C have the *same* average kinetic energy as molecules in water at 0 °C. The freezing point of any substance is the temperature at which both solid and liquid phases can co-exist. The same principle applies at the boiling point: at 100 °C, molecules in the liquid phase (water) have the *same* average kinetic energy as molecules in the gas phase (steam).

Pattern of movement in solids, liquids and gases compared

As a solid is heated, its temperature rises, and the kinetic energy of its molecules therefore increases. However, because it is solid, the position of each molecule cannot change. The increase in kinetic energy therefore results in greater vibration around its equilibrium position.

In a liquid the same effect takes place. But this time, a small amount of translational kinetic energy will be added to the increase in vibrational kinetic energy, since the molecules are now able to move from place to place.

Things are very different in a gas. Here, the chaotic movement of the gas results in almost all of the kinetic energy being translational.

Figures 1(a) for a solid, 1(b) for a liquid and 1(c) for a gas summarise the pattern of movement and the position of molecules in the three phases.

Brownian motion

The motion of molecules in a gas is invisible to the naked eye. If, however, some smoke is introduced into a small glass container and the container is well illuminated and viewed through a microscope, the effect of molecular motion can be seen. This setup is shown in Figure 2. The microscope needs to be focused on the smoke, which you will see as tiny dots of light. If you cannot see anything, it is probably because either the microscope is not focused in the place where the illumination is strong or, more likely, you were expecting to see something much larger than it actually is. The dots will be only just visible.

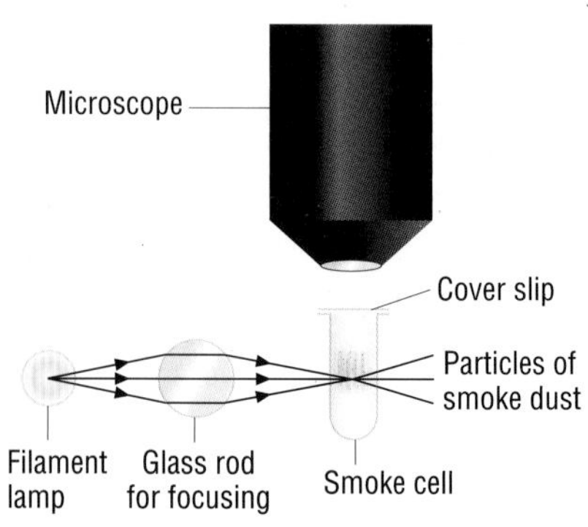

Figure 2 The experimental setup for viewing Brownian motion

The motion, known as Brownian motion, was first observed in 1827 by Thomas Brown when he was examining pollen grains in water. He noticed that they never remained absolutely still but always shuddered around. He put this down to continuous molecular bombardment. It was the first direct evidence that molecules are in perpetual motion. When you look at the smoke particles in the way described above, you should be able to see this shuddering movement. It only happens with very small particles because the molecules around them do not hit them equally from all directions, so the impulse gained by the particles is not zero. If a large particle is used, the individual impulses tend to average out to zero, and the increased mass of the particle changes its velocity less.

STRETCH and CHALLENGE

In any gas with millions upon millions upon millions of molecules, there is a wide variety of speeds at any one point in time. Having some idea of the range of speeds is useful to explain the different properties of gases. For this reason, the histogram (bar chart) shown in Figure 3 is given. The histogram has been constructed for nitrogen gas (basically air) at a temperature of 300 K, about room temperature.

On the vertical axis the percentage of all the molecules in a particular speed range is given. On the horizontal axis the speed is divided into ranges. For example, 10% of the molecules in the gas travel with speed between 350 and 400 m s^{-1}.

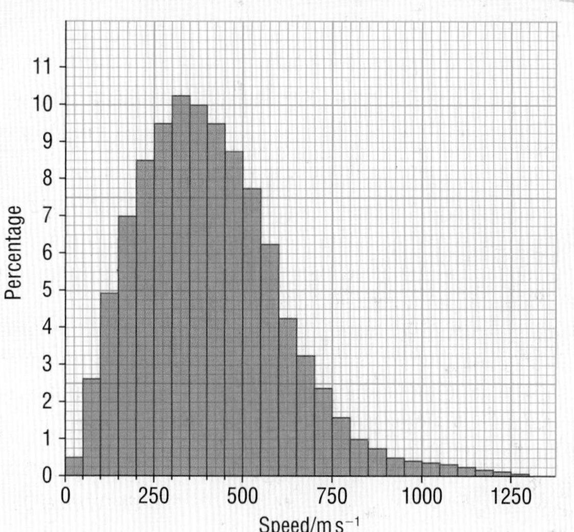

Figure 3 A histogram showing the range of speeds in nitrogen gas at 300 K

Question

Most people know that if you want to find the distance you are from a lightning flash, you count the number of seconds between the flash and the thunder. Then you divide by five to get the distance in miles.

(a) What value does this give for the speed of sound in air?

(b) The value of the speed of sound in air using SI units is 340 m s^{-1}. How does this value give evidence for the speed of molecules quoted above?

(c) Why do smells travel through the air slowly if molecules are moving so fast?

Questions

1 The speed of the smoke particles in the air in the small glass cell can be measured by observing Brownian motion. Although the direction of motion of the smoke particles changes many times per second, they move at about 10 mm s^{-1}.
In the cell the average air molecule and the average smoke particle have the same kinetic energy. Take the mass of a smoke particle to be 1×10^{-16} kg and the mass of an air molecule to be 5×10^{-26} kg. Estimate the average speed of air molecules between collisions at room temperature.

2 A typical speed (in fact the r.m.s. speed, spread 1.3.3) of an air molecule at room temperature is 500 m s^{-1}. When an air freshener spray is used, the scent gradually fills the room. The more massive scent molecules travel at about 400 m s^{-1}.

(a) How long would it take a scent molecule to travel 5.0 m across a room if there were no other molecules along its path?

(b) In fact it will take at least 1000 times longer. Explain why.

(c) Suggest how the rate of diffusion (that is, the continuous movement of mixing) of scent molecules through the room compares with that of the air molecules.

1.3 (3) The kinetic theory and gas pressure

By the end of this spread, you should be able to …

- ✱ **Define pressure.**
- ✱ **State the basic assumptions of the kinetic theory of gases.**
- ✱ **Use the kinetic model to explain the pressure exerted by a gas.**

Pressure

Pressure is defined as the force per unit area. The force required is the force perpendicular to the area. The SI unit of pressure, the pascal (Pa), is one newton per square metre. In equation form this is

$$\text{pressure } (p) = \frac{\text{force } (F)}{\text{area } (A)}$$

The kinetic model of a gas

There are two distinct ways of describing a gas. Historically, the first is called the macroscopic description.

A macroscopic description of a gas is on a large scale. A gas is a phase of matter generated when a liquid boils. It has mass, and a volume equal to the volume of the container it is in. The gas exerts a pressure on the walls of the container.

The microscopic description of a gas is as a collection of a large number of moving molecules that hit one another and the walls of their container. The diagram in Figure 1 shows this.

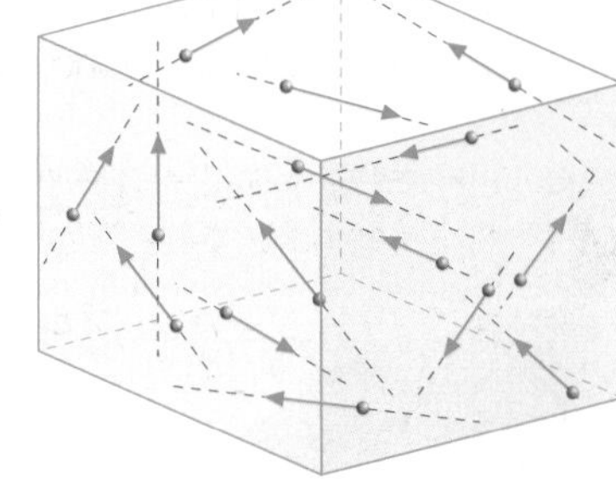

Figure 1 A container showing the collisions of molecules and their random speed and direction

To relate these two descriptions, macroscopic and microscopic, we need to work out the pressure a gas exerts in terms of the movement of its molecules. To do this we need to make some simplifying assumptions:

- A gas consists of a large number of molecules in rapid, random motion.
- Collisions between molecules and between the molecules and the walls of a container are elastic.
- The gravitational force on the molecules is negligible.
- No intermolecular force exists except during collisions.
- The total volume of the molecules is negligible compared with the volume of the container.

Examiner tip

Atmospheric pressure has a value close to 100 000 Pa, so when dealing with the pressure of gases, you are quite likely to get large numerical values of pressure. As always, it helps if you have some idea of the expected size of a numerical answer. This is particularly so when dealing with the forces exerted by molecules. In the last spread you learnt that molecules in the air may be travelling at 500 m s^{-1}. With perhaps 10^{28} molecules in the air around you hitting your 1 square metre of skin every second it is not surprising that the pressure on you is large – even if the molecules have a mass of only 10^{-26} kg each. The reason you are not crushed by this large pressure is that there is a large pressure inside your body as well.

Using models in science

When we say a model, we mean a way of thinking about something that enables us to understand and predict its behaviour. A kinetic model of a gas describes the motion of that gas.

The kinetic model used to find pressure

Figure 2 shows three molecules moving in a cubic box of side length d. The molecules have mass m and are travelling with speed v. Molecule A is travelling horizontally from right to left, molecule B is travelling vertically from bottom to top and molecule C is travelling horizontally from front to back.

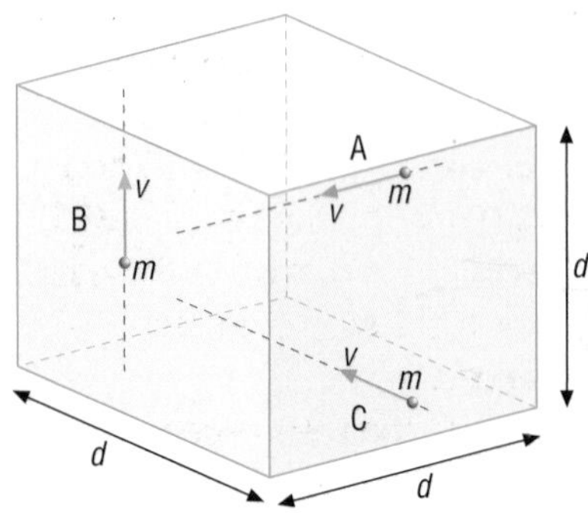

Figure 2 An imaginary situation in which a cubic container has just three molecules moving inside it

Consider molecule A. When it hits the wall, it will bounce back with velocity v since we are assuming elastic collisions with the wall.

- Its momentum will change from mv to the left to mv to the right: a change in momentum of $2mv$.
- The next time it hits that wall will be after it has travelled a distance $2d$ across the box and back.

- The time it takes to do this will be $2d/v$, so it will make $v/2d$ collisions with the wall per unit time.

(Note that if it takes one thousandth of a second to go across the box and back, it will make one thousand collisions per second.) This gives the rate of change of momentum, which is the force F on the wall, as

$$F = 2mv \times \frac{v}{2d} = \frac{mv^2}{d}$$

When there are n molecules going left and right, the force will be nmv^2/d.

This will give a pressure p on a face area d^2 as $nmv^2/d^3 = nmv^2/V$, where V is the volume of the box.

Of course, all the molecules moving in just one of three directions is impossible, but if one molecule collides with another, it will transfer its momentum to the other one, so the total in any direction will still be the same.

The total number of molecules in this box, N, is $3n$, so if we put N rather than n into the pressure equation, we get

$$p = \frac{Nmv^2}{3V} = \frac{Mv^2}{3V} = \frac{1}{3}\rho v^2$$ where M is the total mass of gas and ρ its density.

This analysis is a simplified version, but it does show you the sequence of applying Newton's second law to find the pressure of a gas in terms of its density and the speed of its molecules. The full theory gives the same equation, but instead of a simple v^2, an average value of all the v^2 of all the molecules has to be used. This value is called the mean square speed of the molecules. It is not quite the same as the mean speed squared and is usually given the symbol $\overline{c^2}$.

Worked example

A cylinder has a volume of 500 cm^3. It is filled with gas of density 1.4 kg m^{-3}, and the pressure in the cylinder is 2.5×10^5 Pa. Calculate **(a)** the mean square speed of all the molecules, **(b)** the square root of the mean square speed of all the molecules and **(c)** the kinetic energy of all the molecules.

Answer

(a) Using the equation

$$p = 1/3\, \rho\overline{c^2} \text{ gives } \overline{c^2} = \frac{3p}{\rho} = \frac{3 \times 2.5 \times 10^5}{1.4} = 5.36 \times 10^5 \text{ m}^2\text{ s}^{-2}$$

(b) The root mean square (r.m.s.) speed is simply the square root of **(a)**, that is, 732 m s^{-1}

(c) What is wanted here is $\tfrac{1}{2}mv_1^2 + \tfrac{1}{2}mv_2^2 + \tfrac{1}{2}mv_3^2 + \tfrac{1}{2}mv_4^2 + \ldots\ldots\ldots\ldots + \tfrac{1}{2}mv_n^2$, where n will be some vast number equal to the total number of molecules, and m the mass of one molecule.
The equation can be rewritten as $\tfrac{1}{2}m(v_1^2 + v_2^2 + v_3^2 + v_4^2 + \ldots\ldots\ldots + v_n^2)$.
The term in the brackets is now easy to find, since it is the mean square speed of all the molecules × the number of molecules, that is, the answer to **(a)** × the number of molecules = $5.36 \times 10^5 n$.
This gives the kinetic energy of all the molecules as $\tfrac{1}{2}m \times 5.36 \times 10^5 n$.
Since mn is the total mass of gas, this is volume × density = 500×10^{-6} m^3 × 1.4 kg m^{-3} = 7.0×10^{-4} kg, and the total kinetic energy is $0.5 \times 7.0 \times 10^{-4} \times 5.36 \times 10^5$ = 190 J to 2 sig. figs.

Questions

1 1 mole of hydrogen has a mass of 2.0×10^{-3} kg. At 0 °C and one atmosphere pressure, 1.0×10^5 Pa, it occupies a volume of 0.022 m^3. Calculate **(a)** the r.m.s. speed of a hydrogen molecule and **(b)** the kinetic energy of one mole of the gas.

2 The volume of one mole of gas is the same for all gases at the same temperature and pressure. The heaviest gas is radioactive, radon, with a molar mass of 0.22 kg mol^{-1}. Calculate the r.m.s. speed of this gas at 0 °C and one atmosphere pressure. Remember that the volume of the gas is the same as that in Question 1.

3 The mean kinetic energy of a molecule of any gas is the same at a given temperature. Using the fact that 1 mole of gas contains 6.02×10^{23} particles, find the value of the mean kinetic energy using the data from Question 1. Check that the value is the same for radon (see Question 2).

4 A nitrogen molecule has a mass of 4.7×10^{-26} kg. Six nitrogen molecules in a sample of air have velocities 300, 450 and 500 m s^{-1} to the left, and 350, 400 and 550 m s^{-1} to the right. For these six molecules, calculate:

(a) **(i)** the mean speed
(ii) the mean velocity
(iii) the r.m.s. speed.

(b) **(i)** the mean momentum
(ii) the mean kinetic energy.

Internal energy

By the end of this spread, you should be able to ...

- **Define internal energy of a body.**
- **Explain that the rise in temperature of a body leads to an increase in its internal energy.**
- **Explain the effect of a change in state of a substance on internal energy.**
- **Use a simple kinetic model to describe melting, boiling and evaporation.**

Introduction

The example at the conclusion of spread 1.3.3 showed that it is possible to calculate the total kinetic energy of all the molecules of a gas in a container. This is the energy that the molecules have as a result of continual movement within their container. Under fixed conditions of temperature, pressure and volume the total kinetic energy remains constant. Indeed, once the conditions are fixed for a quantity of gas, the total kinetic energy of the molecules is also fixed. Clearly, individual molecules sometimes move quickly and sometimes slowly, but if they slow down as a result of a collision with another molecule, they simply transfer some of their kinetic energy to the other molecule. In other words, the total kinetic energy is unchanged.

Now consider what happens if you carry the container on board a plane. The container and the molecules within it may now be travelling at 250 m s^{-1}. They all have increased kinetic energy. However, the temperature, pressure and volume can still be the same. Their kinetic energy *within the container* has not changed. The temperature, pressure and volume of the gas control the random kinetic energy within the container. They have no control over the kinetic energy caused by being in the moving plane.

Internal energy

Key definition

The **internal energy** of a body is the sum of the random distributions of kinetic and potential energies of all the molecules in the body.

A definition of internal energy is:

> **The internal energy of a body is the sum of the random distributions of kinetic and potential energies of all the molecules in the body.**

Internal energy includes only the random kinetic energy. The word 'random' is crucial if you are asked to define internal energy. Using the figures for the cylinder in spread 1.3.3, we found the random kinetic energy to be 190 J. The gas had mass of 7.0×10^{-4} kg, and therefore when travelling at 250 m s^{-1} it has kinetic energy of $\frac{1}{2} \times 7.0 \times 10^{-4} \times 250^2 = 22$ J due to its movement in the plane. When finding internal energy, the 22 J is ignored.

Key definition

An **ideal gas** is a gas that has internal energy only in the form of random kinetic energy.

There is something else to consider, however, when calculating internal energy. One of the simplifications we make when we work out the pressure of a gas is to assume that there are no intermolecular attractions. In an **ideal gas**, this is true. For an ideal gas the random kinetic energy of the gas is the only internal energy the gas possesses. But for a real gas, with intermolecular attractions, the molecules may have potential energy, and this potential energy must be included. Again, it is only potential energy between individual molecules that counts. Just lifting the whole gas upwards makes no difference to the internal potential energy.

In practice it is usually *changes* in internal energy that need to be calculated. While it is relatively easy to calculate the actual random kinetic energy for a gas, it is not so easy to give actual values of the random potential energy. Sometimes you will see negative values for the potential energy. This means simply that the random potential energy has fallen by that amount.

Factors affecting internal energy

Temperature

If the temperature of a system rises, the molecules travel more rapidly, their kinetic energy rises and so, therefore, will the internal energy.

Pressure

If the pressure falls with no change in temperature, then the internal energy is unaltered in an ideal gas. If the gas is not ideal, then the molecules will attract one another, which means that if the gas is expanding, there must have been some work done on the molecules to pull them apart. This means that there is a higher potential energy and a higher internal energy, even though the temperature has not changed.

State

The state of a system includes what phase it has (solid, liquid or gas) and other things such as the crystalline structure and atomic rearrangements within a molecule.

Any change in state does not involve a change in temperature. Therefore, the kinetic energy component of the internal energy does not change. However, the molecules do alter their random potential energy considerably. Liquid water changes to steam when it boils at 100 °C. Molecules in boiling water at 100 °C have the same average random kinetic energy as molecules in steam at 100 °C. The molecules in the steam, however, have a far greater random potential energy than those in the boiling water.

For most substances, changing a solid into a liquid at the same temperature involves an increase in volume and a consequent rise in internal potential energy. Liquid water is unusual in that it is more dense than ice, so you might think that the internal potential energy of liquid water would be lower than for ice. But this is not the case. Because breaking down the crystal structure of ice to form liquid water at 0 °C *does* involve work being done, there is a rise in internal energy as ice melts.

Factors that have no effect on internal energy

- The speed of the whole body does not contribute to the internal energy at all.
- A change in the position of the whole body in a gravitational field does not contribute to the internal energy at all.

Questions

1 Figure 1 is the graph of the cooling curve of a substance between 250 °C and room temperature.
Over which sections of the curve is:
(a) the internal energy of the substance decreasing?
(b) the random kinetic energy of the molecules decreasing?
(c) the random potential energy of the molecules almost constant?

2 Explain, in terms of internal energy, why a liquid cools when it evaporates, e.g. a layer of ether or ethanol on the skin feels cold.

3 Give one everyday example of a situation where:
(a) external energy is converted into internal energy, and
(b) internal energy is converted into external energy.

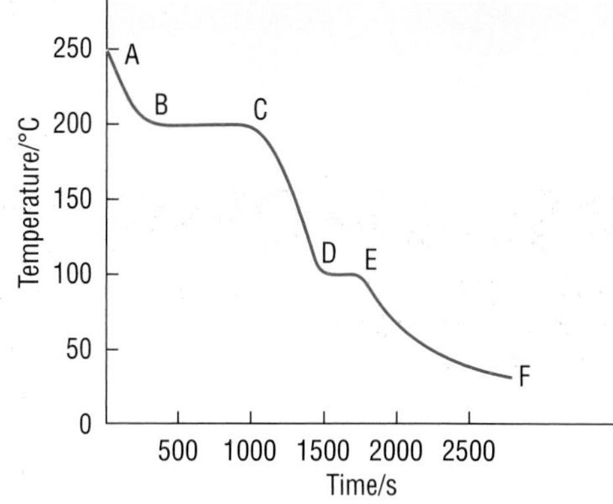

Figure 1

1.3 5 Temperature

By the end of this spread, you should be able to …

* **Explain that regions of equal temperature are in thermal equilibrium.**
* **Explain the relationship between temperature and energy transfer.**
* **Describe what is meant by an absolute scale of temperature and absolute zero.**
* **Convert temperatures measured in kelvin to degrees Celsius (or vice versa).**

Thermal equilibrium

Figure 1 The interchange of energy between the Earth and the Sun

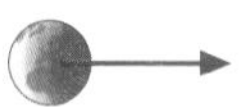

Figure 2 The loss of energy by the Earth at night

Thermal equilibrium concerns energy transfer. We all know that the Earth receives energy from the Sun. This is because the Sun is at a higher temperature than the Earth, so the flow of energy from the Sun to the Earth is much greater than the flow of energy from the Earth to the Sun. The Earth really does send some energy back to the Sun, but it is a very small quantity compared with that flowing the other way. This is illustrated in Figure 1. The energy is transferred by electromagnetic radiation.

At night, cooling takes place because the Earth radiates infrared radiation out into space. Space is at a much lower temperature than Earth, so the energy flow to space is much greater than the energy flow from space to Earth (Figure 2). This is most noticeable on a clear winter night when the temperature of the Earth's surface may fall below freezing point.

Over the course of a year the energy gain from the Sun very nearly equals the energy losses out to space. The scientific arguments about global warming concerns any small difference between energy gains and energy losses. Because the figures for gains and losses are both around 5.5×10^{24} joules per year, it is difficult to get measurements of both to accuracy good enough for any difference between them to be reliable.

Key definition

Two objects at the same temperature will be in **thermal equilibrium.**

Now consider food that has been cooking in an oven for a couple of hours. The walls of the oven are at a fixed temperature, and the temperature of the food will have risen after this amount of time to the same temperature as the walls of the oven. No matter how long the oven is on, the food cannot get any hotter. The food is then said to be in **thermal equilibrium** with the oven.

Conditions of thermal equilibrium apply to two objects when there is zero resultant energy transfer between them. This will happen when the temperatures of the two objects are equal. Temperature determines the direction in which thermal energy will be transferred. Thermal energy is transferred from a region at a higher temperature to a region of lower temperature.

Absolute measurement of temperature

The measurement of temperature has always posed problems. Early thermometers were very unreliable, and different types of thermometers gave different results. Even through the first half of the twentieth century, when an accurate temperature was required it was necessary to state on which thermometer it had been measured. A temperature measured using a mercury-in-glass thermometer agreed only with the reading from a thermocouple thermometer at zero degrees centigrade and at a hundred degrees centigrade. This was not because the thermometers were inaccurate, but because they were using different substances which responded differently to temperature.

This unsatisfactory situation was tackled by an international conference in 1947. It was decided that an absolute scale of temperature was required and that it must not depend on the way any property of a substance varied with temperature. The scale decided on is called the thermodynamic scale of temperature. This scale is related to the efficiency of heat engines and can be shown theoretically to be identical with a scale called the ideal gas scale of temperature. The details of how temperatures are found using the absolute scale of temperature are not required at A level, but you do need to know that:

- The absolute scale of temperature exists.
- It does not depend on any property of a substance.
- It starts from zero at absolute zero, that is, the temperature at which a substance has minimum internal energy. (Spreads 1.3.6 and 1.3.7 will deal with temperature and absolute zero in more detail.)

Numerical values on temperature scales

Further problems were also tackled at the 1947 conference. Different countries used different numerical values both for the freezing point of water and for the boiling point of water, and a completely new pattern of numbers would have been very difficult for people to get used to.

It was decided to use numbers that would make temperature values for weather reports and cooking almost the same as the old centigrade values. The general public in areas of the world that used centigrade would then have no need to adjust their thinking. Those who had used Fahrenheit scales are still adapting to the new scales.

The absolute thermodynamic scale of temperature

Absolute zero is zero kelvin, 0 K. The triple point of water, that is the point at which it can exist in the solid, liquid and gas states simultaneously, is 273.16 K exactly.

The advantage of having absolute zero as 0 K is obvious. The triple point of water is this peculiar number so as to make the old temperature values agree with the new and to fix the point at a temperature that is easy to arrange practically.

The Celsius temperature

This is an absolute scale. It is the absolute thermodynamic scale minus 273.15 exactly. This gives the values in the following table.

	Absolute scale	Celsius scale
Absolute zero	**0 K**	**–273.15 °C**
Triple point of water	**273.16 K**	**0.01 °C**
Ice point	273.15 K	0.00 °C
Steam point	373.15 K	100.00 °C
Room temperature	293 K	20 °C

Table 1

In the table, the figures in bold are exact by definition. The figures not in bold are measured values. An equation that relates absolute thermodynamic temperature, often simply called the kelvin scale, is

$$T/\mathrm{K} = t/°\mathrm{C} + 273.15$$

Questions

1 Convert the following to degrees Celsius:
- **(a)** the boiling point of helium, 4.25 K
- **(b)** the boiling point of oxygen, 90.2 K
- **(c)** the freezing point of mercury, 234 K
- **(d)** the boiling point of sulfur, 718 K
- **(e)** the freezing point of gold, 1340 K.

2 There are four laws of thermodynamics. The first one, called the zeroth law, defines the quantity temperature. The zeroth law of thermodynamics states: when two bodies A and B are separately in thermal equilibrium with a third body C, then A and B are in thermal equilibrium with each other. By considering C to be a thermometer, explain how this law defines temperature.

1.3 (6) Specific heat capacity

By the end of this spread, you should be able to ...

* **Define and apply the concept of specific heat capacity.**
* **Select and apply the equation $E = mc\Delta\theta$.**
* **Describe an electrical experiment to determine the specific heat capacity of a solid or a liquid.**

Terminology

There are a few problems about terminology that you need to be aware of. The first of these is easy to deal with: it is the meaning of the word 'specific'. Whenever you see this word in this book it means 'per unit mass'. The second problem is the use of the word 'heat'. This is a surprisingly difficult word to define, because in everyday language it has several different meanings, most having nothing to do with physics. Because of this, there is a tendency in physics not to use the word. We have other words that should be used in preference. These are:

- 'internal energy' as the random energy of all the atoms in a substance
- 'thermal energy' as the energy supplied to an object, such as by putting a Bunsen burner under it.

These quantities are always measured in joules.

Note that temperature is an altogether different physical quantity. Temperature is measured in °C or K – heat is *never* measured in °C or K.

Think of heating as a process. One particular reason for avoiding the word 'heat' is that, for example, the Sun heats the Earth because the temperature of the Sun is greater than the temperature of the Earth. The Sun radiates electromagnetic waves mostly in the light and infrared regions. If you refer to light as 'heat', it can get very confusing.

Examiner tip

$\Delta\theta$ causes an unexpected problem in practice. If candidates see temperatures in °C and a specific heat capacity unit as J kg^{-1} K^{-1}, they will often take a temperature rise of 20 °C and write it as 293 K. Note the following, however:

temperature rise = 55 °C – 35 °C
= 20 °C

or, exactly the same calculation in kelvin becomes

temperature rise = 328 K – 308 K
= 20 K.

In other words, temperature *changes* in kelvin or degrees Celsius have exactly the same value.

Specific heat capacity (s.h.c.)

Here the word 'heat' is used simply for historical reasons. Use the term as a physical quantity, called **specific heat capacity**, or s.h.c.

The definition of s.h.c. is the quantity of thermal energy required to raise the temperature of a unit mass of a substance by a unit temperature rise. Put another way, it is 'the amount of heating required' to achieve that. The symbol used for s.h.c. is c. In equation form, the definition becomes

$$c = \frac{E}{m\Delta\theta} \quad \text{or} \quad E = mc\Delta\theta$$

where E is the quantity of thermal energy required, m the mass of the material being heated and $\Delta\theta$ the change in the temperature.

Key definition

Specific heat capacity is the quantity of thermal energy required to raise the temperature of a unit mass of a substance by a unit temperature rise.

Knowledge of the s.h.c. of a substance is required whenever you need to calculate the energy required to heat the substance. For example, a manufacturer of dishwashers will know how much hot water is required for a cycle of washing and rinsing and the temperatures required for each part of the process. To ensure the time for a cycle of washing is not too long, the power of the water heater in the machine will have to be determined. This means the s.h.c. of water needs to be known.

Measurement of specific heat capacity

On the base of an electric kettle, you can see its power. If a known mass of water at a known temperature is placed in the kettle and it is switched on, the time taken for it to reach 100 °C can be found. This gives all the information required to find c. A similar experiment can be used to find the s.h.c. of a metal. This is illustrated in Figure 1.

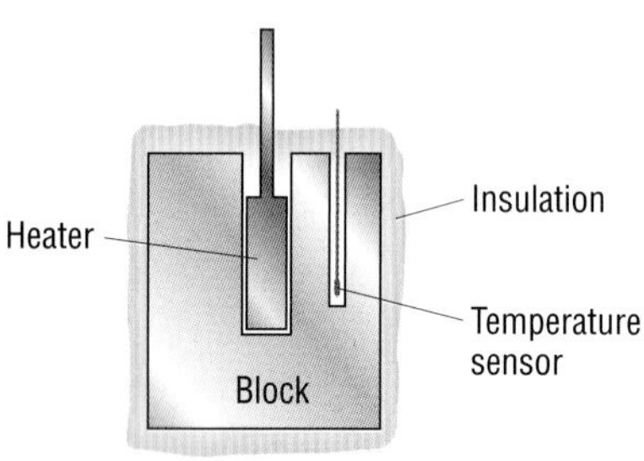

Figure 1 The apparatus used for measuring the s.h.c. of a metal

A block of metal of mass m has two holes drilled in it: one for an electrical heater and the other for a temperature sensor that can be connected to a data logger. The metal is well lagged, and the heater is switched on. A graph of temperature θ against time t is plotted in Figure 2. Either the power P of the heater needs to be known, or both the current I and the potential difference across the heater V need to be measured.

The graph obtained will show a reasonably straight line from a little time after switch-on until switch-off, although the temperature may rise a little after switch-off.

The power of the heater is $P = V \times I$. The equation for s.h.c. gives

$$c = \frac{E}{m\Delta\theta} = \frac{V \times I \times t}{m\Delta\theta} = \frac{V \times I}{m} \times \frac{1}{\text{gradient of graph}}$$

since the gradient of the graph is $\Delta\theta/t$.

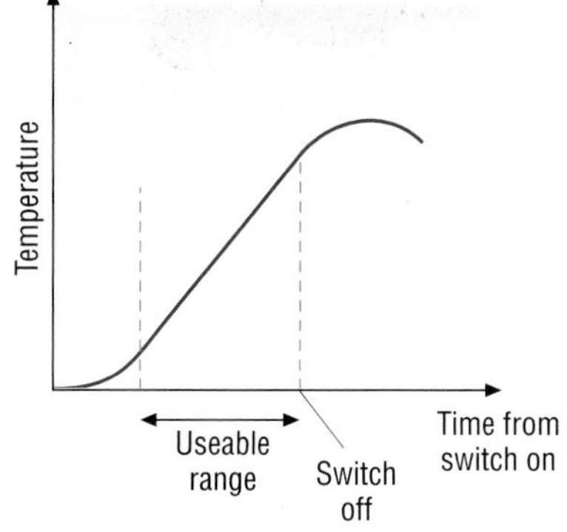

Figure 2 A graph plotted to show how the temperature of the metal rises with time

Worked example

The quantity of hot water required for one part of the cycle in a dishwasher is 4.5 litre. The inlet temperature of the water on a cold day is only 5 °C and is required in the machine at a temperature of 65 °C. The time allowed for heating the water is 15 minutes. What power of heater is required?

Data available: s.h.c. of water = 4200 J kg^{-1} K^{-1}; 1 litre of water has a mass of 1 kg.

Answer

Quantity of thermal energy required = $mc\Delta\theta$

= 4.5 kg × 4200 J kg^{-1} K^{-1} × (65 °C – 5 °C)

= 1.134 × 10^6 J

This energy must be supplied in a time of 15 × 60 s = 900 s.

The power of the heater needs to be 1.134 × 10^6 J/900 s = 1260 W. The manufacturer will therefore probably use a 1200 W heater, and the user would have to wait a little longer for it to heat up on a cold day.

Material	s.h.c./J kg^{-1} K^{-1}
water	4190
ice	2100
copper	385
aluminium	913
mild steel	420
concrete	3350
air at constant pressure	993

Table 1 Values of specific heat capacities of selected materials

Questions

1 One method of heating water using the Sun's rays is to place a tube carrying the water at the focus of a curved mirror (see Figure 3).
For a particular arrangement on a particular day, 820 J of solar energy are absorbed each second by the water, which is flowing at 0.015 kg s^{-1} through the tube. Calculate the maximum possible increase in temperature of the water.

2 A polystyrene cup of soup of mass 400 g is placed in a microwave oven rated at 650 W.
  (a) Calculate the maximum possible increase in temperature of the soup after being heated for two minutes. Assume that the soup has the same thermal properties as water.
  (b) The person heating the soup uses a tight-fitting lid on top of the cup rather than one with a hole in it. Two changes will occur in the vapour above the soup, increasing the pressure there. Name these changes and explain why each causes the pressure to increase.

3 The air in a living room of dimensions 5.5 m × 4.5 m × 2.1 m is heated by a convector heater of power 1.5 kW. Estimate the minimum time required to raise the temperature of the air in the room from 10 °C to 18 °C. The density of air is 1.2 kg m^{-3}. Comment on your answer.

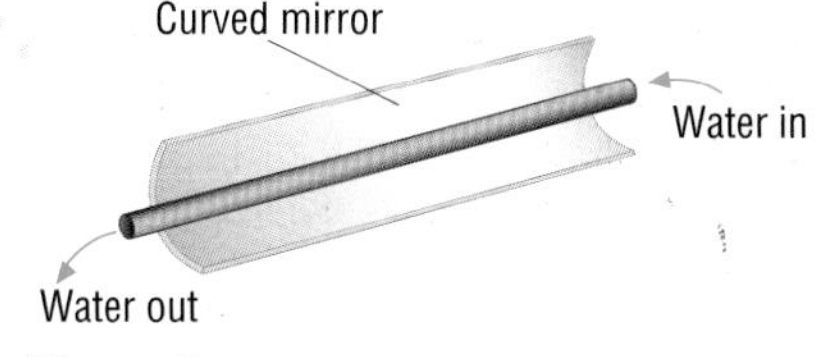

Figure 3

1.3 (7) Latent heat

By the end of this spread, you should be able to ...

*** Describe what is meant by the terms latent heat of fusion and latent heat of vaporisation.**

Introduction

This spread deals with the change of phase of a substance, either from a solid to a liquid or from a liquid to a gas. In spread 1.3.4 these changes were considered from the point of view of internal energy. We saw that, at a substance's melting point, both its solid phase and its liquid phase have the same temperature and that therefore the kinetic energy of the molecules per unit mass of both phases are the same. This is also the case for the liquid and gas phases at the boiling point. Temperature fixes the average kinetic energy of molecules, and so, at the boiling point, liquid and gas have the same internal kinetic energy per unit mass.

Nevertheless, energy is required to change a solid to a liquid or a liquid to a gas. Because this increases the internal energy of the substance, the molecules must gain potential energy when the substance melts or boils. This is shown quite clearly by the numerical values for water shown in the following table. Note that ice is taken as the reference zero.

	Internal kinetic energy per kilogram/J	Internal potential energy per kilogram/J	Total internal energy per kilogram/J
Ice at 0 °C	1.9×10^5	Reference zero	1.9×10^5
Water at 0 °C	1.9×10^5	3.3×10^5	5.2×10^5
Water at 100 °C	2.6×10^5	6.8×10^5	9.4×10^5
Steam at 100 °C	2.6×10^5	27.8×10^5	30.4×10^5

Table 1 Internal energy values for water

Latent heat of fusion

The latent heat of fusion of an object is the amount of thermal energy required to change it at constant temperature from a solid to a liquid. The ice falling into the sea from a glacier in Figure 1 will become an iceberg in the water and will require a very large amount of thermal energy before it all changes into water.

The specific latent heat of fusion of a substance is the quantity of energy per unit mass required to change it at constant temperature from a solid into a liquid.

Its numerical value for ice can be found from the table above to be $(5.2 \times 10^5 - 1.9 \times 10^5) = 3.3 \times 10^5\ \text{J kg}^{-1}$.

Figure 1 An iceberg forming when ice from a glacier falls into the sea

Key definition

The **specific latent heat of fusion** of a substance is the quantity of energy per unit mass required to change it at constant temperature from a solid into a liquid.

Latent heat of vaporisation

Figure 2 shows a familiar situation of boiling water in a saucepan. Bubbles of steam can be seen as they rise through the water at a temperature of 100 °C. Steam itself is invisible. As soon as the bubbles reach the surface they meet colder air and very quickly change back into water droplets. This is what can be seen over the top of the pan. Clouds in the sky are often said to be water vapour. But they are not, because water vapour is also invisible. There is a great deal of water vapour in the room you are sitting in, but you cannot see it. Any clear atmosphere has water vapour in it. When the air in the atmosphere rises, the water vapour in the atmosphere may cool sufficiently to change back to form water droplets. These water droplets are clouds.

One final distinction on terminology is the difference between a vapour and a gas. A vapour can be changed back into a liquid by applying pressure to it. A gas cannot be liquefied by pressure alone.

The definition of latent heat of vaporisation is similar to that for fusion.

The specific latent heat of vaporisation of a substance is the quantity of energy per unit mass required to change it at constant temperature from a liquid into a vapour.

Its numerical value for water is 22.6×10^5 J kg^{-1}. This value is slightly different from the value the table above seems to be giving ($30.4 \times 10^5 - 9.4 \times 10^5 = 21.0 \times 10^5$ J kg^{-1}) because some extra energy is required to do some work against atmospheric pressure to make space for the vapour being created. (This is a good example of the law of conservation of energy in action.)

Figure 2 Water boiling in a glass saucepan

Key definition

The specific latent heat of vaporisation of a substance is the quantity of energy per unit mass required to change it at constant temperature from a liquid into a vapour.

Questions

1 A 3.0 kW electric kettle contains boiling water. It is boiled for 2.00 minutes sitting on a top pan balance. The initial reading is 1.487 kg and the final reading 1.343 kg.

(a) Use these results to calculate the energy required to vaporise **(i)** 1.00 kg of water and **(ii)** 1.00 mole of water. The molar mass of water is 0.018 kg mol^{-1}.

(b) Suggest why the answer to **(a)(i)** differs from the value given in the main text above.

2 One way to reduce the cooking time of food is to use a pressure cooker in which water boils at a temperature above 100 °C. The variation of boiling temperature T with pressure p measured in Pa is shown in the graph of Figure 3.

(a) Verify that the value of p at 373 K is 1.0×10^5 Pa.

(b) Use the graph to find the increase in boiling temperature that occurs when the pressure in the pressure cooker is doubled.

3 In some hot countries, tea is served in a pot with a glass 2/3 full of ice. The boiling tea is poured into the glass to fill it. Estimate the temperature of the resulting drink. (Use data given in this and the last spread to solve this problem.)

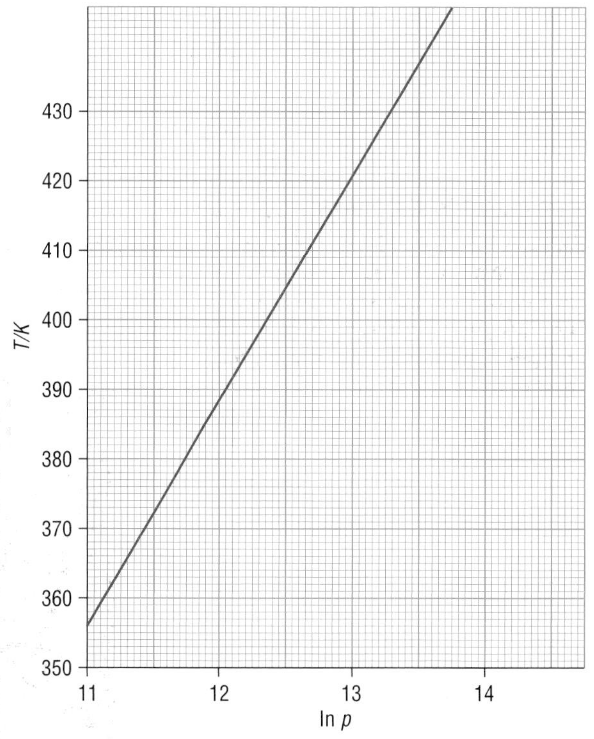

Figure 3

1.3 (8) Boyle's law

By the end of this spread, you should be able to ...

*** State Boyle's law.**

Key definition

Boyle's law states that the volume of a fixed mass of gas is inversely proportional to the pressure exerted on it, provided the temperature is kept constant.

A practical approach to Boyle's law

This spread extends the work on gases started in spread 1.3.3. In that spread we saw that any large-scale theory of a gas – a macroscopic theory – and any molecular theory – a microscopic theory – must agree with one another. Robert Boyle was the first person to investigate a quantitative gas law. He knew nothing about the microscopic properties of a gas, but he investigated how the volume of a gas depended on the pressure exerted on it. His conclusion is now known as **Boyle's law**. A statement of the law is as follows.

The volume of a fixed mass of gas is inversely proportional to the pressure exerted on it, provided the temperature is kept constant.

A piece of apparatus that can be used to demonstrate this law is shown in Figure 1. It consists of a long tube, closed at one end and containing air above some oil. The pressure on the oil can be increased by means of a pump, and the pressure exerted on the air by the oil is indicated by a pressure gauge. The volume of the air in the tube can be measured from a scale behind the tube. A typical set of results from the experiment is given in Table 1.

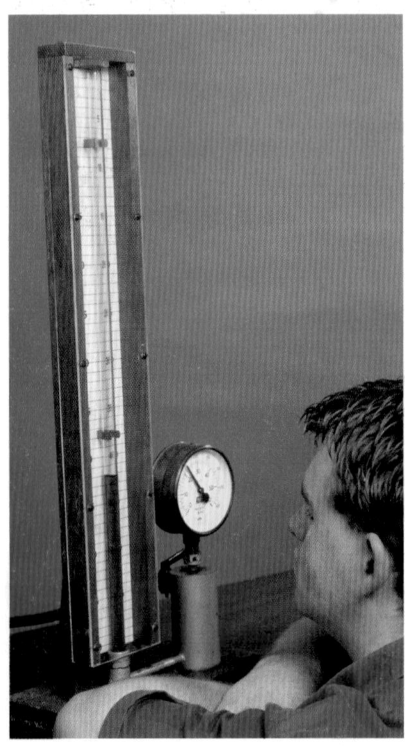

Figure 1 A piece of apparatus used to demonstrate Boyle's law

Pressure $p/10^5$ Pa	Volume V/cm^3	$1/V$/cm^{-3}	pV/N m
4.0	7.7	0.130	3.08
3.5	9.0	0.111	3.15
3.0	10.5	0.0952	3.15
2.5	12.5	0.0800	3.20
2.0	15.5	0.0645	3.10
1.5	21.0	0.0476	3.15
1.0	31.5	0.0317	3.15
0.7	49.0	0.0204	3.13
0.5	62.8	0.0159	3.14

Table 1 Results from the experiment shown in Figure 1

A few points to note about this experiment:

- The apparatus can be pumped up to a high pressure and then very slowly vented. As the pressure gauge reads the values given, the volume is recorded.
- It is important to do the experiment slowly so that the temperature will always be room temperature. A gas cools as it expands, and time must be allowed for the temperature to be constant.
- The unit given for pV is correct as N m. To get the value in N m, the volume needs to be in m^3 and the pressure in Pa. (The first line will be 4.0×10^5 Pa $\times$ 7.7×10^{-6} m^3 = 3.08 N m.) You should check that the unit N m is indeed the unit of pV.

- It is very difficult to check the shape of a graph that shows the inverse proportion of p and V if p is plotted directly against V. If a graph is to be plotted, then a straight-line graph will be obtained if p is plotted against $1/V$. Here the product pV can be seen to be constant.
- The pressure gauge records total pressure. Since atmospheric pressure is around 1×10^5 Pa, some suction is necessary to get the last two readings, as they are below atmospheric pressure.

Worked example

The pressure in the Bournemouth Eye helium balloon, Figure 2, is kept at 3000 Pa above atmospheric pressure. On a day when the atmospheric pressure is 101 000 Pa, the volume of helium is 5500 m³. What will be the volume V_2 of helium when the temperature is unchanged but atmospheric pressure is only 98 000 Pa?

Answer

Total pressure on the first day = 3000 + 101 000 = 104 000 Pa

$p_1V_1 = 104\,000 \times 5500 = p_2V_2 = (98\,000 + 3000) \times V_2$

$$V_2 = \frac{104\,000 \times 5500}{101\,000} = 5660 \text{ m}^3$$

Figure 2 The Bournemouth Eye helium-filled balloon

Questions

1 A bubble of diameter 1.5 mm escapes from a diver's helmet at a depth of 40 m where the pressure is 5.0 atmospheres.
  (a) Calculate the minimum diameter at the surface.
  (b) Why is the diameter likely to be greater than your calculated answer?

2 A cylinder of volume 0.020 m³ contains nitrogen gas at a pressure of 80 atmospheres. The valve is opened and gas is collected at atmospheric pressure until the pressure in the cylinder has fallen to 60 atmospheres. What is the volume of the released nitrogen gas?

3 A simple mercury barometer consists of a vertical glass tube sealed at its upper end containing a column of mercury. The space between the top of the mercury column and the upper end of the tube is a vacuum. A mercury column height of 760 mm is equivalent to atmospheric pressure 1.0×10^5 Pa.
  A school experiment to find atmospheric pressure before the days of modern health legislation was as follows. A length of air was trapped in a capillary tube sealed at one end by a thread of mercury. When the tube was held horizontally, the length of the trapped air column was 82 mm and the length of the thread of mercury was 39 mm. When the tube was held vertically with the open end upwards, the air column was squashed to 78 mm.

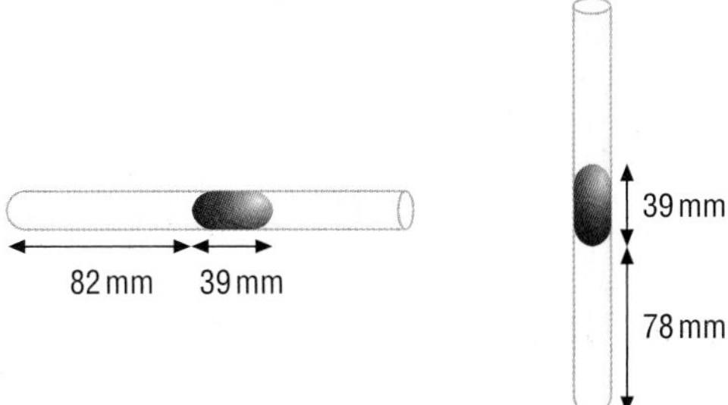

Figure 3

  Find the value of atmospheric pressure in mm of mercury (mmHg).

The ideal gas equation

By the end of this spread, you should be able to ...

- **Select and apply pV/T = constant.**
- **Use the ideal gas equation.**

Temperature

In spread 1.3.5 some details were given about the absolute scale of temperature. We saw that it is a scale based on an ideal gas. Now that some additional work has been done on gas pressures and volumes, we can state what is meant by an ideal gas and show how the behaviour of an ideal gas leads to an absolute scale of temperature.

Boyle's law

In the last spread, an experiment was described that showed how the pressure of a gas affected its volume. That experiment showed that the volume was inversely proportional to the pressure. If gases such as hydrogen, helium, oxygen and nitrogen are used instead of air, the law still holds, but it breaks down if either:

- the gas in close to its boiling point or
- if very high pressures are used.

Under these conditions the molecules themselves are occupying a considerable fraction of the volume of their container. The kinetic theory of gases is therefore not as accurate under these circumstances.

The ideal gas

If a gas behaved ideally, Boyle's law would apply exactly. The gas molecules in an ideal gas would have zero volume, and except when they are colliding with one another, they would exert zero force on one another. All their energy would be internal kinetic energy: they would have no internal potential energy at all. They would exactly obey the kinetic theory equation

$$p = 1/3\rho\overline{c^2}$$

An ideal gas is imaginary, but at low pressures, gases such as hydrogen, helium and air do behave in a very similar way to an ideal gas. The basic reason for this arises from the spacing of their molecules. At atmospheric pressure the volume of the gas molecules themselves is around a thousandth of the volume of their container. By working at much lower pressures, the fraction becomes even smaller.

The ideal gas scale of temperature

The concept of the ideal gas is taken a step further in the definition of this temperature scale. Its definition is as follows.

For a fixed mass of an ideal gas at constant pressure, its volume V is proportional to the **ideal gas temperature** T. T will be a temperature in kelvin.

i.e. $V \propto T$

By combining this proportionality with the corresponding Boyle's law proportion at constant temperature, we get

$$\frac{V}{T} = \text{a constant and } pV = \text{another constant}$$

$$\text{so } \frac{pV}{T} = \text{a third constant}$$

From the definition of the ideal gas scale, this equation is exactly true for an ideal gas.

Key definition

For a fixed mass of an ideal gas at constant pressure, its volume V is proportional to the **ideal gas temperature** T. T will be a temperature in kelvin.

Worked example

In one cylinder of a diesel engine, a piston compresses air at a temperature of 23 °C and pressure 1.00×10^5 Pa to 1/25 of its original volume. (That is, its compression ratio is 25.) The pressure rises to 9.06×10^6 Pa. What will be the temperature of the air after this compression?

Answer

First sort out the information given:

	Initial values	Final values
pressure	$p_1 = 1.00 \times 10^5$	$p_2 = 9.06 \times 10^6$
volume	V_1	$V_2 = V_1/25$
temperature	$T_1 = (23 + 273) = 296$ K	T_2

Now use the ideal gas equation $\dfrac{p_1V_1}{T_1} = \dfrac{p_2V_2}{T_2}$

$$\frac{1.00 \times 10^5 \times V_1}{296} = \frac{9.06 \times 10^6 \times V_1}{25 \times T_2}$$

V_1 cancels to give $T_2 = \dfrac{9.06 \times 10^6 \times 296}{1.00 \times 10^5 \times 25} = 1070\text{ K} = 797\,°\text{C}$

This answer will not be accurate to 3 sig. figs, as we have made the assumption that the gas is an ideal gas. Even at these pressures the equation will give accuracy to 2 sig. figs, so the answer can be given as 800 °C to 2 sig. figs. These high temperatures are important in diesel engines, which do not have spark plugs to ignite the fuel. Diesel fuel is squirted into the hot air and ignites spontaneously.

Examiner tip

Some candidates have difficulty rearranging equations that include proportion signs. This table contains some artificial values for *p*, *V* and *T* with arbitrary units so that you can see the value of *pV* staying constant when the temperature is constant, and the value of *V*/*T* staying constant when the pressure is constant. *pV*/*T* is constant throughout.

p	*V*	*pV*	*T*	*V*/*T*	*pV*/*T*
144	100	14 400	300	⅓	48
72	200	14 400	300	⅔	48
48	300	14 400	300	1	48
24	600	14 400	300	2	48
24	400	9600	200	2	48
24	300	7200	150	2	48
24	200	4800	100	2	48

Questions

1 A meteorological balloon has a volume of 6.0 m^3 when at ground level where the temperature is 293 K. The gas in it is at atmospheric pressure 1.0×10^5 Pa. The balloon rises to a height where the pressure has fallen to 4.4×10^4 Pa and the temperature to 257 K. Calculate the volume of the balloon at this height.

2 The inner tube of a bicycle tyre contains a volume of 8.0×10^{-4} m^3 of air. The pressure of the gas in the tyre is 4.0×10^5 Pa, and the temperature is 20 °C. Towards the end of a race the outer tyre splits and the inner tube expands to 8.3×10^{-4} m^3. The pressure in the tube is 4.1×10^5 Pa. Estimate the temperature in °C of the gas in the tube when the accident occurred.

3 A cylinder in a diesel engine contains a mixture of fuel and air at a temperature of 330 K and a pressure of 1.0×10^5 Pa. The volume of the mixture is reduced by a factor of 18, and the temperature rises to 1100 K. Calculate the resulting pressure in the cylinder.

4 Two containers of volume *V* and 4*V* are connected by a capillary tube of negligible volume. Both are initially at room temperature, 293 K, and contain air at atmospheric pressure 1.0×10^5 Pa. The larger container is placed in boiling water and is heated to 373 K. Calculate the final pressure of the gas in the two containers. Hint: the total mass of gas in the two containers must remain constant.

1.3 (10) The amount of substance

By the end of this spread, you should be able to ...

*** Define a mole of a substance and use the Avogadro constant.**

Background information

In the early nineteenth century, Avogadro carried out a series of experiments on gases. He measured the volumes of gases undergoing chemical reactions. Working with gases at constant temperature and pressure, he found that there was always a simple relationship between the volumes. For example, he found that

> 1 volume of oxygen combined with 2 volumes of hydrogen to produce 2 volumes of steam.

This reinforced his acceptance of the idea of molecules of matter, and he formulated a law, now called Avogadro's law, which states that equal volumes of gases under conditions of equal temperature and pressure contain the same number of molecules.

The Avogadro constant and the mole

The Avogadro constant

This constant can now be used to determine the number of molecules in any quantity of any substance.

Finding the mass of individual molecules with great accuracy was not possible until the twentieth century. By that time a great deal of detail concerning the Periodic Table of the elements and their atomic and nuclear structure had been obtained, and a standard of quantity was needed. The mass of 12 grams of an isotope of carbon called carbon-12 was used as a reference, and it contained 6.02214×10^{23} atoms (see spread 2.3.4). This number is now called the **Avogadro constant** and is represented by the symbol N_A.

Key definition

The Avogadro constant, N_A, is 6.02×10^{23} mol^{-1}.

The amount of substance and the mole

In most scientific experiments even small quantities of material contain vast numbers of individual molecules. Because working with very large numbers can lead to unnecessary mistakes, a new quantity called the *amount of substance* was introduced into the SI system. Its unit is the **mole** (abbreviated to mol), and the mole is defined by the statement:

One mole of any substance contains 6.02×10^{23} (to 3 sig. figs) particles.

Key definition

The **mole** of any substance contains 6.02×10^{23} particles.

That is, anything with a number of particles equal to the Avogadro constant is 1 mole of those particles.

Those of you who study chemistry as well as physics may already be very familiar with using moles for quantitative work.

There is a need to be careful over the distinction between particles, atoms and molecules here. (The word 'particle' is used to cover both atoms and molecules.) For example:

- A mole of hydrogen atoms is 6.02×10^{23} hydrogen atoms.
- A mole of hydrogen molecules is 6.02×10^{23} hydrogen molecules.
- A mole of hydrogen molecules is 2 moles of hydrogen atoms since each molecule has two atoms.

In all the work done on atomic particles so far, the word 'molecule' has been used rather than 'atom'. Most gases are molecular rather than atomic, for example H_2, O_2, N_2 and CO_2. Helium is an exception: each of its particles comprises just one atom of helium.

The statement made by Avogadro quoted at the start of this spread – 1 volume of oxygen combines with 2 volumes of hydrogen to produce 2 volumes of steam – can now be written as:

1 molecule of oxygen combines with 2 molecules of hydrogen to produce 2 molecules of steam

or as:

1 mole of oxygen combines with 2 moles of hydrogen to produce 2 moles of steam.

See Figure 1.

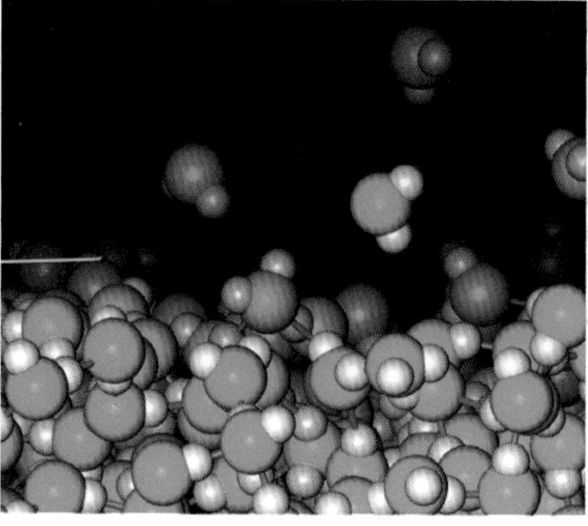

Figure 1 A model showing water molecules on a surface, with some of them evaporating into the space above the surface

The molar gas constant R

In spread 1.3.9 we finished by stating that when an ideal gas undergoes changes in pressure, volume and temperature, pV/T is a constant. We can now go one stage further and state what this constant is for: an amount of substance n (that is, it is for n moles).

$$\frac{pV}{T} = nR$$

where R is known as the molar gas constant (often called simply the gas constant).

Reorganising the equation gives

$$pV = nRT$$

where R has the value 8.3145 J mol^{-1} K^{-1}.

Worked example

What is the volume occupied by a mole of oxygen molecules at standard pressure and temperature (to 4 sig. figs)? (Standard pressure = 101 300 Pa, and standard temperature = 273.2 K.)

Answer

$pV = nRT$, so $101\,300 \times V = 1 \times 8.315 \times 273.2$

$V = 2272/101\,300$ m^3

$= 22.43 \times 10^{-3}$ m^3

(Chemists should recognise this value as 22.43 dm^3.)

Note that if the same calculation had been done for any other gas, the answer would have been the same, that is, in agreement with Avogadro's initial experiments.

Questions

$R = 8.31$ J mol^{-1} K^{-1}, molar volume = 22.43×10^{-3} m^3 and $N_A = 6.02 \times 10^{23}$ mol^{-1}.

1 The density of air is 1.29 kg m^{-3}. Calculate:
   (a) the molar mass of air
   (b) the number of molecules in 1.0 kg of air.

2 A cylinder of volume of 0.020 m^3 at room temperature (290 K) contains nitrogen gas of molar mass 0.028 kg mol^{-1} at 70 atmospheres (atm) pressure (70×10^5 Pa).
   (a) How many moles of gas does the cylinder contain?
   (b) What mass of gas does the cylinder contain?
   (c) When the gas is released into the atmosphere, what volume does it fill?
   (d) An identical cylinder contains hydrogen gas of molar mass 0.02 kg mol^{-1} at the same temperature (290 K) and pressure (70 atm). How many moles of hydrogen does it contain?

3 A spherical flask of volume 2.0×10^{-3} m^3 contains air at 300 K. Air, molar mass 0.029 kg mol^{-1}, behaves as an ideal gas at room temperature. The air is removed from the flask using a vacuum pump until the pressure is reduced to 150 Pa.
   Calculate **(a)** the number of air molecules remaining in the flask and **(b)** the density of the air.

4 The flask in Question 3 is returned to atmospheric pressure 1.0×10^5 Pa and sealed with a rubber stopper.
   (a) Calculate the number of gas molecules in the flask.
   (b) The flask is heated until at 400 K the rubber stopper pops out of the flask. Calculate the pressure in the flask.
   (c) Suppose the rubber stopper did not seal the flask because it had a hole in it. How many gas molecules would remain in the flask at 400 K?

1.3 (11) The Boltzmann constant

By the end of this spread, you should be able to ...

- **Select and apply the equation $E = 3/2kT$ for the mean translational kinetic energy of atoms.**
- **Explain that the mean translational kinetic energy of an atom of an ideal gas is directly proportional to the temperature of the gas.**

Microscopic behaviour of gases

So far in this module, some spreads have concentrated on the microscopic properties of matter, and some on the macroscopic properties. When dealing with the gas laws, however, the emphasis has been on quoting the pressure and the volume in terms of the large-scale, macroscopic properties, the amount of gas n (in moles) and the gas constant R. This spread concludes the module by considering the behaviour of a gas in terms of microscopic quantities.

The Boltzmann constant, *k*

Key definition

The **Boltzmann constant** is the gas constant for a single molecule.

The **Boltzmann constant** is useful when considering the gas equation for molecules rather than moles. R is the gas constant for one mole of molecules. The Boltzmann constant, k, is the gas constant for one single molecule. In the equation $pV = nRT$, nR is the constant for n moles of gas. The same value for this in terms of k must then be Nk, where N is the total number of molecules.

Either of the following two gas equations can be used, depending on whether a problem is set in terms of molecules or large-scale phenomena.

$$pV = nRT \quad \text{or} \quad pV = NkT$$

The numerical value of the Boltzmann constant is 1.3807×10^{-23} to 5 sig. figs. It is measured in J K^{-1}.

We can check that nR and Nk are equal if we consider 2 moles of a gas:

$$nR = 2\ \text{mol} \times 8.31\ \text{J mol}^{-1}\ \text{K}^{-1} = 16.62\ \text{J K}^{-1}$$

$$Nk = 2\ \text{mol} \times N_A \times k = 2\ \text{mol} \times 6.02 \times 10^{23}\ \text{mol}^{-1} \times 1.38 \times 10^{-23}\ \text{J K}^{-1} = 16.62\ \text{J K}^{-1}$$

Examiner tip

Unsurprisingly, the meanings of n, N and N_A cause much confusion. Whenever you use one of these terms, think carefully about its meaning and its probable size. After using one of the terms, consider the magnitude of your answer. If you have made a mistake in its use, your answer will probably seem ridiculous.

These are the definitions of the terms:
***n* is the number of moles** and will probably be in a range of 0.01–10 mol.
***N* is the number of atoms/molecules** and will be a huge number, maybe around 1×10^{24}.
N_A is the Avogadro constant and will always be 6.02×10^{23} mol^{-1}.

STRETCH and CHALLENGE

In spreads 1.3.3 and 1.3.4, the pressure a gas exerted on the walls of its container was deduced in terms of the density of the gas and the mean square speed of the molecules. From this equation a worked example was done that allowed us to determine the kinetic energy of all the molecules. For an ideal gas, the random kinetic energy of the molecules equals its internal energy. The theory of this calculation is as follows.

Pressure p exerted by a gas of density ρ is given by

$p = \frac{1}{3}\rho\overline{c^2} = \frac{M\overline{c^2}}{3V}$ where M is the total mass of the gas, V its volume and $\overline{c^2}$ the mean square speed.

This gives $3pV = M\overline{c^2}$, but from the gas law $3pV = 3NkT$

so $M\overline{c^2} = 3NkT$

giving the mean kinetic energy of one molecule as $E = \frac{1}{2}\frac{M}{N}\overline{c^2} = \frac{3}{2}kT$

Question

Five molecules in a gas have speeds 100, 200, 300, 400 and 500, all in m s^{-1}. What is the square root of the mean square speed of these five molecules? (Note: you do not get the answer by working out the mean speed squared. This is the square root of the mean square speed.)

The kinetic energy of a gas molecule

The theory given in the Stretch and Challenge box shows that the mean kinetic energy E of a single molecule can be obtained in terms of the Boltzmann constant. The relationship is

$$E = \frac{3}{2}kT$$

This gives the mean random translational kinetic energy of an ideal gas, that is its internal energy. It also shows that this energy is directly proportional to the temperature, measured in kelvin.

Worked example

Complete the table below to show the mean values of the kinetic energies and speeds of oxygen and hydrogen molecules at temperatures of −100 °C, 27 °C and 727 °C.

Answer

	Temperature /°C	Temperature /K	Mean kinetic energy/J	Mass of molecule/kg	Mean speed /m s^{-1}
Oxygen	−100	173	$3kT/2 = 3.58 \times 10^{-21}$	5.31×10^{-26}	367
	27	300	6.21×10^{-21}		484
	727	1000	20.7×10^{-21}		883
Hydrogen	−100	173	3.58×10^{-21}	3.32×10^{-27}	1470
	27	300	6.21×10^{-21}		1940
	727	1000	20.7×10^{-21}		3530

Table 1

Note that the mean kinetic energy at any given temperature is the same for both gases. The mass of an oxygen molecule is 16 times the mass of a hydrogen molecule, so hydrogen molecules travel four ($\sqrt{16}$) times faster. This is why there is very little hydrogen in the Earth's atmosphere: hydrogen molecules can travel faster than the escape velocity of the Earth.

Questions

1 A 1.0 mole sample of gas is contained in a cylinder of volume V at a temperature of 300 K. The mean pressure exerted by each molecule of the sample is 5.0×10^{-19} Pa.
   (a) What is the volume V of the cylinder?
   (b) What is the pressure in the cylinder?
   (c) Would either or both of the answers to **(a)** and **(b)** have been different if the cylinder had contained 2.0 moles of gas?

2 **(a)** The r.m.s. speed of nitrogen molecules at 273 K is 490 m s^{-1}. Calculate:
   (i) the mean translational kinetic energy of a molecule **(ii)** its mass.
   (b) The mass of a helium atom is 1/7 that of a nitrogen molecule. Calculate:
   (i) the mean translational kinetic energy at 273 K and at 820 K
   (ii) the speed of a helium atom at 273 K and at 820 K.

3 The escape velocity from the Earth is 11 km s^{-1}. This means that a gas molecule at the top of the atmosphere travelling upwards at 11 km s^{-1} will escape into space.
   (a) The upper atmosphere is at about 1000 K. Calculate the mean kinetic energy of a molecule at this temperature.
   (b) Calculate the r.m.s. speeds of **(i)** hydrogen, with molar mass 0.002 kg mol^{-1}, and **(ii)** helium, with molar mass 0.004 kg mol^{-1}, at this temperature.
   (c) If the r.m.s. speed of the molecules of a gas is greater than 0.2 of the escape velocity, then over the period of the Earth's existence all of the gas will have escaped. Use this fact to explain whether we expect to find any hydrogen or helium in the atmosphere.

4 Estimate the melting point of a solid if the energy required to separate its molecules is 1.1×10^{-20} J.

1.3 Module summary

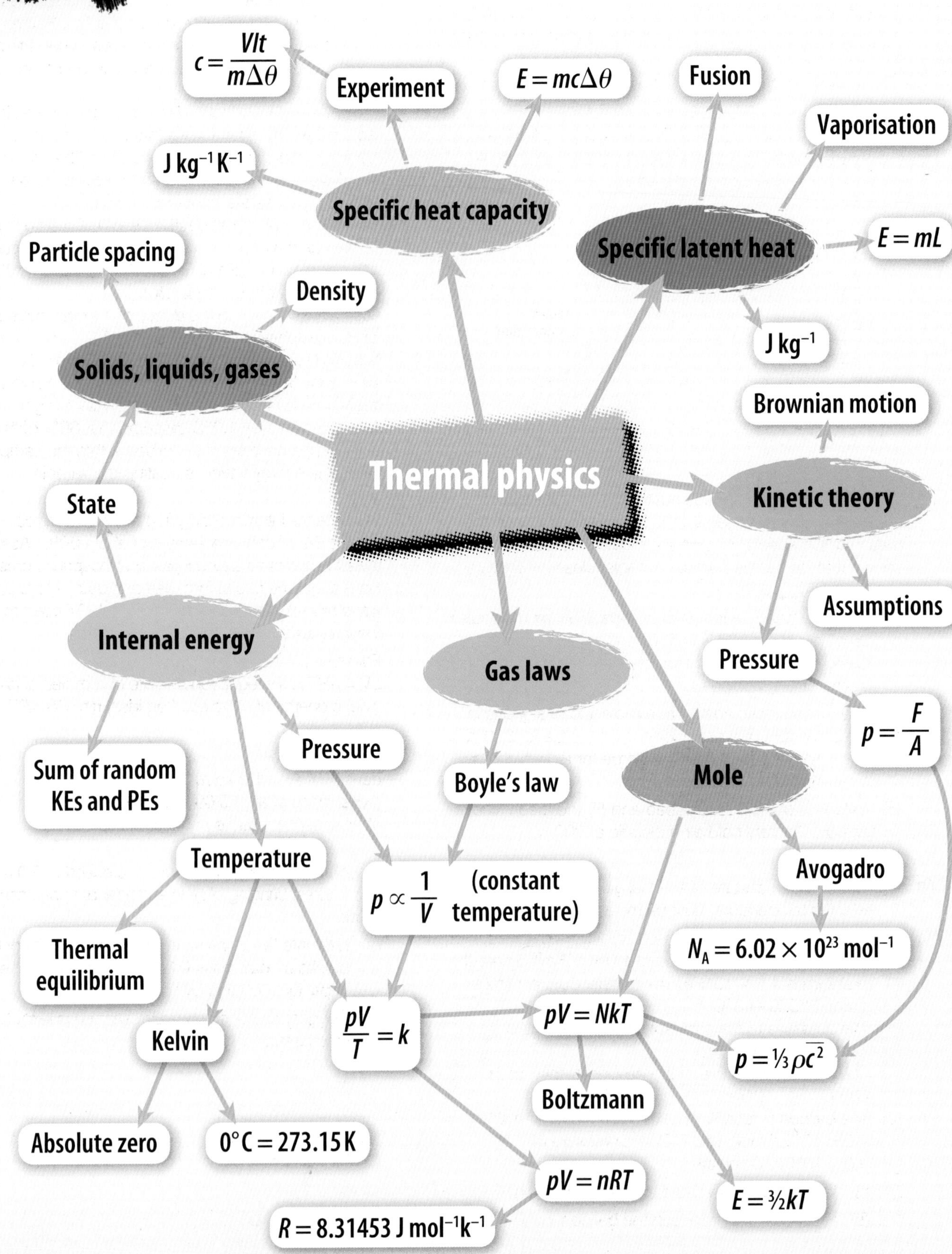

Practice questions

1 A night storage heater can be considered as a stack of bricks which is warmed in the night by electric power and then cools down in the day, heating a room. Calculate the energy in J given out by such a heater of mass 600 kg, as it cools from 70°C to 30°C.
The specific heat capacity of brick = 1.1×10^3 J kg^{-1} K^{-1}.

2 The graph in Figure 1 is called the Maxwellian distribution. It plots the number of molecules with speeds in a small range of speeds Δv against speed v.

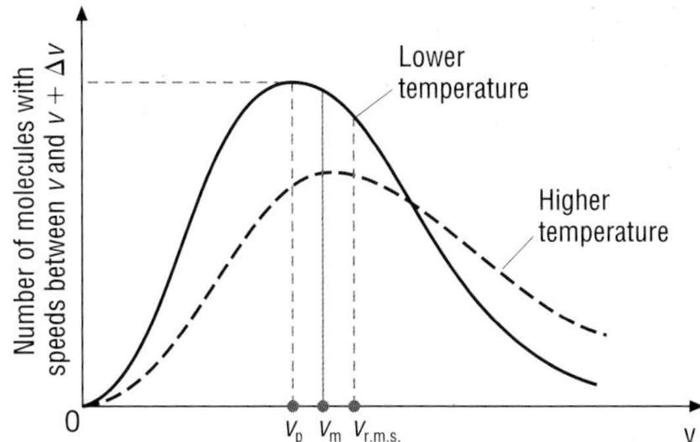

Figure 1

We can define three speeds relating to this distribution: the most probable speed v_p, the mean speed v_m and the mean square speed $v^2_{r.m.s.}$ of the molecules. It can be shown that for a large number of molecules $v_p = 0.8v_{r.m.s.}$ and $v_m = 0.9v_{r.m.s.}$.

(a) The root mean square (r.m.s.) velocity of air molecules on a hot day at 300 K is 510 m s^{-1}.
Calculate **(i)** the most probable speed and **(ii)** the mean speed of the molecules.

(b) The mean kinetic energy of a molecule of any gas is the same at a given temperature. Its value for 300 K is 6.2×10^{-21} J. Verify that this is true for air, which has a molar mass of 0.029 kg mol^{-1}.

(c) Calculate **(i)** the r.m.s. speed and **(ii)** the mean kinetic energy of a very cold air molecule at 200 K.

3 **(a)** The equation of state of an ideal gas is $pV = nRT$. Explain why the temperature must be measured in kelvin.

(b) A meteorological balloon rises through the atmosphere until it expands to a volume of 1.0×10^6 m^3, where the pressure is 1.0×10^3 Pa. The temperature also falls from 17°C to –43°C.
The pressure of the atmosphere at the Earth's surface = 1.0×10^5 Pa.
Show that the volume of the balloon at take-off is about 1.3×10^4 m^3.

(c) The balloon is filled with helium gas of molar mass 4.0×10^{-3} kg mol^{-1} at 17°C at a pressure of 1.0×10^5 Pa. Calculate:

(i) the number of moles of gas in the balloon

(ii) the mass in kg of gas in the balloon.

(d) The internal energy of the helium gas is equal to the random kinetic energy of all of its molecules. When the balloon is filled at ground level at a temperature of 17°C, the internal energy is 1900 MJ. Estimate the internal energy in MJ of the helium when the balloon has risen to a height where the temperature is –43°C.

4 The scientists who first isolated the radioactive element radium were amazed to see that it self-heated, apparently breaking the laws of thermodynamics. They did not know that the energy release in the decay by alpha-particle emission causes the temperature rise.
The historic unit of radioactivity is called the curie and is defined as the number of disintegrations per second from 1.0 g of radium $^{226}_{88}$Ra. One curie equals 3.7×10^{10} decays per second, or becquerels (Bq).
The energy release in the decay of a single nucleus of $^{226}_{88}$Ra by alpha-particle emission is 7.9×10^{-13} J. The specific heat capacity of radium is 110 J kg^{-1} K^{-1}.
Use these data to estimate the time in s it would take a freshly made sample of radium of mass 1.0 g to increase its temperature by 1.0°C. Assume that 80% of the energy of the alpha particles is absorbed within the sample so that this is the energy which is heating the sample.

5 Estimate the internal energy in J of the air in a room of volume 24 m^3 at a temperature of about 20°C. Assume that the air behaves as an ideal gas at atmospheric pressure. Here are some useful formulae and data. *There are several ways to make this estimate. You do NOT need to use all of the information.*

Formulae:
$pV = nRT$ is the equation of state of n moles of an ideal gas
kinetic energy of n moles of an ideal gas = $\frac{3}{2}nRT$

Data:
$R = 8.31$ J mol^{-1} K^{-1}
density of air = 1.2 kg m^{-3}
molar mass of air = 0.030 kg mol^{-1}
atmospheric pressure = 1.0×10^5 Pa

6 A cyclist is pedalling her bicycle at a speed of 5.0 m s^{-1}. She brakes, bringing bicycle and rider of total mass 80 kg to a halt.

(a) Estimate the increase in temperature in °C of her brake blocks of total mass 0.080 kg and specific heat capacity 1600 J kg K^{-1}.

(b) Suggest reasons why your estimate is likely to be inaccurate.

1.3 Examination questions

1 **(a)** Very high temperatures, for example, the temperature of the solar corona at half a million degrees, are often stated without a complete unit, i.e. degrees Celsius or kelvin.
Suggest why it is unnecessary to give degrees Celsius or kelvin in this case. [2]

(b) Describe how the concept of an absolute zero of temperature arises from

(i) the ideal gas laws [2]

(ii) the kinetic theory of an ideal gas. [2]

(c) Two students attempt the same experiment to find how air pressure varies with temperature. They heat identical sealed glass flasks of air, to be considered as an ideal gas, in an oil bath. The flasks are heated from 300 K to 400 K. The pressure in flask A rises from atmospheric pressure, p_o, as expected, but the pressure in flask B remains at p_o because the rubber bung is defective and air leaks out of the flask.

(i) Calculate the pressure in flask A at 400 K in terms of p_o. [2]

(ii) Calculate the fraction, f, of gas molecules in flask B compared to flask A at 400 K where

$$f = \frac{\text{number of gas molecules in B at 400 K}}{\text{number of gas molecules in A at 400 K}}$$ [2]

(OCR 2824 Jan04)

2 **(a)** The equation of state of an ideal gas is $pV = nRT$. State the meaning of each term in the equation. [2]

(b) The oven of a domestic cooker has a volume of 0.10 m^3. The pressure in the oven is 1 atmosphere 1.0×10^5 Pa.

(i) Calculate the mass in kg of air in the oven at 27 °C.
molar mass of air = 0.030 kg mol^{-1}. [3]

(ii) At constant atmospheric pressure the density of the air at 227 °C is x times the density of the air at 27 °C. Calculate the value of x. [3]

(iii) The average speed of the air molecules in a hot oven at 227 °C is greater than those in a cold oven at 27 °C. Explain why. [1]
Calculate the factor f by which the average speed is increased. [2]

(OCR 2824 Jun03)

3 **(a)** Explain what is meant by *internal energy*. Hence suggest how the internal energy of a *real* gas differs from that of an *ideal* gas. [4]

(b) Describe the changes which occur to the *internal energy* and the *state of matter* as a gas is cooled towards absolute zero. Include in your answer, where appropriate, a description of the changes on the molecular scale. [8]

(OCR 2824 Jan02)

4 **(a)** Explain the term *internal energy* and define *the specific heat capacity* of a body. [3]

(b) Outline a method of measuring the specific heat capacity of aluminium. [4]

(c) Consider a 2.0 kg block of aluminium. Assume that the heat capacity of aluminium is independent of temperature and that the internal energy is zero at absolute zero. Also assume that the volume of the block does not change over the range of temperature from 0 K to 293 K.

(i) Show that the internal energy of this block of aluminium at 20 °C is 540 kJ.

specific heat capacity of aluminium = 920 J kg^{-1} K^{-1} [2]

(ii) Hence show that the mean energy per atom in the 2.0 kg aluminium block at 20 °C is about 1.2×10^{-20} J. [3]

molar mass of aluminium = 0.027 kg mol^{-1}

(iii) In 1819 Dulong and Petit measured the heat capacities of many bodies made of different substances and found that for one mole of each substance the molar heat capacity was about 25 J mol^{-1} K^{-1}. Starting from any of the data in **(i)** or **(ii)** show that this is true for aluminium. [2]

(OCR 2824 Jan06)

5 This question is about the atmosphere treated as an ideal gas.

(a) The equation of state of an ideal gas is $pV = nRT$. Data about gases are often given in terms of density ρ rather than volume V. Show that the equation of state for a gas can be written as

$$p = \rho RT/M$$

where M is the mass of 1 mole of gas. [3]

(b) One simple model of the atmosphere assumes that air behaves as an ideal gas at a constant temperature. Using this model the pressure p of the atmosphere at a temperature of 20 °C varies with height h above the Earth's surface as shown in Figure 1.

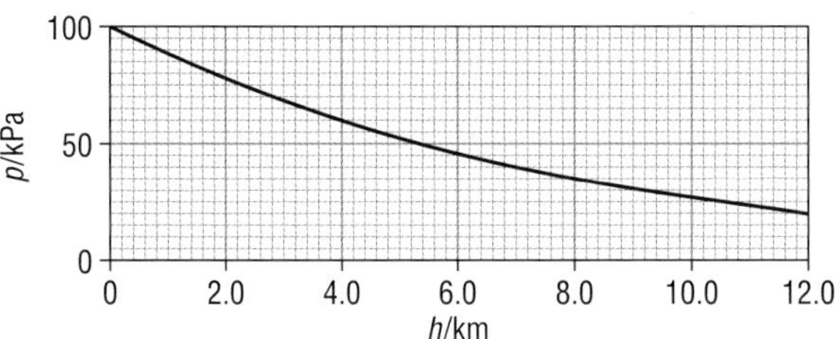

Figure 1

Use data from the graph to show that the variation of pressure with height follows an exponential relationship, that is, the pressure decreases by a constant factor for equal increments in height. [2]

(c) The ideal gas equation in **(a)** shows that, at constant temperature, pressure p is proportional to density ρ. Use data from Figure 1 to find the density in kg m^{-3} of the atmosphere at a height of 8.0 km. [3]

density ρ of air at $h = 0$ is 1.3 kg m^{-3}

(d) In the real atmosphere, the density, pressure and temperature all decrease with height. At the summit of Mt. Everest, 8.0 km above sea level, the pressure is only 0.30 of that at sea level. Take the temperature at the summit to be –23 °C and at sea level to be 20 °C. Calculate, using the ideal gas equation, the density in kg m^{-3} of the air at the summit. [3]

density ρ of air at sea level = 1.3 kg m^{-3}

(OCR 2824 Jun07)

6 This question is about the behaviour of gases.

The average translational kinetic energy per molecule of gas, $\frac{1}{2}m\overline{c^2}$, is related to the absolute temperature T by the relationship $\frac{1}{2}m\overline{c^2} = \frac{3}{2}kT$ where k, the Boltzmann constant, is 1.4×10^{-23} J K^{-1}.

(a) Show that the root mean square speed $\sqrt{\overline{c^2}}$ is proportional to $1/\sqrt{m}$ when T is kept constant. [1]

(b) The table below shows the root mean square (r.m.s.) speed of molecules for three gases at 293 K.

Gas	Mass/10^{-27} kg	r.m.s. speed/m s^{-1}
helium	6.7	1400
neon	33	600
carbon monoxide	47	510

Propose and carry out an arithmetic test to decide whether the data in the table support the statement that the r.m.s. speed is proportional to $1/\sqrt{m}$ when T is kept constant. [4]

Figure 2 shows the distribution of molecular speeds in a sample of oxygen gas.

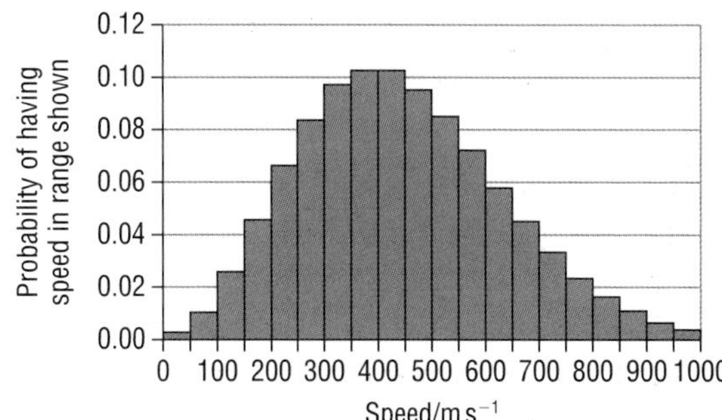

Figure 2

The area of each bar is proportional to the fraction of molecules having a speed within that range. The chart shows that the molecules have a range of speeds.

(c) Use ideas from kinetic theory to explain why:

(i) gas molecules have a range of speeds [2]

(ii) gas molecules are very unlikely to have speeds much greater than the most common speed. [2]

(d) (i) Figure 2 shows that the most probable speed is 400 m s^{-1}.

Use the equation *root mean square speed* = 1.2 × *most probable speed* to calculate the mean square speed in m^2 s^{-2} of the molecules in the sample of gas. [2]

(ii) Use your answer to **(d)(i)** to estimate the temperature in K of the gas. [2]

mass of O_2 molecule = 5.3×10^{-26} kg

(OCR 2863 Jun05)

Further questions A

Newton's laws and momentum

1 (a) Two identical pendulums are constructed from steel balls suspended by strings in a V shape, called a bifilar suspension. The balls just touch. See Figure 1.

Figure 1

Ball 1 is moved to the left and released. It hits stationary ball 2 elastically with speed u. Suppose that immediately after collision ball 1 moves with speed v_1 and ball 2 moves with speed v_2.

(i) Write down equations for the conservation of momentum and of energy in the elastic collision in terms of m, u, v_1 and v_2.

(ii) Put the values $v_1 = 0$ and $v_2 = u$ into your equations in **(i)** to show that they are solutions.

(b) Five identical pendulums are now suspended so that they touch. This arrangement is often called *Newton's Cradle*. See Figure 2.

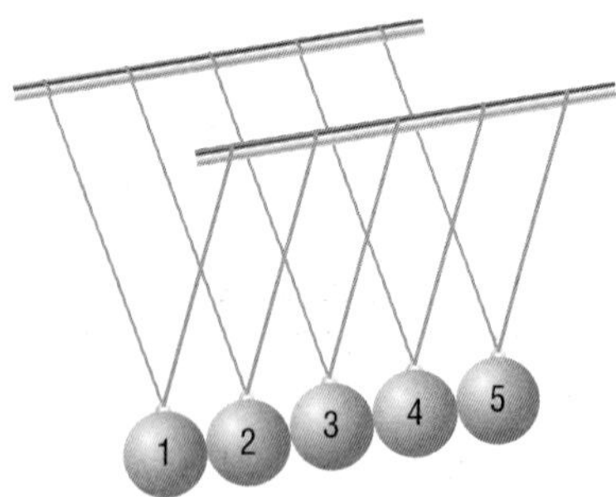

Figure 2

Ball 1 is moved to the left and released, hitting ball 2 with speed u.

(i) After the collision, balls 1 to 4 remain at rest and ball 5 moves away with speed u. Use your answer to **(a)** to explain this observation.

(ii) Explain what happens when balls 1 and 2 are moved to the left and are released together so that ball 2 hits ball 3 with speed u.

(iii) Balls 2 to 5 are now glued together. Describe without calculation or explanation what happens in this situation when ball 1 is released towards ball 2, as before in **(i)**.

2 This question is about kicking a football.

(a) Figure 3 shows how the force F applied to a ball varies with time t whilst it is being kicked horizontally. The ball is initially at rest.

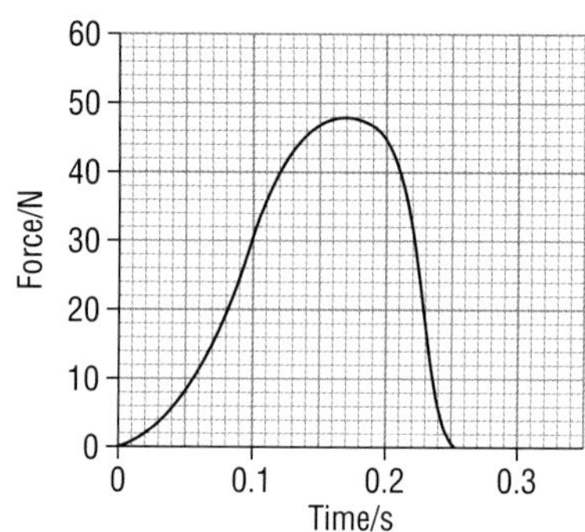

Figure 3

(i) Use the graph to find

1 the maximum force in N applied to the ball

2 the time in s the boot is in contact with the ball.

(ii) The mean force multiplied by the time of contact is called the impulse delivered to the ball. Use the graph to estimate the impulse in N s delivered to the ball.

(b) The mass of the ball is 0.50 kg. Use your answers to **(a)** to calculate

(i) the maximum acceleration in m s^{-2} of the ball

(ii) the final speed in m s^{-1} of the ball

(iii) the kinetic energy in J of the ball after the kick.

(c) The ball hits a wall with a speed of 14 m s^{-1}. It rebounds from the wall along its initial path with a speed of 8.0 m s^{-1}. The impact lasts for 0.18 s. Calculate the mean force in N exerted by the ball on the wall.

Damping

3 A moving-coil ammeter has a damped movement; otherwise it would oscillate for a long time before coming to rest at the correct angle θ on the scale. See Figure 4. The coil is wound on an aluminium former so that eddy currents are set up in the former opposite to its motion when it moves in the magnetic field. Suggest why it is most effective to have the system slightly less than critically damped.

Figure 4

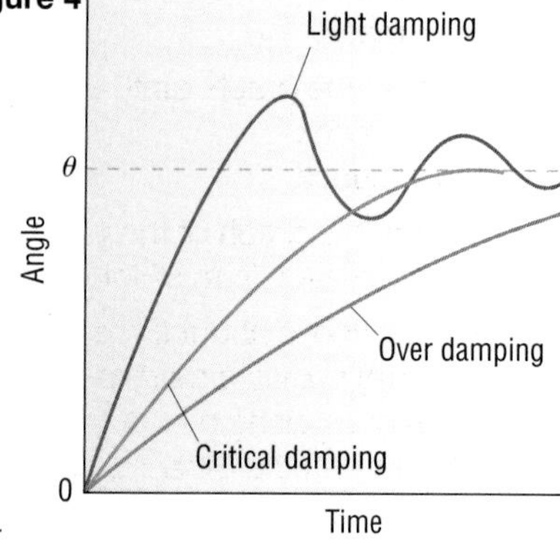

Gravitational field

4 (a) It is possible to find the mass of a planet by measuring the gravitational field strength at the surface of the planet and knowing its radius.

(i) Write down an expression for the gravitational field strength g at the surface of a planet in terms of its mass M and radius R.

(ii) Use the expression in **(i)** to show that the mass of the Earth is 6.0×10^{24} kg. Take the radius of the Earth to be 6400 km.

(iii) Use the data
mass of Earth = 81 × mass of Moon, and radius of Earth = 3.7 × radius of Moon
to show that the value of g at the Moon's surface is about $1.7\ \text{N kg}^{-1}$.

(b) The distance between the centres of the Earth and the Moon is 3.8×10^8 m. Assume that the Moon moves in a circular orbit about the centre of the Earth. Estimate the period of this orbit to the nearest day. Note that 1 day = 8.6×10^4 s.

Harmonic motion

5 A mass suspended from a spring is pulled downwards and released. It oscillates with simple harmonic motion. Figure 5 shows the displacement of the mass from its rest position against time from the moment of release.

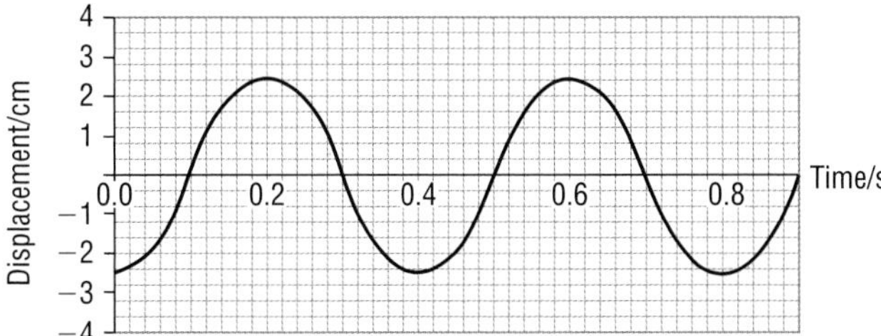

Figure 5

(a) (i) Use data from the graph to determine the amplitude in m of the oscillation and the frequency in Hz of the oscillation.

(ii) Hence find the maximum acceleration in m s^{-2} of the mass.

(b) Using the graph, state a time at which the mass has maximum:
(i) speed **(ii)** acceleration.

(c) Sketch a graph of the variation with time in s of the acceleration in m s^{-2} of the mass.

6 This question is about a mass–spring system.
Figure 6(a) shows a mass attached to two springs. The mass moves along a horizontal tube with one spring stretched and the other compressed. An arrow marked on the mass indicates its position on a scale. Figure 6(a) shows the situation when the mass is displaced through a distance x from its equilibrium position. The mass is experiencing an acceleration a in the direction shown. Figure 6(b) shows a graph of the magnitude of the acceleration a against the displacement x.

(a)

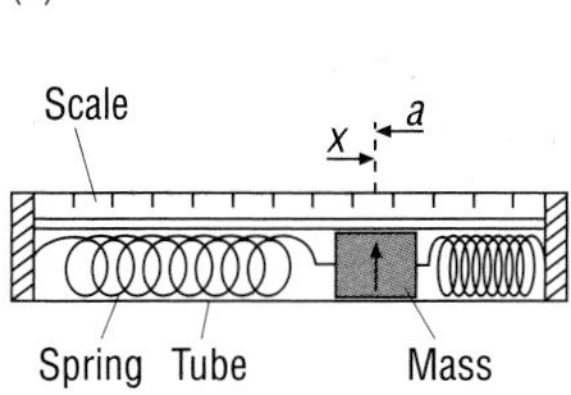

(b)

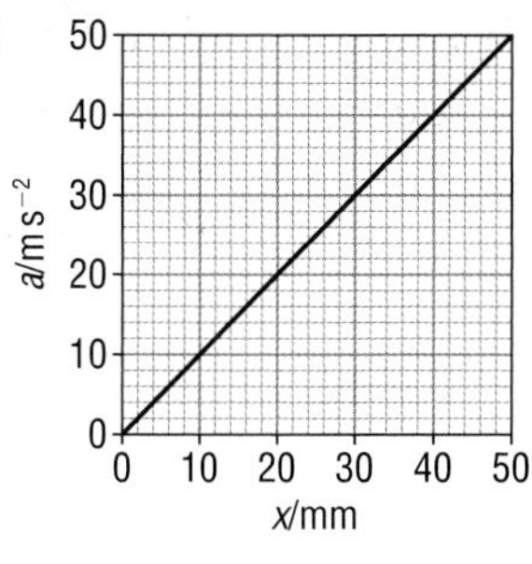

Figure 6

(a) (i) State one feature from each of Figures 6(a) and 6(b) which shows that the mass performs harmonic motion when released.

(ii) Use data from Figure 6(b) to show that the frequency of simple harmonic oscillations of the mass is about 5 Hz.

(iii) The mass oscillates in damped harmonic motion before coming to rest. Sketch a graph of the damped harmonic oscillation of the mass, from an initial displacement of 25.0 mm from $t = 0$ to $t = 0.6$ s.

(b) The mass–spring system of Figure 6(a) can be used as a device to measure acceleration, called an accelerometer. It is mounted on a rotating test rig, used to simulate large g-forces for astronauts. Figure 7 shows the plan view of a long beam rotating about axis **A** with the astronaut seated at end **B**, facing towards **A**. The accelerometer is parallel to the beam and is fixed under the seat 10 m from **A**.

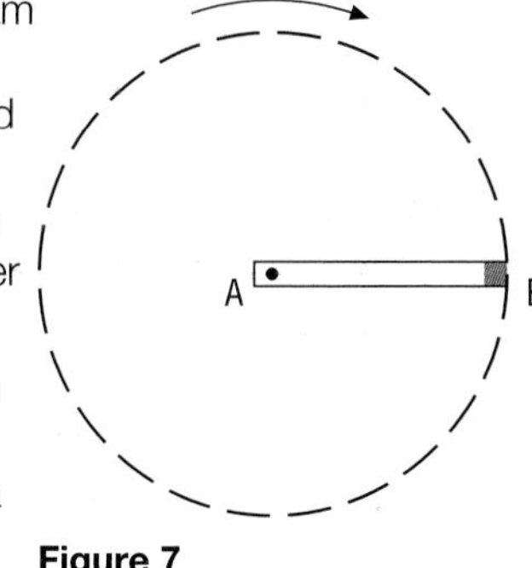

Figure 7

(i) When the astronaut is rotating at a constant speed the mass has a constant deflection. Explain why.

(ii) Calculate the speed $v\ \text{m s}^{-1}$ of rotation of the astronaut when the deflection is 50 mm.

Thermal physics

7 (a) Explain what is meant by the *internal energy* of a gas.

(b) A bicycle tyre has a volume of $2.1 \times 10^{-3}\ \text{m}^3$. On a day when the temperature is 15 °C the pressure of the air in the tyre is 280 kPa. Assume that air behaves as an ideal gas.

(i) Calculate the number of moles n of air in the tyre.

(ii) The bicycle is ridden vigorously so that the tyres warm up. The pressure in the tyre rises to 290 kPa. Calculate the new temperature in °C of the air in the tyre. Assume that no air has leaked from the tyre and that the volume is constant.

(iii) Calculate, for the air in the tyre, the ratio

$$\frac{\text{internal energy at the higher temperature}}{\text{internal energy at 15 °C}}$$

Justify your reasoning.

UNIT 2 Module 1 Electric and magnetic fields

Introduction

You have lived all your life in a gravitational field. The effect of the field on your mass is a gravitational force on you towards the centre of the Earth. Gravitational field obeys an inverse square law: if the distance from the centre of the field is doubled, the force exerted will be reduced to a quarter. The influence therefore falls away rapidly with distance – but never becomes zero.

Similarly, electric fields are caused by electric charge. They exert an electrical force on any charge in the field. As with a gravitational field, the influence follows an inverse square law. However, mass can only be positive, so gravitational force is always attractive, but charge can be positive or negative, so the force can be attractive or repulsive.

If you have ever used a compass you know that the Earth has a magnetic field. You may not know that magnetic field is caused by moving electrical charges. *All* substances respond to magnetic field. The effect is tiny for most objects, but in a few, like iron, the effect is large.

The Earth is showered with charge from the Sun. When this charge arrives it is deflected towards the poles by the Earth's magnetic field. There it ionises particles in the atmosphere, causing the atmosphere to glow. The effect over the north pole is called the aurora borealis or northern lights, shown in the photograph, taken in Alaska.

In this module you will learn about:

- the effect of an electric field on a charge and on a current
- the units used for magnetic field
- creating an electric current by moving a wire through a magnetic field
- transformers.

Test yourself

1 Electric field is force per unit charge. What unit will be used for electric field strength?

2 Two charges are placed near to one another. What force, attraction or repulsion, will there be when the charges are (a) both positive, (b) both negative, (c) one positive and one negative?

3 Do you know what Fleming's left-hand rule is?

4 Give one example of the use of a magnetic field other than for navigation or as provided by a magnet.

Module contents

2.1 (1) Electric fields

By the end of this spread, you should be able to ...

* **State that electric fields are created by electric charges.**
* **Define electric field strength.**
* **Describe how electric field lines represent an electric field.**

Introduction

All fields are regions where a force is exerted on an object at a distance. In the case of an electric field, it is not only caused by an electric charge; the field also exerts an electrical force on any charged object in that field. A radio transmitter, for example, creates a varying electric field, and this causes varying forces on the electrons, and hence a tiny current in an aerial in your radio a large distance from the transmitter. Although you have probably never realised it, you have lived all your life in the Earth's electric field. This does not usually cause any electrical force on you, because you are normally electrically neutral. The number of positive protons in your body is usually equal to the number of negative electrons. Any slight imbalance, for instance when your hair stands on end after combing, results in a very small force in comparison with your weight. Clearly there must be appreciable electrical activity in the Earth's atmosphere to produce lightning.

Electric field definition

In the same way that gravitational field strength was defined in spread 1.2.5 as force per unit mass, electric field strength is defined as force per unit positive charge. In the SI system of units, it will therefore be measured in newtons per coulomb. In equation form this becomes

Key definition

Electric field strength *E* is defined as the force per unit positive charge.

$E = \frac{F}{Q}$ where E is the **electric field strength**, F the force and Q the positive charge.

Note that the word 'positive' has to be included. With mass this was unnecessary because there is no such thing as negative mass. With charge, there are two kinds, positive and negative, so it is necessary to stipulate that the direction of the electric field is the direction in which a force acts on a positive charge, that is, the field is away from a positive charge and towards a negative one. The force on a negative charge will be in the opposite direction to that on a positive charge.

Electric field patterns

An electric field always starts on a positive charge and finishes on a negative charge. If there is no negative charge on the system you are considering, the field lines will finish on a negative charge on the space enclosing the positive charge. (It is always assumed that the universe has an equal number of positive and negative charges – though no one has yet been able to count them!)

Electric field lines not only show the direction of the electric field but also give a guide to its strength. In regions where the field is strong, the lines will be close together. One other feature of electric fields results from the fact that when charges are stationary on a metal surface the field must be at right angles to the surface. If the field were not, there would be a component of the force along the surface that would cause charge to flow, so they would not be stationary. The following figures, Figures 1–6, show some of the shapes of electric fields around different charged bodies. Remember, these represent three-dimensional fields.

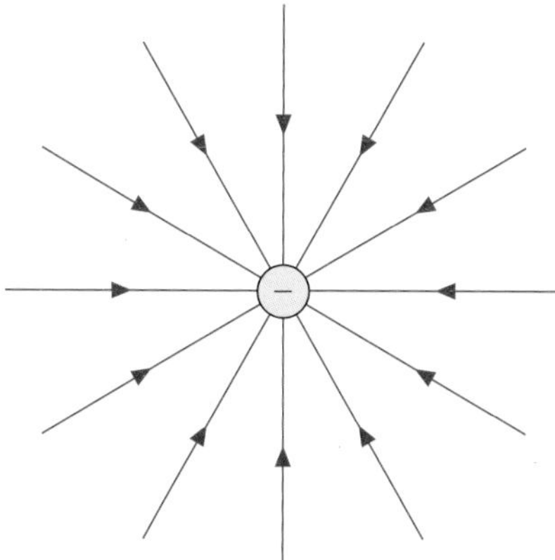

Figure 1 Electric field around a negative point charge

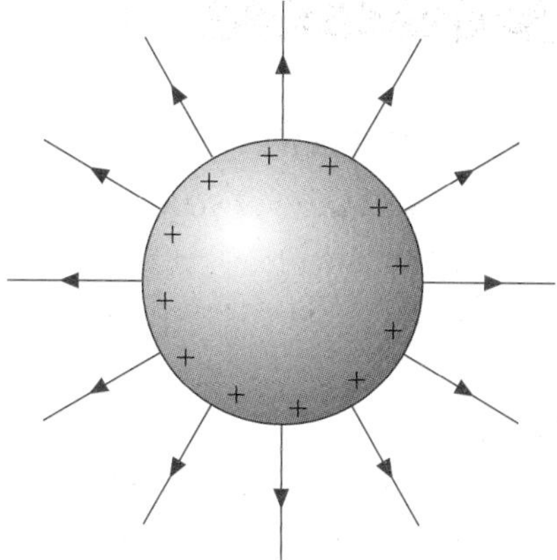

Figure 2 Electric field around a positively charged metal sphere. There is no field inside a metal sphere; the field outside the sphere is the same as it would be if all the charge were concentrated at its centre

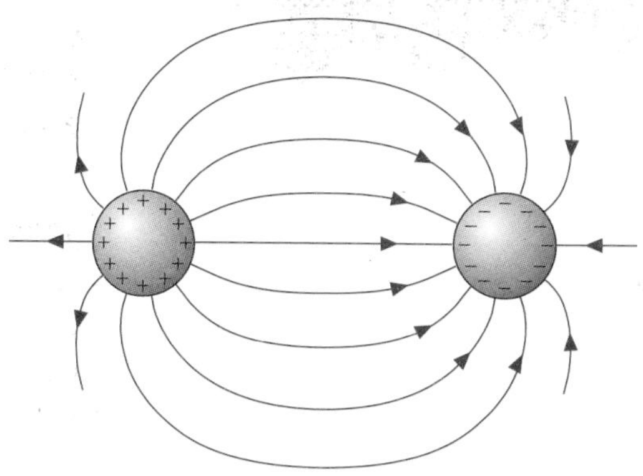

Figure 3 Electric field near one positively charged and one negatively charged small metal sphere

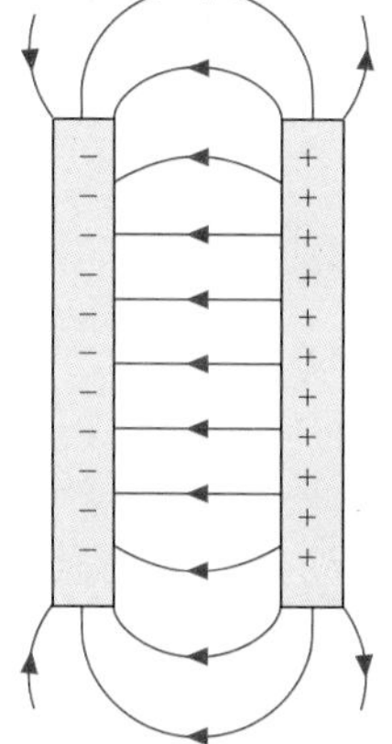

Figure 4 Electric field near two parallel plates, one charged positively and the other negatively. The field in between the plates, but not near their edges, is nearly constant

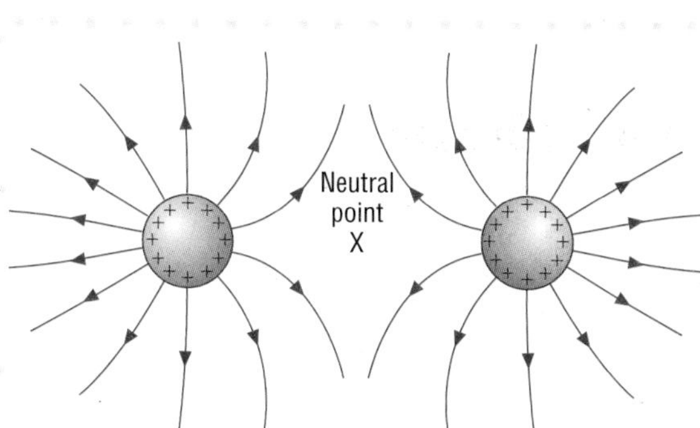

Figure 5 Electric field near two positively charged small metal spheres

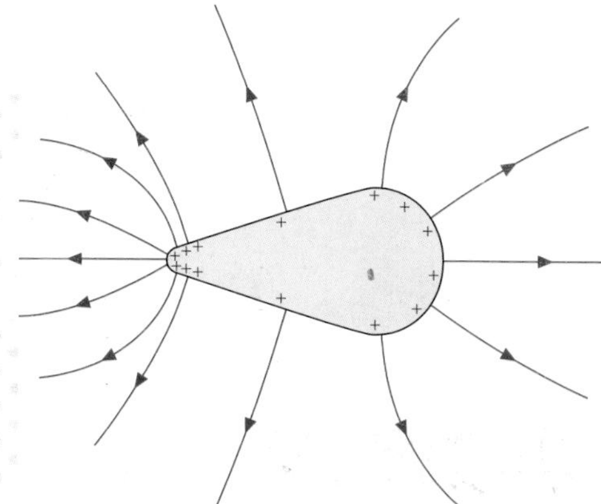

Figure 6 Electric field around a positively charged object rounded at one end and sharp at the other. Electrodes with sharp points are used to provide the strong electric fields in small volumes needed in plasma discharge flat-screen TV displays

Questions

1 There is an electric field at the positively charged sphere in Figure 3. This is caused by the negatively charged sphere. The sphere carries a charge of $+5.0 \times 10^{-9}$ C. It experiences a force of magnitude 1.4×10^{-4} N.
  (a) Calculate the electric field strength at the positive sphere.
  (b) Calculate the force on the negatively charged sphere.

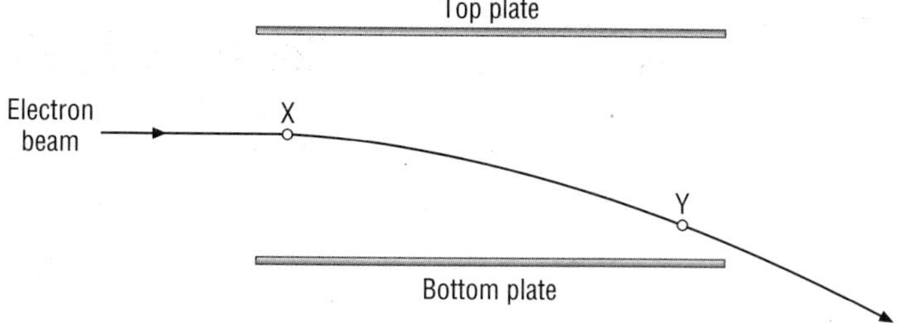

Figure 7

2 Copy Figure 7, which shows an electron beam passing between a pair of parallel conducting plates.
  (a) Label the plates positive and negative.
  (b) Draw arrows to indicate the relative magnitudes and directions of the force on the electron beam at points X and Y.
  (c) The electric field strength between the plates is 8.0×10^{4} N C^{-1}. Calculate the magnitude of the force on an electron at point X.

3 Figure 8 shows a positively charged metal sphere held above an earthed metal plate, that is, held at 0 V.
  Copy the diagram and draw at least five electric field lines between the sphere and the plate.

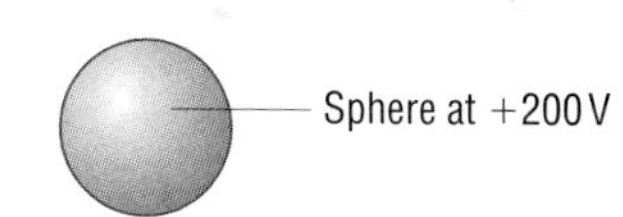

Figure 8

Coulomb's law

By the end of this spread, you should be able to …

* **Select and use Coulomb's law.**
* **Determine electric field strength.**
* **Select and use $E = V/d$ for the magnitude of the uniform electric field strength between charged parallel plates.**

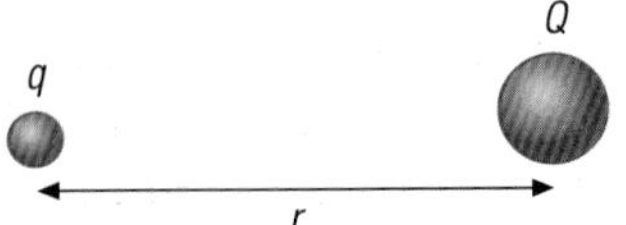

Figure 1 A charge q is placed a distance r from another charge Q

Examiner tip

Q or q can be used to represent charge. Here we have used both to represent two different charges, but you may see one or the other used in equations.

Coulomb's law

At the end of the eighteenth century, Coulomb performed some meticulous and very difficult experiments using isolated charges. An example with two charges is shown in Figure 1. He carefully measured the force between small charged spheres and concluded that the force F between two electric charges q and Q is:

- proportional to $q \times Q$
- inversely proportional to the square of the distance r between them.

This gives, in equation form, $F \propto \frac{qQ}{r^2}$, so $F = \frac{kqQ}{r^2}$

The numerical value of the constant k in this equation can be determined to be 8.99×10^9 N m^2 C^{-2}.

Because of its connection with the theory of electromagnetic waves, the constant is usually written another way. This does not alter its value, but it does make the equation look different. k is written as

$k = \frac{1}{4\pi\varepsilon_0}$, giving the equation as $F = \frac{qQ}{4\pi\varepsilon_0 r^2}$.

In order to make $k = 8.99 \times 10^9$, the value of ε_0 must be given by $\varepsilon_0 = 1/4\pi k = 1/(4\pi \times 8.99 \times 10^9)$.

This gives $\varepsilon_0 = 8.85 \times 10^{-12}$ C^2 m^{-2} N^{-1}. ε_0 is called the permittivity of free space.

Worked example

In a classical model of a hydrogen atom, the electron revolves around the proton in a circle of radius 5.3×10^{-11} m. What force does the proton exert on the electron?

Answer

The charge on a proton is $+1.60 \times 10^{-19}$ C, and the equal and opposite charge on the electron is -1.60×10^{-19} C. Substituting into the equation for force gives

$$F = \frac{+1.60 \times 10^{-19}\ \text{C} \times -1.60 \times 10^{-19}\ \text{C}}{4\pi \times 8.85 \times 10^{-12}\ \text{C}^2\text{m}^{-2}\ \text{N}^{-1} \times (5.3 \times 10^{-11}\ \text{m})^2} = -8.19 \times 10^{-8}\ \text{N}$$

Note how the units coulomb (C) and metre (m) cancel to give the answer in newtons. The negative sign shows the force to be in the opposite direction to r. Therefore the force is inwards and hence attractive, thus causing the centripetal acceleration of the electron.

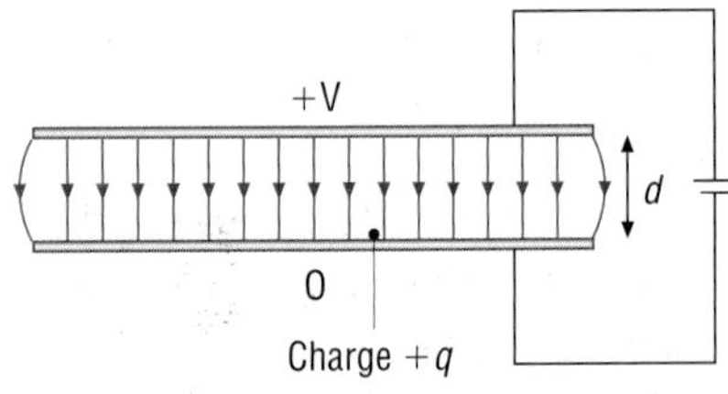

Figure 2 A pair of parallel plates with a battery connected across them has a uniform electric field between all but the edges of the plates

Potential gradient

In Figure 2, two parallel plates that are a small distance d apart are connected to a battery so that the potential difference across the plates is V. The plates carry equal and opposite charges, so that there is a uniform electric field between the plates except just at the edges. A small positive charge q is close to the bottom plate and can be imagined to be moving at constant speed up to the top plate. It will require a constant force F to do this, because the electric field would push it down. The work done on it against the electric field will be the force multiplied by the distance moved, Fd. This quantity of work done can be calculated in another way. Potential difference V is always work done per unit charge, so

$\frac{Fd}{q} = V$, which can be reorganised into $\frac{V}{d} = \frac{F}{q}$

V/d is called the **potential gradient**, and we have already defined F/q (or F/Q) as the electric field strength E. We have therefore two alternative ways of finding the electric field strength E.

$E = \frac{V}{d}$ and also $E = \frac{F}{q}$

Key definition

Potential gradient = electric field strength = V/d.

Examiner tip

Don't forget there are two equations for electric field strength. Some candidates remember only electric field directly from its definition as $E = F/q$. Some others remember it only as the potential gradient $E = V/d$. In practice there are many occasions when *both* equations are required.

Worked example

Oil of density 810 kg m^{-3} is sprayed as a fine mist into the space between two horizontal parallel plates, which are 5.0 mm apart. One oil droplet of radius 5.6×10^{-7} m has a charge on it equal to the charge on a single electron. This droplet is observed through a microscope to remain stationary between the plates when there is a potential difference of 183 V across the plates, as shown in Figure 3. Calculate the charge on an electron.

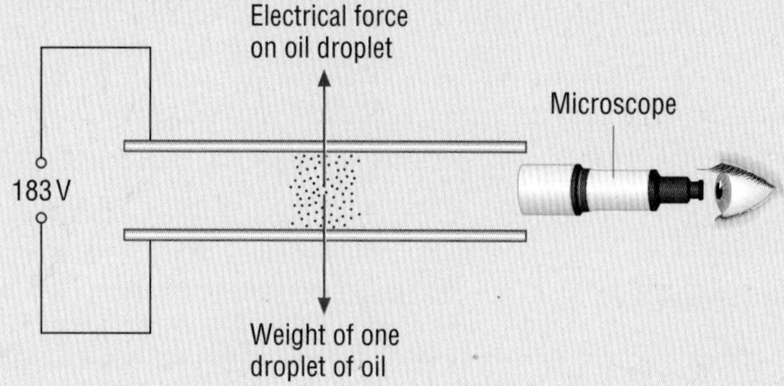

Figure 3 A fine mist of oil drops is viewed in an electric field

Answer

volume of droplet = volume of a sphere of radius r

$= 4\pi r^3/3 = 4\pi \times (5.6 \times 10^{-7})^3/3 = 7.36 \times 10^{-19}$ m^3

mass of droplet = 7.36×10^{-19} m$^3 \times 810$ kg m^{-3} = 5.96×10^{-16} kg

weight of droplet = $mg = 5.96 \times 10^{-16}$ kg $\times 9.81$ N kg^{-1} = 5.84×10^{-15} N

Since the droplet is stationary, the weight of the droplet acting downwards must be balanced by the electrical force acting upwards.

From the definition of electric field strength, $E = F/q$

giving $Eq = 5.84 \times 10^{-15}$.

Now, using the other way of finding the field, $E = V/d = 183$ V/0.0050 m

$= 36\,600$ V m^{-1}.

Finally, $36\,600 \times q = 5.84 \times 10^{-15}$ and $q = 5.84 \times 10^{-15}/36\,600 = 1.60 \times 10^{-19}$ C.

STRETCH and CHALLENGE

Comments on worked example

The worked example is based on the first determination of the charge on the electron, achieved by Millikan. He won a Nobel prize for his work in 1923. The main difficulty he had was in measuring the size of the oil drops he was using. After measuring the p.d. required to hold a droplet still, he switched off the electric field and let them drift downwards in air and then calculated their radius from a measurement of their terminal velocity. Getting a single electron charge on a drop is not that difficult. Most drops will not stay still, because they are uncharged or are charged positively. It is therefore easy to find a drop that can be controlled by the applied voltage.

Question

Millikan, using units other than SI units, found the charge on several oil drops to be –6.0, –12.1, –15.0, –17.8, –27.1 and –32.7. What value does this give for the charge on the electron in his units?

Question

1 The force between two equal point charges of 6.0×10^{-12} C a distance of 9.0 mm apart is 4.0×10^{-9} N.

(a) Calculate the force between the charges when **(i)** one charge changes to 9.0×10^{-12} C or **(ii)** the distance between them changes to 12 mm.

(b) Calculate the magnitude of the electric field strength at either charge.

(c) Use Coulomb's law and the definition of electric field strength to show that the electric field strength E at a distance r from a point charge Q is given by $E = kQ/r^2$.

2.1  Electric fields, gravitational fields and the motion of charged particles

By the end of this spread, you should be able to ...

- **Explain the effect of a uniform electric field on the motion of charged particles.**
- **Describe the similarities and differences between gravitational and electric fields.**

Charged particle movement in an electric field

Introduction

When studying the photoelectric effect during your AS course, you saw how photoelectrons, that is charged particles, could be controlled by a potential difference along their path. If the reverse potential difference was high enough, the photoelectrons were stopped (stopping potential) and sent backwards. This effect is similar to the gravitational effect when a ball is thrown vertically upwards; when the ball loses all its kinetic energy, it falls back to the ground. In this spread, we shall deal with various movements of charge for a variety of directions of electric fields.

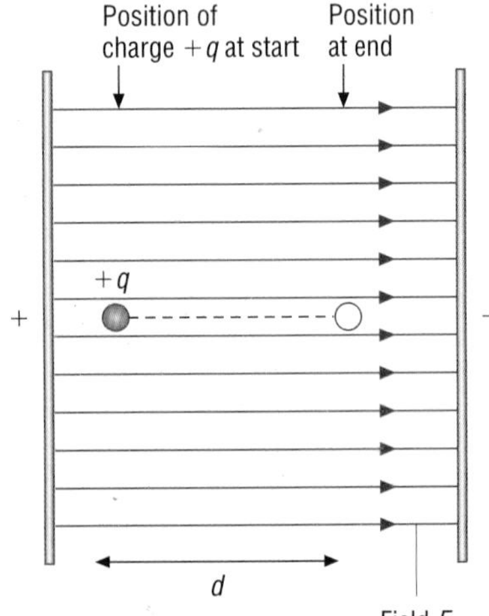

Figure 1 A positive particle moving in a vacuum in the direction of the electric field (or a negative particle moving in the opposite direction to the field)

Charge movement in the direction of the field

This is the simplest arrangement, as shown in Figure 1.

A particle with charge q starts from rest at the point shown. It moves a distance d through the field of electrical field strength E. While it is in the field, a force Eq is acting on it in the direction of the field and therefore work is done on it equal to Eqd.

Since it is in a vacuum its speed will increase and its kinetic energy will rise by Eqd.

Depending on what other information is available (its mass, for example), it would be possible to find its acceleration, its velocity after travelling any particular distance and the time it took to complete that distance. A negatively charged particle travelling in the opposite direction would have the same increase in kinetic energy. A positive particle travelling in the opposite direction would be losing kinetic energy instead of gaining it.

These ideas have considerable practical applications in various types of electronic equipment, for example, in X-ray tubes, particle accelerators, and cathode-ray tubes in oscilloscopes and older television sets, as shown in the following worked example.

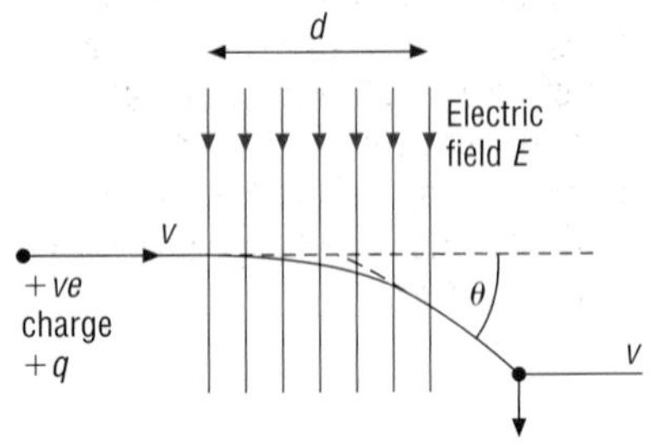

Figure 2 Electrons deflected by an electric field

Charge movement initially at right angles to the direction of the electric field

Consider a positively charged particle q travelling horizontally with velocity v in a vacuum and entering a uniform electric field of magnitude E for a distance d, as shown in Figure 2.

The force that the field exerts on the charge will always be in the direction of the field, so there cannot be any alteration to its horizontal velocity. When the particle emerges from the field, it will have a horizontal velocity equal to its original velocity. It will therefore spend a time d/v in the field. During this time the constant force on it is Eq downwards, giving it a constant acceleration downwards of Eq/m, where m is the mass of the particle.

When it leaves the field, the particle will have a component of velocity downwards of $at = Eq/m \times d/v = Eqd/mv$.

The angle of deflection θ will be given by

$$\tan\theta = \frac{Eqd}{mv^2}$$

Examiner tip

It is not necessary to learn equations such as that given here for the angle of deflection. In fact, doing so is pointless because different information will require different working. What is important is to be able to use the basic facts in different ways according to the information given.

Worked example

In a cathode-ray tube, electrons leave a cathode (which is negative) and are accelerated for a distance of 4.0 cm by a uniform electric field of electric field strength 1.20×10^5 N C^{-1} (Figure 3). They then pass through a hole in the anode (which is positive) and enter a region in which the electric field strength is zero. Calculate:

(a) the speed of an electron when it reaches the anode

(b) the time it takes to reach the screen of the cathode-ray tube, that is 28 cm from the anode.

Answer

(a) Electric field strength = V/d, therefore $V = 1.20 \times 10^5 \times 0.040 = 4800$ V or 4800 J/C.
The charge on an electron is 1.6×10^{-19} C.
Energy gained = 4800 J/C $\times 1.60 \times 10^{-19}$ C $= 7.68 \times 10^{-16}$ J.
This is the kinetic energy of the electron, that is,
$7.68 \times 10^{-16} = \frac{1}{2} mv^2 = 0.5 \times 9.11 \times 10^{-31} \times v^2$, giving

$$v = \sqrt{\frac{2 \times 7.68 \times 10^{-16}}{9.11 \times 10^{-31}}} = 4.11 \times 10^7 \text{ m s}^{-1}$$

(b) The electron then coasts at constant speed until it reaches the screen.
Time taken = 0.28 m/4.11×10^7 m s^{-1} = 6.8×10^{-9} s.

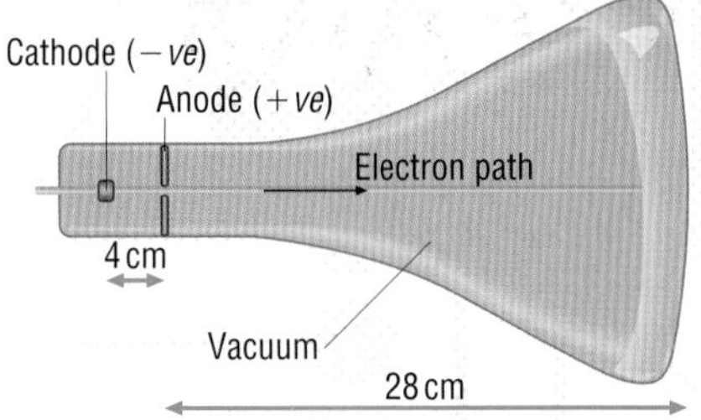

Figure 3 Electrons passing through a cathode-ray tube

Comparison of electric field with gravitational field

The situation described in the previous section has strong similarities with a ball being thrown horizontally in the Earth's gravitational field. The ball has a horizontal velocity unaffected by the downward gravitational force, so (as long as air resistance can be neglected) its horizontal velocity is constant. Its vertical velocity shows a constant downward acceleration. This means that the path followed by a ball in a gravitational field is precisely the same shape as that of a point charge in an electric field.

Other similarities between the fields are given in the table.

	Electric field	Gravitational field
Field symbol	E	g
Force acts on	charge (q)	mass (m)
Field definition	force per unit charge	force per unit mass
Force	$F = Eq$	$F = mg$
Direction of force	in direction of field on positive charge	always in direction of field
Work done (W) in moving distance d	$W = Eqd$	$W = mgd$

Examiner tip

As stated in spread 2.1.1, in electric fields, positive charge experiences a force in the direction of the field and negative charge experiences it in the opposite direction. In a gravitational field, however, there is no such thing as negative mass.

Question

1 Two horizontal parallel metal plates, 1.2×10^{-2} m apart, are connected to a 600 V power supply.

(a) Calculate the electric field strength between the plates.

(b) A tiny sphere of weight 3.3×10^{-14} N has acquired a charge so that it is held in equilibrium midway between the plates by the electric field as shown in Figure 4.

(i) State the magnitude and direction of the electric force on the sphere.

(ii) Calculate the magnitude of the charge on the sphere.

(iii) The voltage between the plates is suddenly doubled. Describe the motion of the sphere.

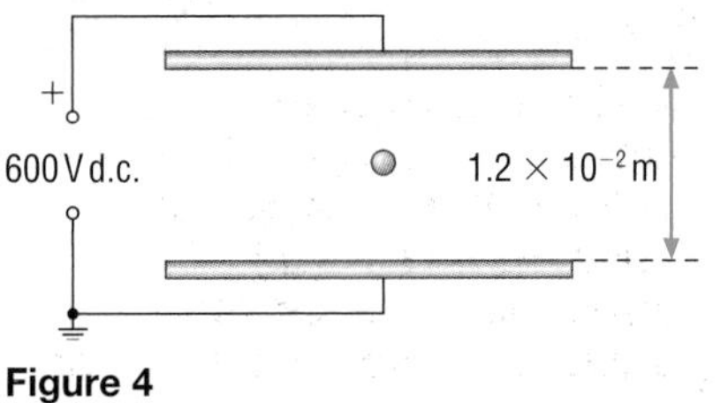

Figure 4

2.1 (4) Magnetic fields

By the end of this spread, you should be able to …

* **Describe the magnetic field patterns of a long conductor and a long solenoid.**

Figure 1 Artwork showing the shape of the Earth's magnetic field

Introduction

This is the third type of field introduced during your course. As with gravitational fields and electrical fields, the term 'field' indicates a region of influence: a place where a force can be exerted on an object. In the case of magnetism, the magnetic field of the Earth has been known for centuries, with the influence of the Earth's magnetic field on a magnet used for navigation. However, its use is fast decreasing now that the Global Positioning System (GPS) is being employed much more. The shape of the Earth's magnetic field is shown in Figure 1 and is similar in shape to the magnetic field of a bar magnet.

Magnetic field of an electric current

As a result of their use in navigation, magnetic fields were associated with the force caused by the effect of the Earth's magnetic field on the north pole of a magnet in a compass. In the modern world, however, it is the magnetic field associated with an electric current in a wire that is more important.

As with electric fields and gravitational fields, the lines drawn to represent the field are close together when the field is strong and further apart when the field is weak. It is not possible for field lines to cross one another as this would mean the field pointing in two directions at one point. Though a magnetic field is represented by two-dimensional diagrams, it is in fact three-dimensional.

(a)

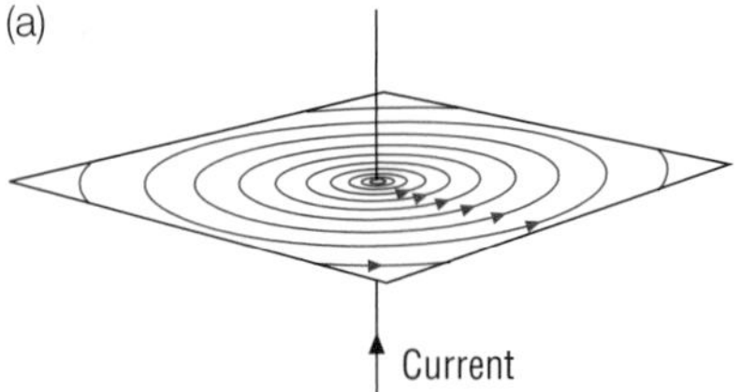

(b)

Figure 2 **(a)** The magnetic field around a wire carrying a current; **(b)** a plan view of the field in **(a)**

The field of a straight, current-carrying wire

The Earth's gravitational field spreads out from the Earth; the electrical field from a charge spreads out from the charge, but the magnetic field associated with a current in a wire does not spread out from the wire in the same way. The field circles the wire as shown in Figure 2(a). A plan of this field is drawn in Figure 2(b). Note that the field is strongest near to the wire and decreases in strength with distance from the wire.

Some conventions are used for directions in these cases. A dot inside the circle representing the wire means current towards you, and a cross means current away from you. A current towards you gives an anticlockwise field. (If you imagine grasping the wire with your right hand and with your thumb pointing in the direction of the current, your fingers will be curling around the wire in the direction of the magnetic field.)

The field around a single coil carrying a current

When a wire carrying a current is formed into a coil, the shape of the magnetic field is as shown in Figure 3. The field around one side of the coil is clockwise; that around the other side is anticlockwise. This is because the current is going one way in one side and the other way in the opposite side. This results in an increase in the strength of the magnetic field within the coil.

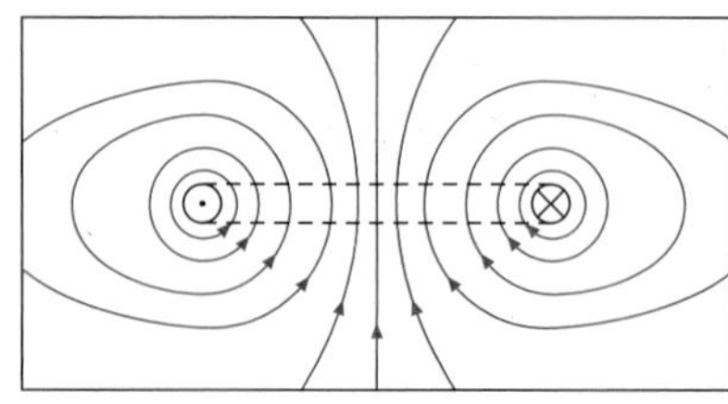

Figure 3 The magnetic field due to a single coil of wire carrying an electric current

The field of a long, current-carrying coil

When the wire is wound into a long coil, the effect is to extend the diagram of Figure 3. The field pattern becomes that shown in Figure 4.

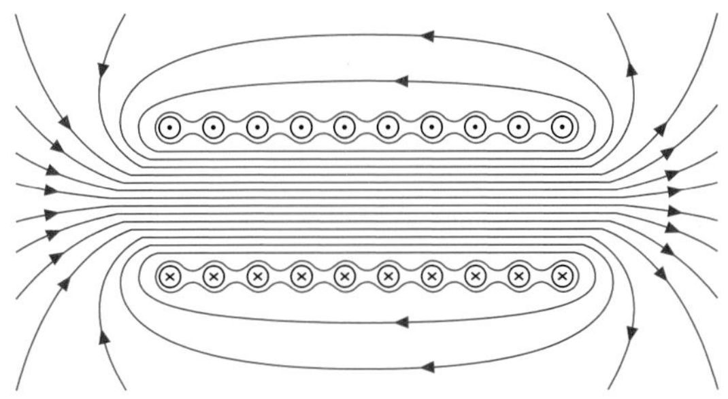

Figure 4 A plan view of the magnetic field of a solenoid

Inside the coil, which is called a solenoid, the field is very uniform; outside the coil, the field is very similar to the magnetic field produced by a bar magnet and similar to the shape of the Earth's magnetic field. If a cylinder of iron is placed inside the solenoid, the magnetic field is increased considerably and the coil and iron core is an electromagnet. More details on this are in the next spread.

Insulating wire in the nineteenth century

At the time of the development of electromagnetism by such people as Oersted, Ampere and Faraday, in the early nineteenth century, insulated wire was unavailable. They had to buy ordinary copper wire and then dip it in a varnish called shellac in order to avoid short circuits in any of the coils they made.

Questions

1 For a long straight wire the magnetic field strength or magnetic flux density B of Figure 2(b) is inversely proportional to the radial distance r from the wire and directly proportional to the current I in the wire.
  (a) How much further apart do you expect the field lines to be at twice the distance from the wire?
  (b) What is the effect on the field lines at a given distance from the wire of doubling the current in the wire?

2 In each of the diagrams of Figure 5 there are two magnetic fields from two different sources. The field lines are shown as solid lines for one and dotted lines for the other. The direction of each field is given by the arrows on the lines. Sketch the resultant field for each of (a), (b) and (c).

(a)
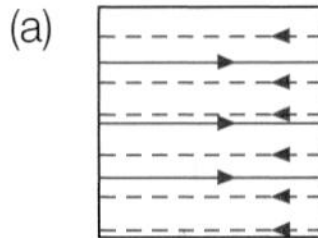
(b)
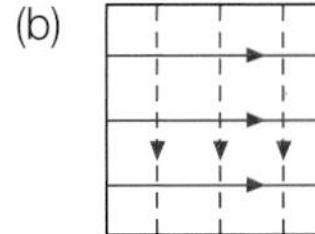
(c)
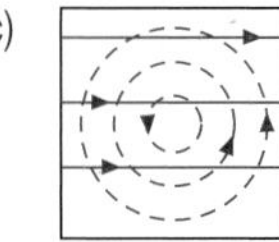

Figure 5

3 Figure 6 is a plan view of the magnetic field pattern of a solenoid with several points within it labelled. Assume that the magnetic field strength at A is 2.0 mT. (The unit T, tesla, will be defined in spread 2.1.6.)

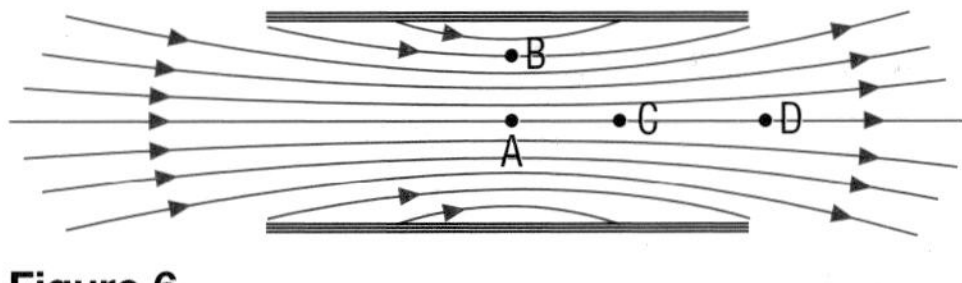

Figure 6

  (a) By looking at Figure 6, suggest values for the field strength at B, C and D.
  (b) The current in the solenoid is doubled. What is the new field strength at A? How is the magnetic field pattern changed?
  (c) The solenoid can be replaced by a bar magnet to give a similar field pattern. Would the north or south pole of this bar magnet be at D?

Electromagnets

By the end of this spread, you should be able to ...

✱ Describe a practical example of the field of a long solenoid.

Figure 1 An electromagnet in an electric bell

Electromagnet structure

While ceramic and metal magnets are still produced in large numbers, when a really large, powerful magnet is required, electromagnets are used. An electromagnet is a long coil of wire, a solenoid, with a current passing through it and with an easily magnetised core (usually made of iron, but now some are made of more readily magnetised materials). Electromagnets can be made stronger by increasing the number of turns and by increasing the current. In many applications it is important that the core demagnetises quickly once the current falls to zero. One example is shown in Figure 1, a picture of a small electromagnet used in a doorbell.

The wire shown in the solenoid in Figure 1 is *insulated* copper wire. Much of the development of small, powerful electric motors is due to improved wire insulation in the coils of the motor. Insulated wire can now be made with an enamelled surface that is not only thin but can withstand high temperatures without melting. The enamelling needs to be removed at the end of the wire to make an electrical connection. A 500 W electric motor used to be 30 cm long and weigh 10 kg. Now, a hand drill can contain a 500 W motor that is only 10 cm long and weighs less than 1 kg.

Electromagnets come in various shapes and sizes. One common shape uses two separate coils as shown in Figure 2. Why is it necessary to be careful over whether each side of the coil is wound clockwise or anticlockwise?

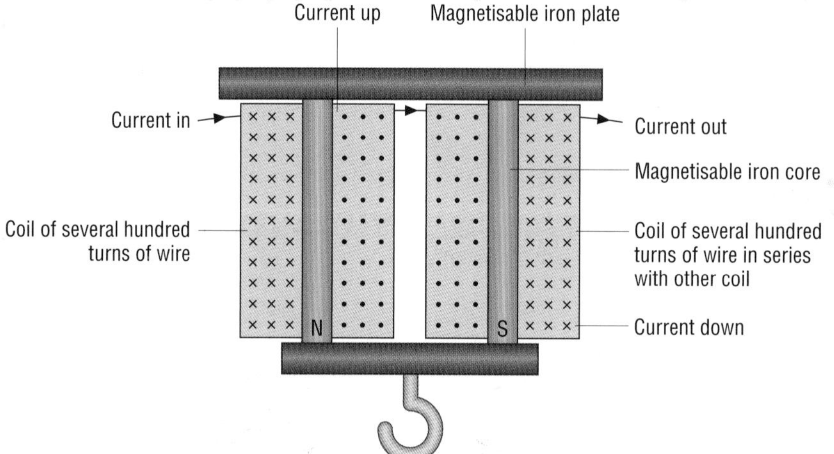

Figure 2 A large electromagnet with two separate coils

Uses of electromagnets

Electromagnets are not used just for lifting old cars in scrapyards. Some of the more important uses are in providing magnetic fields:

- in electric motors and generators
- in transformers
- in mass spectrometers, for analysing matter with great precision
- in magnetic resonance imaging (MRI), for obtaining superb pictures of 'slices' of a living human body
- in fusion reactors, for containing plasma
- in cyclotrons and particle accelerators for nuclear research.

Details of many of these instruments, some of which are shown in Figures 3, 4 and 5, will be given in later spreads.

Figure 3 Part of the magnet in an electric generator

Figure 4 An electromagnet in a mass spectrometer produces a very strong magnetic field

An interesting development concerns the MRI equipment shown in Figure 5. Because the patient is positioned where the core would usually be, no core is possible. This means that the current has to be very large, but a very large current would produce a large heating effect and would also be very expensive. This problem is overcome by using the phenomenon of superconductivity. In this, certain materials at very low temperatures have zero resistance. Currents of the order of tens of thousands of amperes are possible with no heating effect at all. But as the magnet is very large, it costs quite a lot to keep the temperature low.

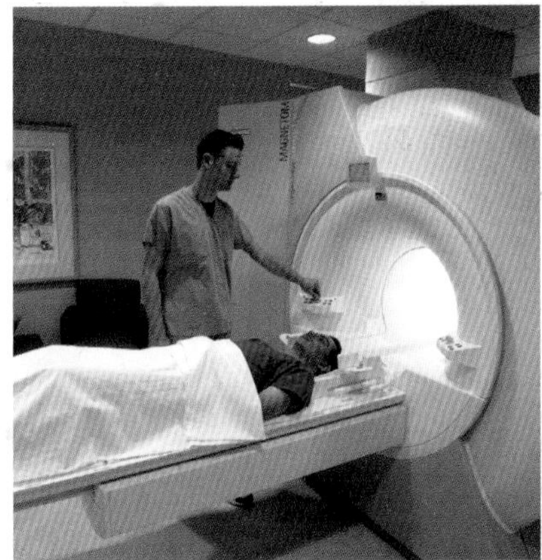

Figure 5 No core is possible in magnetic resonance imaging (MRI) equipment, as the patient has to be in the strong magnetic field

Questions

1 Figure 6 shows a cross-section through an electromagnet. Copy the outline of the diagram. There is a current in the coil of wire.

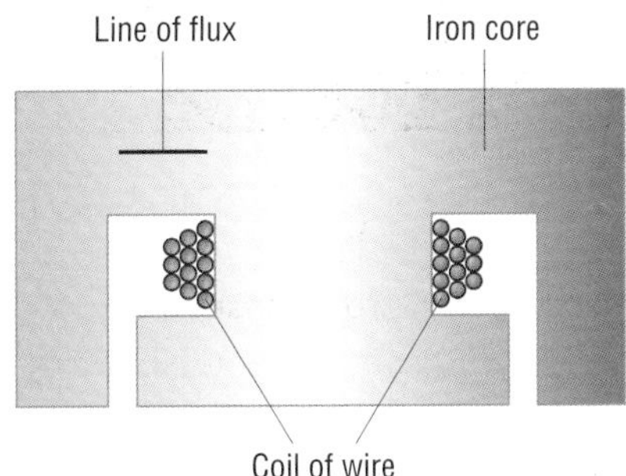

Figure 6

A small length of a magnetic field line, also called a line of flux, is shown on the diagram. Complete this magnetic field line on your diagram and add three more possible field lines.

2 One end of a small rod of soft iron is placed at D in Figure 6 of spread 2.1.4. Explain why it will experience a resultant (net) force. In which direction is this force? What force does it experience when placed in the middle of the solenoid at A? Why?

3 Figure 7 shows a traditional electric doorbell. It rings when the bell push is pressed and held down. It incorporates an electromagnet. Explain how it works.

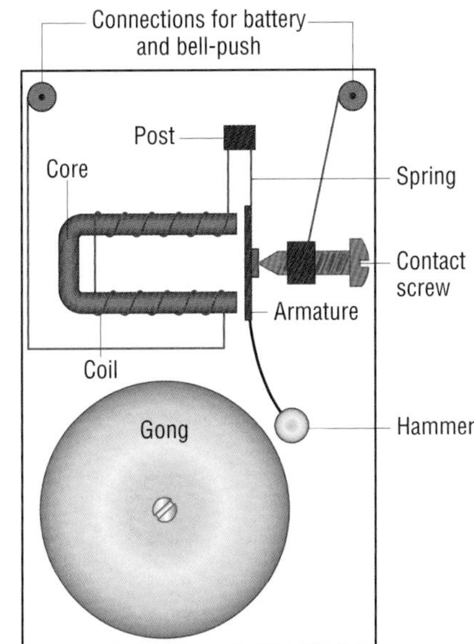

Figure 7

2.1 (6) Definition of magnetic flux density

By the end of this spread, you should be able to ...

- **State and use Fleming's left-hand rule.**
- **Define magnetic flux density and the tesla.**
- **Select and use the equations $F = BIL$ and $F = BIL\sin\theta$.**
- **Select and use the equation $F = BQv$.**

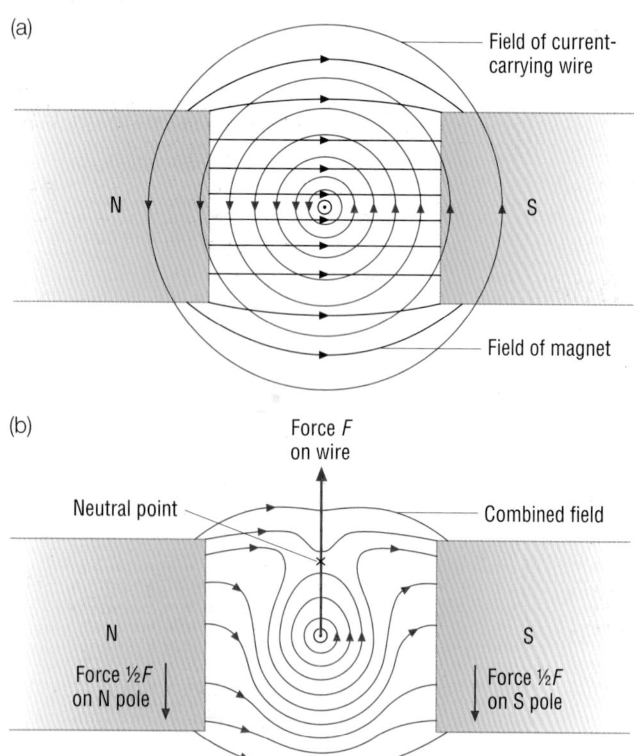

Figure 1 (a) The magnetic field of a current-carrying wire superimposed on the uniform magnetic field between the poles of a horseshoe magnet; **(b)** the two fields from **(a)** added together to get the resultant field

Fleming's left-hand rule

In the last spread various arrangements of wires and shapes of magnetic fields were considered. In this spread, we will look at the interaction between the field of a wire carrying current and a uniform magnetic field. Figure 1(a) shows the magnetic field between the poles of a horseshoe magnet, together with the magnetic field of a wire placed in between the poles and carrying a current. The two fields are superimposed on top of one another. Figure 1(b) shows the resultant field of the wire and the magnet. In Figure 1(a) you can see that the N-pole of the magnet is in the downward (to the bottom of the page) magnetic field of the wire, so the field of the wire is pushing the N-pole downwards. The S-pole of the magnet is in the upward field of the wire. Since it is a S-pole, it will have a force on it that is also downwards. The wire therefore exerts a downward force on the magnet, so by Newton's third law, the magnet must be exerting an upward force on the wire. These forces are shown in Figure 1(b). **Fleming's left-hand rule**, sometimes called the motor rule, gives the three-dimensional arrangement for the directions of the current, the magnetic field and the force on the wire. Use your left hand in the way shown in Figure 2. The direction of:

- your **F**irst finger gives the magnetic **F**ield
- your se**C**ond finger gives the direction of the **C**urrent
- your thu**M**b gives the direction of **M**otion of the wire – the force on it.

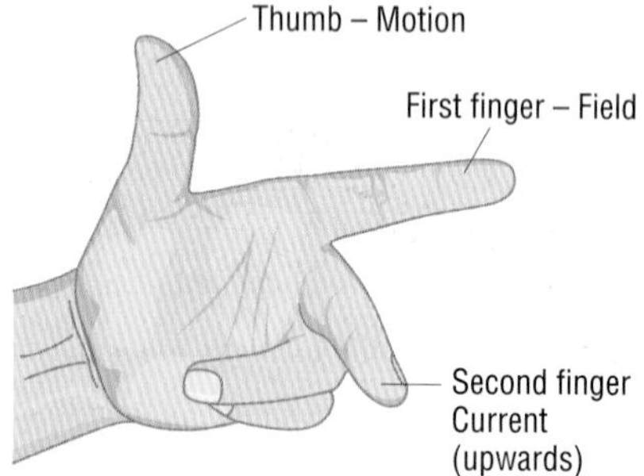

Figure 2 Fleming's left-hand rule

Measuring the magnetic field

The value of the force referred to above is used to measure the strength of the magnetic field. This is measured in terms of a quantity called the **magnetic flux density**. Flux is a term normally associated with the flow of fluids such as water, and the field lines were historically a representation of the water flow. Here there is nothing flowing, but the idea of magnetic field lines travelling from north to south remains, and in the early days of magnetic research, field lines were always used for field descriptions. Density comes about because it was a measure of how concentrated the field lines were. In this case, for instance, the greater the number of field lines per unit area, the greater the field. This early terminology remains, and now the magnetic flux density is a quantitative measure of magnetic field. Its symbol is B.

The magnitude of the force F acting on the wire is proportional to four quantities:

- The current I in the wire.
- The length L of the wire.
- The magnetic flux density B.
- The sine of the angle θ between the wire and the field.

Since force, current, length and angle are already defined and their units are known, we can use these terms to define **magnetic flux density**.

Magnetic flux density is defined by the equation

$$B = \frac{F}{IL\sin\theta}$$

Rearranging this equation gives $F = BIL\sin\theta$.

Provided F is in newtons, I is in amperes and L is in metres, B will be in **tesla**. One tesla, T, is the magnetic flux density when a wire of length one metre and carrying a current of one ampere at a right angle to the field experiences a force of one newton.

Note that if the field and the wire are in the same direction, $\sin\theta$ will be zero, and the force will be zero. When the wire and the field are at right angles to one another, $\sin\theta$ will be 1, and the force will be at its maximum value. One tesla is a large magnetic flux density. In magnetic resonance machines the magnetic field has to be up to 2 T. A good strong bar magnet will have a flux density near its poles of around 20 milliteslas, mT. The magnetic flux density of the Earth in the UK is around 5×10^{-5} T, or 50 μT.

The force on a charged particle moving in a magnetic field

Consider a charge $+Q$ travelling with velocity v at right angles to a magnetic field of magnetic flux density B. In a time t the charge will have moved a distance $L = vt$, and the current I, the charge flowing per unit time, will be Q/t. Using the equation $F = BIL$ and substituting gives for the charged particle

$$F = B \times \frac{Q}{t} \times vt = BQv$$

As with a current in a wire, the force acts in a direction given by Fleming's left-hand rule. The force is at right angles to both the magnetic field and the direction of travel of the particle. You need to be careful when applying Fleming's left-hand rule to charged particles. If the particle is negatively charged, an electron for example, the direction of the current is in the opposite direction to the direction in which it is travelling.

If the particle is initially not travelling at right angles to the field, the situation is as shown in Figure 3, in which a charge Q moves with velocity v at an angle θ to the magnetic field of flux density B. Consider the two components of the velocity. One component, at right angles to the field, has magnitude $v\sin\theta$, and the other in the direction of the field has magnitude $v\cos\theta$. The component at right angles to the field results in the charge experiencing a force $BQv\sin\theta$, and the component in the direction of the field will have no effect whatsoever on the particle's path.

Questions

1 Show that the units of magnetic flux density, usually T (tesla), can be written as N s C^{-1} m^{-1}.

2 Figure 4 shows the directions of the current I in a short section of wire and the magnetic flux density B at the wire.
   (a) The current is in the direction H–G. In which direction is the force on the wire?
   (b) The free electrons are drifting in the direction G–H. In which direction is the average force on them?
   (c) The wire carries a current of 0.24 A. The length of wire in the magnetic field is 60 mm. The magnetic flux density B is 30 mT. Calculate the force on the wire.
   (d) Through what angle must the wire be rotated and in which plane to reduce the force on the wire to **(i)** half the value in (c) and **(ii)** zero?

Key definition

Magnetic flux density B is defined by the equation

$F = BIL\sin\theta$

where F is the force on a wire of length L carrying a current I at an angle θ to the field.

Key definition

One **tesla**, T, is the magnetic flux density when a wire of length one metre and carrying a current of one ampere at a right angle to the field experiences a force of one newton.

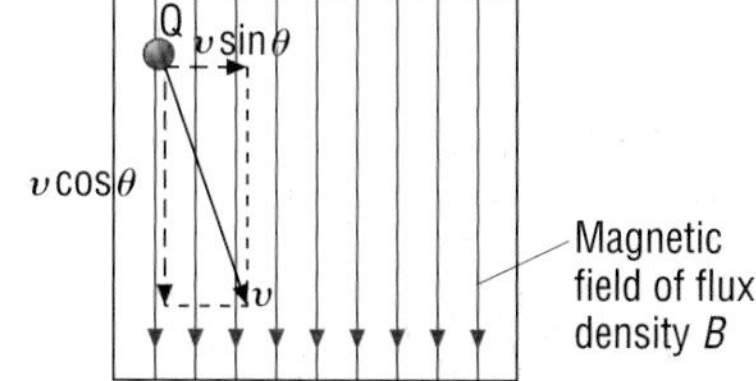

Figure 3 A charged particle moving at an angle θ to the magnetic field will experience a force $BQv\sin\theta$

Key definition

The **force F on a charge Q** moving with velocity v at an angle θ to a magnetic field of flux density B is given by $F = BQv\sin\theta$.

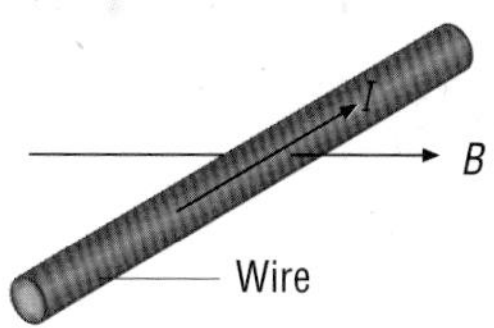

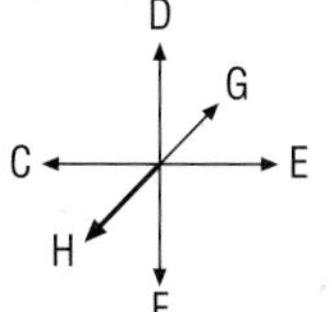

Figure 4

2.1  Particle movement in magnetic fields

By the end of this spread, you should be able to ...

- **Analyse the circular orbits of charged particles.**
- **Analyse the motion of charged particles both in electric and in magnetic fields.**

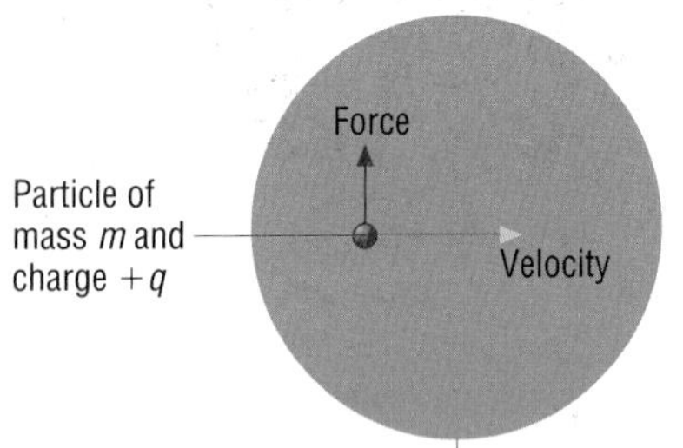

Figure 1 A positively charged particle of mass m moving with velocity v in a direction at right angles to a magnetic field of flux density B. The direction of the field is downwards into the page. Using Fleming's left-hand rule shows the force to be towards the top of the page

Charged particles in a magnetic field

Many modern pieces of equipment function by controlling the movement of charged particles in a vacuum using both electric fields and magnetic fields. The effect of an electric field was dealt with in spread 2.1.3. It can alter the path of a charged particle and also do work on it so that its speed increases. The effect of a magnetic field can also be to alter the direction in which the particle moves, but it cannot increase the speed of a particle. This is because the force applied to the charged particle is always at right angles to its direction of motion.

The shape of the path of a charged particle moving in a magnetic field

Figure 1 shows a positively charged particle of mass m and charge Q moving with velocity v in a direction at right angles to a magnetic field of flux density B. The magnitude of the force on the particle will be BQv as shown. The direction of movement of the charge is to the right, so the direction will be towards the top of the page. This is simply the arrangement for circular motion. The force BQv causes centripetal acceleration v^2/r, where r is the radius of the particle's circular path. This gives

$$Bqv = m\frac{v^2}{r} \text{ that gives when rearranged } r = \frac{mv}{BQ}$$

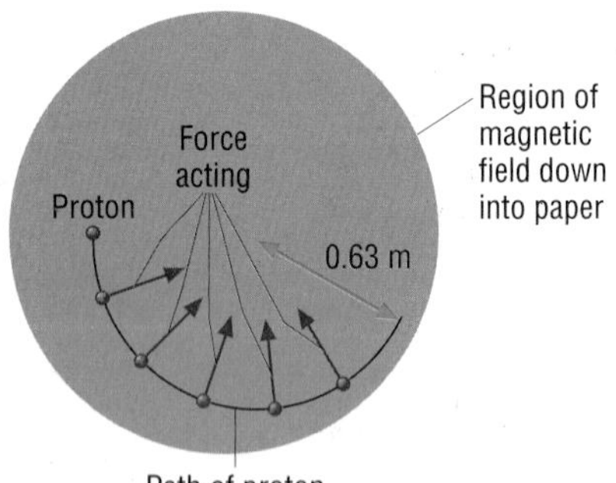

Figure 2 A proton moves in a circle in a magnetic field that is downwards into the page

Worked example

In a particle accelerator, protons are accelerated from rest in a vacuum by a potential difference (p.d.) V and then directed at right angles into a magnetic field of flux density 0.039 T. They travel in a semicircle that must have a radius less than 0.63 m if they are to remain within the magnetic field.

(a) What is the maximum value of V that can be used to satisfy this condition?

(b) How long does a proton take to complete a semicircle of the maximum allowed radius?

Answer

A diagram showing the arrangement is drawn in Figure 2.

The proton has mass 1.67×10^{-27} kg and charge $+1.60 \times 10^{-19}$ C.

(a) For the limiting condition, when the radius is 0.63 m, the velocity v can be obtained from

$$v = \frac{rBQ}{m} = \frac{0.63 \times 0.039 \times 1.60 \times 10^{-19}}{1.67 \times 10^{-27}} = 2.35 \times 10^6 \text{ m s}^{-1}$$

The work done on the proton by the p.d. V is QV, and this becomes the kinetic energy of the electron.

So $\frac{1}{2} mv^2 = QV$, giving

$$V = \frac{mv^2}{2Q} = 1.67 \times 10^{-27} \times \frac{2.35 \times 10^{62}}{2 \times 1.60 \times 10^{-19}} = 2.89 \times 10^4 \text{ V}$$

(b) For a radius of 0.63 m, the semicircle will have a length $\pi \times 0.63 = 1.98$ m. At speed 2.35×10^6 m s^{-1}, this distance will therefore take a time of $1.98/2.35 \times 10^6 = 0.842$ μs.

Examiner tip

You may have noticed a slight discrepancy with the answer to this worked example. It illustrates a problem with significant figures. Working out V from the equation gives 2.88×10^4 V. We obtain 2.89×10^4 by the better method of leaving the answer from the first part of the question in the calculator and using that rather than rounding it up and re-entering it. Since only 2 sig. figs are given in the question, the better final answer would therefore be 2.9×10^4 V.

Charged particles in both electric and magnetic fields

One particular use of the combination of the two fields is in a device called a **velocity selector**. For this device the two fields are arranged at right angles to one another as shown in Figure 3.

The pink circle is a region of magnetic field of flux density B down into the page. In the space between the pair of plates, there is an electric field of field strength E from top to bottom, shown in green. A positively charged particle, with charge Q and shown in red, enters the two fields with velocity v. The force the electric field exerts on the particle will be QE downwards. The force the magnetic field exerts on the particle, found using Fleming's left-hand rule, will be BQv upwards.

Any particle that is undeflected from its straight line path through the fields has zero resultant (net) force acting on it, and therefore $QE = BQv$. Q cancels to give $E = Bv$ or $v = E/B$.

The fact that Q cancels out implies that any charged particle, positive or negative, passing undeflected through the space where both fields exist has a velocity equal to the ratio E/B of the fields. By measuring B and E the value of the velocity of the particle can be determined.

If the particles have a range of speeds when they enter the space where both fields exist, the force due to the electric field will be the same for all particles with the same charge. The force due to the magnetic field will increase with the speed of the particles. Slow particles have a smaller force exerted on them by the magnetic field. QE will be greater than BQv, so the slow particles will be deflected downwards by the fields. On the other hand, a fast particle will have a larger force exerted on it by the magnetic field than by the electric field, so it will be deflected upwards. The result of this is shown in Figure 4.

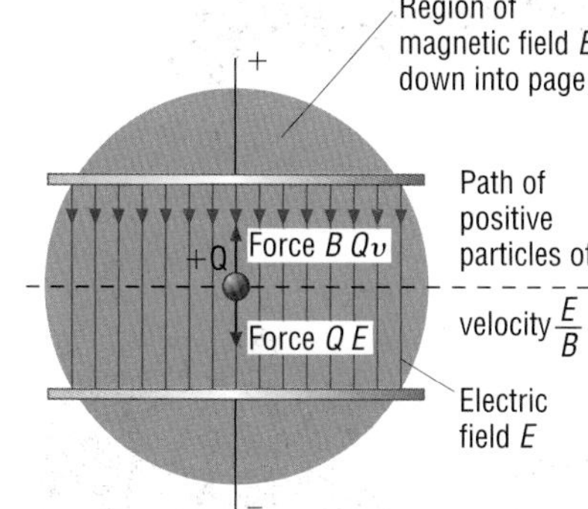

Figure 3 A positive particle travelling in a vacuum and acted upon by both an electric and a magnetic field

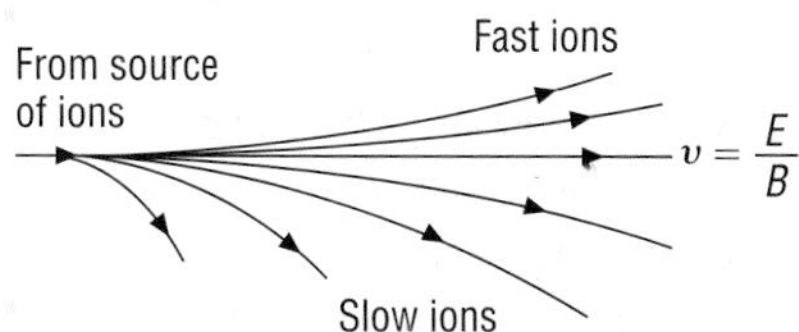

Figure 4 Particles of varying speeds travelling through a velocity selector

Questions

1 Here are three possible paths of an electron in a vacuum: A straight line, B circular path, C parabolic path. Which path best describes the motion of an electron initially moving:
   (a) at right angles to a magnetic field, (b) at right angles to an electric field and (c) parallel to a magnetic field?

2 (a) Calculate the magnitude of the force on an electron moving at 2.0×10^7 m s^{-1} as it enters a region of uniform magnetic field of flux density 5.0×10^{-3} T perpendicular to its path.
   (b) Calculate the acceleration of the electron and hence the radius of its orbit in the field.

3 Figure 5 shows a beam of protons passing through a hole into a region where there is a uniform electric field of strength E.
   (a) Copy the diagram and sketch on it a possible path for the protons.
   (b) A uniform magnetic field of flux density B is now applied at right angles (into the plane of the diagram), and the electric field is switched off. Sketch a possible path for the protons.
   (c) The electric field is switched on again. Explain why it is now possible for some of the protons to pass undeflected to the detector.

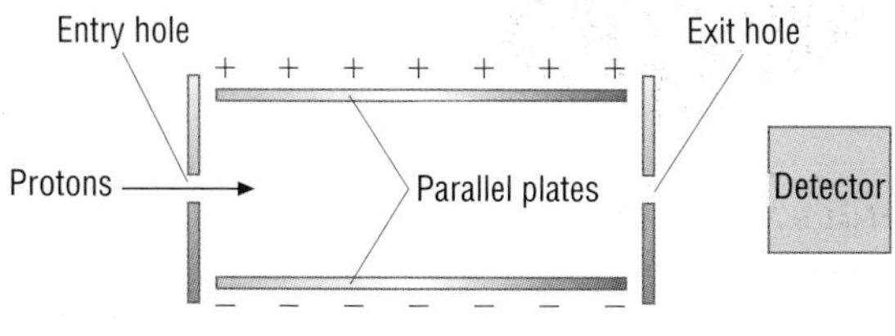

Figure 5

4 The fuel in nuclear fission reactors to generate electricity is $^{235}_{92}U$. In natural uranium over 99% is $^{238}_{92}U$ and only 0.7% is $^{235}_{92}U$. In one 'separation process', each atom of natural uranium is combined with six atoms of fluorine to make the molecule UF_6. The molecules are ionised and, using a velocity selector, made into a beam of particles each with the same velocity.
   (a) Explain why the UF_6 ions of $^{238}_{92}U$ have more momentum than those of $^{235}_{92}U$.
   (b) The ion beam passes through a region of uniform magnetic field directed at right angles to their velocity as shown in Figure 6 before being collected in a trap.
   The figure shows the path of the UF_6 ions of $^{235}_{92}U$. Copy the diagram and add the path of the UF_6 ions of $^{238}_{92}U$.
   (c) Hence explain how this device works as a separator. Why would UF_6 ions of $^{238}_{92}U$ reach the collector if the apparatus was not kept under a good vacuum?

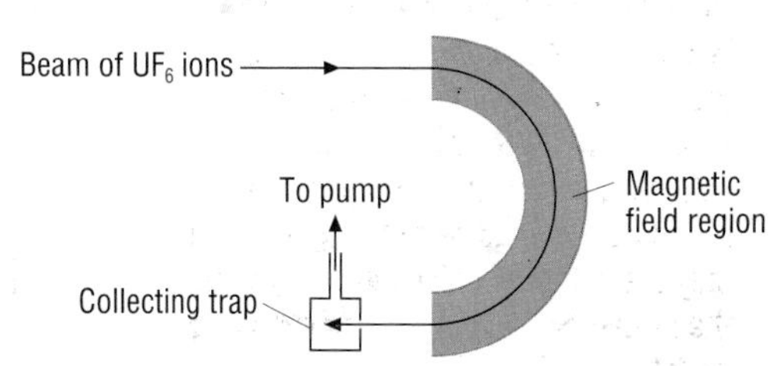

Figure 6

2.1 (8) The mass spectrometer

By the end of this spread, you should be able to ...

* **Explain the use of deflection of charged particles in a mass spectrometer.**

Introduction

Mass spectrometers are used to identify particles. If the particle can be ionised, its movement in electric and magnetic fields can be controlled in such a way that the mass of the particle can be measured. The design of a mass spectrometer varies according to the kind of particle needing identification. Some spectrometers are used to analyse biological specimens in which the particles may be large molecules, while others concentrate on the isotopic analysis of atoms. (See spread 2.3.3. for details about isotopes.)

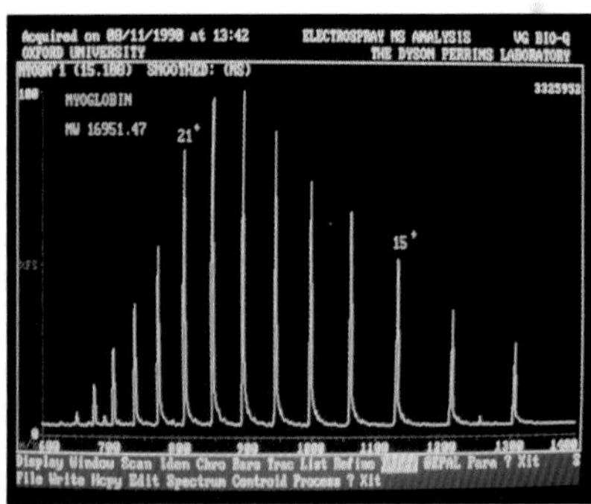

Figure 1 The mass spectrum of myoglobin, the oxygen-storage protein of red muscle, displayed on the computer screen of a mass spectrometer used for protein analysis at Oxford University

Development of mass spectrometry

The mass spectrometer was invented by Francis William Aston in 1919 when he controlled the path of particles accelerating through a near vacuum by using electric and magnetic fields together. In his method, all particles with the same mass arrived at the same point on a photographic plate. On the resulting image, the density of blackening revealed the number of particles arriving, and the position of the point showed the mass of the particles. Since then, the mass spectrometer has resulted in a phenomenal improvement in chemical analysis. Mass spectrometer detectors are now so sensitive that they can detect just a few molecules, and the accuracy of the mass of individual atoms is now known to around 8 significant figures. Mass spectrometers are used extensively in all sorts of chemical analysis, from purity testing to forensic work. For example, in the analysis of pollution, a sample of an oil slick in the sea can be analysed by a mass spectrometer, and this can tell us, almost with certainty, which oilfield produced the slick and probably which tanker was responsible for the spillage. A photo of the type of readout produced by a modern mass spectrometer is shown in Figure 1.

The Bainbridge mass spectrometer

This spectrometer can be used for isotopic analysis. Assume that a fine beam of positively charged neon ions, travelling in a vacuum, can be sent into a velocity selector (see spread 2.1.7), as shown in Figure 2.

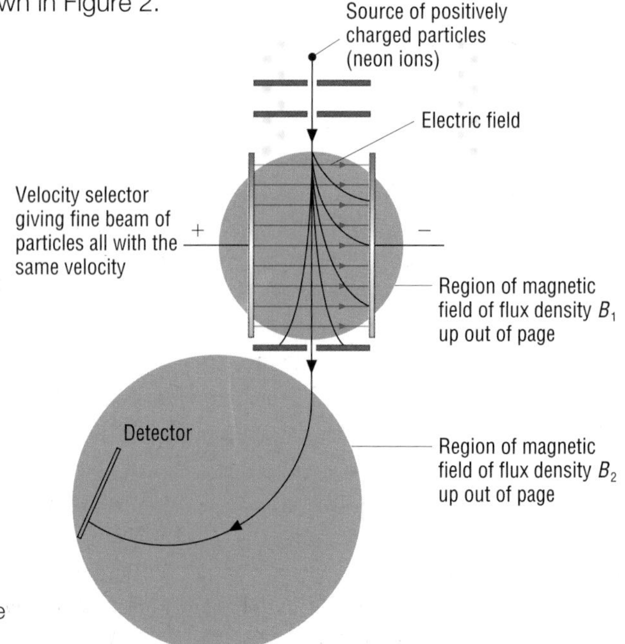

Figure 2 A Bainbridge mass spectrometer

Those ions that go straight through the velocity selector will have speed $v = E/B_1$, where E is the electric field strength and B_1 is the magnetic flux density in the velocity selector. This velocity can be adjusted by controlling the magnitudes of the two fields. The neon ions that travel with this velocity then enter a uniform magnetic field of flux density B_2. In this field they will travel in a circular path. The radius of the path will be given by

Force $= B_2Qv = ma = m\frac{v^2}{r}$ and by rearranging the equation $r = \frac{mv}{B_2Q}$

Eliminating v gives $r = \frac{mE}{QB_2B_1}$

By measuring r, the mass of the ion can be obtained. When this experiment was first performed, the results from it showed that neon ions mostly had a mass of 19.992 u but that 0.26% of the ions had mass 20.994 u and 8.82% had mass 21.991 u. This discovery of isotopes explained why so many atoms had almost whole-number ratios of masses. The differences were explained with the discovery of the neutron.

Key definition

Atomic and nuclear masses are usually measured in terms of the **unified atomic mass unit** u. It is a mass equal to 1/12 the mass of an atom of the nuclide $^{12}_{6}C$. One u = 1.66054×10^{-27} kg, to 6 sig. figs. More detail about this mass unit is given in spread 2.3.3.

Other mass spectrometers

Different manufacturers of mass spectrometers use different methods of producing the initial stream of ions. In one system, samples in liquid form are injected into the machine and the substance is then ionised by bombardment from high-energy electrons.

Another type of mass spectrometer is called a time-of-flight (TOF) spectrometer and is shown in Figure 3.

In a time-of-flight secondary ion mass spectrometer, to give it its full name, a pulsed ion beam or pulsed laser beam is used to remove batches of molecules from the outermost surface of the sample. The molecules are ionised and accelerated towards a detector. The time it takes them to reach the detector depends on their mass. The advantage of this system is that macromolecules (such as polymers or proteins) are not disintegrated by the beam. These instruments are used in coatings research, microelectronics and surface contamination studies.

Figure 3 Researcher observing a time-of-flight secondary ion mass spectrometer (TOF SIMS). The sensor array can be seen through the round window (lower left)

Questions

1 A large ion of mass 5.8×10^9 u and charge $+18e$ is accelerated constantly towards a detector by a potential difference of 870 V. Assuming the ion starts from rest, calculate the time taken for the ion to travel 47 cm to the detector.

2 Figure 2 shows a Bainbridge mass spectrometer.
The beam consists of singly ionised neon-20 atoms all travelling at the same speed, 3.0×10^5 m s^{-1}, through a vacuum. As the beam passes through the magnetic field it follows a circular path of radius 0.125 m.
- **(a)** Explain why the path is a semicircle.
- **(b)** Show that the force on each ion of mass 3.32×10^{-26} kg is 2.4×10^{-14} N. In which direction is this force?
- **(c)** Calculate the magnetic field strength or flux density in teslas.
- **(d)** Suggest where the detector should be positioned to detect ions of neon-22 travelling with the same speed. Explain your decision.

3 The spectrometer of Figure 4 is used to collect the nuclides $^{238}_{92}U$ and $^{206}_{82}Pb$ from a small sample of rock to date it.
- **(a)** Singly ionised nuclei of the two nuclides from the sample of rock pass through the hole in the 200 V electrode with negligible velocity. They are accelerated towards the electrode at 0 V. Show that the momentum gained by an ion of $^{206}_{82}Pb$, mass 3.5×10^{-25} kg, is about 5×10^{-21} N s.
- **(b)** Calculate the radius of the circular path of the lead ion when within the uniform region of magnetic field of flux density 0.12 T.
- **(c)** The lead and uranium ions have the same charge and kinetic energy when they enter the magnetic field, yet the uranium ions follow a path of greater radius. Explain why this is.

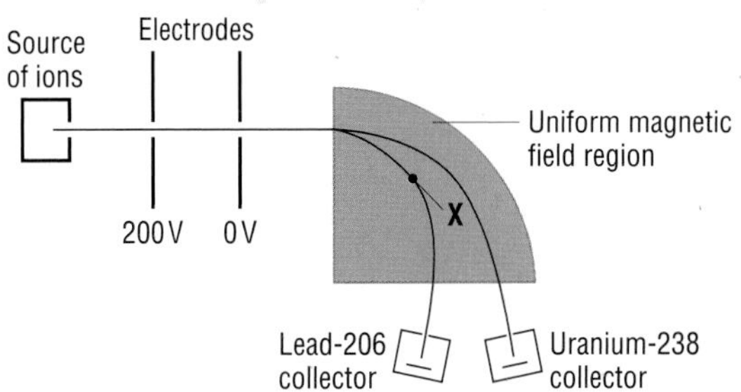

Figure 4

2.1 (9) Electromagnetic induction

By the end of this spread, you should be able to …

- ✱ **Define magnetic flux and the weber.**
- ✱ **Define magnetic flux linkage.**
- ✱ **Select and use the equation for magnetic flux density $\phi = BA\cos\theta$.**

Introduction

In the early part of the nineteenth century, when the importance of electric currents was first recognised with the development of electric motors, the battery was the only available source of current. But the batteries of that time were very inefficient, and alternative sources were needed. Faraday realised that, since an electric current produced a magnetic field, perhaps a magnetic field could produce an electric current. Faraday's investigations led to the discovery of electromagnetic induction, the generation of electric currents by moving or changing magnetic fields.

The fundamental experiment of electromagnetic induction

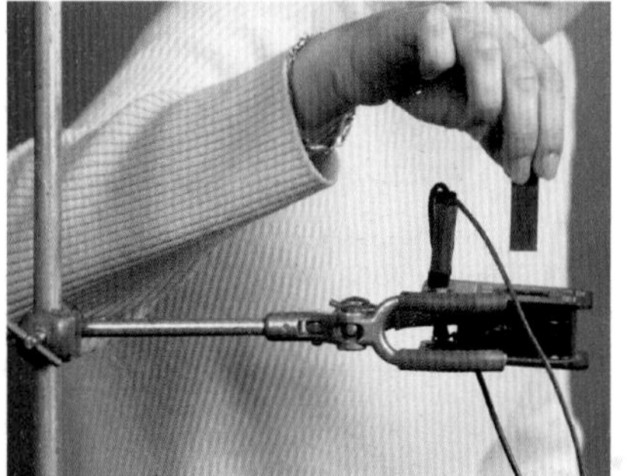

Figure 1 A direct method of demonstrating electromagnetic induction

With sensitive electrical test equipment, it is easy to demonstrate electromagnetic induction. All that is required is a magnet, a piece of wire and a sensitive meter. To produce a current in the wire, the magnet can be moved near it (Figure 1). You will not be able to get any electrical energy out of the system unless some work is done on the wire, which involves moving the wire relative to the magnet. The direction of movement of the wire is important. To create an electric current, that is to move the electrons in the wire, the magnet must be moved *across* the wire. When it is moved across one way, the electrons move. If the magnet moves the other way, the direction of movement of the electrons is reversed.

This simple demonstration produces only a few microwatts of electrical power, but all modern power stations use exactly the same process to produce outputs of thousands of megawatts, still using wires and magnetic fields, although on a much larger scale.

Fleming's right-hand rule

Note that this is *not* the motor effect. The *left*-hand rule was used for the motor effect. Electromagnetic induction is the opposite effect and is sometimes called the dynamo effect. It requires the right-hand rule.

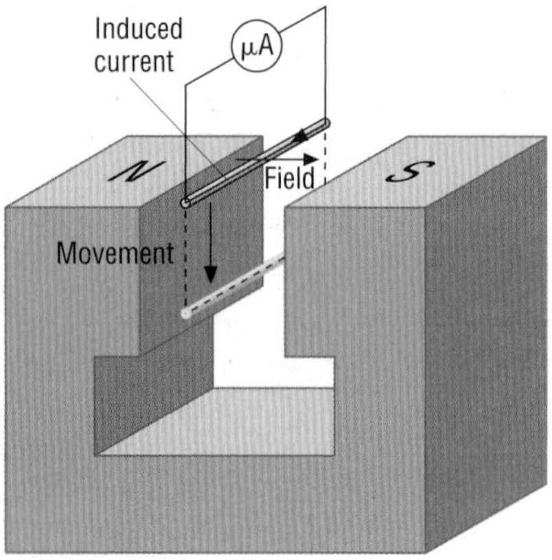

Figure 2 shows another arrangement for demonstrating electromagnetic induction. The magnetic field of the horseshoe magnet has a direction from the north pole to the south pole. The wire is shown to be moving down through the field. The wire is said to 'cut' the magnetic field. As a result, an e.m.f. is set up in the wire, which will cause a current to flow in it, provided there is a complete circuit. The direction of the current is shown.

Figure 2 A wire being moved between the poles of a horseshoe magnet in order to produce an electric current by electromagnetic induction

Fleming's right-hand rule gives these three directions:

- The thu**M**b shows the direction of **M**otion of the wire relative to the field.
- The **F**irst finger shows the direction of the **F**ield.
- The se**C**ond finger shows the direction of the induced **C**urrent. (This is conventional current, not electron flow.)

Note that these directions use the same code as the left-hand motor rule, but here you use your right hand.

Magnetic flux

In the previous section, the expression 'cutting' a magnetic field was mentioned. To quantify how much magnetic field has been 'cut', a new quantity is defined called

magnetic flux. Figure 3(a) shows a rectangular loop of wire of area A in a field at right angles to the loop of magnetic flux density B. The magnetic flux Φ is given by

$$\Phi = BA$$

In Figure 3(b) a side view of the same situation is shown but with the rectangular loop at an angle θ to its original position. Here less of the flux passes through the loop. The new value of the magnetic flux Φ' through the area is

$$\Phi' = BA \cos\theta$$

When the loop is parallel to the field, θ will be 90°, and since cos 90° = 0, the magnetic flux will be zero. Be careful with this angle. It is not the angle between the flux and the area, but the angle the loop has turned through. Make sure you have things the right way around.

The unit of magnetic flux is the **weber**. One weber (Wb) is the magnetic flux when a magnetic field of magnetic flux density one tesla passes at right angles through an area of one square metre.

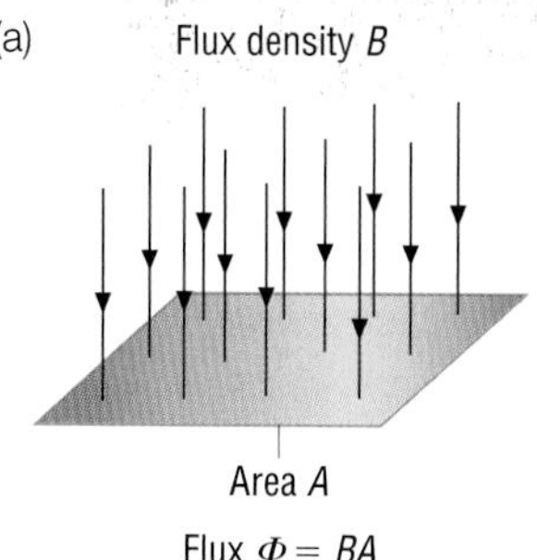

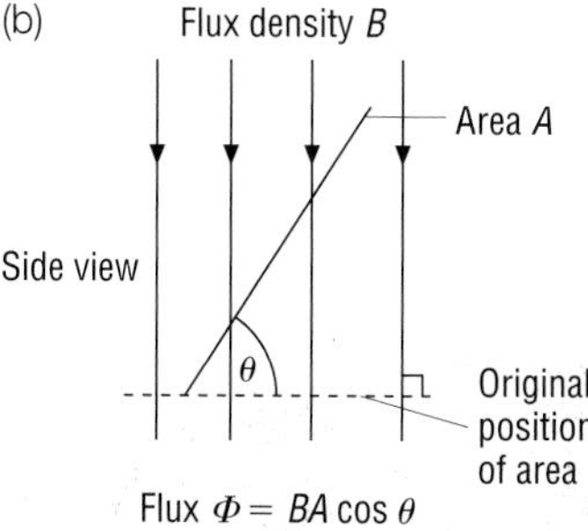

Figure 3 **(a)** Here the loop of area A is at right angles to the field of flux density B so $\theta = 0$, $\cos\theta = 1$ and the flux through the loop is BA; **(b)** here the loop of area A has been rotated through an angle θ from its original position, so the flux through the loop is $BA \cos\theta$

Magnetic flux linkage

In many motors and generators, coils of many turns of wire are used, so it is useful to know not just the flux through one coil but the product of this and the number of turns N. This quantity is called the **flux linkage** and is defined by the equation

$$\text{flux linkage} = N\Phi$$

is simply measured in weber turns, Wb turns.

Worked example

A rectangular coil of 400 turns of wire has length 8.9 cm and width 6.4 cm. It rotates in a magnetic field of flux density 0.045 T. Calculate the flux through the coil and the flux linkage when the plane of the coil is **(a)** at right angles to the field, **(b)** has moved through an angle of 40° and **(c)** has moved through 90° so that it is parallel to the field, as shown in Figure 4.

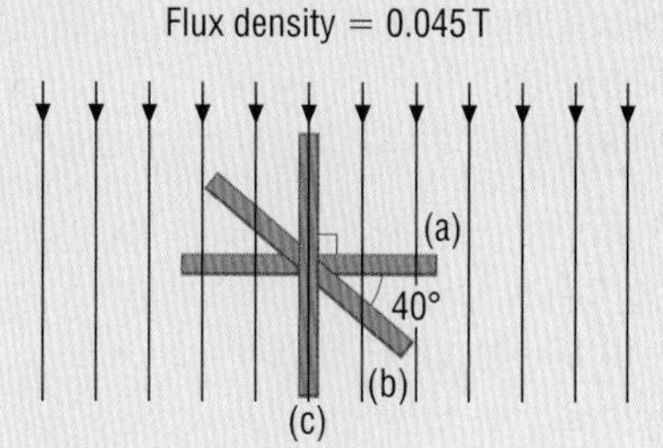

Coil shown in three positions, (a), (b) and (c)

Figure 4 Rectangular coil

Answer

The flux is always given by $\Phi = BA \cos\theta$, and the flux linkage by ΦN.

The area A of the coil is 0.089 m × 0.064 m = 5.7×10^{-3} m². Answers are tabulated so that the pattern is clear.

	(a) Coil at 90° to field	(b) Coil moved by 40°	(c) Coil parallel to field
Flux $\Phi = BA\cos\theta$	$0.045 \times 5.7 \times 10^{-3} \cos 0 = 2.56 \times 10^{-4}$ Wb	$2.56 \times 10^{-4} \times \cos 40 = 1.96 \times 10^{-4}$ Wb	$2.56 \times 10^{-4} \times \cos 90 = 0$
Flux linkage $= \Phi N$	$2.56 \times 10^{-4} \times 400 = 0.102$ Wb turns	$1.96 \times 10^{-4} \times 400 = 0.078$ Wb turns	0

Key definitions

Magnetic flux through an area A is defined as the product of the magnetic flux density B and the projection of area A onto a surface at right angles to the flux. It is given the symbol Φ.

$$\Phi = BA \cos\theta$$

where θ is the angle between the plane of the area and the projection surface.

The unit of magnetic flux is the **weber**. One weber (Wb) is the magnetic flux when a magnetic field of magnetic flux density one tesla passes at right angles through an area of one square metre.

Magnetic **flux linkage** for a coil equals the magnetic flux through the coil multiplied by the number of turns on the coil.

Questions

1 Show that a Tesla, T, is a Weber per square metre, Wb m^{-2}.

2 A long coil or solenoid wound on an iron rod has 300 turns of cross-sectional area 4.0×10^{-5} m². When it carries a certain current the flux linkage of the coil is 6.0×10^{-4} Wb turns.

(a) Calculate **(i)** the flux linking one turn of the coil and **(ii)** the flux density in the iron rod.

(b) Why is it not possible to answer this question when the coil is wound on a wooden dowel?

2.1 Further questions B

Coulomb's law

① A small conducting sphere is attached to the end of an insulating rod (not shown). It carries a charge of $+5.0 \times 10^{-9}$ C. The sphere is held between two parallel metal plates. The plates, which are 4.0 cm apart, are connected to a 50 000 V supply.

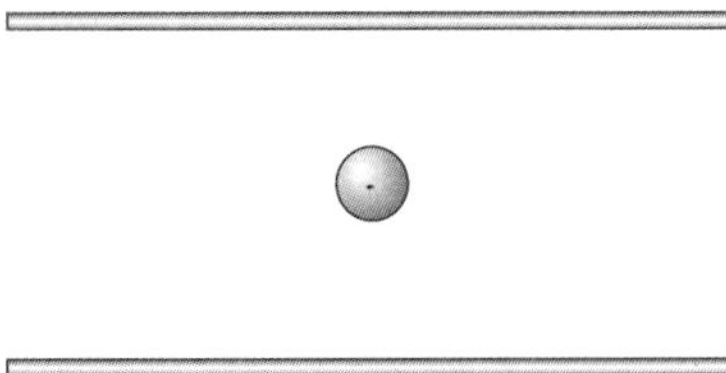

Figure 1

Calculate:

(a) the magnitude of the electric field strength between the plates

(b) the magnitude of the force on the sphere, treated as a point charge of $+5.0 \times 10^{-9}$ C.

② A second identically charged sphere like that in Question 1 above is attached to a top pan balance by a vertical insulating rod. The charged sphere of Question 1 is clamped vertically above the second sphere such that their centres are 4.0 cm apart.

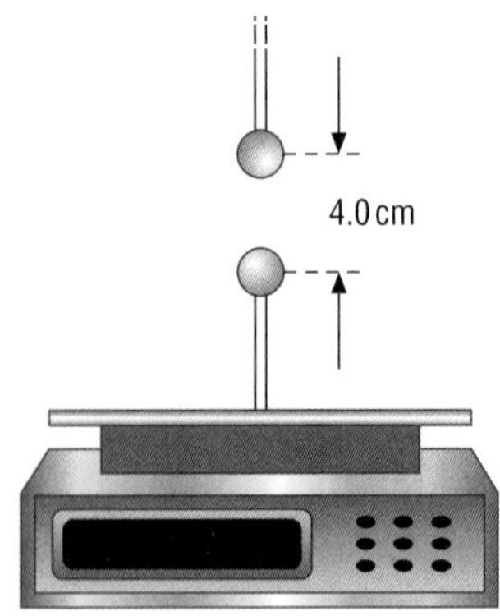

Figure 2

(a) Show that the force between the two spheres acting as point charges is about 1.4×10^{-4} N.

(b) The balance can record masses to the nearest 0.001 g. The initial reading on the balance before the original charged sphere is clamped above the second sphere is 8.205 g. Calculate the final reading in g on the balance.

Electric fields

③ **(a)** Some details of the accelerating plates of an oscilloscope are shown in Figure 3. Electrons leave the cathode with negligible kinetic energy. They are accelerated through a vacuum towards the anode at 0 V.

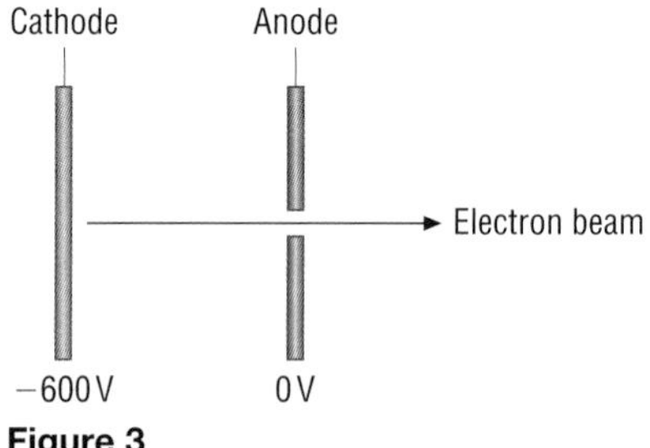

Figure 3

Calculate

(i) the kinetic energy and

(ii) the speed gained by the electrons as they pass through the anode.

(b) The electron beam passes through a pair of deflecting plates before hitting a fluorescent screen as shown in Figure 4.

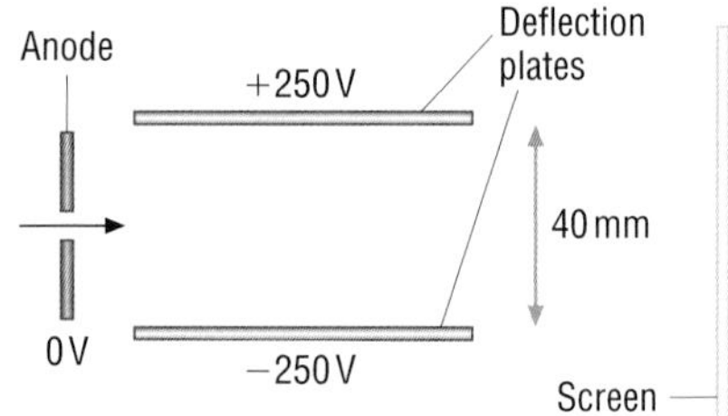

Figure 4

(i) Calculate the electric field strength between the deflecting plates.

(ii) Copy Figure 4 and sketch on it:

1 five lines to represent the electric field in the space between the plates

2 the path of the beam from the anode to the screen.

(iii) Describe and explain the shape of the path of the beam through the region of electric field.

Definition of magnetic flux density

(4) An alpha particle moving horizontally at 1.5×10^7 m s^{-1} enters a uniform vertical magnetic field of flux density 0.20 T. An alpha particle has a mass of 6.6×10^{-27} kg and a charge of 3.2×10^{-19} C.

(a) Calculate

(i) the force on and

(ii) the acceleration of the alpha particle in the field.

(b) Describe

(i) the motion of the alpha particle and

(ii) how its speed changes with time while in the field.

(5) Is it possible to make a wire float in the Earth's magnetic field? Estimate the magnitude of the current in a wire so that the vertical force on it is equal and opposite to its weight. The weight of a 1.0 m length of single-strand connecting wire is 0.06 N. The horizontal component of the Earth's magnetic field is 2×10^{-5} T.

Electromagnetic induction

(6) A loop of wire is connected to a sensitive centre-zero galvanometer. The loop is moved at constant speed vertically upwards between the poles of a strong U-shaped magnet, from well below the magnet to well above it. Describe the movement of the needle on the galvanometer in relation to the position of the loop in its motion.

Faraday's and Lenz's laws of electromagnetic induction

By the end of this spread, you should be able to …

- ✱ **State and use Faraday's law of electromagnetic induction.**
- ✱ **State and use Lenz's law of electromagnetic induction.**
- ✱ **Select and use the equation: induced e.m.f. = – rate of change of magnetic flux linkage.**

Faraday's law of electromagnetic induction

In the last spread you saw a situation in which a current could be generated by electromagnetic induction. The value of such a current depends not only on the generating process but also on the resistance of the circuit. For this reason **Faraday's law** concentrates only on the e.m.f. produced by electromagnetic induction. From the careful definitions of quantities in spread 2.1.9, Faraday's law can be expressed very simply:

The magnitude of the induced e.m.f. is equal to the rate at which magnetic flux is cut.

For a coil this becomes:

The induced e.m.f. is equal to the rate of change of flux linkage.

Key definition

Faraday's law of electromagnetic induction states that the magnitude of the induced e.m.f. is equal to the rate at which magnetic flux is cut.

Worked example

Look back to Figure 2 on spread 2.1.9. The uniform field between the poles of the magnet has flux density 0.062 T, the length of the wire is 5.3 cm and it is moved down a distance of 2.8 cm in 0.060 s.

(a) What e.m.f. is produced by this movement?

(b) What will be the current through the microammeter if the circuit resistance is 8.8 Ω?

Answer

(a) Area of flux cut by the wire = 0.053 m × 0.028 m = 1.48×10^{-3} m^2.
Flux cut by wire $\Phi = BA$ = 0.062 T × 1.48×10^{-3} m^2 = 9.2×10^{-5} Wb.
E.m.f. induced = Φ/t = 9.2×10^{-5} Wb/0.060 s = 1.53 mV.

(b) Current = e.m.f./total resistance = 1.53 mV/8.8 Ω = 174 μA.

Lenz's law of electromagnetic induction

So far in this spread no mention has been made of the direction of any induced current. **Lenz's law** corrects that omission.

The direction of any induced current is in a direction that opposes the flux change that causes it.

Key definition

Lenz's law states that the direction of any induced current is in a direction that opposes the flux change that causes it.

The electromagnetic induction equation

Faraday's law and Lenz's law can be combined into this equation:

$$E = -\frac{\Delta\Phi}{t}$$

where E is the induced e.m.f., $\Delta\Phi$ is the change in flux and t is the time interval.

Practical applications of Lenz's law

The minus sign in the above equation indicates Lenz's law. It shows that the induced e.m.f. opposes any forward e.m.f. and is really an extension of the principle of conservation of energy. The induced e.m.f. is often called the **back e.m.f.**

When a current is being established, in an electromagnet for example, the induced e.m.f. will be set up in such a direction to try to prevent the current increasing. When the current is being switched off, the induced e.m.f. tries to keep the current going. There are practical uses and disadvantages of this.

Some braking systems on lorries, buses, trains and roller-coaster rides use the braking effect of moving an electrical conductor through a strong magnetic field or vice versa. The induced current in the conductor will be in a direction to oppose motion, hence the braking effect. The high-speed ICE-3 trains in Germany produce a large magnetic field across a rail, which is the conductor. The advantage is that no wear takes place on the brake as there is no direct contact between the magnet and the conductor and no friction is involved.

A disadvantage of induced e.m.f. occurs when a large direct current needs to be switched off. As the current falls, a high induced e.m.f. can occur. This produces a large voltage across the switch itself, which causes sparking. Apart from being damaging to the switch, the sparks themselves emit radio waves that cause interference on radios and televisions in the surrounding area. All manufacturers of equipment likely to cause sparking now have to adhere to strict requirements either to prevent sparking or to shield the equipment so these radio waves are not transmitted. One way is to connect a capacitor across the spark gap. This acts as a reservoir for charge and so limits the amount of sparking. More details will be given on capacitors in the next module.

Examiner tip

As usual, extra care must be taken with signs. When applying the equation to a circuit in which a battery is connected to a motor, the battery can be considered to provide a forward e.m.f., and the motor, since it will have a coil rotating in a magnetic field, will cause a back e.m.f. So:

forward e.m.f. – back e.m.f. = p.d. across any resistor.

A correct equation might be

$12\ V - 9\ V = 3\ V$

If you are not careful it is easy to get

$12\ V = -9\ V + x$

which then incorrectly gives $x = 21$ V.

Think of these problems in energy terms; for each coulomb passing through the system:

12 joules supplied by the battery – 9 joules of work done by the motor = 3 joules heating the resistor

OR

12 joules supplied = 9 joules of work done by motor + 3 joules heating the resistor.

Whether or not the minus sign is needed depends on which side of the equation the term is placed.

Questions

1 The magnetic flux linkage of a coil of wire increases steadily by 0.18 Wb in a time of 45 ms.
Calculate the e.m.f. induced across the ends of the coil.

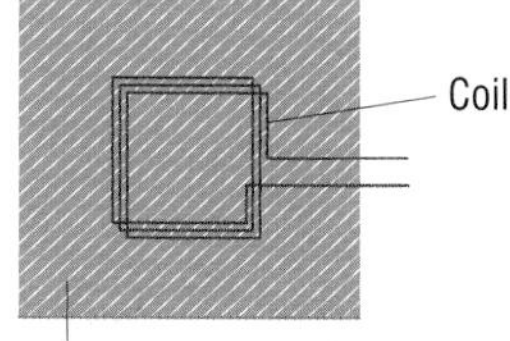

Figure 1

2 An electromagnet produces a uniform field through a coil of 200 turns each of area 4.0×10^{-4} m^2 as shown in Figure 1. The field is directed into the diagram. The ends of the coil of resistance 32 Ω are connected together. The electromagnet is switched off and the flux density falls from 0.20 T to zero in 0.040 s.
   (a) Calculate **(i)** the e.m.f. induced in the coil and **(ii)** the current in the coil while the flux density is being decreased.
   (b) In which direction will the current be, clockwise or anticlockwise? Explain how you made your decision.

3 Figure 2 shows how the flux linking one turn of a coil of wire varies with time.
   (a) Use the graph to calculate the peak value of the e.m.f. induced across the turn of wire.
   (b) Sketch a graph with labelled axes to show how the e.m.f. induced across the turn of wire varies over the same time interval.
   (c) The coil consists of 200 turns of wire. Assuming that the flux links all of the turns, calculate the peak e.m.f. across the whole coil.
   (d) Suggest a way of increasing the e.m.f. induced across the coil without altering the coil.

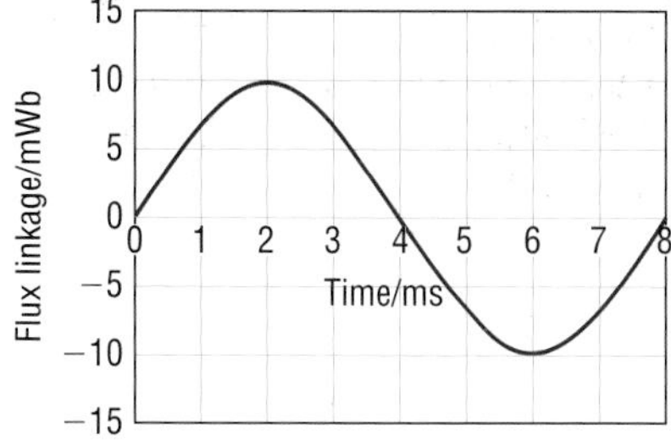

Figure 2

4 A rigid rectangle of wire ABCD is moved at a steady speed of 0.20 m s^{-1} towards the right as shown in Figure 3. Side AB is of length 8.0 cm. There is a uniform magnetic field of flux density 0.40 T into the diagram over the shaded region shown.
   (a) **(i)** Calculate the flux change through the coil per second.
   (ii) Hence calculate the e.m.f. induced across AB.
   (iii) Explain why no e.m.f. is induced in sides AD and BC, which are also in the magnetic field.
   (b) The resistance of the loop is 2.0 Ω. Calculate **(i)** the current in the loop and **(ii)** the energy dissipated as heat in the circuit per second.
   (c) A force is needed to move the rectangle steadily to the right.
   (i) Explain why and calculate the value of the force.
   (ii) Calculate the work that must be done per second to move the wire.

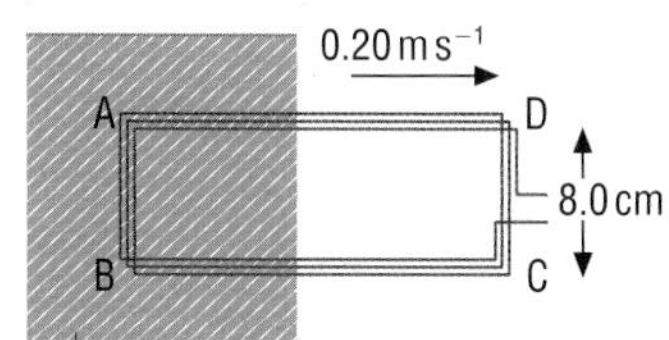

Figure 3

5 The fuselage and wings of an aeroplane are made of metal, so an e.m.f. should be generated between the wingtips when it flies through the Earth's magnetic field.
   (a) Justify the statement above.
   (b) A wire could be connected between the wingtips to create a circuit. The current generated could be used to light the cabin. Explain why this suggestion cannot work.

2.1 (11) The a.c. generator

By the end of this spread, you should be able to …

∗ Describe the function of a simple a.c. generator.

Introduction

Alternating current has been mentioned many times throughout this course, but no explanation has been given of how it differs from direct current or why it is used. Most of the comments about a.c., for example when dealing with the domestic circuit, have simply asked you to just assume it behaves like d.c. This spread will go some way to correcting this simplification, but it will not attempt to cover a.c. theory completely, because of its complexity, especially when other components are also in a circuit.

Alternating current (a.c.)

With a direct current (d.c.), the conduction electrons in a wire drift along the wire, normally at a very slow speed. This was dealt with at AS level (AS book, spread 2.1.1). Batteries always supply direct current. Any magnetic field produced by a constant d.c. will itself be constant.

In contrast, with alternating current (a.c.), the conduction electrons oscillate about their mean position and do not drift along the wire at all. Alternating current is used in all countries for mains electrical distribution for the simple reason that it produces a variable magnetic field. The changing magnetic field means that electromagnetic induction can be used with a.c., in particular in transformers. These will be considered in the next spread.

One problem with a.c. concerns the value given to the current. If the electrons are merely oscillating backwards and forwards, the average current is clearly zero. A graph of a.c. plotted against time is shown in Figure 1. The current is shown starting at zero, rising to a maximum of 10 A after a time of 0.005 seconds, reaching zero after 0.010 s and then another half cycle in the opposite direction, when the current is then negative. The shape of the graph has a sine wave pattern. One complete cycle takes 0.020 s, a frequency of 50 Hz. All European countries use 50 Hz. In the USA, 60 Hz is used.

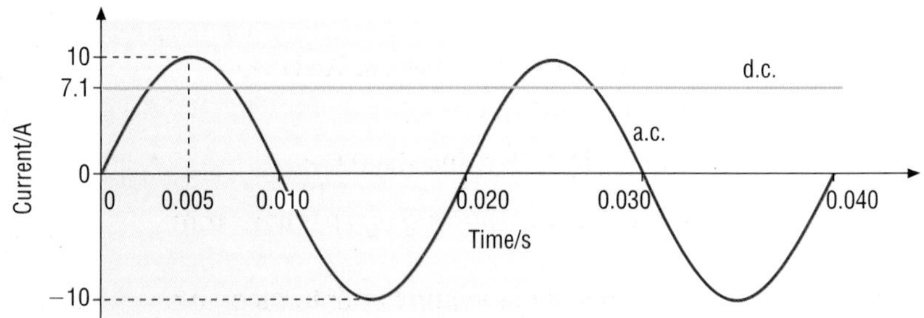

Figure 1 The variation of current with time in an alternating current. The direct current that provides the same heating effect is also shown

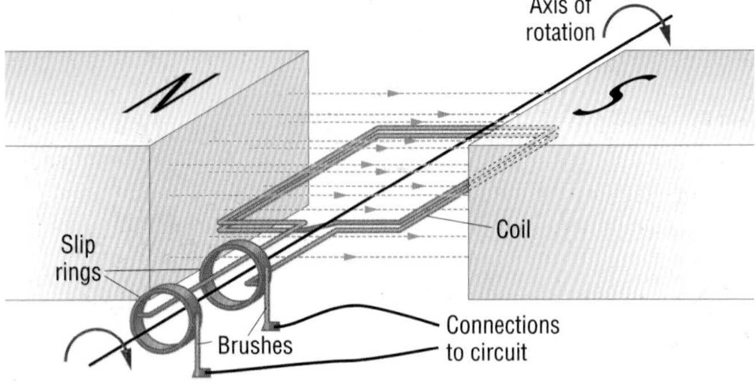

Figure 2 A simplified diagram of an a.c. generator

The a.c. generator

Not only is a.c. useful because it has a varying magnetic field, but it is also easy to produce, using a rotating coil. If a rectangular coil is rotated in a constant magnetic field at a rate of 50 rotations per second it will produce an alternating current of 50 Hz in a sine wave shape in any resistor to which it is connected. Figure 2 shows a simplified version of such a generator. The coil is free to rotate on an axle and the coil is connected to the electrical circuit via two slip rings against which brushes, usually made out of a solid paste of carbon and copper, make contact. When the coil is

STRETCH and CHALLENGE

On Figure 1 a line is also drawn showing a direct current. This has a value of 7.07 A. If these two currents were passing, separately, through the same resistor, they would both produce the same heating effect. For this reason an alternating current that varies between –10 A and +10 A is said to be a 7.1 A r.m.s. current. The term r.m.s. stands for root mean square. This may seem rather odd, but the average current is zero, and the heating effect of a current, I^2R, clearly depends on I^2. The square root of the average value of I^2 is much more useful. All the values you are used to using with a.c. are the r.m.s. values. A 13 A fuse, for example, can carry a current that varies between $+13\sqrt{2}$ A and $-13\sqrt{2}$ A 50 times a second, that is between +18.4 A and –18.4 A.

Questions

Sketch a current/time graph of the 50 Hz alternating current I of peak value 5.0 A in a resistor of resistance 8.0 Ω.

Sketch on the same time axis the values of I^2. (Hint: it never becomes negative and it is still a sine wave pattern.)

in the horizontal position shown it is cutting magnetic field at maximum rate. The e.m.f. generated at this moment is therefore a maximum. When it is in the vertical position the wires at the top are moving in the direction of the field and so no e.m.f. is generated. On the way down, the e.m.f. is in the opposite direction, which will give rise to the reversal of direction of any current the e.m.f. causes. All mains electricity is generated by this basic system. Figure 3 shows the many coils in a large generator. In generators of this size the situation in Figure 2 is reversed. The coils remain fixed in position and the magnet spins inside the coils.

Figure 3 A large commercial generator showing the coils that generate the electrical power. In this instrument it is the magnet that rotates, and the coils remain stationary

Questions

1 A small generator coil is rotated at 60 revolutions per minute in the uniform magnetic field between the poles of an electromagnet. The coil is connected via slip-rings to a resistor and oscilloscope. See Figure 4.

(a) At the instant shown, $t = 0$, in Figure 4, the oscilloscope reading is +0.4 V. State the reading at

$t =$ **(i)** 0.25 s, **(ii)** 0.50 s, **(iii)** 1.75 s and **(iv)** 3.0 s.

(b) Sketch a graph of the oscilloscope reading against time from $t = 0$ to 3.0 s.

(c) How would the graph change if **(i)** the number of turns on the coil were doubled, or **(ii)** the area of the coil were halved, or **(iii)** the speed of rotation were increased to 90 revolutions per minute?

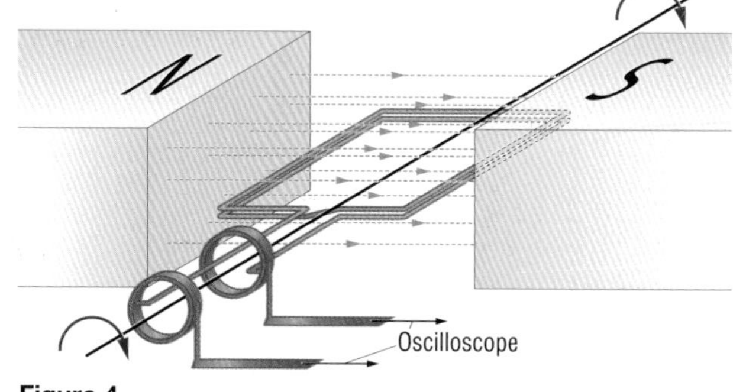

Figure 4

2 Figure 5 shows a cross-section through a simple a.c. generator.

(a) (i) Copy Figure 5 and sketch two complete flux loops which pass through the poles of the rotor.

(ii) The core of the generator is made from iron. Give reasons why iron is used.

(b) Explain how rotating the magnet causes an e.m.f. in the coil.

(c) In which position is the magnet when the e.m.f. is **(i)** a maximum and **(ii)** zero?

(d) Suggest two modifications to the generator and explain how each of these would increase the e.m.f. induced in the coil.

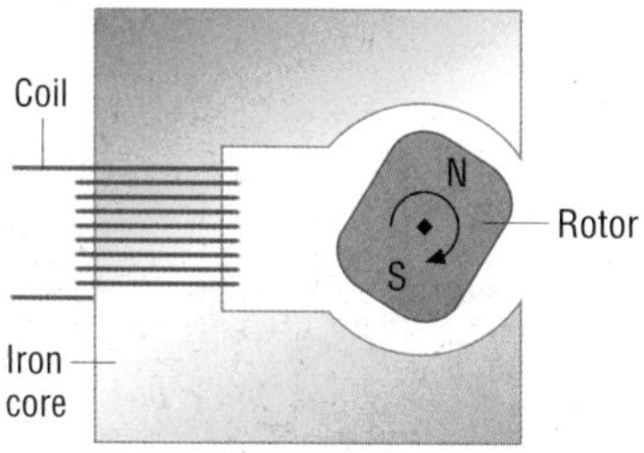

Figure 5

(12) The transformer – 1

By the end of this spread, you should be able to …

* **Describe the function of step-up and step-down transformers.**

Why transformers are necessary

Transformers change electrical supplies from low voltage, high current, to high voltage, low current, or vice versa. They can do this with over 99% efficiency and need virtually no maintenance, because they have no moving parts. If you look around your neighbourhood you will see many small electrical sub-stations containing switch gear and transformers. In the countryside many transformers are set up on the poles that distribute electrical power to farms and houses. Some have been in place for 80 years.

Worked example

Figure 1 shows a power station connected to a small town by cables that have total resistance 0.20 Ω. The town requires power of 460 kW. Find the efficiency of the supply system **(i)** when the voltage of the supply at the town is 230 V and **(ii)** when the voltage of the supply at the town is 2300 V.

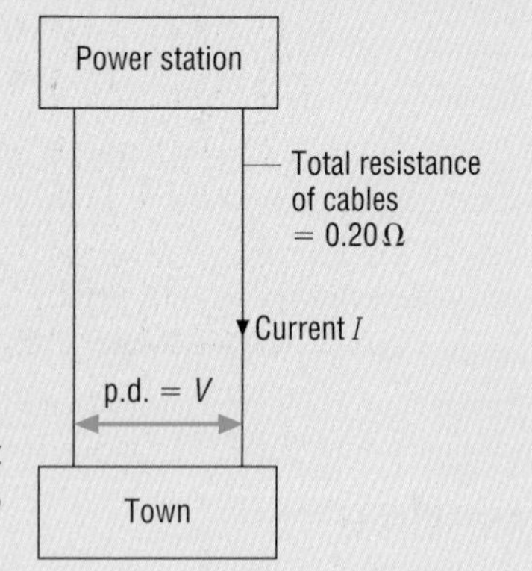

Figure 1 The electrical circuit connecting a power station to a town

Answer

This is laid out in a table so that you can see how the figures for the two supply voltages differ.

p.d. at town (V)	(i) Supply at 230 V	(ii) Supply at 2300 V
Power (P)	460 000 W	460 000 W
Current (I) = P/V	2000 A	200 A
Voltage across cables	2000 A × 0.20 Ω = 400 V	200 A × 0.20 Ω = 40 V
p.d. from power station	230 V + 400 V = 630 V	2300 V + 40 V = 2340 V
Power from power station	630 V × 2000 A = 1 260 000 W	2340 V × 200 A = 468 000 W
Efficiency = $\frac{\text{power used}}{\text{power supplied}}$	460 kW/1260 kW = 0.365 = 36.5%	460 kW/468 kW = 0.983 = 98.3%

The very low efficiency of the 230 V system is not economically viable. On the other hand, the high voltage of 2300 V would be lethal in a house. Low voltage could be used for transmission only by making the resistance of the cables lower, but in this example it is already only 0.20 Ω, and to make this much lower would require very thick, costly, ugly cables. The problem is made worse when much higher powers must be distributed over much larger distances. The answer to the dilemma, in practice, is to use very high voltages for transmission (up to 450 000 V) and to use 230 V for domestic use. To change from high voltage to low voltage efficiently requires a transformer: transformers will work only on a.c., so all mains electrical supplies must be a.c.

Mains distribution

In a typical mains electrical distribution system, a generator will have an output voltage of 6000 V. This will be stepped up at the power station to 275 000 V for transmission. A large electricity sub-station, such as the one in Figure 2, will step down the voltage, usually in stages, to 11 000 V. A small transformer unit, somewhere close to homes and like the one in Figure 3, will further step down the voltage to 230 V. In practice, power stations are linked by a national grid. This grid is also connected to many large sub-stations for area distribution.

Figure 2 A large electricity sub-station

Figure 3 A local transformer unit within a few hundred metres of the houses it is supplying

Questions

The questions below consider one aspect of the cost of distributing power around the country using the national grid. Each pylon supports six transmission lines. Each line consists of four multi-strand cables. The normal rating of a line is 700 MW at 400 kV.

1 This question leads you through the analysis to show that the total power loss per metre due to heating of the cables at 400 kV from a 2000 MW power station is 170 W m^{-1}.

(a) Show that 12 cables are required to transmit 2000 MW.

(b) Calculate the total current in these cables.

(c) Take the resistivity of each cable to be 4.0×10^{-8} Ω m and its area of cross-section to be 4.9×10^{-4} m^2. Hence calculate the power loss per metre.

(d) How far can the power be transmitted before it has dropped to 99% of its initial value?

2 The cost of the energy dissipated in the resistance of a cable depends on the radius of the cable and the current in the cable.

(a) Write down an expression for the power dissipated per metre in a cable in terms of the current I, resistivity ρ and radius r of the cable. (See spreads 2.2.5 and 2.2.7 in the AS book.)

(b) Figure 4 shows how the cost of the energy dissipated per year depends on r for a fixed I.

Describe the shape of this curve in as much detail as you can.

3 **(a)** Assume that the cost per year of the capital (interest charges on borrowed money, etc.) for building new power lines is proportional to the weight of the wire in the cables. Hence show that this cost is proportional to r^2. Copy Figure 4 and add to it a second curve to show how this cost depends on the radius of the cables.

(b) The point where the two curves intersect gives the radius of the cable for which the annual cost is a minimum. Explain why it is undesirable to build cables with wire that is **(i)** too thick or **(ii)** too thin.

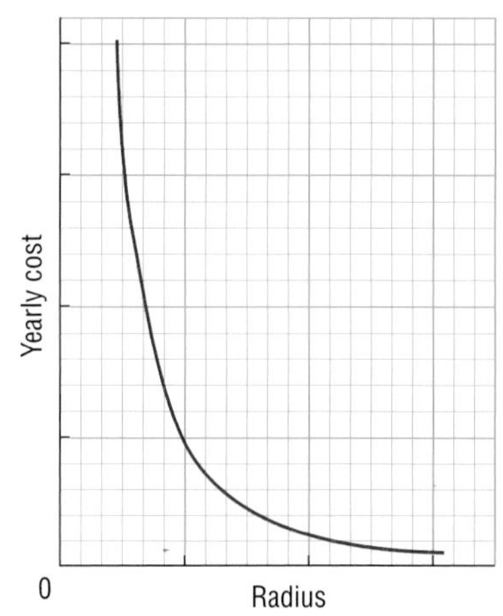

Figure 4

2.1 (13) The transformer – 2

By the end of this spread, you should be able to ...

- **Describe the function of a simple transformer.**
- **Select and use the turns-ratio equation for a transformer.**

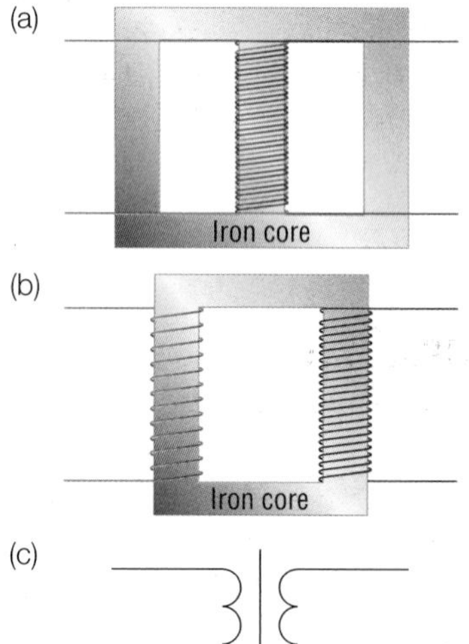

Figure 1 **(a)** The usual arrangement of the coils in a transformer; **(b)** another possible arrangement of the coils in a transformer; **(c)** the circuit symbol for a transformer

Transformer structure

The simplest transformer consists of two coils of insulated copper wire wound on top of one another on a core of easily magnetised iron. One of the coils is connected to the a.c. input and is called the **primary coil**. The second is connected to the output and is called the **secondary coil**. In order to get as strong a magnetic field as possible, the core is usually a complete loop of iron, as shown in Figure 1(a). Figure 1(b) is an arrangement sometimes used for small transformers where maximum efficiency is not so important, and Figure 1(c) shows the electrical symbol for a transformer.

The function of a transformer

When there is an alternating current in the primary coil, this causes the iron core to be magnetised and then remagnetised in the opposite direction 50 times per second. This rapid change in magnetic flux means an equally fast change in magnetic flux through the secondary coil. If there was just one turn in the secondary coil, the e.m.f. generated in that coil would, according to Faraday's law, be equal to the rate of change of flux through the coil. If there are, say, 100 turns in the secondary coil, then the e.m.f. generated will be 100 times larger, as each turn has the same change of flux through it, and because all the turns are in series.

In spread 2.1.10 Faraday's law of electromagnetic induction was stated for a coil as 'the induced e.m.f. is equal to the rate of change of flux linkage'. This is the principle being used here. The more rapidly the flux changes and the more coils on the secondary coil, the larger the induced e.m.f.

The effect of the number of turns in the primary coil also has to be considered, but the theory of this depends on the behaviour of a coil when supplied with an alternating e.m.f., and this is not part of the A2 course. This theory shows that the ratio of the output to input e.m.f. equals the **turns ratio**. This gives the following equation.

$$\frac{\text{number of turns on secondary}}{\text{number of turns on primary}} = \text{turns ratio} = \frac{\text{e.m.f. across secondary}}{\text{e.m.f. across primary}}$$

In symbols this is written as $\frac{N_s}{N_p} = r = \frac{E_s}{E_p}$

Examiner tip

Be careful with the symbols in the turns-ratio equation, as you could see V (voltage) replacing E (e.m.f.).

Transformers can be used to increase or to decrease the e.m.f. supplied to the primary coil. Those that increase the e.m.f. are called step-up transformers. Those that decrease the e.m.f. are called step-down transformers. These will have a turns ratio less than one.

The efficiency of a transformer

Needless to say, you can never get more power out of a transformer than you put into it. On the other hand, transformers are very efficient machines and can be nearly 100% efficient. The equation above assumes that the transformer is 100% efficient. Under perfect conditions the input power will equal the output power. This is possible only when the resistance of the coils is negligible. To minimise resistance the wires of the copper coils are often quite thick. This makes large transformers expensive, so a balance has to be struck between the economics of low cost and the physics of high efficiency. If you look at a transformer on a distribution pole you will often see tubes protruding from the sides, as shown in Figure 2. These contain oil in which a convection current is set up when the inside of the transformer gets hot. The oil is cooled by the air outside the transformer.

For a 100% efficient transformer:

power input = power output
so $E_pI_p = E_sI_s$

If this equation is combined with the previous equation, we get

$$r = \frac{N_s}{N_p} = \frac{E_s}{E_p} = \frac{I_p}{I_s}$$

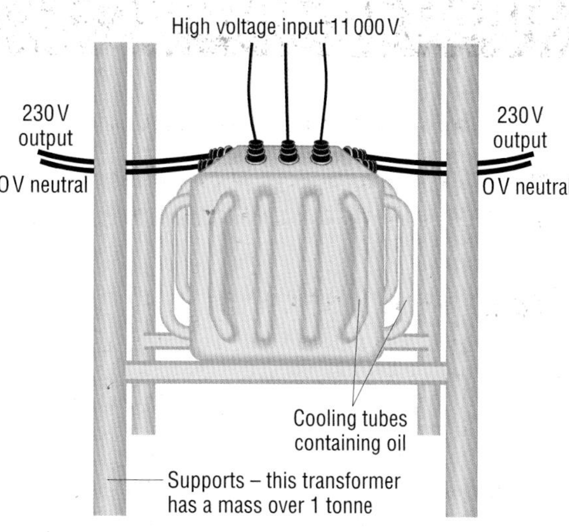

Figure 2 A local mains transformer with an input at 11 000 V and an output at 230 V. The high-voltage input terminals must be well insulated. The output wires need to be thicker than the input wires. The pipes outside the body of the transformer contain cooling oil

Worked example

A transformer similar to the one shown in Figure 2 has an input at 11 000 V and an output at 230 V. It supplies power of 150 kW to a locality and has an efficiency of 98%.

(a) Calculate **(i)** the turns ratio of the transformer
(ii) the output and the input currents
(iii) the total resistance of the locality's electrical circuits
(iv) the power wasted in heating the transformer.

(b) How will the values in (a) change at night when the power requirement is only 20 kW?

Answer

(a) (i) $r = \frac{N_s}{N_p} = \frac{E_s}{E_p} = \frac{230\text{ V}}{11\,000\text{ V}} = 0.021$

(ii) Output current = output power/E_s = 150 000 W/230 V = 652 A
Power out = power in × 0.98
so power in = power out/0.98 = 150 000 W/0.98 = 153 000 W

$$\text{input current} = \frac{\text{input power}}{\text{input e.m.f.}} = \frac{153\,000\text{ W}}{11\,000\text{ W}} = 13.9\text{ A}$$

(iii) Resistance of locality = V/I = 230V/652 A = 0.35 Ω
(iv) Power wasted = 153 kW – 150 kW = 3 kW

(b) Working through in exactly the same way for the reduced output gives the answers:
(i) unchanged at 0.021, **(ii)** output current = 87 A, input current = 1.9 A, **(iii)** resistance = 2.6 Ω, **(iv)** power wasted = 400 W.

The above worked example shows two key facts about transformers:

- The transformer can cope with varying output without any need for manual adjustment. It automatically adjusts to different demands for power.
- Several of the equations used in the example were, theoretically, for a 100% efficient transformer, yet they have been used for one that is only 98% efficient. This method of working will not give highly accurate answers, but as long as the transformer is working at a percentage approaching 100%, the answers obtained are accurate to 2 sig. figs. It would be sensible, in (a), to change 652 A to 650 A and 13.9 A to 14 A. On the other hand, the 153 000 W is reliable to 3 sig. figs because the 2% loss is 2% of 150 000 W, which is 3000 W.

Questions

1 A mobile phone charging unit contains a 230 V mains transformer. The output is a 6.0 V a.c. supply.
(a) What is the frequency of the output supply?
(b) The output coil on the transformer has 48 turns. How many turns are there on the primary coil?

2 A 12 V a.c. laboratory power supply contains a mains transformer. This has 400 turns on its primary coil.
(a) How many turns are there on the secondary coil?
(b) The primary circuit contains a 0.5 A fuse. Estimate the maximum current which can be drawn from the secondary coil. Why is this only an estimate and not an accurate calculation?

3 The primary and secondary coils of a transformer are wound on the same iron core. Each coil has a different cross-sectional area and number of turns.
(a) Which one of the following three quantities will be the same for each coil: magnetic flux, magnetic flux linkage or magnetic flux density?
(b) Explain the reason that the iron core is made from thin sheets of iron glued together. What would be the result of using a transformer having a solid iron core?

2.1 Electric and magnetic fields summary

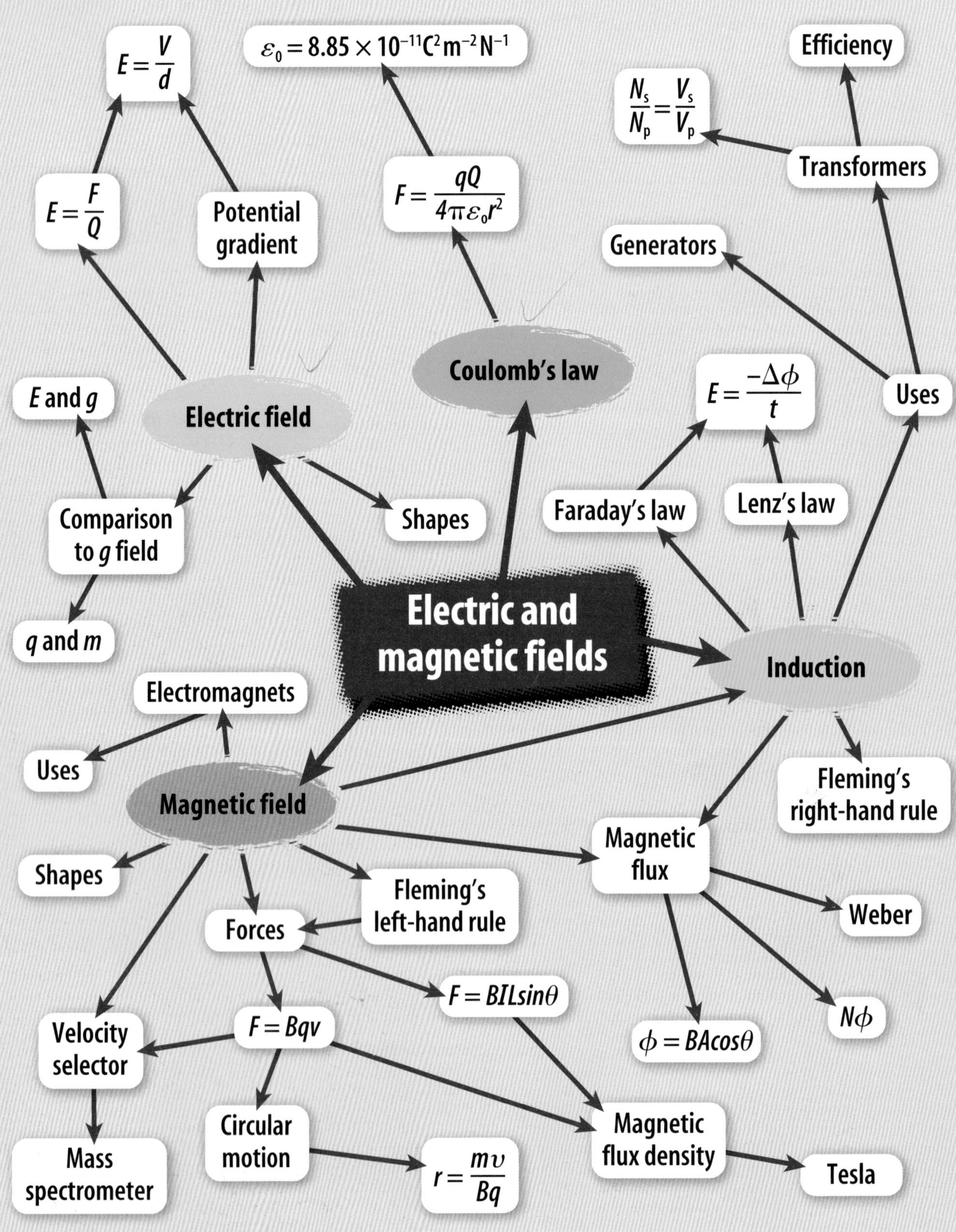

Practice questions

1 A device called a Hall probe is often used to measure magnetic flux density. The potential difference across a strip of semi-conducting material placed in the field is proportional to its flux density. This question explains the basic principles.
In Figure 1, part of a strip of conducting material (the Hall probe) lies in a region of uniform magnetic field perpendicular to the strip. Usually the field covers a region much larger than the strip.

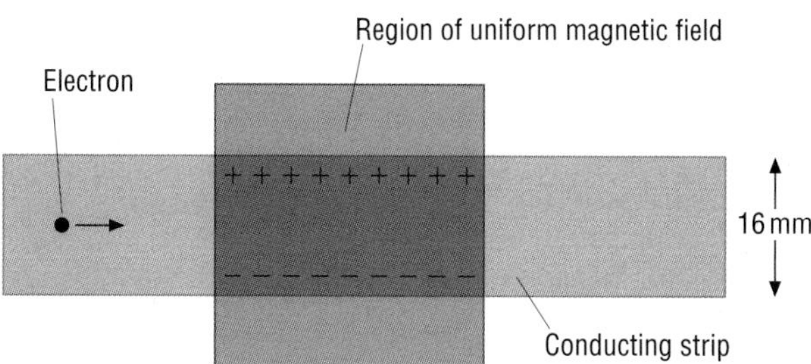

Figure 1

The strip is part of an electric circuit. Electrons pass through the strip from left to right at a steady speed *v*.

(a) The magnetic field of flux density 0.20 Wb m^{-2} is directed into the strip so that there is a magnetic force of 1.6×10^{-22} N on each electron that enters the field. Calculate the speed *v* of the electrons as they enter the field.

(b) Suggest why the magnetic force on the moving electrons results in opposite charges appearing at the edges of the conducting strip as shown in Figure 1.

(c) The charges shown in Figure 1 set up an electric field. State the direction of this electric field and calculate its strength given that there is a potential difference *V* across the strip of 16 μV. Hence show that when the electrons pass through the magnetic field region, the electric force cancels the magnetic force.

(d) Show that the p.d. *V* across the strip is related to the magnetic flux density *B* by the equation $V = vdB$ where *v* is the speed of the electrons and *d* is the width of the strip.

2 Figure 2 shows the initial path of an electron observed in a nuclear particle detector. The electron has been created along with another particle, not shown here, in the detector at point A. There is a uniform magnetic field perpendicular to the plane of Figure 2.

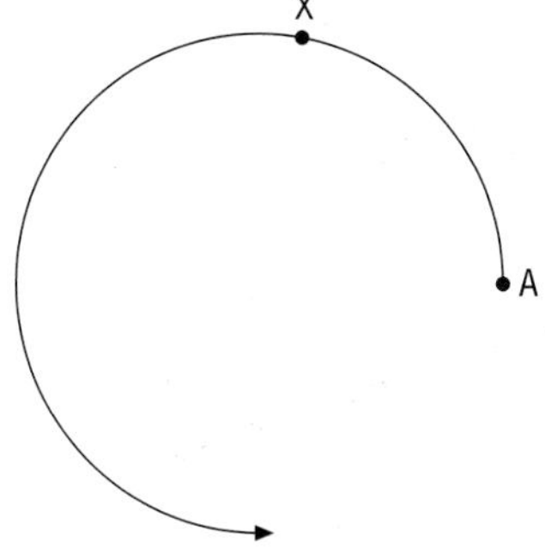

Figure 2

(a) Explain how you can tell that there is a magnetic field in the particle detector.

(b) (i) The speed of the electron at point **X** is 1.0×10^{8} m s^{-1}. The radius of curvature of the electron path is 0.040 m. Calculate the magnitude of the force in N on the electron.

(ii) State the direction of the force on the electron at **X**.

(c) Calculate the magnitude of the magnetic flux density *B* in the detector.

3 Electromagnetic brakes can help slow vehicles, such as large lorries and express trains, but will not bring them to a halt. There is also no actual contact between the moving parts, which makes the brakes safer and more reliable at high speeds.

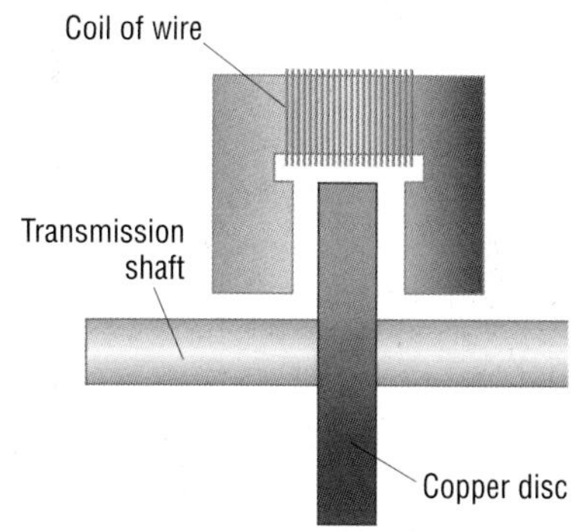

Figure 3

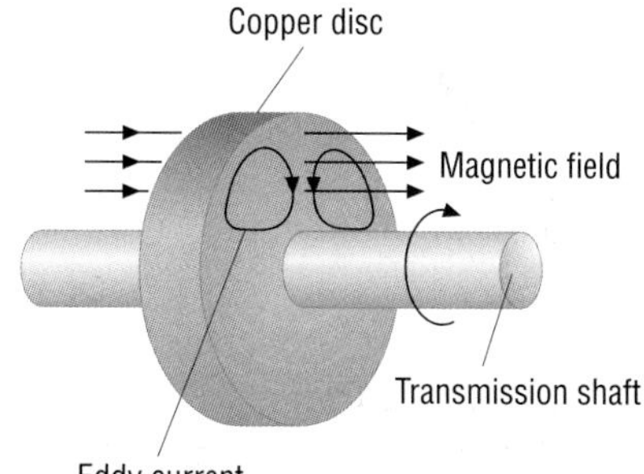

Figure 4

A copper disc is fastened to the transmission shaft of a vehicle. To slow the vehicle, a current is switched on in the coil, Figure 3, which creates a magnetic field that passes through part of the disc as shown in Figure 4.

(a) (i) Sketch Figure 3 and draw two magnetic flux loops produced by the current in the coil.

(ii) Suggest with a reason a suitable material for the core of the electromagnet.

(b) As the copper disc rotates, eddy currents apply a braking force to the shaft. Use Faraday's laws to explain why:

(i) eddy currents are induced in the copper disc

(ii) eddy currents cause a force on the disc that brakes its rotation

(iii) the braking force decreases as the speed of the disc decreases.

2.1 Examination questions – 1

1 Two very small identical conducting balls, each of mass 8.0×10^{-4} kg, are suspended from a single point by insulating threads of negligible mass as shown in Figure 1. Each sphere has been given the same charge of 3.0×10^{-8} C so that they repel each other and are in equilibrium with their centres a distance 6.0×10^{-2} m apart.

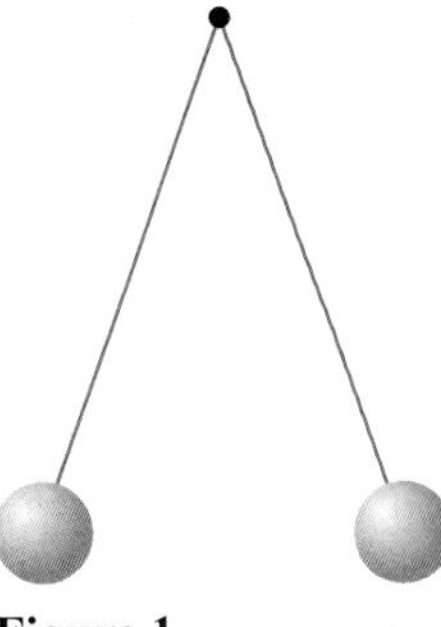

Figure 1

(a) (i) Copy Figure 1 and draw on it two arrows, each labelled F_e, to show the direction of the electrostatic force on each ball. [1]

(ii) Show that the value of F_e is about 2.3×10^{-3} N. [2]

(b) Each ball experiences three forces. On your copy of Figure 1, draw and label arrows to represent the other two forces acting on one ball. [1]

(c) Using the data above, calculate the angle between the threads. [4]

(d) The gravitational force F_g between the two balls is much smaller than the electrostatic force F_e between them. Calculate F_g/F_e. [4]

(OCR 2824 Jun02)

2 **(a)** Define *electric field strength at a point in space.* [2]

(b) Figure 2 shows two point charges of equal magnitude, 1.6×10^{-19} C, and opposite sign held a distance 8.0×10^{-10} m apart at points A and B. The charge at A is positive.

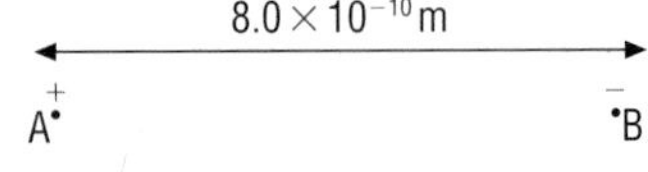

Figure 2

(i) Copy Figure 2 and draw on it electric field lines to represent the field in the region around the two charges. [3]

(ii) Calculate the magnitude of the electric field strength at the midpoint between the charges. [5]

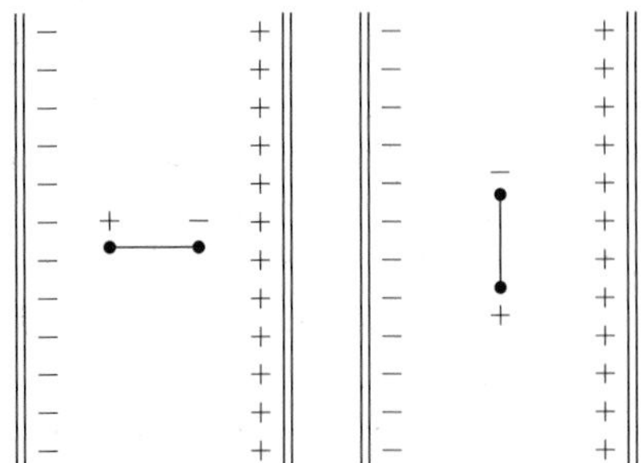

Figure 3 **Figure 4**

(c) Imagine two equal masses, connected by a light rigid link, carrying equal but opposite charges: a system called *a dipole*. Figure 3 and Figure 4 show the dipole placed in different orientations between two uniformly and oppositely charged plates.

Any effects of gravity are negligible. Describe the electric forces acting on the charges by drawing suitable arrows on the diagrams. Explain the motion, if any, of the dipole when it is released from rest **(i)** in Figure 3 and **(ii)** in Figure 4. [5]

(OCR 2824 Jan04)

3 This question is about changing the motion of electrons using electric fields. Figure 5 shows a horizontal beam of electrons moving in a vacuum. The electrons pass through a hole in the centre of a metal plate **A**. At **B** is a metal grid through which the electrons can pass. At **C** is a further metal sheet. The three vertical conductors are maintained at voltages of +600 V at **A**, 0 V at **B** and +1200 V at **C**. The distance from plate **A** to grid **B** is 40 mm.

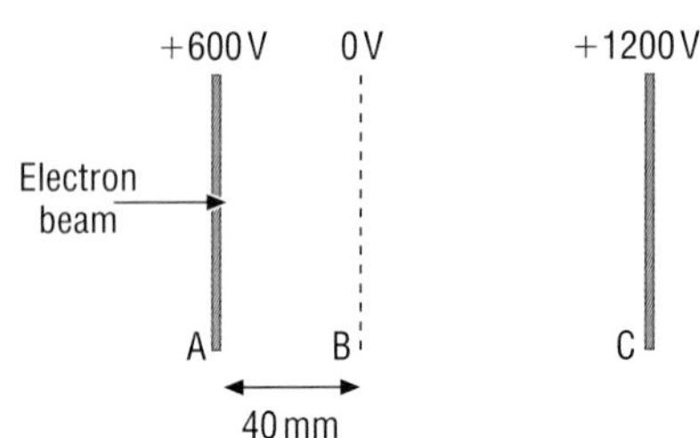

Figure 5

(a) Copy Figure 5 and draw on it electric field lines to represent the fields in the regions between the three conductors. [3]

(b) Show that the magnitude of the electric field strength between plate **A** and grid **B** is 1.5×10^4 V m^{-1}. [2]

(c) Calculate the horizontal force in N on an electron after passing through the hole in **A**. [2]

(d) Show that the minimum speed that an electron in the beam must have at the hole in **A** to reach the grid at **B** is about 1.5×10^7 m s^{-1}. [2]

(e) Calculate the speed in m s^{-1} of these electrons when they collide with sheet **C**. [1]

(f) Describe and explain the effect on the current detected at **C** when the voltage of the grid **B** is raised. [2]

(OCR 2824 Jan05)

4 This question is about electric forces.

A very small negatively charged conducting sphere is suspended by an insulating thread from support **S**. It is placed close to a vertical metal plate carrying a positive charge. The sphere is attracted towards the plate and hangs with the thread at an angle of 20° to the vertical as shown in Figure 6.

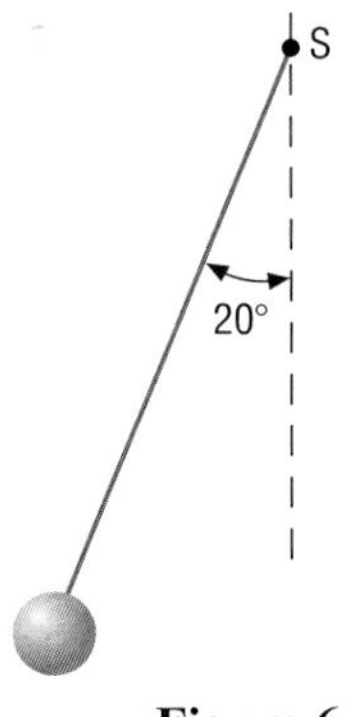

Figure 6

(a) Copy Figure 6 and draw at least five electric field lines on it to show the pattern of the field between the plate and the sphere. [3]

(b) The sphere, of weight 1.0×10^{-5} N, carries a charge of -1.2×10^{-9} C.

(i) Show that the magnitude of the attractive force between the sphere and the plate is about 3.6×10^{-6} N. [3]

(ii) Hence show that the value of the electric field strength at the sphere, treated as a point charge, is 3.0×10^{3} N C^{-1}. [2]

(c) The plate is removed. Figure 7 shows an identical sphere carrying a charge of $+1.2 \times 10^{-9}$ C, mounted on an insulating stand. It is placed so that the hanging sphere remains at 20° to the vertical. Treating the spheres as point charges, calculate the distance r in m between their centres. [3]

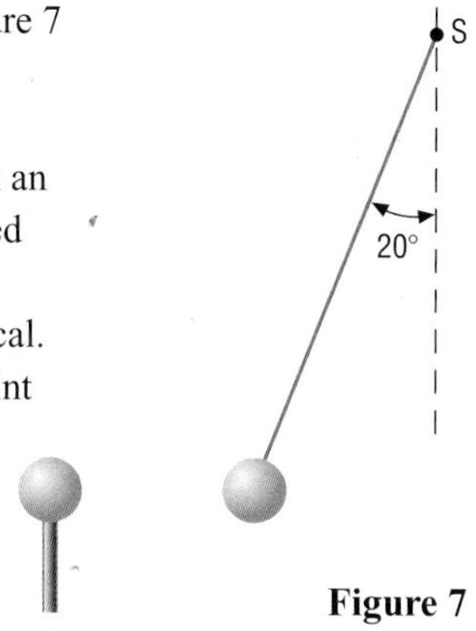

S
20°

Figure 7

(d) Copy Figure 7 and sketch on it the electric field pattern between the two charges. By comparing this sketch with your answer to **(a)**, suggest why the distance between the plate and the sphere in Figure 6 is half of the distance between the two spheres in Figure 7. [2]

(OCR 2824 Jan06)

5 A nitrogen atom is initially stationary at point **P** in Figure 8, midway between two large horizontal parallel plates in an evacuated chamber. The nitrogen atom becomes charged. There is an electric field between the plates. Ignore any effects of gravity.

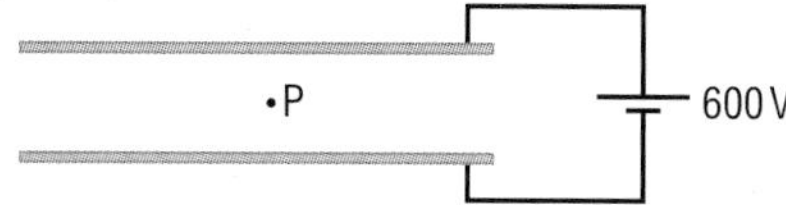

Figure 8

(a) The direction of the electric force on the nitrogen ion is vertically downwards. State with a reason the sign of the charge on the ion. [1]

(b) The voltage between the plates is 600 V. At the instant that the ion, charge 1.6×10^{-19} C and mass 2.3×10^{-26} kg, reaches the lower plate, show that:

(i) the kinetic energy of the ion is 4.8×10^{-17} J [2]

(ii) the speed of the ion is 6.5×10^{4} m s^{-1}. [2]

(c) The electric field strength between the plates is 4.0×10^{4} N C^{-1}. Calculate the separation in m of the plates. [2]

(d) The ion passes through a hole in the lower plate at a speed of 6.5×10^{4} m s^{-1}. It enters a region of uniform magnetic field of flux density 0.17 T perpendicularly into the plane of Figure 9.

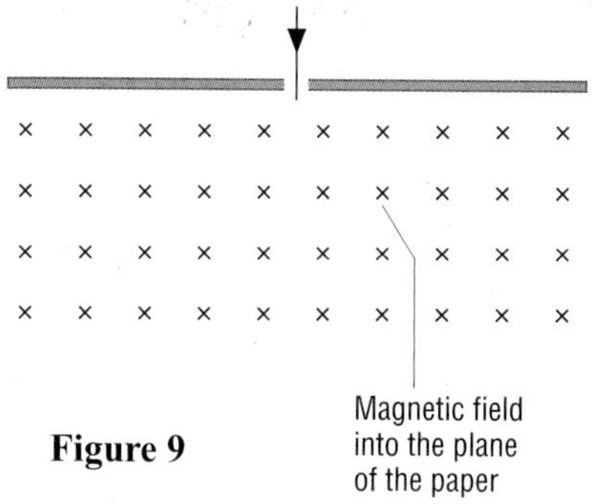

Magnetic field into the plane of the paper

Figure 9

(i) Copy Figure 9 and sketch on it the semicircular path taken by the ion. [1]

(ii) Calculate how far from the hole the ion will collide with the plate. Use data from **(b)**. [5]

(OCR 2824 Jun06)

6 This question is about the electron beam inside a television tube.

(a) Figure 10 shows a section through a simplified model of an electron gun in an evacuated TV tube.

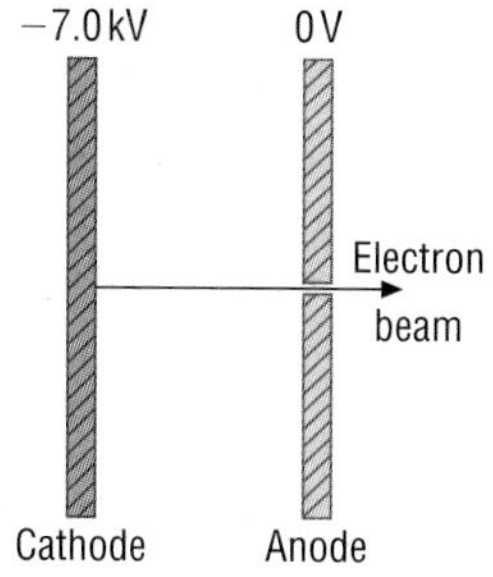

−7.0 kV
0 V
Electron beam
Cathode
Anode

Figure 10

(i) Copy Figure 10 and draw on it electric field lines to represent the field between the cathode and the anode. [2]

(ii) The electrons, emitted at negligible speed from the cathode, are accelerated through a p.d. of 7.0 kV. Show that the speed of the electrons at the anode is about 5.0×10^{7} m s^{-1}. [2]

Figure 11

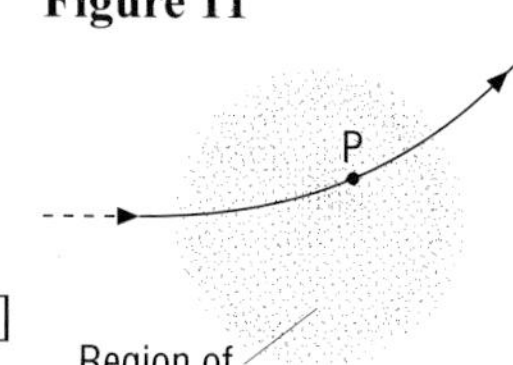

(b) Some electrons pass through a small hole in the anode. They enter a region of uniform magnetic field shown by the shaded area in Figure 11. They follow a circular arc in this region before continuing to the TV screen.

(i) State the direction of the force on the electrons at the point labelled **P**. [1]

(ii) State the direction of the magnetic field in the shaded area. Explain how you arrived at your answer. [2]

(iii) Calculate the radius in m of the arc of the path of the electron beam when the value of the magnetic flux density is 3.0×10^{-3} T. [4]

(c) The region of uniform magnetic field is created by the electric current in an arrangement of coils. Suggest how the end of the electron beam is swept up and down the TV screen. [2]

(OCR 2824 Jan07)

2.1 Examination questions – 2

1 Figure 1 shows a section of a mass spectrometer. A beam of identical positively charged ions, all travelling at the same speed, enters an evacuated chamber through a slit S.
A uniform magnetic field directed vertically out of the plane of the diagram causes the ions to move along the semicircular path SPT. The beam exits the chamber through the slit at T.

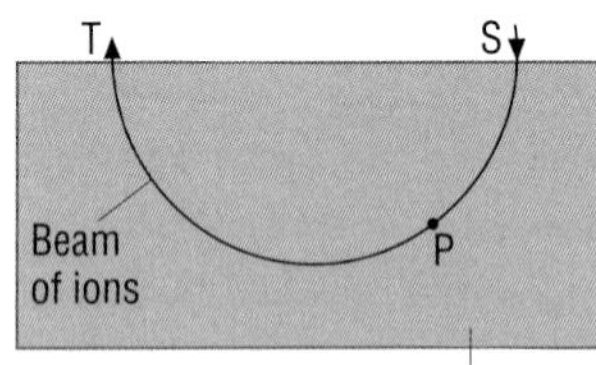

Figure 1

(a) **(i)** Copy Figure 1 and draw an arrow to indicate the direction of the force on the ion beam at P. [1]

(ii) State the rule you would use to verify that the ions are positively charged. [1]

(iii) Explain why the ions follow a circular path in the chamber. [2]

(b) Describe and explain the changes to the path of the ions for a beam of ions of greater mass but the same speed and charge. [3]

(c) The speed of the singly charged ions is 3.0×10^5 m s^{-1} in the magnetic field of flux density 0.60 T. The mass of each ion is 4.0×10^{-26} kg.

(i) Show that the force on each ion in the beam in the magnetic field is about 3×10^{-14} N. [2]

(ii) Calculate the radius in m of the semicircular path. [3]

(OCR 2824 Jan04)

2 Figure 2 shows a square flat coil of insulated wire placed in a region of uniform magnetic field of flux density B. The direction of the field is vertically out of the paper. The coil of side x has N turns.

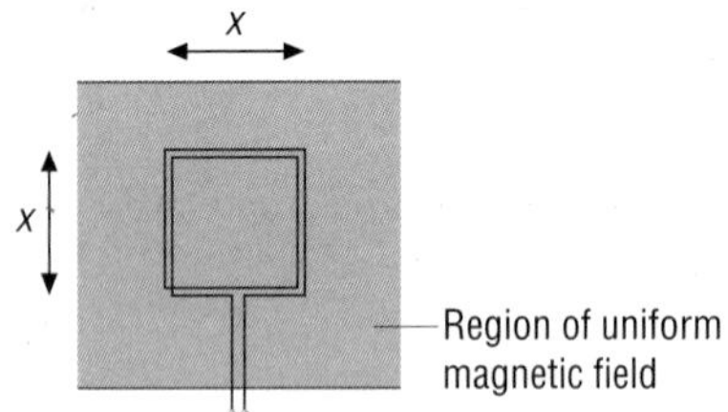

Figure 2

(a) **(i)** Define the term *magnetic flux*. [1]

(ii) Show that the magnetic flux linkage of the coil in Figure 2 is NBx^2. [2]

(b) The coil of side $x = 0.020$ m is placed at position **Y** in Figure 3. The ends of the 1250-turn coil are connected to a voltmeter. The coil moves steadily through the region of magnetic field of flux density 0.032 T at a speed of 0.10 m s^{-1} until it reaches position **Z**. The total motion takes 1.0 s.

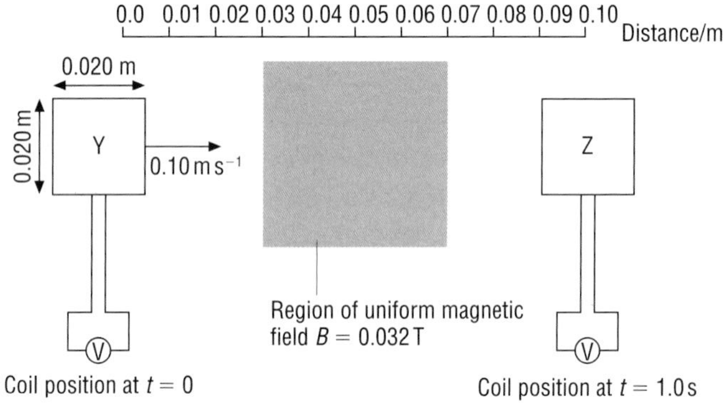

0.0 0.01 0.02 0.03 0.04 0.05 0.06 0.07 0.08 0.09 0.10 Distance/m

0.020 m

0.020 m

Y

0.10 m s^{-1}

Z

Region of uniform magnetic field B = 0.032 T

Coil position at t = 0

Coil position at t = 1.0 s

Figure 3

(i) Show that the voltmeter reading as the coil enters the field region, after t = 0.2 s, is 80 mV. Explain your reasoning fully. [3]

(ii) Draw a graph of the voltmeter reading against time t from 0 to 1.0 s for the motion of the coil from **Y** to **Z**. Label the y-axis with a suitable scale. [4]

(OCR 2824 Jun04)

3 This question is about forcing a liquid metal, such as molten sodium, through a tube.

(a) The liquid metal is in a tube of square cross-section, side w, made of electrically insulating material. See Figure 4. Two electrodes are mounted on opposite sides of the tube, and a magnetic field of flux density B fills the region between the electrodes. An electric current I passes across the tube between the electrodes, perpendicular to the magnetic field. The interaction between the current and the field provides the force to move the liquid.

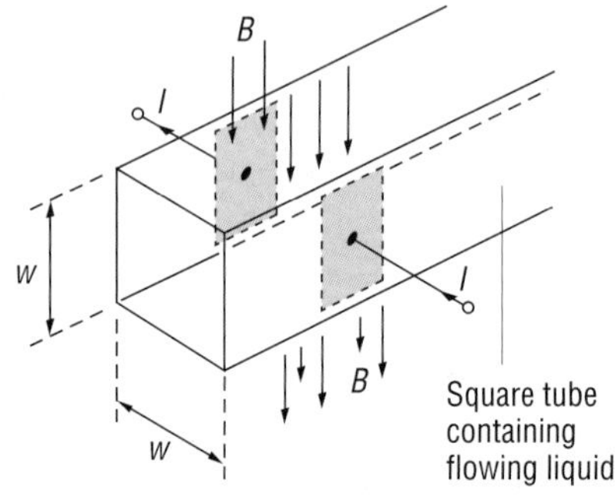

Figure 4

(i) State the direction of the force on the liquid metal. Explain how you determined the direction. [2]

(ii) State a relationship for the force F in terms of the current I, the magnetic field B and the width w of the tube. [1]

(iii) Data for this device is as follows: $B = 0.15$ T, $I = 800$ A and $w = 25$ mm.
Calculate the force in N on the metal in the tube. [2]

(b) To monitor the speed of flow of the liquid metal, a similar arrangement of electrodes and magnetic field is set up further down the tube (Figure 5). A voltmeter is connected across the electrodes instead of a power supply.

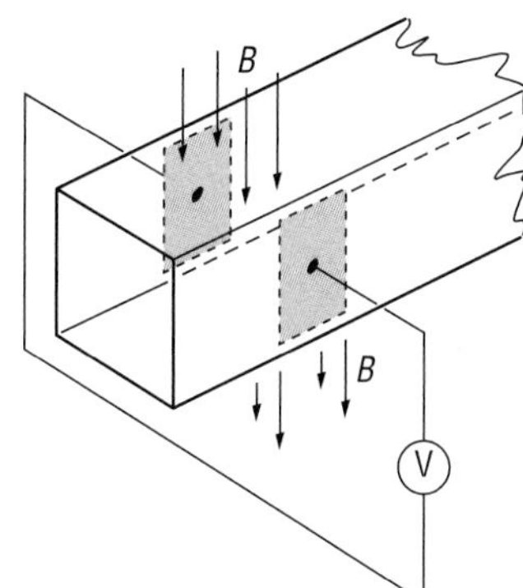

Figure 5

(i) Explain, using the law of electromagnetic induction, why the voltmeter will register a reading which is proportional to the speed of flow of the metal. [3]

(ii) State how and explain why the voltmeter reading changes when the magnetic flux density across the tube is doubled. [2]

(OCR 2824 Jan06)

4 This question is about using changing magnetic flux to control the current in an electric circuit.

(a) Figure 6 shows a fluorescent tube.

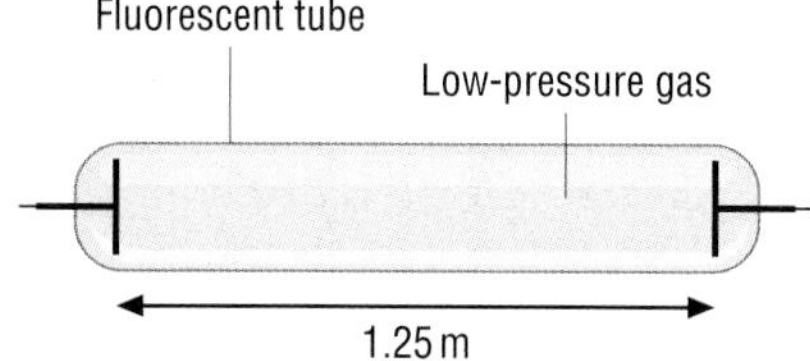

Figure 6

The tube contains a low-pressure gas. The gas is normally an electrical insulator. When an alternating potential difference is applied across the tube, the electric field between the electrodes helps to ionise the gas, making it into a conductor.

(i) The maximum potential difference across the electrodes is 325 V. The distance between the electrodes is 1.25 m. Calculate the maximum electric field strength in V m^{-1} between the electrodes. [2]

(ii) Suggest how the electric field helps to ionise the gas. [2]

(b) Figure 7 shows the fluorescent tube in series with a choke.

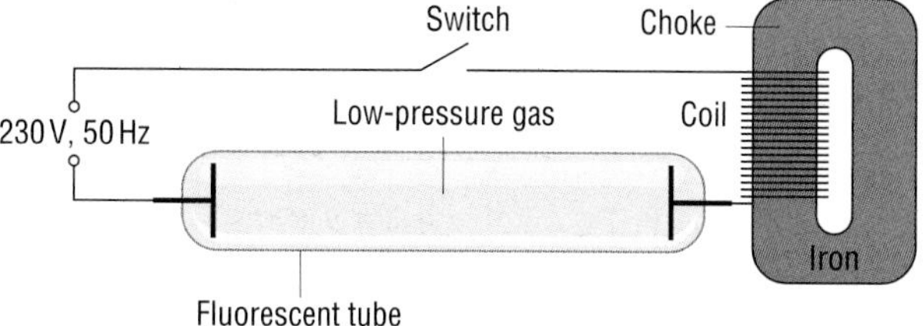

Figure 7

The choke is a low-resistance coil of wire wound on a loop of iron. This controls the current in the tube when it is conducting. The graph of Figure 8 shows how the flux linkage through the choke coil changes with time when the tube is conducting.

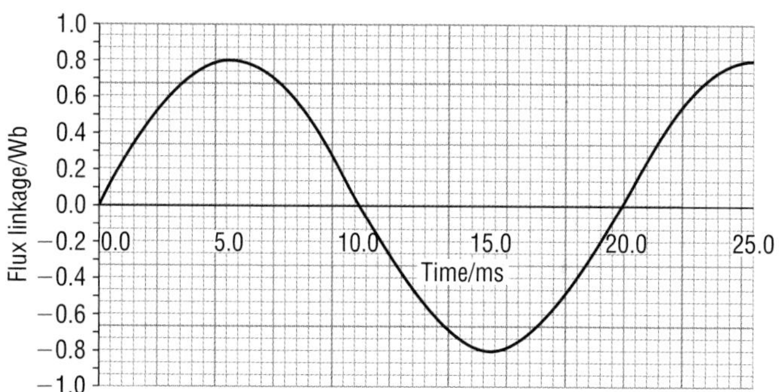

Figure 8

(i) By measuring a suitable gradient on the graph, find the peak voltage across the coil. [2]

(ii) Explain, with reference to the time scale on the graph, how the voltage across the coil varies with time. [1]

(c) Use ideas about electromagnetism to suggest how the choke in Figure 7 prevents the alternating current in the tube from becoming too large. [2]

(OCR 2864 Jun03)

UNIT 2 Module 2
Capacitors and exponential decay

Introduction

Mobile phones, cameras, toys, cars, laptops, toothbrushes and many other pieces of familiar electrical equipment seem to be designed to hide anything electrical. The only clue is a compartment for a battery somewhere. Many devices that would not have required any electrical supply 50 years ago now incorporate sophisticated electronic circuitry. The development of the microprocessor and its subsequent reduction in size means that many of these devices contain more electronic circuitry than mainframe computers once did.

The chip itself processes digital information supplied from a series of switches and sensors; the output from the chip is passed to other switches and controls. For example, in modern car engines sensors in each cylinder measure the pressure and temperature of the fuel/air mixture, other sensors record engine speed and road speed, and the quantity of fuel supplied and ignition are adjusted to give optimum fuel efficiency.

The microprocessor is a small piece of silicon bearing millions of semiconductor devices, resistors and capacitors, each one so small that it is visible only through a microscope. This module is about one of those components, the capacitor. A capacitor stores charge, and hence energy, in most cases for a very short time; you can see some – the small blue cylinders – in this photograph of a piece of circuit board.

In this module you will learn:

- how to calculate the charge and the energy stored in a capacitor
- how to arrange capacitors in a circuit to perform different functions
- how to calculate the time taken for a capacitor to discharge
- about exponential decay.

Test yourself

1 What is the SI unit of electrical charge?

2 A component has a resistance of 5.0 kΩ and the current in it is 300 μA. What is the p.d. across the component? (You will find μA used a great deal when dealing with capacitors, so you need to be sure you can handle prefixes accurately.)

3 Assume you start with £20 and each day you spend 10% of what you have at the start of the day. Sketch the shape of a graph to show how the amount of money you have changes with time. Why are you never broke?

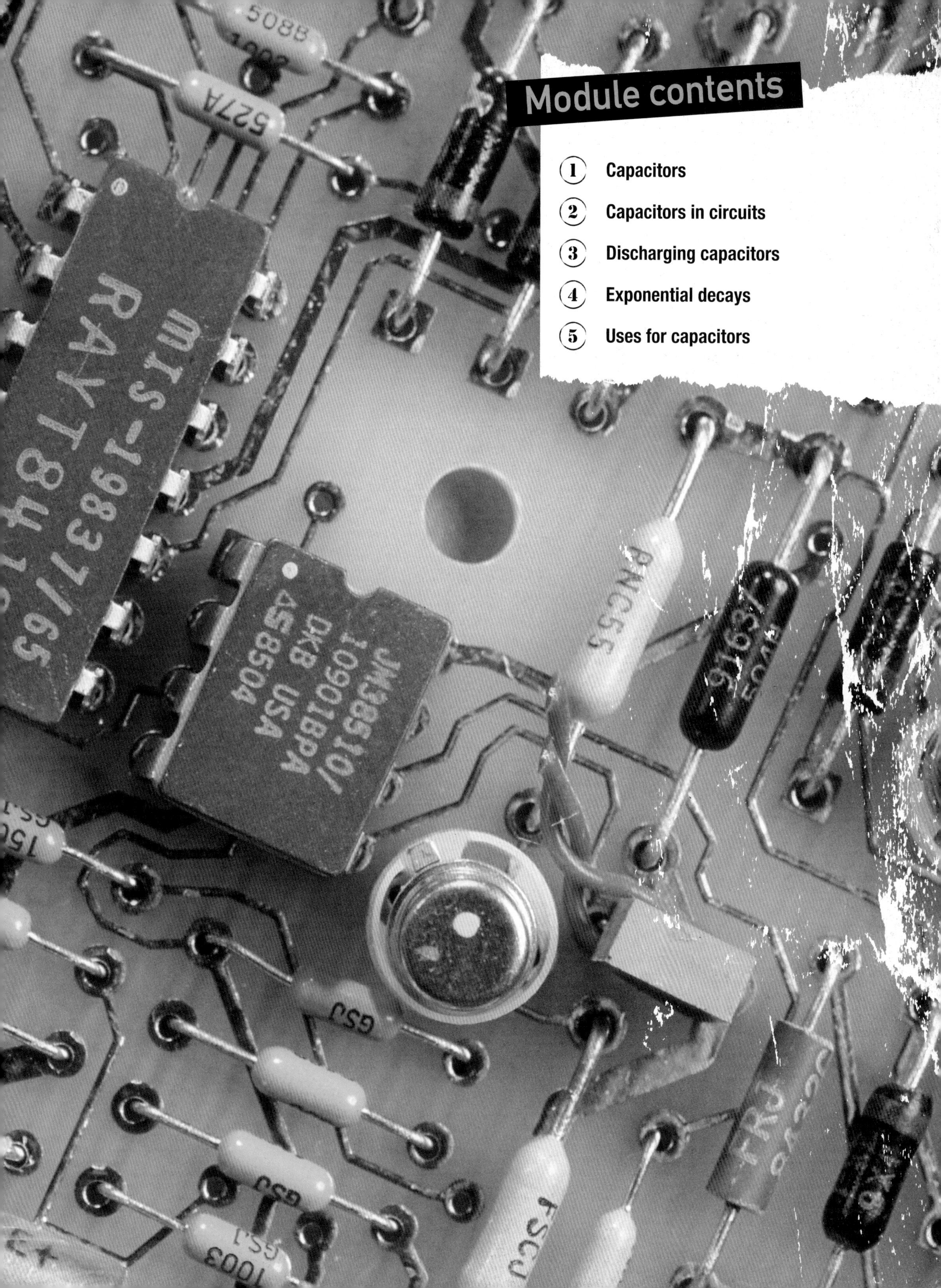

Module contents

2.2 (1) Capacitors

By the end of this spread, you should be able to ...

* **Define capacitance and the farad.**
* **Select and use the equation $Q = VC$.**
* **Explain that the area under a p.d. against charge graph is equal to the energy stored in a capacitor.**
* **Select and use the equations $W = ½QV$ and $W = ½CV^2$.**

Introduction

In your course so far, whenever a source of electrical power has been required, it has always been supplied by transferring chemical energy in a battery into electrical energy in the circuit or by doing some work on moving wires through magnetic fields and providing the electrical energy by electromagnetic induction. What has been lacking is a way of storing the electrical energy.

At some time, you have probably rubbed a balloon on a jumper and charged it up so that it will be attracted to a wall. Although the balloon stores electrical energy, it is in a small quantity and is difficult to retrieve. A capacitor is an electrical component that is easy to charge and from which the electrical energy it stores is easy to retrieve. But with capacitors, it is not possible to store a great deal of energy in a small volume. Luckily, there are many electrical circuits where it is necessary to store minute quantities of charge for a short time. For example, when a radio is tuned, a capacitor in the tuning circuit may store as little as a picojoule (10^{-12} J) of energy for 10 nanoseconds (10^{-8} s) before discharging and then repeating the process 10^8 times in the next second. Larger amounts of energy can be stored in capacitors in cameras, for example, in order to fire the built-in flash. These may store up to a joule of energy and charge and discharge a few times a second. Capacitors are generally used to store electrical energy for short times. They do not replace batteries.

Figure 1 Capacitors are available in a variety of shapes and sizes

The structure of a capacitor

Figure 1 shows a collection of capacitors. They come in all sorts of shapes and sizes; most have a fixed value, but some are variable. All have two terminals, and many can be connected into a circuit either way round, but some, called electrolytic capacitors, have to be connected positive to a positive terminal. This is because of the way they are constructed. If connected the wrong way round, they can be destroyed, so you need to look at the casing of the capacitor to see whether it is marked + and –.

Despite the variety of shapes and sizes, capacitors are basically two metal plates separated from one another by an insulator. In order to keep the overall size of a capacitor down to a suitable size as a circuit component, the plates are usually rolled up into a cylinder by using an additional insulating layer, as shown in Figure 2. This insulating layer is thin. If too high a potential difference is connected across it, there is a danger that it will cease to insulate, and a high current can occur. For this reason capacitors are marked with the maximum p.d. that can be placed across them.

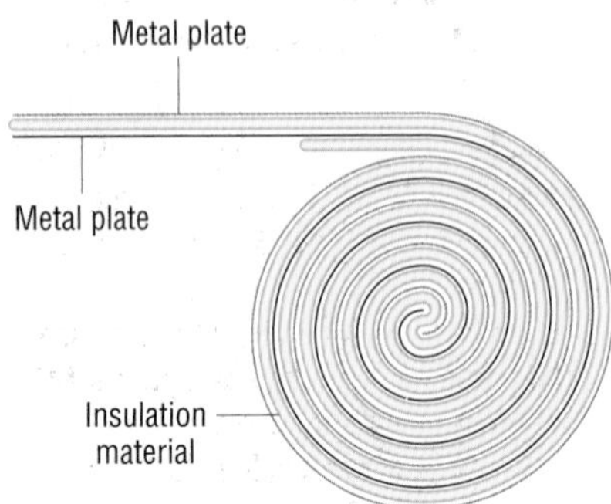

Figure 2 This diagram shows how the plates of a capacitor are rolled up on one another to make the component more compact for fitting into electrical circuits

Current never passes through a perfect capacitor. Electrons flow from the negative terminal of a battery to a capacitor and spread out on one of the plates. As the electrons arrive, they repel electrons on the opposite plate, and these electrons flow to the positive terminal of the battery. This all takes place simultaneously. The end result is that one of the plates has a negative charge, $-Q$, and the other plate an equal and opposite charge, $+Q$.

Capacitance

Capacitors are used for their charge-carrying ability. To quantify this ability the term **capacitance** is used. The capacitance C of a capacitor is defined as the charge stored per unit potential difference across it. Put into equation form this becomes

$$\text{capacitance} = \frac{\text{charge}}{\text{potential difference}} \text{ or in symbols } C = \frac{Q}{V}$$

Key definition

Capacitance is defined as the charge stored per unit potential difference. Its unit is the farad (F). One farad is one coulomb per volt.

The unit of capacitance is the farad (F). One farad is one coulomb per volt. A capacitor with a capacitance of 1 farad has a very large value. It would store 6 coulombs if a 6 volt battery were connected across it. You are much more likely to find electrolytic capacitors with a capacitance of, for example, 200 μF, or ceramic capacitors with values of 0.01 μF, 470 pF, etc.

A 2.2 μF capacitor connected to a 9.0 V battery will store a charge $Q = C \times V = 2.2 \times 10^{-6}\ \text{F} \times 9.0\ \text{V} = 19.8 \times 10^{-6}\ \text{C}$.

The energy stored in a charged capacitor

When a graph is drawn to show how the potential difference V across a capacitor varies with the charge Q stored on it, a straight line through the origin is obtained. Figure 3 shows that the capacitance of a particular capacitor does not depend on the p.d. across it; the capacitance is constant. The graph also enables the energy stored by the capacitor to be calculated. As the charge present on a capacitor increases, so extra work needs to be done to add additional charges. The area beneath the graph directly gives this work done and hence also gives the energy stored by the capacitor.

The work done W to charge a capacitor = the energy stored by the capacitor = area beneath the graph of V against $Q = \frac{1}{2}QV$.

Combining this equation with the equation $Q = CV$ gives two more expressions of W:

$$W = \frac{1}{2}QV = \frac{1}{2}CV^2 = \frac{Q^2}{2C}$$

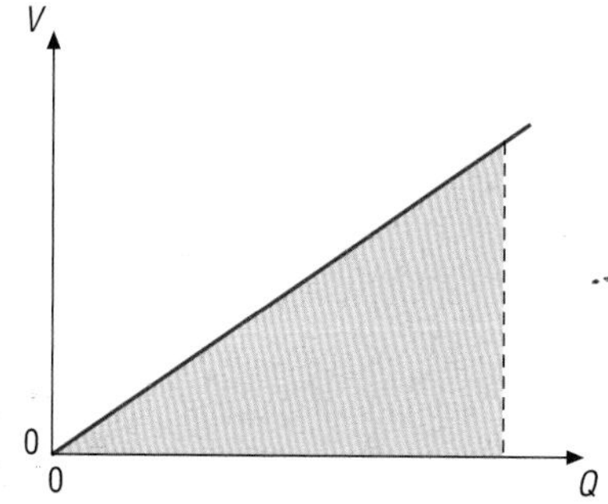

Figure 3 A graph showing how the charge stored by a capacitor varies with the p.d. across it. The area beneath the graph gives the electrical energy stored

Worked example

A 20 μF capacitor has a p.d. across it of 6.0 V. What charge and energy does it store? How would these values change if the p.d. was doubled to 12.0 V?

Answer

Charge $Q = CV = 20 \times 10^{-6}\ \text{F} \times 6.0\ \text{V} = 120\ \mu\text{C}$

Energy $= \frac{1}{2}QV = \frac{1}{2} \times 120 \times 10^{-6}\ \text{C} \times 6.0\ \text{V} = 360\ \mu\text{J}$

When the voltage is doubled, the charge is doubled to 240 μC.

The energy stored is multiplied by 4, since both the charge and the voltage are doubled, to 1.44 mJ.

Note that there are similarities between this situation and stretching a spring. Here, doubling the charge gives four times the energy stored; with a spring, stretching it to twice the extension also multiplies the energy stored by four times. In both cases the energy is the area beneath a straight line graph that passes through the origin.

Key definition

The energy W stored by a charged capacitor

$$= \frac{1}{2}QV = \frac{1}{2}CV^2 = \frac{Q^2}{2C}$$

Examiner tip

Many mistakes with powers of 10 are made for two reasons associated with calculators:

1. When calculating 10^6 say, 10 exp 6 is often inserted. This gives 10^7. You need to insert 1 exp 6 for the correct answer.
2. When calculating with a number such as 4.3×10^{-26}, the minus sign symbol (–) is often forgotten. You need to look critically at all calculator answers to make sure they are sensible. A number of molecules cannot possibly be 8×10^{-16} for instance.

Questions

1. Show that the unit of capacitance, the farad, F, is equivalent to (coulomb)²/joule, C^2J^{-1}.
2. A charge of 1.8×10^{-5} C is stored on a capacitor of capacitance 4.0×10^{-6} F. Calculate the p.d. across the capacitor.
3. A 200 mF capacitor is charged to a p.d. of 40 V.
   (a) Calculate the charge stored on the capacitor.
   (b) The capacitor is discharged in 100 μs through a thick wire. Calculate
   (i) the average current and
   (ii) the average power dissipated in the wire during the discharge.

2.2 ②

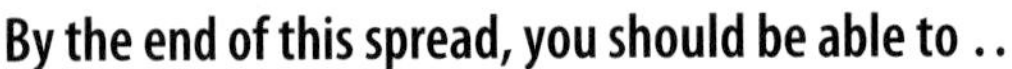

Capacitors in circuits

By the end of this spread, you should be able to ...

* **State and use the equation for the total capacitance of two or more capacitors in parallel.**
* **State and use the equation for the total capacitance of two or more capacitors in series.**
* **Solve circuit problems involving capacitors in series and in parallel circuits.**

Capacitors in parallel

In a circuit, capacitors can often be in parallel with one another. One such circuit is shown in Figure 1. Here three capacitors, C_1, C_2 and C_3, are connected in parallel with one another and have a battery connected to them to provide a potential difference V across each of them. The process of charging each capacitor will be just the same as if they were connected individually to the battery. This means that the charge Q_1 on C_1 will be C_1V, etc. This will give the total charge Q on all the capacitors as

$$Q = C_1V + C_2V + C_3V = (C_1 + C_1 + C_3)V$$

The total capacitance C of all the capacitors is the total charge/p.d. across them, so

$$C = \frac{Q}{V} = C_1 + C_2 + C_3$$

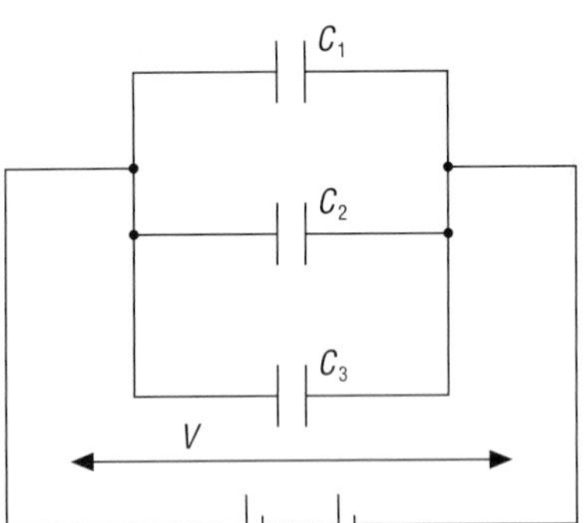

Figure 1 Three capacitors in parallel with the same potential difference V across each one

Note that it is when capacitors are in *parallel* that their individual capacitances can be added directly to find the total capacitance. This has to be so. For a given p.d., more charge is being stored, and so the capacitance must be greater. The above equation can be extended for any number of capacitors in parallel.

Capacitors in series

When three capacitors are in series with one another, the circuit will be as shown in Figure 2.

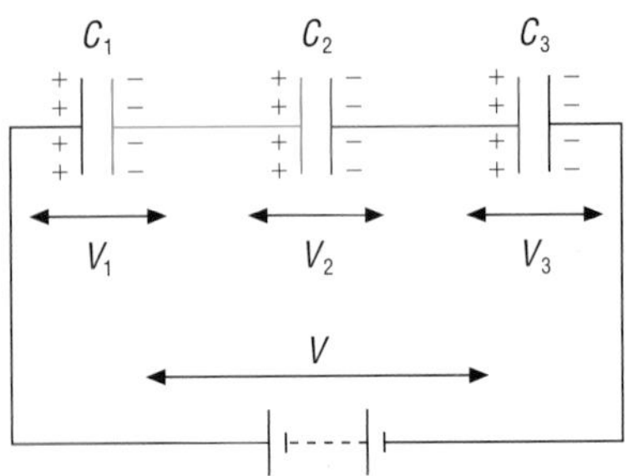

Figure 2 Three capacitors in series. Each has the same charge

The first point to note about the circuit is that the application of Kirchhoff's second law means that

$$V = V_1 + V_2 + V_3$$

To understand the second point, look at the two plates on adjacent capacitors and the wire between them coloured green. These plates and the wire are not actually connected to the battery. As they are uncharged before the battery is connected, they must be uncharged (in total) after connection. Any positive charge on one plate must mean an equal amount of negative charge on the other plate. The same is true for the two plates and connecting wire for the plates coloured red. This is why the charges have been marked on the plates. Every plate has the same magnitude charge on it in a series circuit. The charge Q, supplied from the battery, is equal to the charge on all three capacitors. This instinctively sounds wrong; it seems as though Kirchhoff's first law must be broken when, for instance, 4 mC leaves the battery to charge up three capacitors, each capacitor has 4 mC on it. But the total charge is 4 mC, *not* 12 mC. This now enables the total capacitance of the circuit to be found. Since

$$V = V_1 + V_2 + V_3$$

$\frac{Q}{C} = \frac{Q}{C_1} + \frac{Q}{C_2} + \frac{Q}{C_3}$ and since Q cancels out throughout, we get

$$\frac{1}{C} = \frac{1}{C_1} + \frac{1}{C_2} + \frac{1}{C_3}$$

As before, this expression can be extended for as many capacitors as there are in series.

Examiner tip

Be careful when using the series formula for capacitors. Firstly, make sure that it is the reciprocal formula for capacitors in series, and secondly, remember that, when you have done the reciprocal calculation, you have found the reciprocal of the total capacitance. Far too many candidates in exams get an answer such as 1/20 μF when the correct answer is 20 μF.

Key definition

For capacitors in **parallel**
$C = C_1 + C_2 + C_3 + \ldots\ldots$

For capacitors in **series**
$\frac{1}{C} = \frac{1}{C_1} + \frac{1}{C_2} + \frac{1}{C_3} + \ldots$

Worked example

A capacitor of capacitance 0.00100 μF has a 12.0 V battery connected across it as shown in Figure 3(a).

(a) Calculate the charge on the capacitor.

(b) A break develops in the circuit at A. The two ends of the wire at the break are near to one another, so they behave as a capacitor of capacitance 20 pF. The circuit effectively becomes the circuit in Figure 3(b). When this broken circuit is switched on, with both capacitors initially uncharged, what will be:

(i) the total circuit capacitance?

(ii) the charge on each capacitor?

(iii) the p.d. across each capacitor?

Answer

(a) $Q = CV = 0.00100\ \mu F \times 12\ V = 0.012\ \mu C$ (Note how the μ symbol can be carried through the equation.)

(b) (i) $\frac{1}{C} = \frac{1}{0.00100} + \frac{1}{0.000020} = 1000 + 50000 = 51000$

$$C = \frac{1}{51000} = 1.96 \times 10^{-5}\ \mu F$$

(ii) The charge Q on each capacitor and the total charge are the same, so

$$Q = CV = 12\ V \times 1.96 \times 10^{-5}\ \mu F = 2.35 \times 10^{-4}\ \mu C$$

(iii) The p.d. across the 0.00100 μF capacitor is $Q/C = 2.35 \times 10^{-4}\ \mu C/0.00100\ \mu F = 0.24\ V$. The p.d. across the 0.000020 μF capacitor is $Q/C = 2.35 \times 10^{-4}\ \mu C/0.000020\ \mu F = 11.76\ V$

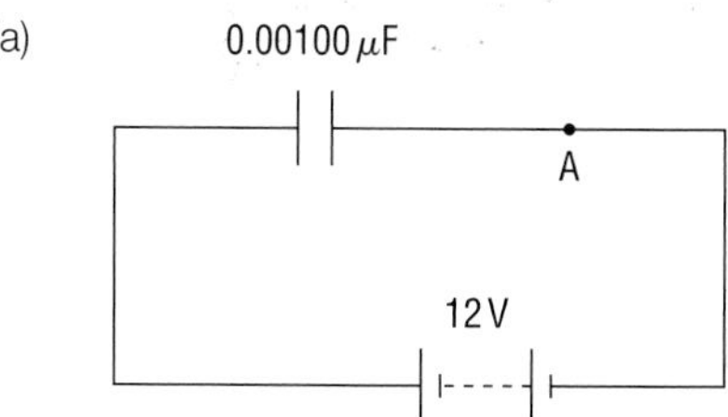

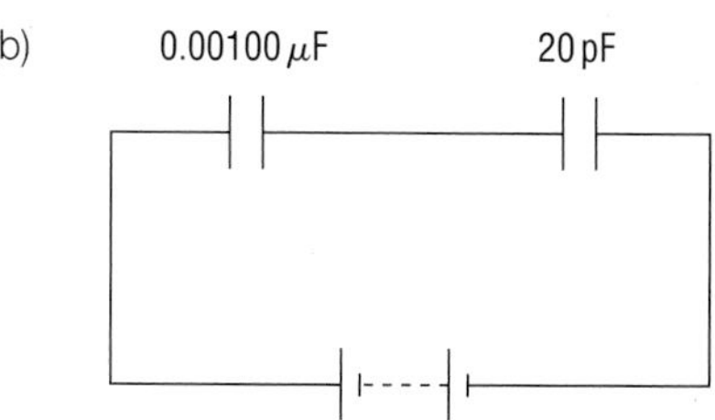

Figure 3 **(a)** A single capacitor in a circuit; **(b)** the modified circuit after a fault develops

The worked example shows again how careful you will need to be with powers of 10. When dealing with numbers less than one, far more mistakes can be made than with numbers greater than one.

Note that in the worked example the large p.d. appears across the small capacitor. An electrician may try to find a fault in a circuit by connecting a voltmeter across various components. The components across which there is zero p.d. are probably working well. If there is a high p.d. across a resistor, then that resistor is probably the one in which there is a break. For the same reason there will normally be a high p.d. across a switch that is off; when it is switched on, the p.d. across it will be zero.

Questions

1 Figure 4 shows three capacitors connected to a d.c. supply.

(a) Calculate **(i)** the total capacitance of the system, **(ii)** the charge on and **(iii)** the p.d. across each capacitor.

(b) One of the 3.0 μF capacitors is replaced by one of an unknown value. The total capacitance of the system is 4.0 μF. Calculate the value of the unknown capacitor.

(c) For the capacitor system of part **(b)**, calculate **(i)** the charge on and **(ii)** the p.d. across each capacitor.

2 A 1000 μF capacitor is charged from a 15.0 V d.c. supply through a two-way switch. The switch is thrown to connect it to an uncharged 500 μF capacitor as shown in Figure 5.

(a) Calculate **(i)** the initial and **(ii)** the final charge on the 1000 μF capacitor.

(b) Calculate the change in p.d. across the 500 μF capacitor after the switch is thrown.

(c) Calculate **(i)** the initial energy stored in the 1000 μF capacitor and **(ii)** the final energy stored in both capacitors.

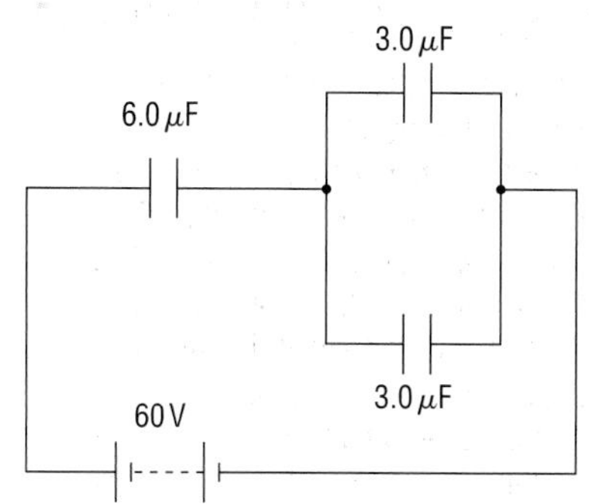

Figure 4

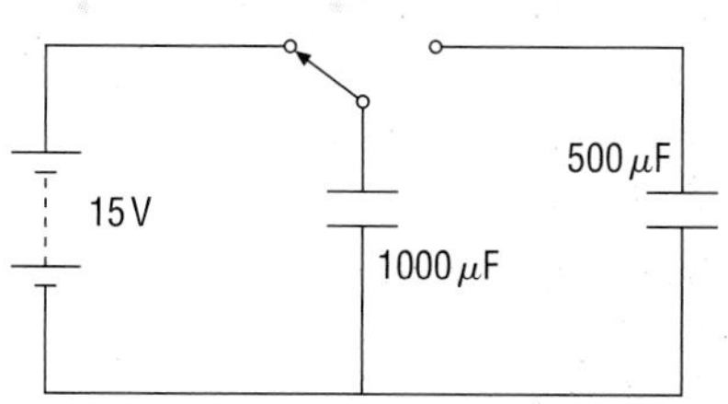

Figure 5

2.2  Discharging capacitors

By the end of this spread, you should be able to ...

*** Sketch graphs showing the discharge of a capacitor through a resistor.**

Introduction

This spread concentrates on one particular aspect of graphical work and introduces you to a very common graphical pattern that you may not have met before. Graphs that are straight lines and square law patterns are familiar in lots of situations, but a decay graph is unlike any of these. For example, if you plot a graph of the temperature of a cup of tea against time as it cools, you get a decay graph. You also get one when you plot the decay of a radioactive substance, or when a capacitor discharges through a resistor. This particular type of graph is called an exponential decay graph.

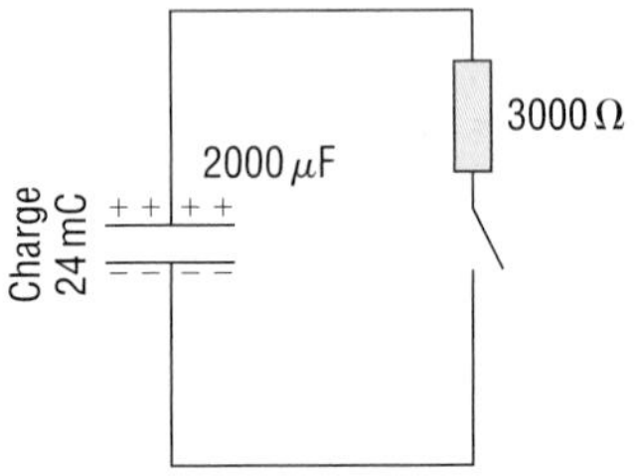

Figure 1 A 2000 μF capacitor, charged and ready to discharge when the switch is closed at time $t = 0$

An exercise to plot an exponential decay graph

Consider the circuit in Figure 1. It shows a capacitor of capacitance 2000 μF having a charge of 24 mC, connected in series with a 3000 Ω resistor. A switch in the circuit is open, and at the instant it is closed, time $t = 0$, the capacitor will start to discharge through the resistor.

Time/s	Q/mC	V_C/V = Q/C	V_R/V = $-V_C$	I/mA = V_R/R	Δt/s	ΔQ/mC = I Δt
0	24	12.0	−12.0	−4.0	1.0	−4.0
1	20	10.0	−10.0	−3.3	1.0	−3.3
2	16.7	8.4	−8.4	−2.8	1.0	−2.8
3	13.9	7.0	−7.0	−2.3	1.0	−2.3
4	11.6	5.8	−5.8	−1.9	1.0	−1.9
5	9.7				1.0	
6					1.0	
7					1.0	
8					1.0	
9					1.0	
10					1.0	
11					1.0	
12					1.0	
13					1.0	
14					1.0	
15					1.0	
16	1.30	0.65	−0.65	−0.22	1.0	−0.22
17	1.08	0.54	−0.54	−0.18	1.0	−0.18
18	0.90	0.45	−0.45	−0.15	1.0	−0.15
19	0.75	0.38	−0.38	−0.13	1.0	−0.13
20	0.62	0.31	−0.31	−0.10	1.0	−0.10
21	0.52	0.26	−0.26	−0.09	1.0	−0.09
22	0.43	0.22	−0.22	−0.07	1.0	−0.07
23	0.36	0.18	−0.18	−0.06	1.0	−0.06
24	0.30	0.15	−0.15	−0.05	1.0	−0.05

The table shows what happens during the next 24 seconds. You should make a copy of the table and complete it by working along each line and filling in the spaces between 5 seconds and 16 seconds. Do not worry about significant figures, just keep two or three. The sequence is as follows.

- The charge Q on the capacitor at the start of each time interval is known.
- The p.d. across the capacitor V_C can then be found.
- Since only the capacitor and the resistor are in the circuit, the p.d. across the resistor V_R must have the same magnitude as that across the capacitor but in the opposite direction, hence the minus sign.
- This enables the current I in the circuit at that time to be calculated. The minus sign indicates discharging.
- Then assume that for the next short time Δt, taken as one second, the current stays constant. In this time the current results in charge ΔQ flowing from the capacitor.
- This value is taken off the charge Q to start the next line.

STRETCH and CHALLENGE

Electrical energy per unit charge is being supplied by the capacitor, that is, it has an e.m.f. Because this energy per unit charge is being used by the resistor to produce thermal energy, it has a potential difference across it. An equation for this could be $E_C + V_R = 0$.

Question

Explain why the values for V_R are numerically equal to the values for V_C but are all negative.

Figure 2 shows how Q, the charge on the capacitor, varies with time. Copy and complete it with your data from the table on the previous page. Q is decreasing all the time but at a slower and slower rate. However far the time scale is extended, the quantity of charge on the capacitor never reaches zero. A graph showing how V_C, the p.d. across the capacitor, varies with time will have exactly the same shape as the charge/time graph because V_C is directly proportional to Q. It will start at 12 V when $t = 0$.

Figure 3 shows how I, the current in the circuit, varies with time. It is shown as having a negative value to indicate discharge.

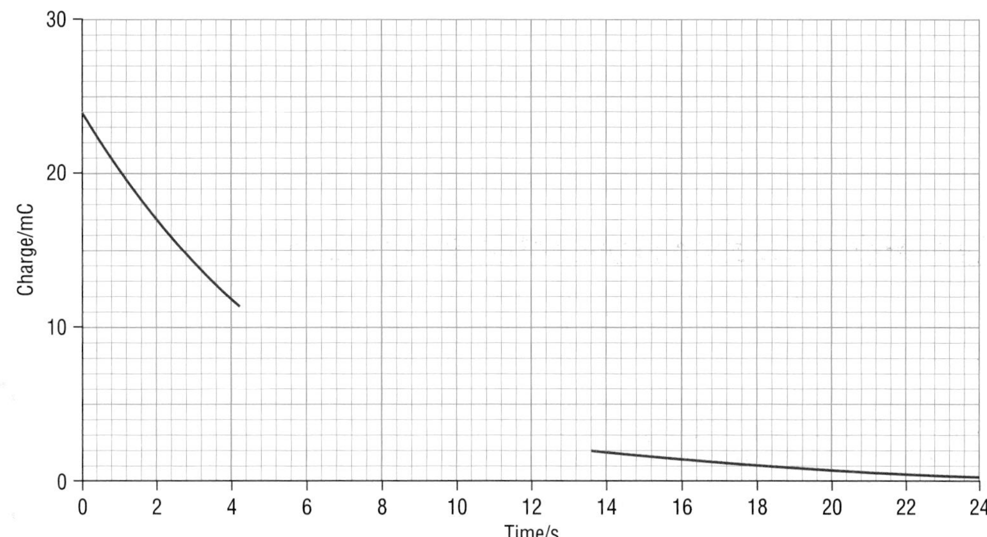

Figure 2 The variation of charge with time

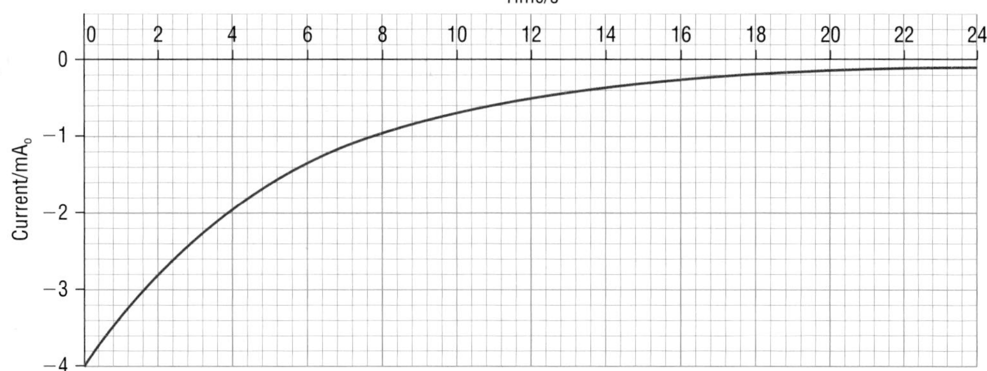

Figure 3 The variation of current with time

Question

1 A capacitor discharges through a resistor. Figure 4 shows the variation in current in the resistor against time for part of the discharge. The graph is an exponential decay curve. For this to be true the ratio of the values of the current will be the same at equal intervals of time.

(a) Estimate the values of the current $I_{0.5}$, $I_{1.0}$ and $I_{1.5}$ at $t = 0.5$, 1.0 and 1.5 ms.

(b) Calculate the values of $I_{0.5}/I_{1.0}$ and $I_{1.0}/I_{1.5}$. These should be approximately equal.

(c) Repeat **(a)** and **(b)** to find the ratios at $t = 1.5$ to 2.0 ms, etc. up to 3.0 ms.

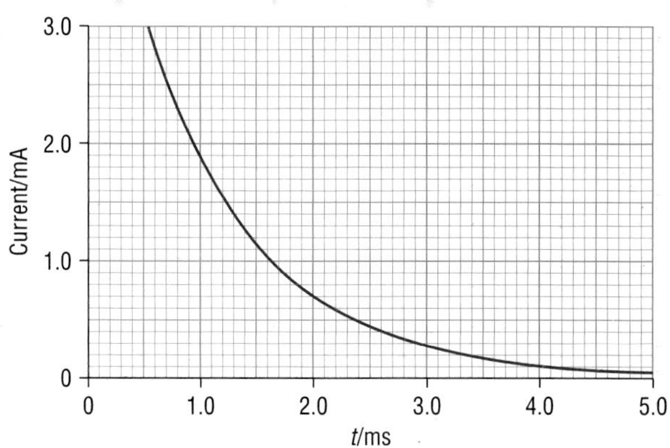

Figure 4

Exponential decays

By the end of this spread, you should be able to …

- **Explain the constant-ratio property of an exponential decay.**
- **Define the time constant of a circuit.**
- **Analyse the discharge of capacitor using equations of the form $x = x_0 e^{-t/CR}$.**
- **Select and use *time constant* = *CR*.**

Exponential decays

The exercise on the previous page showing how a capacitor discharges has involved making a few approximations, but it illustrates what is happening to current, charge and p.d. during discharge. If a better approximation is required, then the time interval of one second could be shortened – but this would need even more calculations. The graphs obtained are quite accurate but slightly exaggerate the rate of decay because of the assumed constant current during each interval of one second.

Certain characteristics of exponential graphs can be seen using these two graphs.

- Any given time interval results in the same ratio of final current/starting current.
  For example, on the current graph use a time interval of 4 seconds
  0 s → 4 s; current drops to 1.96 mA from 4.0 mA; a ratio of 0.49
  4 s → 8 s; current drops to 0.95 mA from 1.96 mA; a ratio of 0.48
  8 s → 12 s; current drops to 0.45 mA from 0.95 mA; a ratio of 0.47
  12 s → 16 s; current drops to 0.22 mA from 0.45 mA; a ratio of 0.49.
- The time taken to reach half value is always the same.
  For example, to fall from 4.0 mA to 2 mA takes 3.8 s
  To fall from 3 mA to 1.5 mA takes from 1.6 s to 5.4 s, which is also 3.8 s
  To fall from 1.6 mA to 0.8 mA takes from 4.9 s to 8.8 s, which is 3.9 s.

Time constant

When a capacitance is multiplied by a resistance, the units are rather surprising. The unit of capacitance is the farad, which is the coulomb per volt, and the unit of resistance is the volt per ampere.

$$\text{So unit of capacitance} \times \text{resistance} = \frac{\text{coulomb}}{\text{volt}} \times \frac{\text{volt}}{\text{ampere}} = \frac{\text{coulomb}}{\text{ampere}}$$

$$= \frac{\text{ampere second}}{\text{ampere}} = \text{second}$$

In other words, for a circuit containing a capacitor of capacitance *C* and a resistor of resistance *R*, the value of *C* × *R* can be given in seconds. In the previous spread the value of *CR* was given by

$2000\ \mu\text{F} \times 3000\ \Omega = 6\,000\,000\ \mu\text{s} = 6.00$ seconds

The term *CR* is used a great deal in capacitor circuits and is called the **time constant** of the circuit.

Key definition

The **time constant** of a circuit containing a capacitor of capacitance *C* and a resistor of resistance *R* is given by *time constant* = *CR*.

The exponential symbol 'e'

The symbol **e** is used in equations of exponential decay. e is just a number; it has no units. In that respect, and because it is a number with no end of decimal places, it is similar to π. The numerical value of e can be obtained using your calculator. You need to be able to do this. On any scientific calculator you will find the symbol e^x, which you can usually activate using the shift key. To find e itself you want the *x* to be 1, that is, e^1. The value you will obtain after pressing 'shift' 'e^x' '1' 'EXE' is 2.718 281 828. The mathematical reason for using this number is that the gradient of the graph $y = e^x$ is e^x. So, when $x = 1$, $y = 2.718\ldots$ and the gradient is also 2.718…. If you now repeat this with $x = 3$, $y = 20.09\ldots$ and the gradient is also 20.09….

Exponential decay equations

The need for using **e** becomes apparent when you are told that the equation for the charge on a capacitor as it discharges through a resistor is

$$Q = Q_0\, e^{-\frac{t}{CR}}$$

where Q is the charge at time t, Q_0 is the charge at the start, C is the capacitance of the capacitor and R is the resistance of the resistor. The corresponding equation for the current in the circuit is

$$I = -I_0\, e^{-\frac{t}{CR}}$$

where I is the current at time t and I_0 the current at the start. The minus sign indicates discharge. Note how these equations can be used in the following worked example.

Worked example

A 22.2 μF capacitor is connected to a 9.00 V battery and fully charged. The battery is then removed and the capacitor is discharged through a 90.1 kΩ resistor, starting at time $t = 0$.

Calculate

(a) the time constant for the discharge circuit,
(b) **(i)** the charge on the capacitor when $t = 0$
(ii) the current when $t = 0$
(c) **(i)** the charge on the capacitor when $t = 1.50$ s
(ii) the current when $t = 1.50$ s
(d) **(i)** the charge on the capacitor at a time equal to the time constant.

Answer

(a) $CR = 22.2 \times 10^{-6} \times 90.1 \times 10^3 = 2.00$ s
(These figures were arranged to make the time constant equal to 2.00 s.)

(b) **(i)** $Q_0 = CV = 22.2 \times 10^{-6} \times 9.00 = 200\ \mu C$
$I_0 = -V_C/R = -9.00/90.1 \times 10^3 = -99.9\ \mu A$
(the minus sign indicates discharge).

(c) **(i)** $Q = Q_0\, e^{-\frac{t}{CR}} = 200 \times 10^{-6}\, e^{-\frac{1.5}{2.0}} = 200 \times 10^{-6}\, e^{-0.75}$
$= 200 \times 10^{-6} \times 0.472 = 94.5\ \mu C$

(ii) $I = I_0\, e^{-\frac{t}{CR}} = -99.9 \times 10^{-6}\, e^{-\frac{1.5}{2.0}} = 99.9 \times 10^{-6}\, e^{-0.75}$
$= 99.9 \times 10^{-6} \times 0.472 = 47.2\ \mu A$

(d) $Q = Q_0\, e^{-\frac{CR}{CR}} = 200 \times 10^{-6}\, e^{-\frac{2.0}{2.0}} = 200 \times 10^{-6}\, e^{-1.0}$
$= 200 \times 10^{-6} \times 0.368 = 73.6\ \mu C$

The charge remaining on any capacitor after one time constant is always 36.8% of the charge at time $t = 0$.

Question

1 A 200 μF capacitor is charged to 26 V and then discharged through a 40 kΩ resistor.

(a) Calculate the initial current in the resistor.
(b) **(i)** After 5.5 s the p.d. has fallen to 13 V. Find the p.d. after another 5.5 s.
(ii) Calculate the current in the resistor at 11 s.
(c) Calculate **(i)** the p.d. and **(ii)** the current in the resistor after 8.0 s.
(d) Show that the values in (c) are related to the values in (b) by a factor close to 0.69, which is ln 2.
(e) How long does it take for the p.d. to fall to 1.0 V?

5 Uses for capacitors

By the end of this spread, you should be able to …

* **Describe the uses of capacitors for the storage of energy.**

Introduction

This spread will give you some idea of the large range of uses for capacitors. You should be able to quote a few specific uses.

One factor about capacitor behaviour that has not been mentioned in this module so far is that the ability of a capacitor to store charge depends on the distance between the plates. In most capacitors this separation is fixed, but if the plates can move towards or away from one another, the charge-storing ability changes. In fact, the closer the plates are to one another, the larger the capacitance. This is because the force of attraction between the positive and negative charges increases. (Capacitance has nothing to do with the volume of a capacitor.) This also explains why some capacitors that have the largest capacitance can have only a small p.d. across their plates. A high p.d. would break down the very thin insulator between the plates.

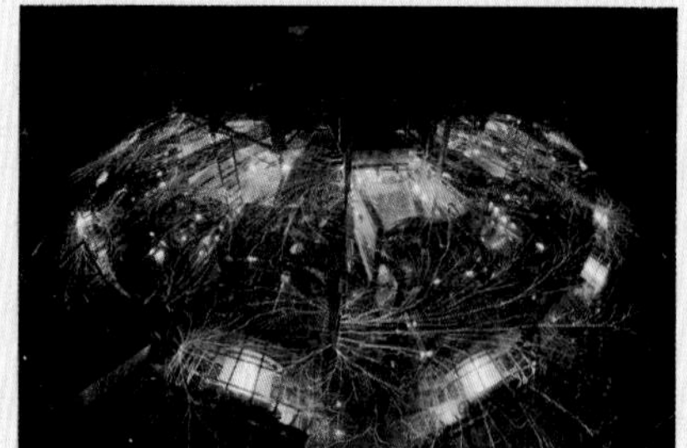

Figure 1 The Z machine (Sandia National Laboratories)

The charge and energy storage ability of a capacitor

In the introduction to capacitors in spread 2.2.1, the way a battery in a camera can charge up a capacitor in a flash unit was mentioned. Typically, with 9 V across it, a 5000 μF capacitor can store 0.2 J for a flash that probably lasts for only a few microseconds.

Capacitors can supply back-up power to prevent data loss in a computer when power cuts out briefly.

The same arrangement, on a huge scale, can be used to cause the fusion of nuclei in a nuclear reactor. (See spread 2.3.15 for details about fusion.) The Z machine in New Mexico (Figure 1) has a very large number of high-voltage capacitors that are charged slowly and then discharged in only a few billionths of a second. The power output has a peak value of around 300 terawatts (300 million million watts). Electrical energy may be generated from fusion in the future, but at present, far more energy is required to create the discharge than is gained from the fusion reaction.

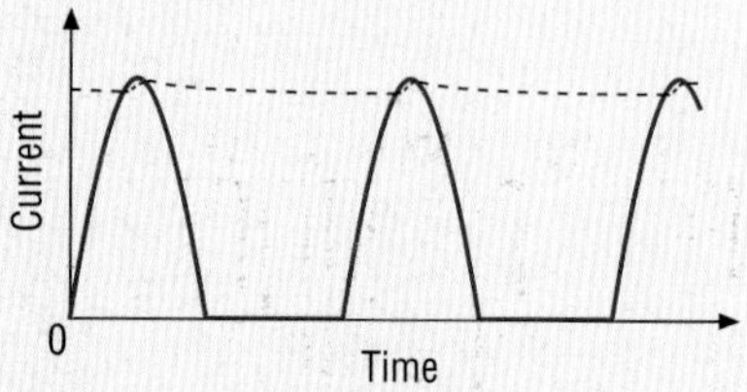

Current
0
Time

Figure 2 A rectified alternating current (a.c.)

Rectifier allowing current in one direction only

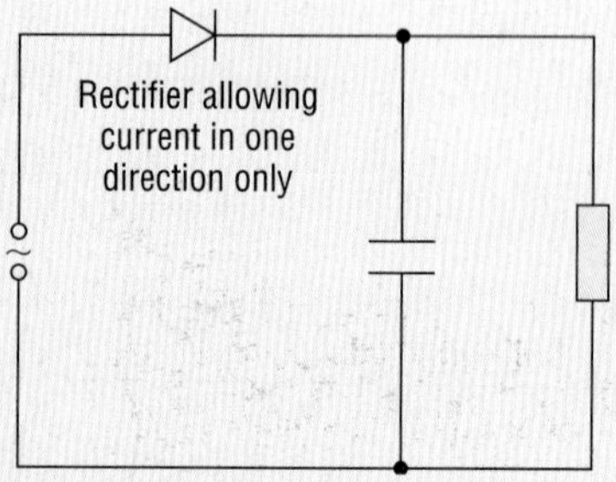

Figure 3 A smoothing circuit

Capacitors in a.c. circuits

Smoothing circuits

When a direct current (d.c.) is required from a mains a.c. circuit, a device called a rectifier is required, which will allow current through a load resistor in one direction only. A rectifier will supply a current that varies with time (Figure 2). In order to obtain a smooth d.c., a capacitor can be placed across the load resistor (Figure 3). During a cycle, the capacitor charges up when current is supplied and discharges through the load resistor when no current is supplied. The current with the capacitor in place is shown by the dotted line in Figure 2.

V
Graph of input voltage
Time
V
Graph of output voltage
Time

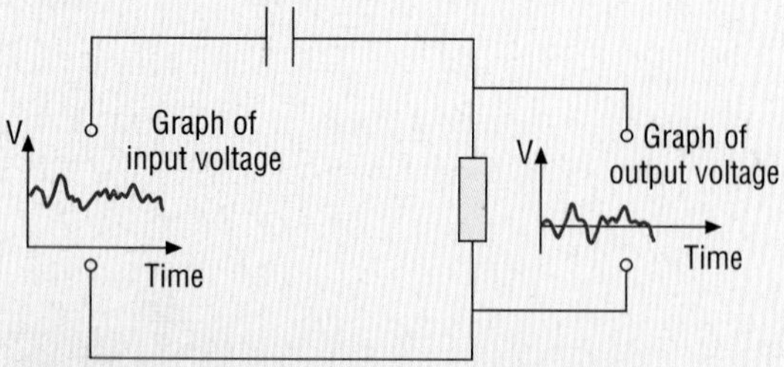

Figure 4 A direct current (d.c.) blocking circuit

Filter circuits

These are very important uses for capacitors. The effective resistance of a capacitor (called its reactance) varies with the frequency of the a.c. supply. This makes it possible to design circuits in which high-frequency signals travel in one direction in a circuit and low frequencies travel in another. For example, unwanted noise can be diverted from entering a loudspeaker. Another example of a filter circuit is shown in Figure 4. Here a supply is giving a fluctuating output. It is a combination of a.c. and d.c. The capacitor can charge up and discharge with the variations in output, but the d.c. component results in a fixed charge on the capacitor. The effect is to allow the a.c. through the capacitor but to block the d.c. Capacitors are frequently used to block d.c.

Tuning circuits

Combining a capacitor with a coil makes electrical resonance possible. The circuit is shown in Figure 5(a) in which an aerial is connected to a coil and a variable capacitor in series. In old radios the variable capacitor was like the one shown in Figure 5(b) and was right behind the tuning knob. The output across the capacitor varies with capacitance as shown in Figure 5(c). A signal of a particular frequency will give a large output. Notice that the shape of this graph is similar to that of one for mechanical resonance. This is electrical resonance, and as with mechanical resonance, the amplitude of the output can be much larger than the amplitude of the input.

Figure 5 (a) A tuning circuit containing a coil and a capacitor; **(b)** a variable tuning capacitor; **(c)** the variation of output with capacitance

Other uses

- *Capacitor microphones*: One plate of a capacitor in the microphone is free to vibrate. Its capacitance varies as sound waves cause it to vibrate. With a fixed p.d. across it, the charge on the capacitor must vary. The variations in the current to the microphone can be detected and amplified. A similar system is sometimes used for computer keyboards. When you depress a key you are not operating a switch but changing the capacitance of a capacitor.
- *Displacement sensors*: Moving your hand near a charged plate can alter the capacitance in a circuit and hence cause a small current. This can be used to sense the presence of a person.
- *Preventing sparking*: A capacitor across a switch will limit the damage caused by sparking and limit the amount of radio frequency interference a spark causes. It does this by allowing high-frequency a.c. to charge and discharge itself.
- *As a counter in digital electronics (an integrator)*: If a digital signal, such as that shown in Figure 6, is used to charge up a capacitor, it will charge in steps and effectively count the number of pulses. It integrates. Other capacitor circuits can be used to differentiate.

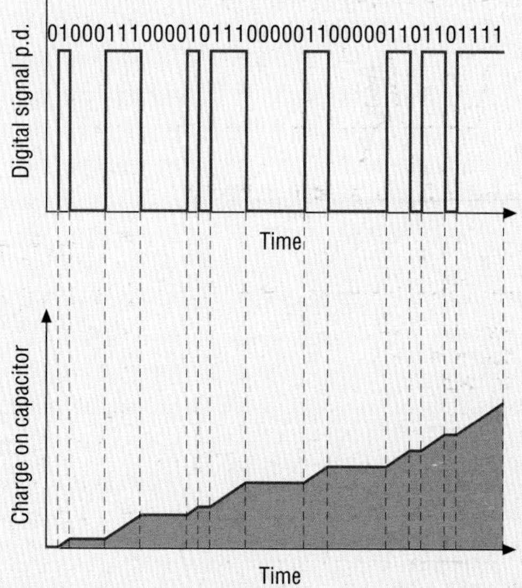

Figure 6 A digital signal

Question

1 Describe how capacitors are used in
 (a) loudspeakers;
 (b) microphones;
 (c) some radios.

2.2 Further questions C

Capacitors and exponential decay

1 The discharge of a capacitor can be used to measure reaction times. The capacitor in Figure 1 begins to discharge when switch A is moved from P to Q. The discharge is stopped when switch B is opened. As soon as the voltmeter reading is observed to fall, the student under test opens switch B. The student's reaction time can now be calculated.

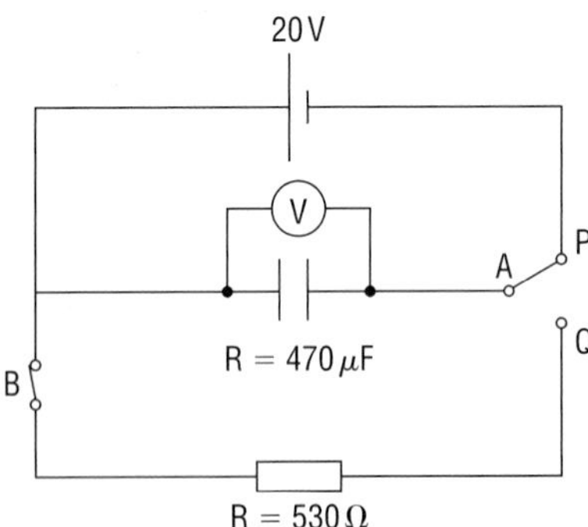

Figure 1

(a) Show that the time constant *RC* of the circuit is 0.25 s.

(b) Every 0.25 s the p.d. across the capacitor falls to approximately 0.37, that is 1/e, of its previous value. Show that the p.d. across the capacitor at t = 0.25 s after switch A is moved to Q is 7.4 V.

(c) Calculate the p.d. at t = 0.5, 0.75 and 1.0 s. Plot a graph to show how the p.d. across the capacitor varies with time to 1.0 s.

(d) The student under test stopped the discharge when the p.d. had fallen to 12 V. Use **(i)** your graph and **(ii)** the equation $V = V_0e^{-t/CR}$ to find the reaction time of the student.

(e) How could you modify the circuit to measure times of a few milliseconds?

2 Figure 2 shows how the charge on a capacitor varies with the p.d. across it.

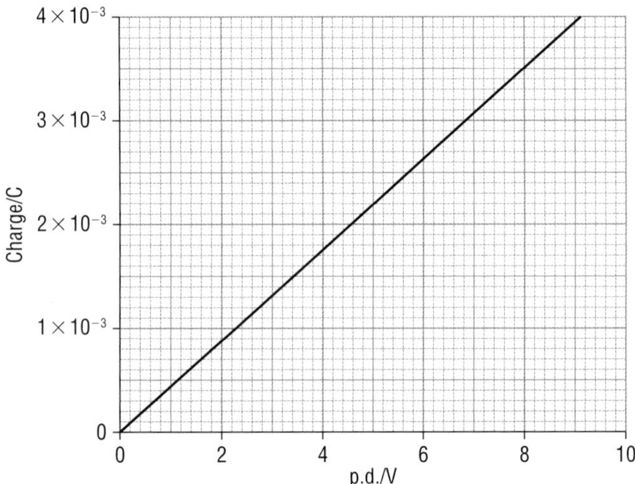

Figure 2

Use the graph to find **(a)** the energy stored in the capacitor when charged to a p.d. of 8.0 V and **(b)** the capacitance of the capacitor.

3 Figure 3(a) shows two capacitors connected in series, and Figure 3(b) shows them connected in parallel to the same d.c. supply.

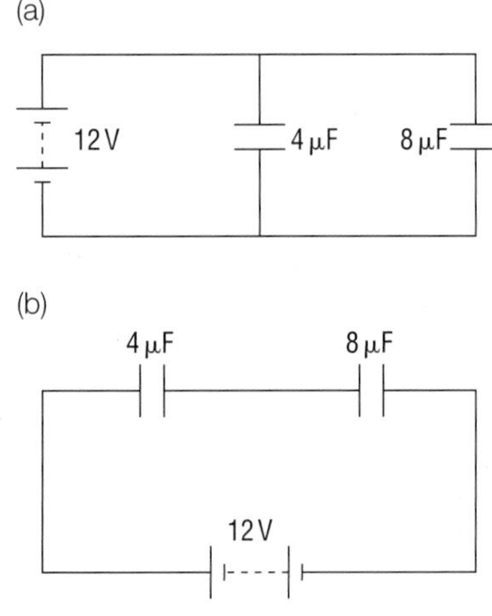

Figure 3

Calculate the values of the charge on and p.d. across each capacitor in each circuit.

4 You are given three capacitors each of the same value, 6.0 μF. By arranging some or all of them in as many ways as possible, you can obtain seven different values of capacitance. What are they? Draw the capacitor arrangement for each value.

5 One simple model of the atmosphere assumes that air behaves as an ideal gas at a constant temperature. Using this model the pressure p of the atmosphere at a temperature of 20 °C varies with height h above the Earth's surface as shown in Figure 4.

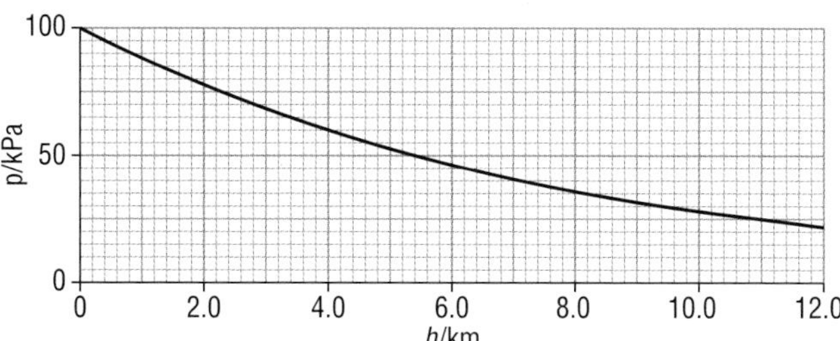

Figure 4

Use pressure values from the graph at equal increments of height to show that the variation of pressure with height follows an exponential relationship.

6 Figure 5 shows a circuit diagram of a capacitor discharging through a resistor.

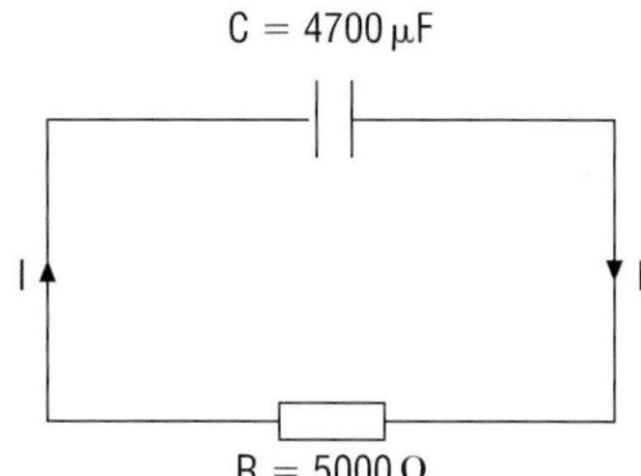

Figure 5

The mathematical model of the discharge of the capacitor is shown in Figure 6. It is the same as that in spread 2.2.3 and assumes that the current I is constant over each small time interval Δt. This process is repeated as shown.

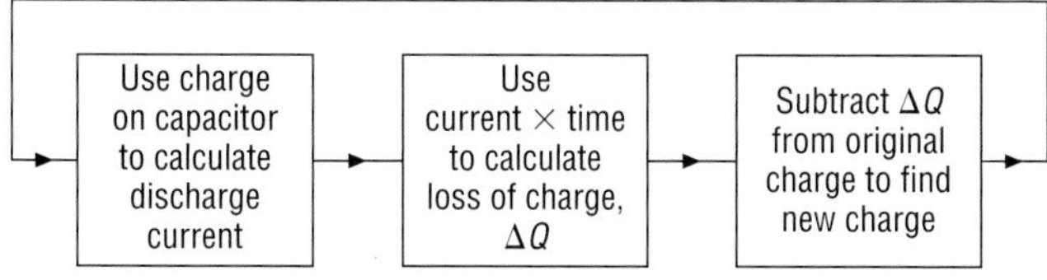

Figure 6

Complete the table for the discharge of the 4700 μF capacitor. The small time interval used is $\Delta t = 2.0$ s.

Q	$I = V/R = Q/RC$	$\Delta Q = I\Delta t$	$Q_{new} = Q - \Delta Q$
5.64×10^{-2} C			5.16×10^{-2} C
5.16×10^{-2} C			

7 Figure 7 shows two capacitors, A, of capacitance C, and B, of capacitance $2C$, connected in parallel. Figure 8 shows them connected in series. The capacitors can be connected by a two-way switch S either to a d.c. supply, of e.m.f. V, or to a voltmeter.

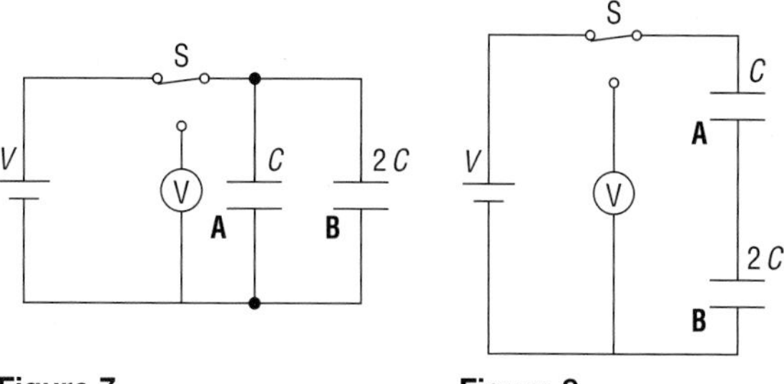

Figure 7 **Figure 8**

(a) In terms of C, find the total capacitance of the capacitors:
   (i) when connected as in Figure 7
   (ii) when connected as in Figure 8.

(b) For the circuit shown in Figure 7, find:
   (i) in terms of V, the voltage across capacitor A
   (ii) in terms of V and C, the total charge stored on the capacitors.

(c) For the circuit shown in Figure 8, find, in terms of V and C, the total energy stored in the two capacitors.

(d) The switch S is changed to connect the charged capacitors to the voltmeter in both circuits.
   (i) Explain why the capacitors will discharge, although possibly very slowly.
   (ii) State which system will discharge more rapidly. Give a reason for your answer.

2.2 Capacitors and exponential decay summary

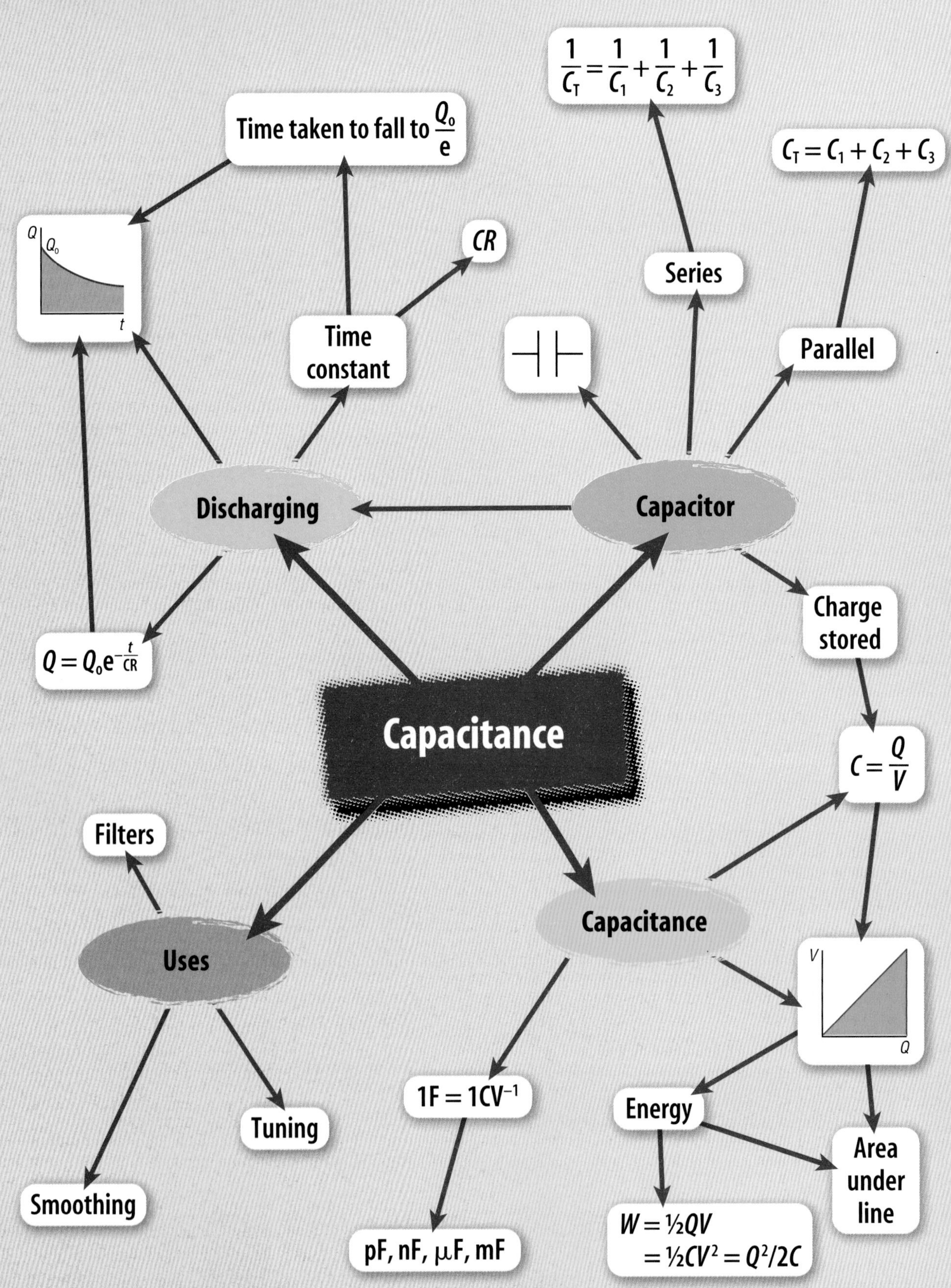

Practice questions

1. Two horizontal parallel metal plates are connected to a 600 V power supply.
   (a) Explain how the plates act as a capacitor.
   (b) The capacitance of the plates is 1.2 pF (1.2×10^{-12} F). Calculate:
   (i) the charge stored on the plates
   (ii) the energy stored in the charged capacitor.

2. A variable capacitor is set to 200 pF. It is connected across a 6.0 V cell.
   (a) Calculate or state the values of the stored charge Q, the capacitance C, the p.d. V across the capacitor and the energy E stored in the capacitor.
   (b) The capacitance is reduced to 100 pF with the capacitor still connected to the cell. Which of the four quantities in (a) is unchanged? Calculate or state the new values of Q, C, V and E.
   (c) The capacitor is disconnected from the cell. The capacitance is increased back to 200 pF. Which value of the four quantities in (b) is unchanged? Calculate or state the final values of Q, C, V and E.

3. **(a)** One expression for the energy W stored on a capacitor is
   $$W = \tfrac{1}{2} QV$$
   where Q is the charge stored and V is the potential difference across the capacitor.
   Show that another suitable expression for the energy stored is
   $$W = \tfrac{1}{2} CV^2$$
   where C is the capacitance of the capacitor.
   (b) Draw a graph to show how the energy W in J stored on a 2.2 F capacitor varies with the potential difference V from 0 to 5.0 V across the capacitor.

4. The radioactive nickel nuclide $^{63}_{28}$Ni decays by beta-particle emission with a half-life of 120 y.
   A student designs an electronic clock, powered by the decay of nuclei of $^{63}_{28}$Ni. One plate of a capacitor of capacitance 1.2×10^{-12} F is to be coated with this isotope. As a result of this decay the capacitor becomes charged. The capacitor is connected across the terminals of a small neon lamp. See Figure 1. When the capacitor is charged to 90 V, the neon gas inside the lamp becomes conducting, causing it to emit a brief flash of light and discharging the capacitor. The charging starts again. Figure 2 is a graph showing how the voltage V across the capacitor varies with time.

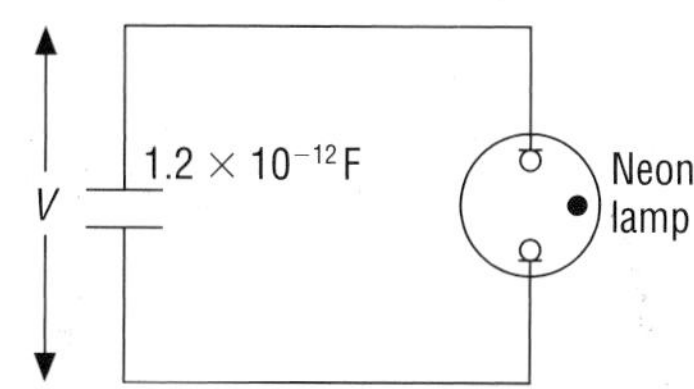

Figure 1

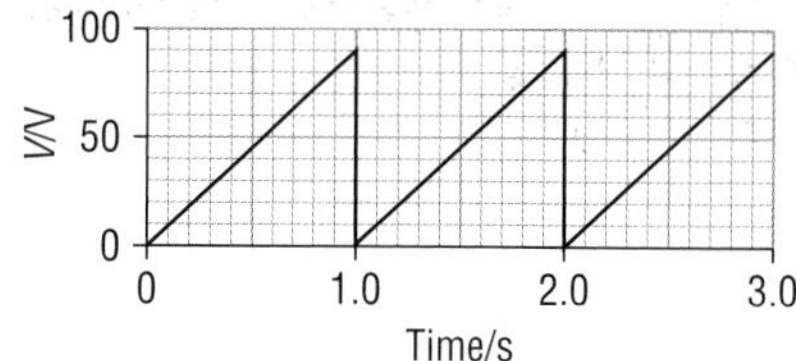

Figure 2

   (a) Show that the maximum charge stored on the capacitor is 1.1×10^{-10} C.
   (b) When a nickel atom emits a beta-particle a positive charge of 1.6×10^{-19} C is added to the capacitor plate. Show that the number of nickel nuclei that must decay to produce 1.1×10^{-10} C is about 7×10^{8}.
   (c) The neon lamp is to flash once every 1.0 s. Calculate the number of nickel atoms needed in the coating on the plate. Use the fact that the number of nickel nuclei decaying per second equals 1.8×10^{-10} × number of undecayed nickel atoms present.
   (d) (i) Show that the energy stored on the capacitor just before the discharge is about 5 nJ.
   (ii) For a visible flash, the neon lamp must transfer energy at an average rate of at least 0.01 W. Calculate the duration of the flash if this is to happen.
   (iii) Explain the flaw in the student's design.

5. A 2.2 F capacitor is connected in parallel with the power supply to a digital display for a video/DVD recorder. The purpose of the capacitor is to keep the display working during any disruptions to the electrical power supply. Figure 3 shows the 5.0 V power supply, the capacitor and the display. The input to the display behaves as a 6.8 kΩ resistor. The display will light up as long as the voltage across it is at or above 4.0 V.

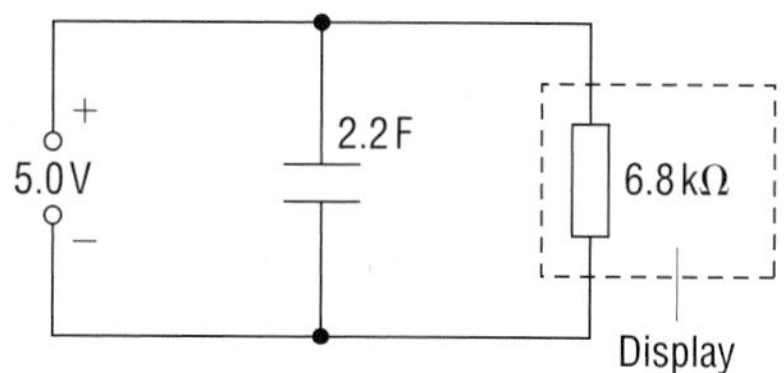

Figure 3

   Suppose the power supply is disrupted.
   (a) Show that the time constant of the circuit of Figure 3 is more than 4 hours.
   (b) Find the energy lost in J by the capacitor as it discharges from 5.0 V to 4.0 V.
   (c) The voltage V across the capacitor varies with time t according to the equation
   $$V = V_0 e^{-t/RC}.$$
   Calculate the time in s that it takes for the voltage to fall to 4.0 V.
   (d) Calculate the mean power consumption in W of the display during this time.

2.2 Examination questions

1 Figure 1 shows two large, parallel, insulated capacitor plates, separated by an air gap of 4.0×10^{-3} m. The capacitance of the arrangement is 200 pF. The plates are connected by a switch to a 2000 V d.c. power supply. The switch is closed and then opened.

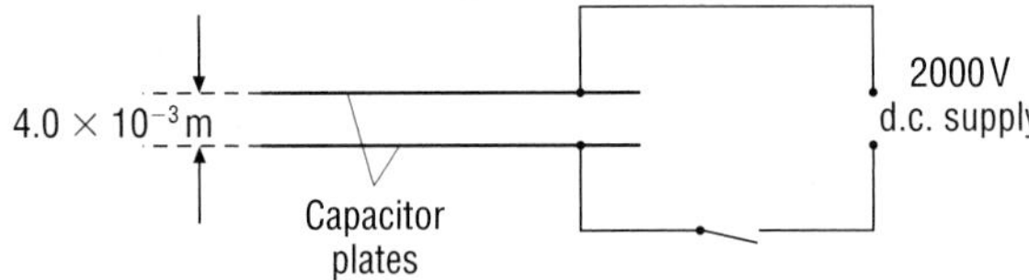

Figure 1

(a) Calculate:

(i) the magnitude of the electric field strength between the plates [2]

(ii) the magnitude in μC of the charge on each plate [3]

(iii) the energy in μJ stored in the capacitor. [3]

(b) With the switch remaining open, the plates are pulled apart until their separation is doubled. The capacitor maintains the same charge. The electric field strength between the plates is unchanged. State the new:

(i) voltage in V between the plates

(ii) capacitance in pF of the plates

(iii) energy stored in μJ in the capacitor. [3]

(c) The energy stored in the capacitor has increased. State the source of this energy. [1]

(OCR 2824 Jan03)

2 **(a)** Figure 2 shows the graph of charge Q stored against potential difference V across a capacitor.

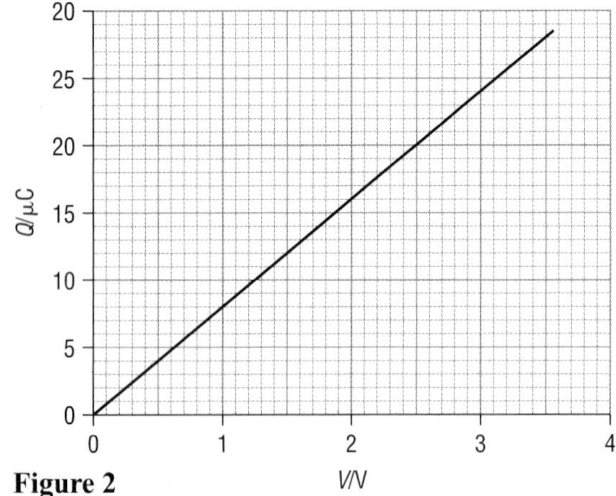

Figure 2

(i) Use the graph to find the capacitance in μF of the capacitor. [2]

(ii) Calculate the energy in μJ in the capacitor when it is charged to 3.0 V. [2]

(iii) The capacitor is discharged through a resistor. The charge falls to 0.37 of its initial value in a time of 0.040 s. This is the time constant of the circuit. Calculate the resistance in Ω of the resistor. [2]

(iv) Explain why the discharge time of the capacitor is independent of the initial charge on the capacitor. [2]

(b) You are provided with a number of identical capacitors, each of capacitance 3.0 μF. Three are connected in a series and parallel combination as shown in Figure 3.

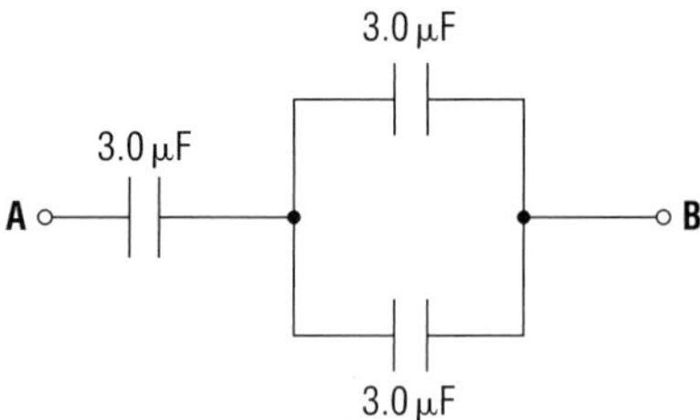

Figure 3

(i) Show that the total capacitance between the terminals **A** and **B** is 2.0 μF. [3]

(ii) Draw a diagram in the space below to show how you can produce a total capacitance of 2.0 μF using **six** capacitors of 3.0 μF. [2]

(OCR 2824 Jan05)

3 This question is about the discharge of combinations of capacitors.
In Figures 4 and 5 the capacitors are charged through a 10 kΩ resistor from a 10 V d.c. supply when the switch **S** is connected to **X**. They discharge when the switch is moved to **Y**. The ammeters A_1, A_2, A_3 and A_4 monitor the currents in the circuits. Initially the switch is connected to **X** and the capacitors are fully charged.

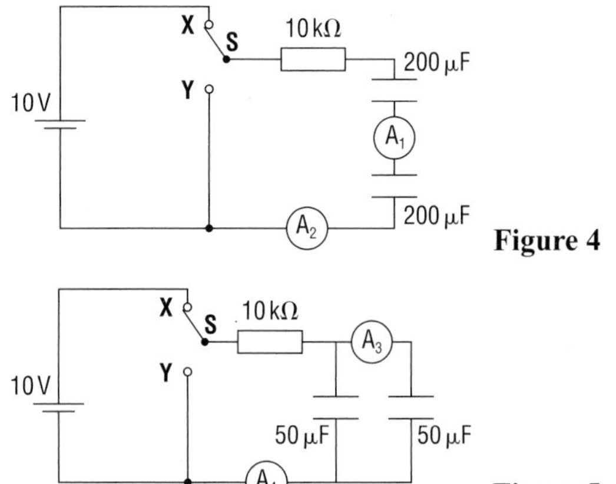

Figure 4

Figure 5

(a) State:

(i) the voltage in V across each capacitor in Figure 4 [1]

(ii) the voltage in V across each capacitor in Figure 5. [1]

(b) **(i)** Calculate the total charge in C stored in the circuit of Figure 5. [2]

(ii) Explain why the total charge stored in the circuit of Figure 4 is the same as in the circuit of Figure 5. [2]

(c) Figure 6 shows how the reading I on ammeter A_2 in the circuit of Figure 4 varies with time t as the capacitors discharge, after the switch is moved from **X** to **Y** at $t = 0$.

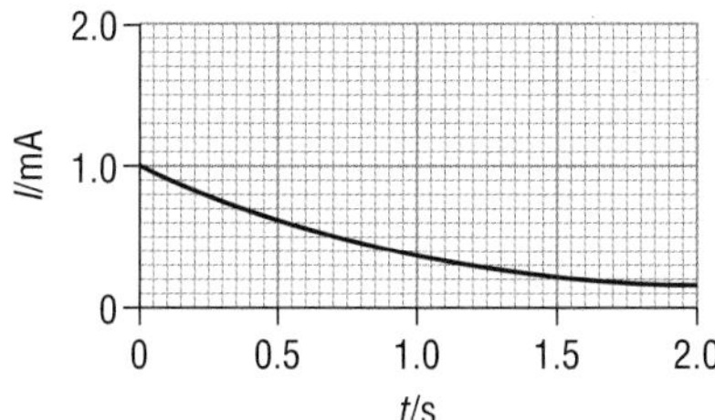

Figure 6

(i) Describe how and explain why the reading on ammeter A_1 varies, if at all, over the same time interval. [2]

(ii) Copy Figure 6 and sketch curves on it to show how you expect the readings on ammeters A_3 and A_4 to vary with time from $t = 0$, when the switch is moved from **X** to **Y** in Figure 5. Label your curves **3** and **4** respectively. [3]

(OCR 2824 Jun06)

4 **(a)** Define the *capacitance* of a capacitor. [1]

(b) Figure 7 shows a circuit in which a 0.47 μF capacitor may be connected by a two-way switch S either to an 11.0 V d.c. supply or to a 2200 Ω resistor.

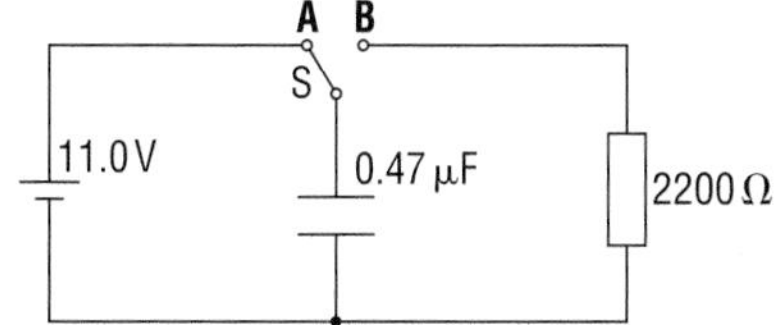

Figure 7

(i) The capacitor is charged with switch S in position A. Calculate:

1 the charge in C stored in the capacitor [2]

2 the energy in J stored in the capacitor. [2]

(ii) The switch is moved to position B at time $t = 0$ to discharge the capacitor. Calculate:

1 the initial current in A in the resistor [2]

2 the time constant in s of the circuit. [2]

(c) Figure 8 shows the variation in current in the resistor with time for part of the discharge.

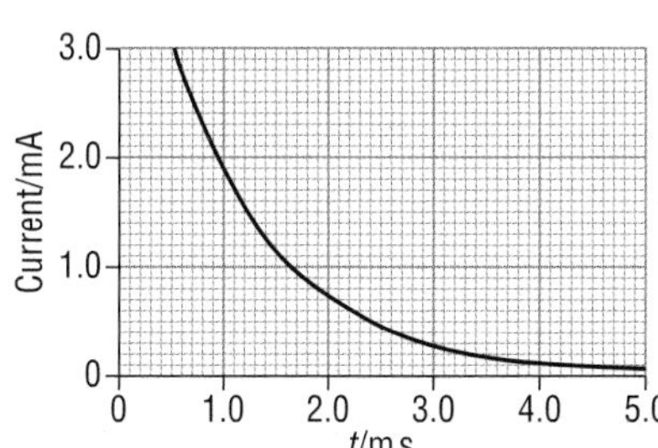

Figure 8

(i) Show that the shape of the graph is exponential. [2]

(ii) Estimate the charge in C which flows from the capacitor during the time $t = 1.0$ ms to $t = 2.0$ ms. [3]

(OCR 2824 Jun04)

5 **(a)** A capacitor C of capacitance 500 μF is connected either to a 12 V battery or to a resistor R through a switch S, as shown in Figure 9. The capacitor is initially uncharged and connected across R.

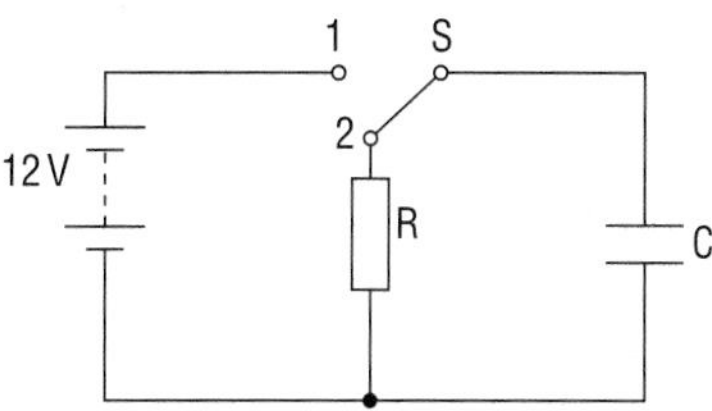

Figure 9

(i) Describe the movement of charge in the circuit which takes place after the switch S is moved from position 2 into position 1. [1]

(ii) Calculate the final charge in μC stored on the capacitor. [1]

(b) The switch is moved back to position 2 so that the capacitor discharges through the resistor R. Figure 10 shows the variation with time t of current I during the discharge.

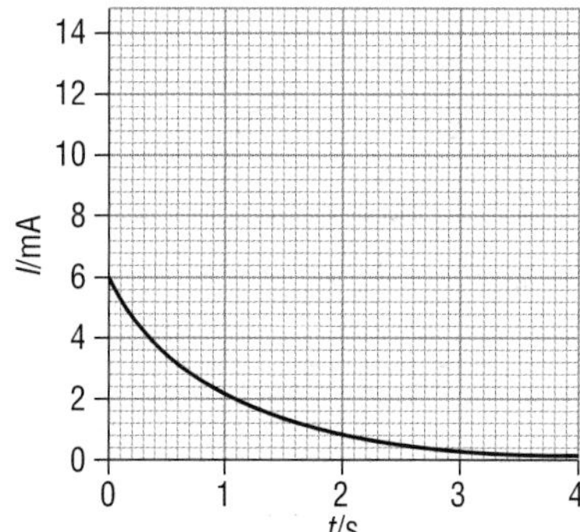

Figure 10

(i) Use data from the graph and Figure 9 to calculate a value for the resistance of R. [2]

(ii) Determine the time constant in s of the circuit. [1]

(iii) The curve of Figure 10 can be described in the form $I = I_0 e^{-t/RC}$. Substitute values into the equation to give an expression for I in terms of t. [1]

(iv) Explain how you could use Figure 10 to verify the charge calculated in **(a) (ii)**. [2]

(v) The resistor R is replaced by one of half the resistance. Copy Figure 10 and sketch on it the discharge curve you would predict. [2]

(OCR 2824 Jun02)

UNIT 2

Module 3 Nuclear physics

Introduction

The smaller a particle is, the greater the energy required to experiment with it is. The early experiments on the breakdown of nuclear particles used the high-energy cosmic radiation from the Sun and other stars. Balloons carrying unexposed photographic films were flown into the upper atmosphere (leading to a sudden increase in the number of sightings of unidentified flying objects), where collisions between high-energy particles from space and nuclei in the film clearly showed that nuclear particles called mesons existed.

Now apparatus for this type of experiment exists on Earth. The image on this double page is a computer-generated model of a particle detector called ALICE. It is part of the Large Hadron Collider (LHC) at CERN, the European particle physics laboratory near Geneva. The LHC consists of an underground circular tunnel 27 kilometres long within which beams of charged particles are accelerated almost to the speed of light and travel around the ring in opposite directions before colliding in ALICE. The collisions will generate temperatures more than 100 000 times hotter than the heart of the Sun. These conditions may free quarks from their bonds, and detectors spaced around the point of collision might find quark-like material, as probably existed just after the Big Bang when the Universe was still extremely hot. The diameter of the rings in the image is 10 metres and the overall height is 16 m; the mass of the whole detector is 10 000 tonnes.

In this module you will learn about:

- the nuclear atom and fundamental particles
- radioactivity
- nuclear fission and fusion.

Test yourself

1. What are the two particles in the nucleus of most atoms? What is the other particle in an atom?
2. What is an ion?
3. Correct these spellings: neucleus, nutron, neuclide, neuclear, nutral. Devise a rule for yourself to make certain you spell each one correctly.
4. What is Einstein's most famous equation? What does each symbol stand for?

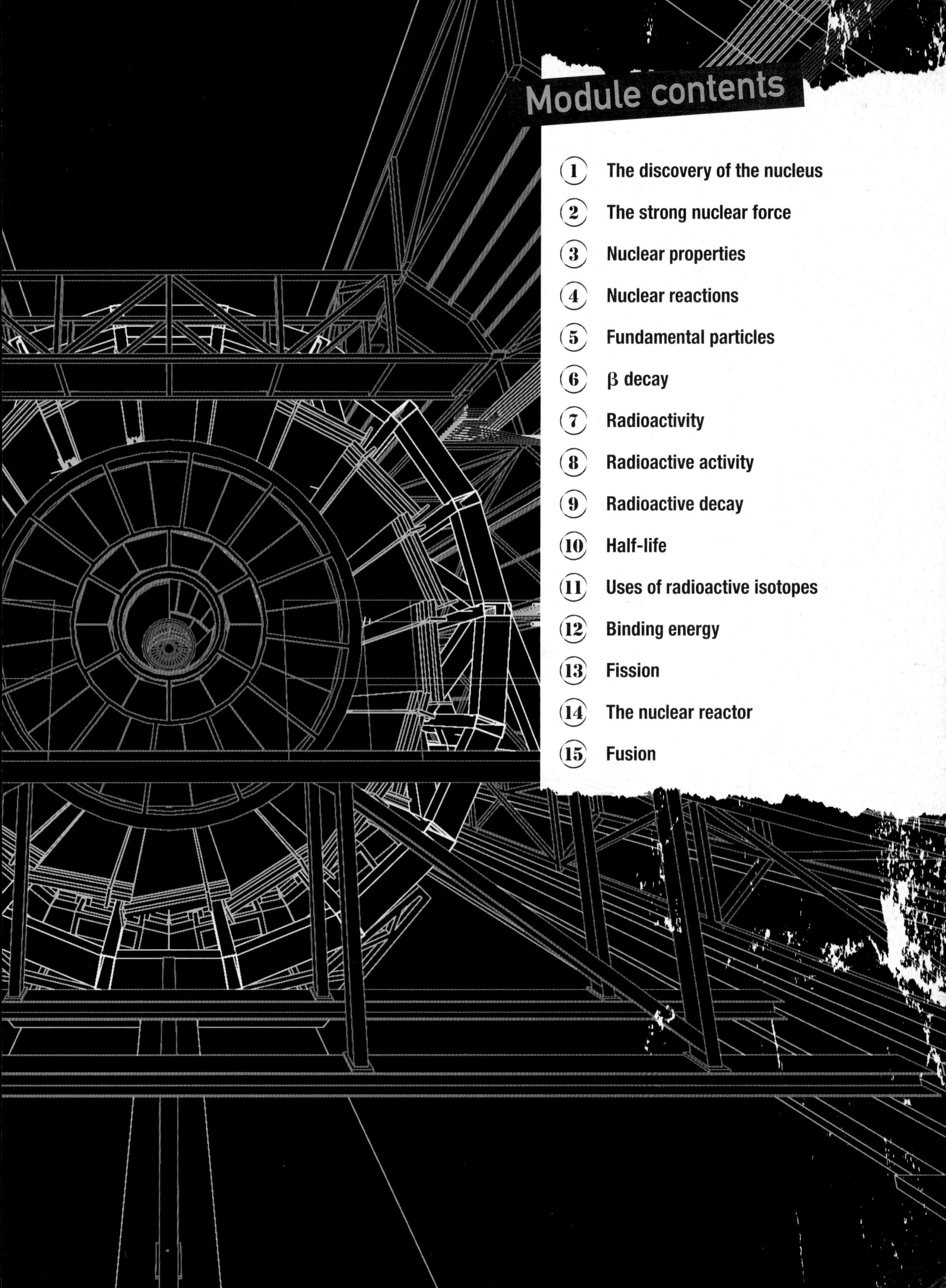

Module contents

2.3 ① The discovery of the nucleus

By the end of this spread, you should be able to ...

- **Describe qualitatively the alpha-particle scattering experiment.**
- **Describe the basic atomic structure of the atom and the relative sizes of the atom and the nucleus.**

Figure 1 The interior of the 27 km-long tunnel housing the Large Hadron Collider at the CERN laboratory near Geneva

Introduction

Early scientific investigation introduced the word 'atom' for a particle so small that further division was impossible. Indeed, the word itself, from the Greek, means 'indivisible'. An atom is still defined as the smallest particle that can take part in a chemical reaction. Then, at the end of the nineteenth century, Thomson discovered the electron. This particle had a charge-to-mass ratio that was about 1800 times larger than that for any known particle. That is, for its mass it had a huge charge. It soon became clear that it was far less massive than the smallest atom, so the search was on for other subatomic particles. That search is still going on today with massive atom-smashing machines such as at the CERN particle accelerator near Geneva (Figure 1). Well over 300 subatomic particles are now known, and a few new ones seem to be found every year.

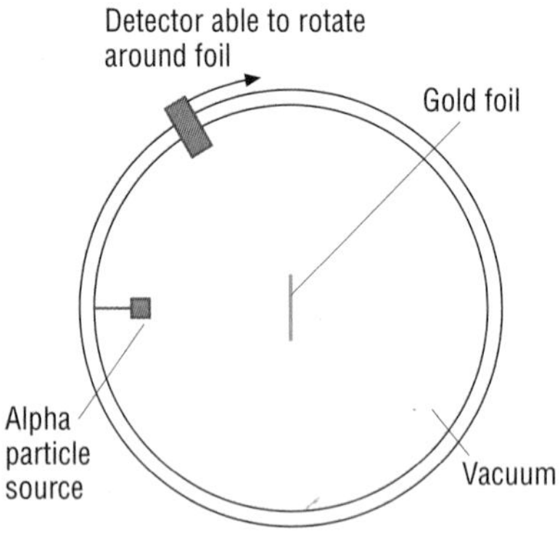

The alpha-particle scattering experiment

In the early years of the twentieth century, the atom was imagined to be a bundle of positive charges, with most of the mass, and negative electrons. But radioactivity had been discovered by this time, and it was known that alpha particles had high energies. Rutherford decided to fire alpha particles as bullets in a vacuum to shatter atoms to see what happened. Two of his colleagues, Geiger and Marsden, were given the task. They decided that it would be advantageous to have a very thin layer of atoms as a target so that, if anything unusual did happen, it was likely to be from at most only a few collisions, and it would then be easier to interpret their results. They chose a thin gold foil as a target (Figure 2). Their detector was a zinc sulfide screen that produced a tiny flash of light when an alpha particle hit it, and it was not very sensitive. As expected, not much happened. The kinetic energy of the alpha particles was so large (around 6 000 000 eV compared with 0.02 eV vibrational energy for the gold atom) that even when a collision did occur, it just knocked a gold atom out of the way. However, a few stray particles on their detector could not be explained as part of background radiation, and so they persevered and found that about 1 in 10 000 alpha particles were deflected by more than 90° (Figure 3). This could not be explained at the time.

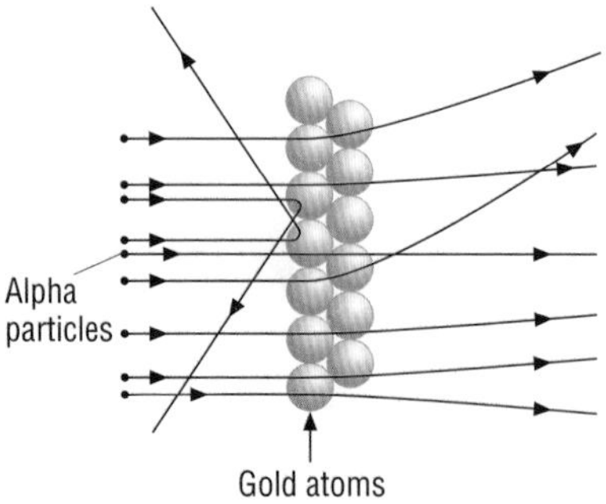

Detector able to rotate around foil

Gold foil

Alpha particle source

Vacuum

Figure 2 Apparatus for the alpha-particle scattering experiment

Alpha particles

Gold atoms

Figure 3 The pattern of scattering of alpha particles by a gold atom. The number of undeflected alpha particles for this number of deflected nuclei would be of the order of a hundred thousand

Deductions from alpha-particle scattering

Using the equation from spread 2.1.2 for the force acting between point charges, the force between the positive charge Q in a gold atom (79e) and the positive charge q in an alpha particle (2e) is given by

$$F = \frac{qQ}{4\pi\varepsilon_0 r^2} = \frac{2 \times 1.6 \times 10^{-19} \times 79 \times 1.6 \times 10^{-19}}{4\pi \times 8.9 \times 10^{-12} \times r^2} = \frac{3.6 \times 10^{-26}}{r^2}$$

Figure 4 shows that if r is of the order of atomic separation, say 2×10^{-11} m, then F is about 10^{-4} N. Calculating from the energy and the momentum of the alpha particle shows that this force is nowhere near large enough. To get a large enough force of repulsion on the positive charge on the alpha particle, the magnitude of the force necessary is around 300 N. This large force requires the value of r to be about 10^{-14} m.

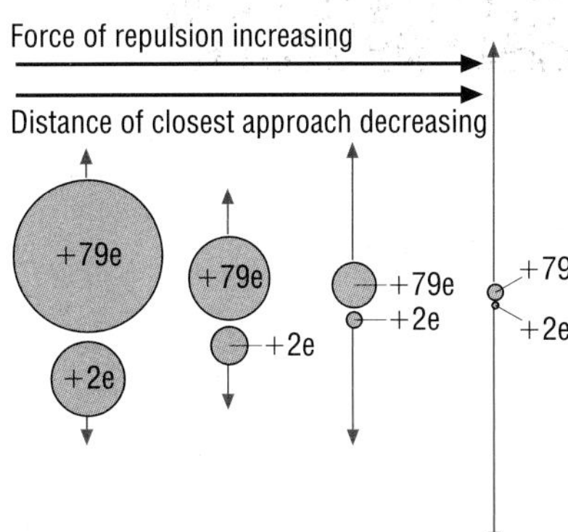

Figure 4 The force between a charge 2*e* and 79*e* increases as the charges get closer together

The only way the charge on the alpha particle can get this close to the charge of the gold atom is for the alpha particle to be very small and for all the positive charge in the gold atom to be concentrated in a particle of diameter about 10^{-14} m. It was this experiment that led to the model of an atom as having a small positive nucleus where almost all the mass is concentrated, surrounded by orbiting electrons (Figure 5).

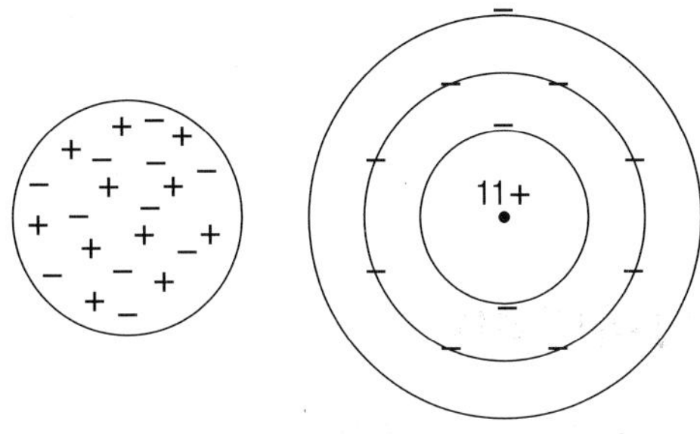

Figure 5 **(a)** The assumed structure of a sodium atom before the alpha-particle scattering experiment; **(b)** the assumed structure of the atom after the alpha-particle scattering experiment

The neutron

For a long time before the nucleus was discovered, chemists had been finding the mass of atoms. Many of the masses proved to be almost whole-number multiples of the mass of the smallest atom, hydrogen. They used oxygen as 16.00 units and found the mass of hydrogen to be 1.008 units, fluorine 19.00 units, nitrogen 14.01 units, chromium 52.00 units and helium 4.003 units. Although there are some striking exceptions to this pattern, notably chlorine at 35.5 units, it was too much of a coincidence that so many were whole numbers.

Gradually, it was seen that all 90 or so atoms had a similar structure, but the missing piece from this model, the neutron, was not discovered until the 1930s when some strange neutral emission occurred from beryllium after it had been bombarded by alpha particles. At this stage it seemed as though the structure of atoms had been established, with all atoms consisting of:

- a very small nucleus containing protons mass 1.0 u charge +*e*
- and neutrons mass 1.0 u charge 0
- surrounded by orbiting electrons mass 0.00055 u charge –*e*.

A mass of 1 u is 1.6605×10^{-27} kg; a charge of +*e* is 1.6022×10^{-19} C.

This simple pattern can explain many phenomena, but future studies would show that things are actually more complex than this.

Questions

1 Calculate the force of attraction between the proton and the electron in a hydrogen atom. The radius of the orbit of the electron is 5.3×10^{-11} m.

2 Calculate the charge-to-mass ratio of **(a)** an electron, **(b)** a proton and **(c)** a helium nucleus. Give your answers in both *e*/u and in C kg^{-1}.
Data: mass of electron = 1/1840 u, mass of helium-4 = 4u.
1 u = 1.66×10^{-27} kg, $e = 1.60 \times 10^{-19}$ C.

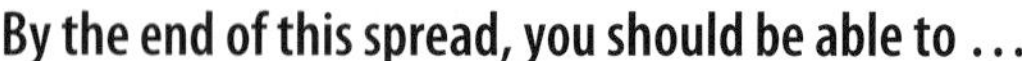

The strong nuclear force

By the end of this spread, you should be able to ...

- **Select and use Coulomb's law and Newton's law of gravitation.**
- **Describe the properties of the strong nuclear force.**

Forces on nuclear particles

In the previous spread, the force between the positive charge on a gold atom and the positive charge on an alpha particle was calculated using the equation

$$F = \frac{qQ}{4\pi\varepsilon_0 r^2} = \frac{2 \times 1.6 \times 10^{-19} \times 79 \times 1.6 \times 10^{-19}}{4\pi \times 8.9 \times 10^{-12} \times r^2} = \frac{3.6 \times 10^{-26}}{r^2}$$

This equation can be modified slightly to find the force between two protons in a nucleus, each with charge 1.6×10^{-19} C, when a distance 2.0×10^{-15} m apart. It is

$$F = \frac{qQ}{4\,\pi\varepsilon_0 r^2} = \frac{1.6 \times 10^{-19} \times 1.6 \times 10^{-19}}{4\pi \times 8.9 \times 10^{-12} \times (2.0 \times 10^{-15})^2} = 57 \text{ N}$$

This force is an extremely large force of repulsion and is acting on a very small mass. The force between all the protons in any nucleus is repulsion – so why do they not all fly apart from one another? What holds them together?

The first possible answer is gravity, because they are very close together. The following calculation gives the value of the gravitational force of attraction between two protons, each of mass 1.67×10^{-27} kg, the same distance apart.

$$F = \frac{Gm^2}{r^2} = \frac{6.7 \times 10^{-11} \times (1.67 \times 10^{-27})^2}{(2.0 \times 10^{-15})^2} = 4.7 \times 10^{-35} \text{ N}$$

As you can see, there is a vast difference between the force needed to keep the protons together and the force provided by gravitational attraction. Gravity forces will be completely ignored throughout the rest of this module when dealing with nuclear forces. They are always far too small to have any significant effect.

Now we understand that the electrical force between two protons is a force of repulsion and that the force of gravity is far too small to keep them together, we know there must be a different kind of force altogether acting between protons keeping them together. This force is called the **strong nuclear force**.

The properties of the strong nuclear force

- Since the force acts within the nucleus of atoms but not outside the nucleus, the force must have a very small range. Electrical and gravitational forces decrease with distance according to an inverse square law; if you double the distance between two charges or masses, the force between them decreases by a factor of four. The strong nuclear force decreases much more rapidly with distance and does not extend much beyond adjacent protons and neutrons within the nucleus.
- The strong nuclear force must act between **nucleons**, whether they are protons or neutrons. It is a genuine nuclear force between the particles in a nucleus and is independent of charge.
- The force must bind nucleons together, but if it was only an attractive force the nucleons would collapse in on themselves. It must therefore become a force of repulsion when the nucleons are very close together.
- When the structure of nuclei is examined, it is found that the only nucleus that does not contain neutrons is the hydrogen nucleus, which contains only one proton. Two protons cannot exist in a nucleus unless a neutron is present. Similarly, two neutrons cannot exist in a nucleus unless a proton is present. Both particles are needed for a stable nucleus. The resultant (net) force on any neutron will be the strong force on it:

Key definition

A **nucleon** is a nuclear particle. That is, it is either a proton or a neutron.

the resultant force on any proton will be the vector sum of the strong force and the electrical force. For light nuclei, the number of protons is approximately equal to the number of neutrons. For heavier nuclei, there are more neutrons than protons. The largest stable nucleus is that in the bismuth atom, which has 83 protons and 126 neutrons. Any larger nucleus, such as one in a uranium atom with 92 protons and 146 neutrons, is radioactive. More details about this will be given in spread 2.3.7.

Figure 1 is a graph showing how the strong force F varies with the distance between the centres of adjacent nucleons. You can see that the strong force provides repulsion for distances up to 2.4×10^{-15} m, is attractive for distances from about 2.4×10^{-15} m to a distance of about 5.0×10^{-15} m and is zero for any larger distance. You can also see that the strong force can be as large as a few hundred times greater than the electrical force of repulsion.

Figure 2 shows the forces acting on two nucleons of a nucleus. Inside the nucleus, the nucleons have a resultant force on them of zero. However, if a nucleon near the surface of the nucleus moved only slightly further away, it would have a very large resultant force on it pulling it back. This has the effect of keeping nuclei very stable.

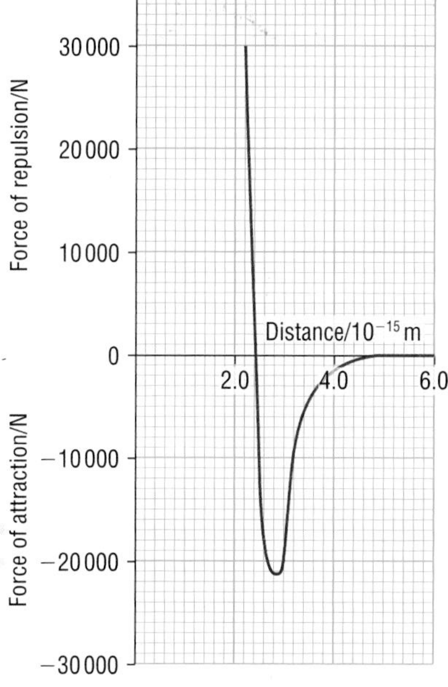

Figure 1 A graph showing how the strong nuclear force varies with the distance between nuclei

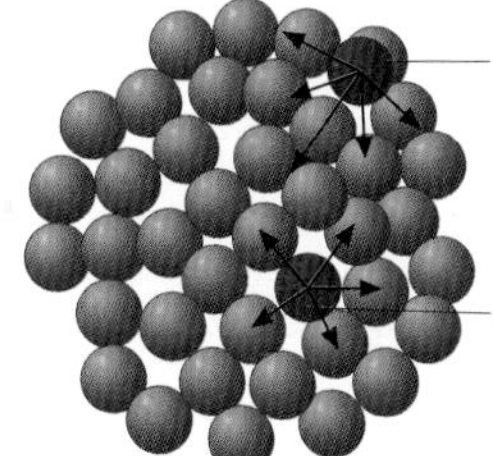

Figure 2 The forces acting on two of the nucleons within a nucleus

Equilibrium separation of nuclear particles

Using data from the graph, it is now possible to estimate the size of different nuclei. Figure 3(a) shows two neutrons separated by a distance d. When the neutrons are in equilibrium, the resultant force on them must be zero. The graph shows this to occur when $d = 2.4 \times 10^{-15}$ m. If these two neutrons moved a bit further away from one another, they would each have a large force of attraction pulling them back together. If they moved closer, a large force of repulsion would push them back towards equilibrium. In Figure 3(b) two protons are considered. Here they will have an electrical force of repulsion that must be balanced by the attraction provided by the strong force. Since the electrical force will be only a few hundred newtons (at most only half a square on the vertical axis of the graph), the separation of the protons will be almost exactly the same as that for the neutrons. Figure 3(c) shows the situation for more protons and neutrons in a real nucleus. The separation of nucleons within any nucleus is virtually independent of how many nucleons there are in the nucleus.

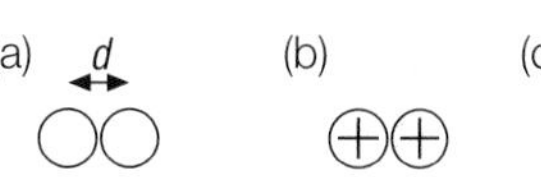

Figure 3 (a) Two neutrons in equilibrium, **(b)** two protons in equilibrium, **(c)** a real nucleus in equilibrium

Questions

1 Figure 1 shows how the strong force varies with distance between nuclei. A positive value indicates repulsion.
   (a) Use the graph to state the distance between the centres of two neutrons in equilibrium.
   (b) Calculate the electrostatic force between two protons when their centres are 2.4×10^{-15} m apart. Assume that all the charge on a proton is at its centre.
   (c) Estimate the equilibrium separation of two protons.

2 It has been suggested that the strong force F acting between two nucleons is of the form

$$F = \frac{A}{x^4} - \frac{B}{x^8}$$

where x is the distance between the two nucleons in metres, and A and B are constants. A has a numerical value around 10^{50} times greater than B.
   (a) What happens to the sign of F when x changes from 10^{-15} m to 10^{-12} m? (You will need to do some cancelling in evaluating this, because otherwise your calculator will give you an ERROR message, since the numbers would be bigger than 10^{99}.)
   (b) Is F, as used here, the force of repulsion or the force of attraction?
   (c) What will be the relationship between A and B when the force is zero?

Examiner tip

Get the terminology right from the start:

Anything or any particle that has no charge on it is *neutral*. So the neutral fundamental particle is the **neutron** (and another neutral particle, to be considered later, is called the neutrino.)

Anything that is in the *centre* of an atom is in the **nucleus** (plural **nuclei**). So the particles in the nucleus are **nucleons**, and the science dealing with them is nuclear physics (and a term, to be considered later in this book, for a particular type of nucleus is nuclide.)

Note how these terms are used in the remaining spreads.

2.3 (3) Nuclear properties

By the end of this spread, you should be able to …

* **Estimate the density of nuclear matter.**
* **Define proton and nucleon number and define and use the term *isotopes*.**
* **State and use the notation ^A_ZX for the representation of nuclides.**

Nuclear density

At the end of the previous spread, it was stated that the separation of nucleons is almost independent of the number of nucleons in a nucleus. Since protons and neutrons have nearly the same mass, the implication of this is that the density of nuclear matter is constant, because as the number of nucleons in nuclei increases, its volume V and its mass M are in direct proportion. In equation form this becomes

$V = cM$ where c is a constant.

Since the volume is proportional to the radius R cubed and $M = A \times m_p$, where A is called the **nucleon number** and is the number of nucleons in any nucleus, and m_p is the mass of a proton, this can be written

$R^3 = c'Am_p$ where c' is a different constant.

By taking the cube root, the value of the radius of a nucleus becomes

$R = (1.2 \times 10^{-15}\text{ m}) \times \sqrt[3]{A}$

The values of c' and m_p have been included in the numerical value of the constant given in the equation. Notice that when $A = 1$, the radius of the nucleon is 1.2×10^{-15} m, so the distance separating two nuclei is 2.4×10^{-15} m as was shown in Figure 1 of spread 2.3.2.

Now that we can find the radius of any nucleus, it is possible to calculate the diameter of a nucleus and to find the density of nuclear matter, as shown in the following worked example.

Key definitions

The **nucleon number** A is the number of nucleons in any nucleus.

The **proton number** Z is the number of protons in a nucleus.

Worked example

Calculate the **(a)** the mass, **(b)** the radius, **(c)** the volume and **(d)** the density of a nickel nucleus containing 28 protons and 36 neutrons. The mass of both protons and neutrons to 3 sig. figs is 1.00 u (1 u = 1.66×10^{-27} kg).

Repeat the process for a uranium nucleus containing 92 protons and 146 neutrons. Assume that both nuclei are spherical in shape. (Any distortion from the spherical shape of all nuclei is small.)

Answer

	values for nickel nucleus	values for uranium nucleus
Number of nucleons	64	238
(a) mass	$64 \times 1.66 \times 10^{-27}$ kg $= 1.06 \times 10^{-25}$ kg	$238 \times 1.66 \times 10^{-27}$ kg $= 3.95 \times 10^{-25}$ kg
(b) radius	$R = (1.2 \times 10^{-15}\text{ m}) \times \sqrt[3]{64}$ $= 4.8 \times 10^{-15}$ m	$R = (1.2 \times 10^{-15}\text{ m}) \times \sqrt[3]{238}$ $= 7.4 \times 10^{-15}$ m
(c) volume = $4\pi R^3/3$	$V = 4.6 \times 10^{-43}\text{ m}^3$	$V = 1.7 \times 10^{-42}\text{ m}^3$
(d) density = m/V	$2.3 \times 10^{17}\text{ kg m}^{-3}$	$2.3 \times 10^{17}\text{ kg m}^{-3}$

Note that the densities of both nuclei are the same – which is what they must be.

Densities of this massive amount actually occur in some stars in which matter has collapsed. Neutron stars are probably only a few kilometres in diameter yet have a mass larger than the Sun.

Nuclear terminology

The nucleon number A was defined above and is the number of protons plus neutrons in a nucleus.

The **proton number** Z is the number of protons in a nucleus. It also indicates the positive charge on the nucleus, in terms of e, the elementary charge, and for a neutral atom it will be the number of orbiting electrons.

A **nuclide** is a term used to describe a particular nucleus.

To designate a nuclide, the following arrangement of numbers and letters is used:

$^{\text{nucleon number}}_{\text{proton number}}$element symbol

$^{A}_{Z}$element symbol e.g. $^{4}_{2}$He, $^{64}_{28}$Ni, $^{238}_{92}$U

The first of these three examples gives a nuclide of helium with proton number $Z = 2$ and nucleon number $A = 4$, so it must have two neutrons. The second is a nickel nuclide with 28 protons and 36 neutrons, and the third is a uranium nuclide with 92 protons and 146 neutrons. These nuclides are also often referred to as helium-4, nickel-64 and uranium-238 respectively.

Figure 1 gives a diagrammatic representation of the structure of the nucleus for some other nuclides.

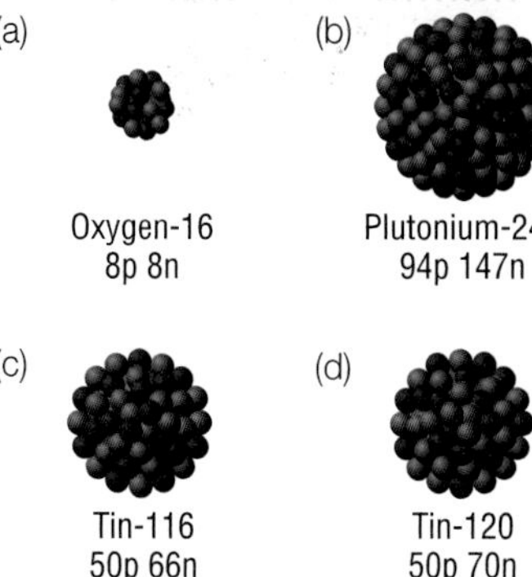

Figure 1 Artwork representing the nucleus of the nuclides: **(a)** oxygen-16, **(b)** plutonium-241, **(c)** tin-116 and **(d)** tin-120

Isotopes

Figure 1 shows the nuclei of two nuclides of tin. This is possible because a stable tin nucleus must have 50 protons but can have anything from 62 to 74 neutrons. The number of protons in a nucleus always determines the element. Different numbers of neutrons affect the mass of an atom but do not alter its chemical properties. Two nuclides with the same number of protons but different numbers of neutrons are called **isotopes** of one another. The mass spectrometer described in spread 2.1.8 can be used to determine the masses of various isotopes.

Key definition

Two nuclides with the same number of protons but different numbers of neutrons are **isotopes**.

Data

The following table is a small part of a much larger table covering all known nuclides. It is set out here to give you some idea of the pattern of the complete table and to provide the data you will need to answer the questions in this book. Some of the information given will be explained in later spreads.

Element	Symbol	Proton number Z	Neutron number	Nucleon number A	Atomic mass/u	Percentage abundance
proton	p	1	0	1	1.00728	
neutron	n	0	1	1	1.00867	
electron	e	−1	0	0	0.00055	
hydrogen	H	1	0	1	1.00783	99.99
(deuterium)	(D)	1	1	2	2.01410	0.01
helium	He	2	1	3	3.01603	0.00013
		2	2	4	4.00260	~100
carbon	C	6	6	12	12.00000	98.9
		6	7	13	13.00335	1.1
oxygen	O	8	8	16	15.99492	99.76
		8	9	17	16.99913	0.04
		8	10	18	17.99916	0.20
sodium	Na	11	12	23	22.98977	100
calcium	Ca	20	20	40	39.96259	97
uranium	U	92	143	235	235.04393	0.7
		92	146	238	238.05080	99.3

Questions

1 Using the table where necessary, state the number of protons, neutrons and electrons in the following particles:

(a) A carbon-14 atom

(b) An oxygen-19 atom

(c) A calcium-44 atom

(d) An oxygen-16 singly ionised negative ion

(e) A water molecule comprising oxygen-16 and hydrogen-1 atoms.

2 A nucleus containing A nucleons is a uniformly dense sphere of approximate radius $1.2\,A^{1/3}$ fm.

(a) What distance, in metres, is a femtometre (fm)?

(b) Calculate the radius and the volume of a uranium nucleus that contains 238 nucleons.

(c) The mass of a nucleon is 1.66×10^{-27} kg. What is the approximate density of the uranium nucleus?

2.3 (4) Nuclear reactions

By the end of this spread, you should be able to …

- **Use nuclear decay equations to represent simple nuclear reactions.**
- **State the quantities conserved in a nuclear decay reaction.**

Introduction

So far in this module, we have looked at some basic nuclear facts. The purpose of this spread is to introduce various nuclear reactions and to express them in the form of a nuclear equation. Many of the reactions themselves, and the particles that are mentioned, will be dealt with in more detail in the spreads that follow. It has already been stated that many fundamental particles have now been discovered, and these will be included as they become required by the equations.

Conservation laws in nuclear physics

Conservation laws in the classical physics of subjects such as chemistry, Newtonian mechanics and thermal physics are the laws of conservation of mass, conservation of energy, conservation of momentum and conservation of charge. Various principles have been established that are effectively statements of these laws for particular applications. Kirchhoff's first law, for example, is a law of conservation of charge with particular application to currents at a junction.

The application of conservation laws to nuclear physics requires special care. Many of the phenomena of nuclear physics involve extreme situations. In Newtonian mechanics a speed of 10 kilometres per second would be thought of as a high speed. In nuclear physics a high speed might be 299 000 kilometres per second. At these speeds Einstein's theory of relativity must be used, which says that energy and mass can be interconverted. If you look carefully at the table on the previous spread, you will find, for example, that the mass of 6 protons, 6 electrons and 6 neutrons in a carbon-12 atom does not come to 12 u exactly. This is because some mass/energy is converted in forming the carbon-12 atom from the individual particles. We have to combine conservation of energy and conservation of mass when dealing with nuclear reactions.

The following conservation laws, which you have met earlier, also apply to nuclear reactions:

- conservation of mass/energy
- conservation of momentum
- conservation of charge.

Nuclear equations

Natural radioactivity

In 1896, Becquerel discovered radioactivity when some sealed photographic plates became exposed because they were near a piece of rock containing uranium. The equation representing the emission of an alpha particle – a helium nucleus – is

$$^{238}_{92}\text{U} \rightarrow {}^{234}_{90}\text{Th} + {}^{4}_{2}\text{He} + 4.2\text{ MeV}$$

Conservation of mass/energy results in the release of 4.2 MeV of energy. Most of this energy is gained by the alpha particle. This is because the momentum of the massive thorium nucleus recoiling in one direction must be equal to the momentum of the alpha particle, of a smaller mass, travelling in the opposite direction at a much greater speed. Some energy is also released in the form of gamma radiation.

Artificial transmutation

Throughout recorded history, various people have tried to make a valuable element, such as gold, from cheaper elements. This transmutation of elements had never been possible until the following reaction produced a few atoms of oxygen from some atoms of nitrogen by bombarding air with alpha particles. The reaction could be seen by using a device called a cloud chamber (shown in Figure 1). The equation showing what happened is

$${}^{4}_{2}\text{He} + 7.7\ \text{MeV} + {}^{14}_{7}\text{N} \rightarrow {}^{1}_{1}\text{H} + {}^{17}_{8}\text{O} + 6.5\ \text{MeV}$$

The energy of the alpha particle is necessary to initiate the reaction, but there is energy remaining after the reaction so that the proton produced emerges at high speed. Various electrons are not accounted for in this nuclear reaction, but electron energies will be small compared to the alpha particle and proton energies. Stray electrons are always around in the atmosphere and will be attracted to any positive ion or proton.

Fission

This is the reaction that releases a large amount of energy in nuclear reactors. A typical fission reaction takes place when a slow neutron collides with a uranium-235 nucleus. In this reaction:

$${}^{1}_{0}\text{n} + {}^{235}_{92}\text{U} \rightarrow {}^{93}_{39}\text{Y} + {}^{140}_{53}\text{I} + 3\,{}^{1}_{0}\text{n} + 200\ \text{MeV}$$

Conservation of energy and momentum results in high-speed neutrons being emitted. These are slowed down by a moderator, their energy provides the power output of the reactor and then one of the neutrons is used to produce another reaction. This sequence is called a chain reaction.

Induced nuclear reactions in particle accelerators

High-energy particle accelerators are huge and accelerate particles to within 0.00005% of the speed of light. Protons can now reach a final energy of 1 TeV. (T means tera, or 10^{12}, so this is 1 000 000 MeV.) When a proton of this energy collides with a stationary proton, a pattern similar to that in Figure 2 can be produced. The false-colour tracks are mostly of new particles. The nine positive particles (red), which deflect to the right in the strong magnetic field, are a kaon, a proton and seven pions. In addition, seven negative pions (blue) are produced, together with a neutral lambda. The lambda is invisible because it is uncharged. However, it travels on to produce another proton (yellow) and another negative pion (purple). The equation for the proton–proton collision is

$$\text{p} + \text{p} + \text{energy} = \text{p} + 7\pi^{+} + 7\pi^{-} + \text{K}^{+} + \Lambda$$

This type of equation is completely new. More details about elementary particles will be given in the next few spreads.

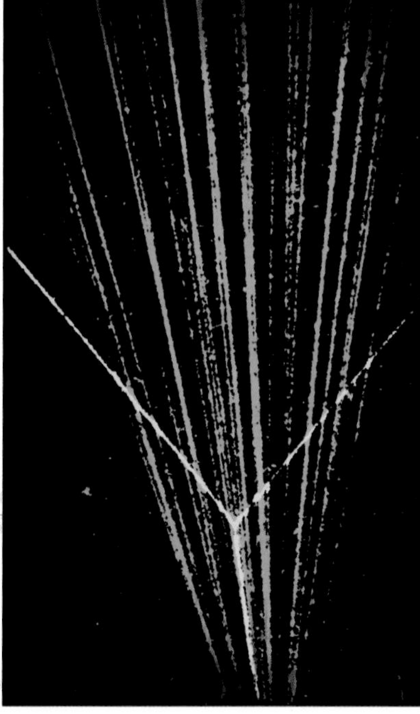

Figure 1 A typical view of a cloud chamber in which a forked track indicates a nuclear reaction

Figure 2 A high-energy proton collides with a stationary proton in a bubble chamber to produce 17 other particles

Questions

1 In Figure 2, there is a small green spiral at the bottom left-hand side. Explain how the features of the spiral's pattern indicate that it is caused by an electron. Suggest why the radius of curvature of the electron's path gets smaller and smaller.

2 Write a charge equation for the proton–proton collision shown in Figure 2 in order to show that charge is conserved in the reaction.

3 A plutonium-240 nucleus emits an alpha particle (helium-4) to form a uranium-236 nucleus. The masses of the nuclei are, for plutonium-240, 240.0022 u, uranium-236, 235.9951 u and helium-4, 4.0015 u.

   (a) Write a nuclear equation for this reaction.

   (b) Calculate the loss of mass that appears to take place. Convert this value into kilograms.

   (c) Use Einstein's $E = mc^2$ equation to calculate the energy equivalence of this mass.

   (d) Assuming that all this energy becomes kinetic energy of the alpha particle, find its speed of emission.

   (e) Explain why the assumption in **(d)** is appropriate.

2.3 (5)

Fundamental particles

By the end of this spread, you should be able to ...

- **Explain that protons and neutrons are not fundamental particles but are made of quarks.**
- **Describe a quark model of hadrons and how this can be extended.**
- **State that electrons and neutrinos are members of a group of particles known as leptons.**

Categories of particles

In the mid-twentieth century, studies of cosmic radiation (radiation from the Sun and outer space) found that, occasionally, an extremely energetic particle, when colliding with a nucleus, produced a particle whose mass was larger than an electron but smaller than a proton. These particles were called mesons (for 'intermediate masses'). Since then, such particles have been created in the laboratory as a result of the development of particle accelerators capable of giving huge energy to nuclear particles.

At the end of spread 2.3.4 the names of some of these particles were given. Now we will put these and other particles into categories. The categories were chosen initially according to the mass of the particles they categorised. Heavy particles such as protons and neutrons are called **baryons**, light particles such as electrons and neutrinos are called **leptons** and, as has already been stated, those of mass between these two are called **mesons** (although some mesons are now known with mass greater than the mass of the proton). There are too many to state all of them. The following lists give some of the properties of the particles. Apart from knowing that the proton and the neutron are baryons and that the electron and neutrinos are leptons, you need not memorise any detail of this data.

Baryons	Symbol	Mass/u	Mesons	Symbol	Mass /u	Leptons	Symbol	Mass /u
Proton	p	1.007	Pion-zero	π^0	0.144	Electron	e	0.00055
Neutron	n	1.009	Pion-plus	π^+	0.149	Muon	μ	0.113
Lambda	Λ	1.188	Pion-minus	π^-	0.149	Neutrino	ν	0(?)
Sigma-plus	Σ^+	1.267	Kaon-zero	K^0	0.531	Muon neutrino	ν_μ	0(?)
Omega-minus	Ω^-	1.408	Kaon-plus	K^+	0.526			

The CERN Large Hadron Collider (LHC)

This huge particle accelerator was planned in 1993 at an estimated cost of £2000 million. It is an international project and uses a 27 kilometre-long circular ring tunnel outside Geneva to reach energies of 14 TeV (1.4×10^{13} eV) for collisions between protons and antiprotons:

- There are over 3000 magnets around the tube through which the particles travel. Some are 4 metres in diameter, and most are 5 metres or more long.
- The whole apparatus is kept at a temperature of 1.8 kelvin. It needs to be this cold so that the magnets can use superconducting materials and hence huge currents.
- The magnetic fields are up to 8 T. (A normal strong magnet is only about 0.02 T.)

Antiparticles

As well as this long list of known particles, every known particle has its opposite particle. For a proton, there is an antiproton; for an electron, an antielectron, called a positron. All antiparticles are opposite in charge to the particle itself but have the same mass and any other properties. The extraordinary property of antiparticles is that they are made of antimatter. If a proton meets an antiproton, they are both annihilated with a release of a large equivalent amount of energy. When a proton and a neutron join together to form deuterium, about 2.2 MeV of energy is released. In contrast, when a proton and antiproton annihilate, nearly 1900 MeV is released.

It may be that at the Big Bang, when the universe was formed, there happened to be more matter than antimatter created leaving the universe with a lot of matter and not much antimatter – though a few astronomers wonder whether some distant galaxies could be made entirely of antimatter. Luckily, there is not much antimatter around on the Earth!

Fundamental particles

With so many particles, it seems unlikely that they are all elementary particles incapable of being broken down into something more fundamental. The search is on for fundamental building blocks out of which the particles can be formed. It is much like the developments in chemistry during the nineteenth century when lots of different atoms were found and people successfully sought to determine the simpler structure of all atoms with the discovery of electrons, protons and neutrons.

The situation today is that, when two protons collide with enormous energy, the bits that emerge are mesons and leptons. This is not much help with trying to find the basic building blocks. However, theoretical physicists have proposed a **quark** model of matter that successfully explains most of the structure of all the known particles.

Much research shows that fundamental particles have many different properties besides the familiar ones such as mass and charge. Some of these properties have been given the following names: spin, baryon number, lepton number, strangeness, charm. Associated with each name is a number that measures the amount of each property the particle has. Thus, a proton has a charge number of +1, a baryon number of +1, a spin number of +½, a strangeness of 0 and, since it is not a lepton, a lepton number of 0. All the numbers for the antiparticles have the opposite sign to those for the particle itself.

The quark theory

In the quark theory, all the leptons, and their antiparticles, are fundamental particles that cannot be broken down any further. They are thought to be structureless point particles and are not influenced by the strong force.

The baryons and mesons, and their antiparticles, collectively known as **hadrons**, can be broken down into quarks and are influenced by the strong force. All baryons are composed of three quarks, and all mesons of a quark and an antiquark. The three quarks initially proposed, together with their antiquarks, were called **up**, **down** and **strange**. The properties of these three quarks are in the table.

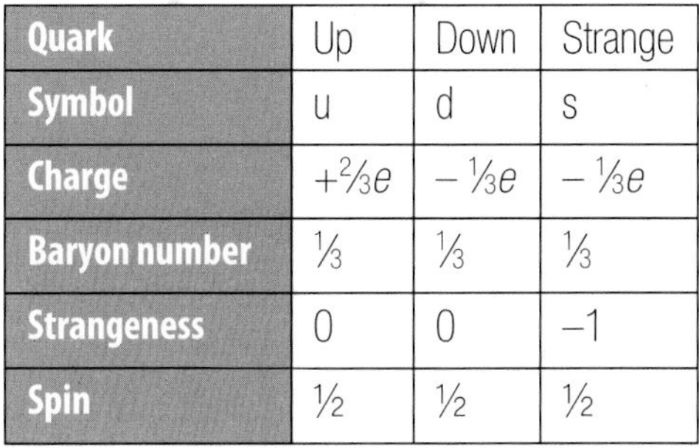

Quark	Up	Down	Strange
Symbol	u	d	s
Charge	$+\frac{2}{3}e$	$-\frac{1}{3}e$	$-\frac{1}{3}e$
Baryon number	⅓	⅓	⅓
Strangeness	0	0	−1
Spin	½	½	½

Using these quarks and their antiparticles it is possible to see how the following particles are constructed. When a line is placed over the top of a quark, it indicates that it is the antiquark. Note that uud means u + u + d, but the + signs are usually omitted.

proton	**uud**	charge $(\frac{2}{3} + \frac{2}{3} - \frac{1}{3})\,e = +e$,	baryon number 1,	strangeness 0
neutron	**udd**	charge $(\frac{2}{3} - \frac{1}{3} - \frac{1}{3})\,e = 0$,	baryon number 1,	strangeness 0
antiproton	$\bar{u}\bar{u}\bar{d}$	charge $(-\frac{2}{3} - \frac{2}{3} + \frac{1}{3})\,e = -e$,	baryon number −1,	strangeness 0
π^+ meson	$u\bar{d}$	charge $(+\frac{2}{3} + \frac{1}{3})\,e = +e$,	baryon number 0,	strangeness 0

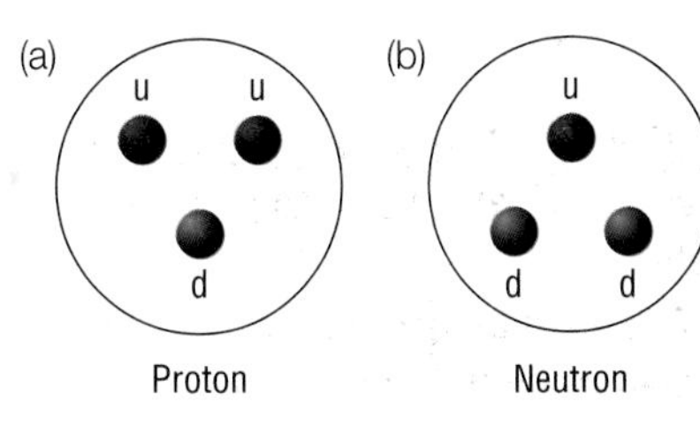

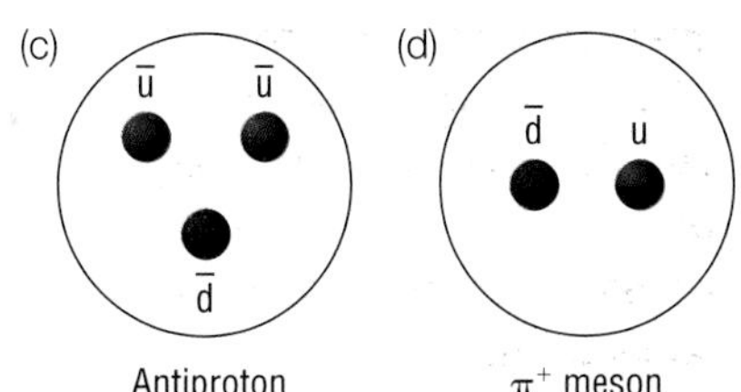

Figure 1 The quark arrangement of four hadrons: **(a)** a proton, **(b)** a neutron, **(c)** an antiproton, **(d)** a π+ meson

These four particles are illustrated in Figure 1. Quarks are much smaller than the particles they make up, so these diagrams exaggerate the size of the quarks.

This list can be extended to include all the known particles, but to do so, three other quarks, called **charm**, **top** and **bottom** have to be added.

There are many more questions about the structure of matter:

- What gives matter its mass?
- What is the 96% of the universe that is invisible made of?
- Why does nature prefer matter to antimatter?
- How did matter evolve from the first instant after the Big Bang?

Looking for smaller and smaller fundamental particles requires larger and larger, and more expensive, apparatus.

Questions

1 **(a)** State the charge, in terms of the elementary charge e, on the up quark and the down quark.

(b) State the quark composition of the proton and neutron.

2 The π^+ meson can be produced in a reaction between two protons, as shown by the equation

$$p^+ + p^+ \rightarrow p^+ + n^0 + \pi^+$$

(a) Simplify the equation and write the equation in terms of quarks.

(b) How many quarks are there in a meson?

(c) What is the quark composition of the π^+ meson?

2.3 (6) β decay

By the end of this spread, you should be able to ...

- **Describe the weak interaction between quarks.**
- **State that there are two types of β decay and describe these in terms of the quark model.**
- **State that neutrinos and antineutrinos are produced in β^+ and β^- decays, respectively.**

The weak interaction

Certain behaviour of some particles cannot be explained by the strong interaction between hadrons. A second nuclear interaction must therefore exist. It is called the **weak interaction**.

The introduction of another interaction might seem an admission that some of the earlier ideas are incorrect, but it is really not very much different from a time when it was realised that the gravitational force could not explain why solids were solid. The gravitational force between atoms is so small that some other force must keep them together. The electrical force between charged particles was therefore introduced. In other words, there is an interaction between positively and negatively charged particles. An interaction implies a force. With the weak interaction, there is a (relatively) weak force. It is much less than the strong nuclear force, only about a millionth of its value, and its range is less, at 10^{-17} m.

The strong interaction acts on hadrons but not on leptons. The weak interaction acts on both leptons and hadrons.

Additional conservation laws in nuclear physics

In any nuclear reaction, the usual conservation laws must always be obeyed, as was explained in spread 2.3.4. Now some unfamiliar conservation laws must be added to the list to get:

- conservation of mass/energy
- conservation of charge
- conservation of momentum
- conservation of spin
- conservation of baryon number (meaning that the number of baryons at the start of a reaction must equal the number of baryons after the reaction)
- conservation of lepton number (meaning that the total lepton number is the same before and after a reaction).

Mass and energy are combined together because, with the high energies involved, Einstein's $E = mc^2$ equation becomes highly relevant. (In practice, nuclear physicists usually work in units of energy only. They quote mass in units of MeV/c^2.)

Examiner tip

Remember, a β^- particle is an electron and β^+ particle is a positron.

β decay

The weak interaction between quarks is responsible for β decay (beta decay). It is also responsible for the fact that a free neutron is an unstable particle that will decay into a proton, an electron and a neutrino. Many unstable particles decay as a result of the weak interaction.

There are two types of β decay. These can best be described by nuclear equations. Two of these equations are as follows. In both cases the nucleus produced is a nitrogen-14 nucleus. Note the use of superscripts and subscripts in front of particles that are not nuclides. The superscripts give the mass number, and subscripts give the charge. This gives consistency with nucleon number and proton number for nuclides. In an equation, the total number for superscripts and that for subscripts must be the same on both sides.

1 ${}^{14}_{6}\text{C} \rightarrow {}^{14}_{7}\text{N} + {}^{0}_{-1}\text{e} + {}^{0}_{0}\bar{\nu}$ (β^- decay)

2 ${}^{16}_{8}\text{O} \rightarrow {}^{16}_{7}\text{N} + {}^{0}_{1}\text{e} + {}^{0}_{0}\nu$ (β^+ decay)

In the first case the unstable nucleus that decays is a carbon-14 nucleus. It emits an electron and an antineutrino. The electron is the β^- particle.

Breaking this equation down into particles it becomes

6 protons and 8 neutrons become 7 protons, 7 neutrons, an electron and an antineutrino.

By removing the 6 unchanged protons and 7 unchanged neutrons, we have an overall change of

a neutron changes into a proton, an electron and an antineutrino.

This equation can be put into quark terms as follows:

Particle equation $n \rightarrow p^+ + e^- + \bar{\nu}$
quark equation $udd \rightarrow uud + e^- + \bar{\nu}$
that simplifies to $d \rightarrow u + e^- + \bar{\nu}$

Conservation of energy/mass and momentum will be satisfied by the velocity of the emitted particles. Conservation of charge is seen as $-\frac{1}{3} = \frac{2}{3} - 1 + 0$.

Conservation of spin is provided by the antineutrino, which has zero mass and zero charge but does have spin.

Conservation of baryon number is seen as $\frac{1}{3} = \frac{1}{3} + 0 + 0$ (or from the full equation, $1 = 1 + 0 + 0$).

Conservation of lepton number is given by $0 = 0 + 1 - 1$ as all leptons have a lepton number of 1, antileptons have a lepton number of –1 and all other particles have a lepton number of zero.

Question 1 below asks you to repeat this process for the second equation. If you do this correctly you will find that the conservation laws hold for that equation too. The β^+ particle in this case is a positive electron, which is the positron, the antimatter of an ordinary electron. (The answers are given at the back of the book so that you can check you have done it correctly.)

Neutron decay

A free neutron, which is a neutron not bound in a nucleus, is an unstable particle. It will decay into a proton, an electron and an antineutrino. The equation for this is the same as the one given above, namely

Particle equation $n \rightarrow p^+ + e^- + \bar{\nu}$
quark equation $udd \rightarrow uud + e^- + \bar{\nu}$
that simplifies to $d \rightarrow u + e^- + \bar{\nu}$

This, and all of the reactions dealt with in this spread, involve the weak force acting on quarks.

Questions

1 Complete the particle equation and the quark equation for the following β^+ decay:

$$^{16}_{8}O \rightarrow {}^{16}_{7}N + {}^{0}_{1}e + {}^{0}_{0}\nu$$

Show that charge, lepton and baryon numbers are conserved by the reaction.

2 A nucleus of carbon-14 is radioactive and emits a β-particle and an antineutrino.

(a) Write a particle equation and a simplified quark equation for the reaction.

(b) Calculate the maximum kinetic energy of the β-particle emitted. The mass of a nucleus of carbon-14 is 14.003 24 u, and that of nitrogen-14 is 14.003 07 u.

(c) Why is the value you have quoted the *maximum* kinetic energy?

Radioactivity

By the end of this spread, you should be able to ...

* **Describe the spontaneous and random nature of radioactive decay.**
* **Describe the nature of α-particles, β-particles and γ-rays.**

Figure 1 A spinthariscope

The discovery of radioactivity

As mentioned in spread 2.3.4, in 1896 Becquerel found that some photographic plates were being fogged, despite the fact that they were still wrapped in light-proof paper. He realised that the fogging was being caused by some nearby uranium minerals. He was the first person to become aware of a nuclear reaction. When he published his results, many people started working to establish:

- that the phenomenon actually happened and was not fogging through other causes than uranium minerals
- whether other minerals would produce the same results
- what the properties of the radiation were, apart from its ability to penetrate materials
- what caused the radiation.

This sequence of events usually happens in scientific experimentation. Frequently, with a new discovery, both theoretical and practical investigations take place soon after the initial publication. One key piece of work is always for experimental results to be reproducible. That means that a different scientist working in a different laboratory must be able to get the same results. In this case, there was no shortage of people working on radioactivity, as it was called, and they had plenty of rewarding lines of enquiry.

Natural radioactivity

In this context, natural means not induced. The radioactivity came from minerals found in the ground. Nothing had to be done to the minerals to make the radioactivity happen. In fact, nothing could be done to stop it happening, apart from just absorbing it by putting the mineral in a box with thick walls. Several other things made no difference whatsoever. The experiments tried were:

- heating the mineral to a high temperature
- cooling the mineral
- dissolving it in acid
- altering the pressure on it
- putting it in strong magnetic fields
- electrically charging it or putting it in an electric field.

None of these caused any change in the amount of radiation emitted. The radioactivity was therefore said to be **spontaneous**. It just happens.

Detecting radioactivity

In the early days, blackening of a film was the only way to detect the radiation. But soon it was found that fluorescent materials such as zinc sulfide, when examined under a microscope, showed tiny flashes of light when radiation fell on them. This was a big advantage in the investigation of radioactivity because it enabled actual counts to be made. The science thus became quantitative. Using these so-called scintillations, it was soon realised that the radiation was not continuous but **random**. Flashes on the zinc sulfide screen were very irregular. Many schools have small instruments called spinthariscopes (Figure 1). They have a very weak radioactive source, a phosphor as a fluorescent screen and a magnifying glass. It is fascinating to look at almost individual atoms decaying in one of these instruments, but you must wait for about 10 minutes for your eyes to become accustomed to the dark before you will see anything at all.

(a)

Radioactive source | Alpha particle tracks | Transparent lid | Black surface with layer of cooled air above it | Sponge to hold carbon dioxide up | Solid carbon dioxide | Removable base

(b)

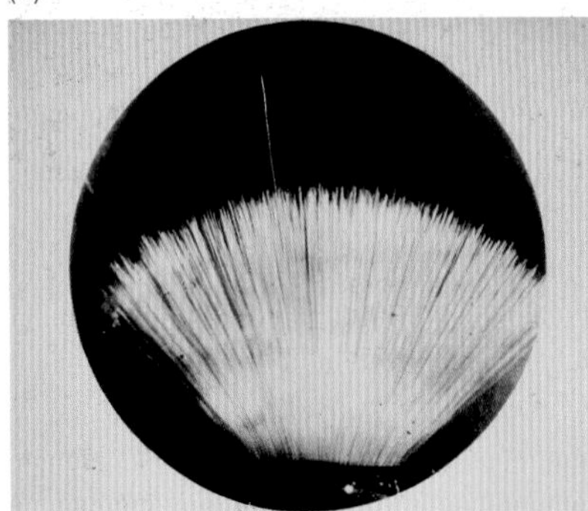

Figure 2 **(a)** A cloud chamber; **(b)** trails of alpha particles in a cloud chamber. One alpha particle, perhaps from a different source, has much greater energy than all the others

Later, cloud chambers became available. These show vapour trails of particles from radioactive sources. Later still the Geiger tube was invented, which allows accurate counts of radioactivity to be made. Trails made in photographic plates and in liquid hydrogen are also important ways of detecting and measuring radioactivity, and the simple scintillation method has been upgraded by combining it with a photomultiplier tube to get a large electrical count rate from the tiny flash of light. All of these methods rely on using the charge and high energy of radioactive emissions. Figures 1, 2, 3 and 4 show some of these instruments and the type of information they give.

The nature of natural radioactivity

It was quickly established that there were three types of radiation from radioactive materials. They are called alpha (α), beta (β) and gamma (γ) radiations. It was comparatively easy to discover this fact because in an electric field the three types of radiation were seen to behave differently. Alpha radiation moved slightly in the direction of the electric field, so it was obviously positively charged. Beta radiation moved a very large amount in the electric field in the opposite direction to the alpha particles, so the beta radiation was obviously negatively charged and either had a much larger magnitude charge than the alpha particle or had much less mass. In fact, beta radiation was so easily deflected by fields that any field strong enough to deflect alpha particles simply deflected any beta radiation through 90° immediately. Gamma radiation was not affected by electric or magnetic fields, so was understood to be uncharged. Investigations over about 40 years established the following properties of these three types of radiation.

Radiation	Symbol	Nature		Mass/u	Charge	Typical speed of emission
alpha	α	helium nucleus: 2 protons, 2 neutrons	particle	4.00	$+2e$	5% of speed of light: $0.05c$
beta	β	electron	particle	0.00055	$-e$	99% of speed of light: $0.99c$
gamma	γ	electromagnetic radiation	wave	zero	zero	speed of light: c

Typical nuclear equations for each of these emissions are:

Alpha: ${}^{238}_{92}\text{U} \rightarrow {}^{234}_{90}\text{Th} + {}^{4}_{2}\alpha + \text{energy}$

Beta: ${}^{241}_{94}\text{Pu} \rightarrow {}^{241}_{95}\text{Am} + {}^{0}_{-1}\beta + \text{energy}$

Gamma: ${}^{60}_{27}\text{Co} \rightarrow {}^{60}_{27}\text{Co} + {}^{0}_{0}\gamma + \text{energy}$

In this last reaction, the supply of energy for the gamma-ray photon is obtained by the cobalt-60 nucleus going down to a lower energy state. In many alpha and beta emissions, gamma rays are also emitted.

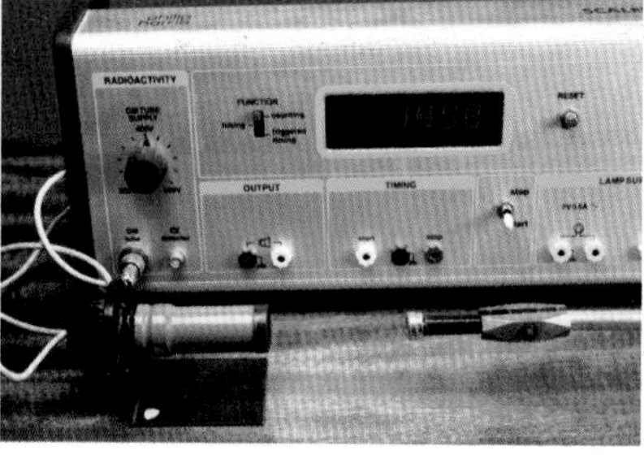

Figure 3 A Geiger tube in front of a counter used to measure individual radioactive decays

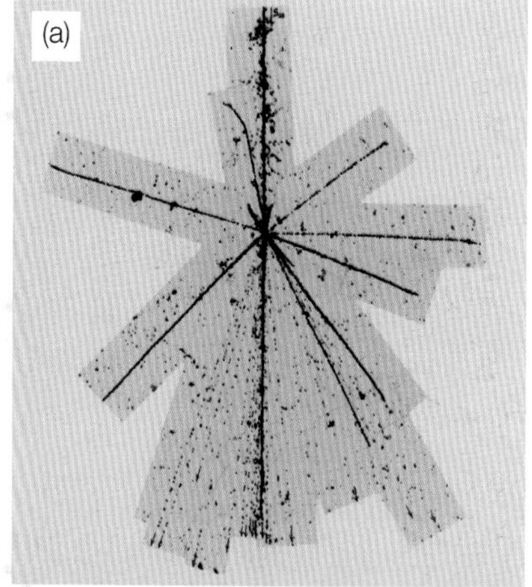

Figure 4 **(a)** A high-energy nucleus from a cosmic source collides with a nucleus in a piece of photographic emulsion. The collision produces a spray of nuclear fragments (dense tracks) and 16 pions (fainter tracks); **(b)** a photo of particles travelling in liquid hydrogen in a bubble chamber. A positive kaon, coming from the top, decays into two positive and one negative pion. The other tracks and spirals are not part of the kaon's decay. Deciphering such photos can be difficult!

Questions

1 What is the difference in meaning of the two words *spontaneous* and *random* when applied to radioactivity?

2 **(a)** Calculate the kinetic energy, in MeV, of an alpha particle travelling with a speed of 1.5×10^7 m s^{-1}.

(b) Why is it not possible to carry out a similar calculation for a beta particle travelling with a speed of 2.9×10^8 m s^{-1}?

3 **(a)** The mass of a nuclide can be determined from the energy of a beta particle emitted from it. The maximum energy of beta particles emitted from the decay of magnesium-27 is 2.610 MeV. The mass of an atom of aluminium-27 is 26.981541 u. Calculate the mass of a magnesium atom.

(b) Justify the number of significant figures you give in your answer to **(a)**.

2.3 (8) Radioactive activity

By the end of this spread, you should be able to …

* **Describe the energy, penetration and range of α-particles, β-particles and γ-rays.**

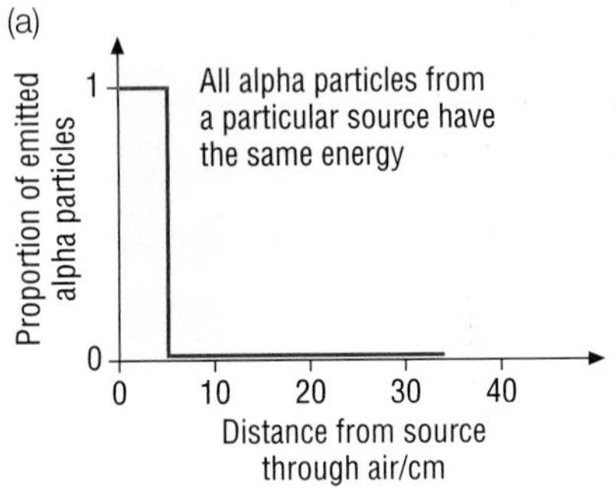

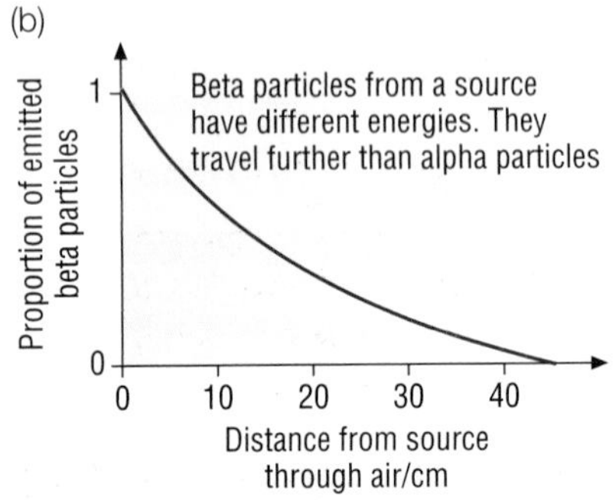

(a)

Proportion of emitted alpha particles

All alpha particles from a particular source have the same energy

Distance from source through air/cm

(b)

Proportion of emitted beta particles

Beta particles from a source have different energies. They travel further than alpha particles

Distance from source through air/cm

Figure 1 **(a)** A graph of intensity against distance for a stream of alpha particles travelling through air; **(b)** a graph of intensity against distance for a stream of beta particles travelling through air.

The energy of radioactive emissions

One startling fact about the discovery of natural radioactivity was quickly recognised when electric and magnetic fields were applied to determine the charge on the particles. Very strong fields were required to get alpha particles deflecting at all, because the kinetic energy of the alpha particles was so large. Typical energies of some particles, in electronvolts, are as follows:

- Mean kinetic energy of an oxygen atom at 300 K = 0.04 eV.
- Electrical energy of an electron leaving a cell of a battery = 1.5 eV.
- Energy given to an electron just to enable it to be freed from a hydrogen atom (ionising it) = 13.6 eV.
- Energy of an electron in a cathode-ray tube = 6000 eV.
- Energy of an alpha particle from a uranium atom = 4 200 000 eV.
- Energy of a beta particle = 1 200 000 eV.
- Energy of a gamma ray photon = 400 000 eV.

As you can see, the energies associated with radioactivity are many thousand times greater than energies involved with electrons in atoms. This is because nuclear energies are much larger than the electron energies involved in chemical reactions.

The range of radioactive emissions in air

It might be expected from the above figures that alpha particles would have the greatest range when emitted into the air and that gamma rays would have the least range. In fact, the reverse is true.

Alpha particles are charged and are relatively massive. They therefore interact strongly with the molecules of the air through which they are travelling. They crash through the molecules, attracting electrons and so pulling them off molecules. This is why, in a cloud chamber, a clearly visible vapour trail is left behind. Many hundreds of thousands of ions are formed in this way, so that alpha particles lose all their energy after travelling a few centimetres. Since all the alpha particles from a particular nuclear reaction usually have the same energy, all the alpha particles travel about the same distance in air. Figure 1(a) is a graph of this, and Figure 2(b) on the previous spread shows this clearly. Figure 2 on this spread shows the effect of having a source in which alpha particles of various energies are present.

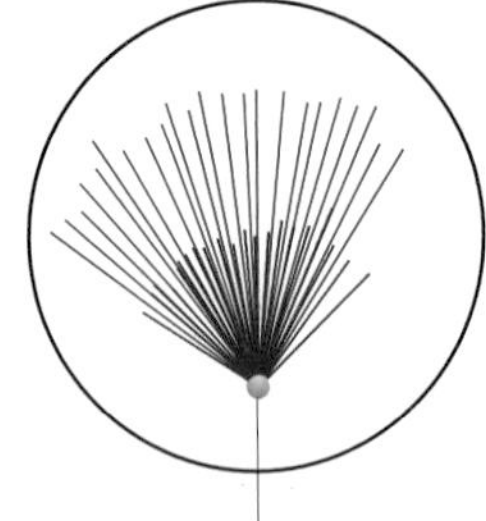

Figure 2 Tracks of alpha particles of two different energies

Beta particles are also charged but are far less massive than alpha particles. They therefore cause far less ionisation than alpha particles when travelling through air. Beta-particle tracks are much less dense and difficult to see. As a result, beta particles can travel much further than alpha particles through air. They also have different energies on emission, so the number reaching any distance gradually decreases, as shown in the graph of Figure 1(b).

Gamma rays barely interact with air molecules at all. They can therefore travel large distances, spreading out as they go, so the intensity reduces as the beam's area increases. See Figure 3.

A simple demonstration of the penetrating ability of the three types of naturally occurring radiation can be done by putting absorbing sheets in between a source and a detector.

- Alpha radiation will be completely stopped by a normal sheet of paper.
- Beta radiation will be stopped by a sheet of aluminium about 2–3 mm thick.
- Gamma radiation will be reduced considerably by a centimetre-thick piece of lead, but even with extra thickness some of this radiation will still penetrate. To protect the environment from the radiation from a nuclear power reactor, several centimetres of steel and several metres of concrete are used.

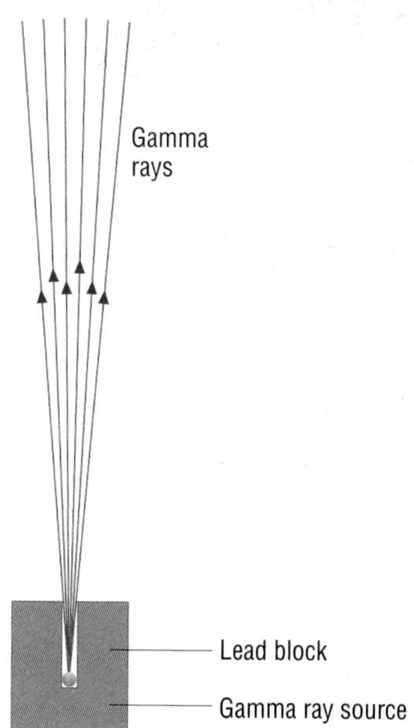

Figure 3 The intensity of gamma radiation falls only a little owing to interaction with air molecules, but it does fall because of the beam widening

Protection against radiation

Complete protection against radiation is impossible. The Earth receives a great deal of radiation from the Sun, much of which we are protected against by the atmosphere. Because many rocks are radioactive, we live in a background of radiation from the soil and rocks around us. Certain towns and cities are more radioactive than others. (Some are more than 100 times more radioactive than the average value.) A radioactive gas called radon leaks out of the ground in many parts of the country. Government Building Regulations now insist that houses in some parts of Cornwall, Somerset, Northamptonshire and Derbyshire are fully protected from radon gas getting into houses, by putting a radon-proof barrier under the floor and using extraction pumps. Background radiation is small but not zero.

Radioactive activity

The rate at which any source emits radioactive particles is called its **activity (*A*)**. An activity of one particle per second is one **becquerel (Bq)**. Strong sources may have activities of many millions of becquerels. Background radiation can be of the order of 20 Bq for each cubic metre of air, but as explained above, this can vary hugely from place to place.

Be careful to distinguish between count rate and activity. A source in a laboratory may have an activity of 2000 Bq. When you put an instrument in front of it you may get a count rate of only 400 counts per second. This is because not all of the particles will be going in a direction to enter your counter and some of the particles that started from the source may be absorbed within the source itself or on the path from the source to the counter or may enter the counter but not be detected. Because any radioactivity is random, it is sensible to count for a reasonable length of time in order to get a reliable value for the count rate.

Key definition

The rate at which a source emits radioactive particles is called its **activity** (*A*). An activity of one particle emitted per second is called a **becquerel (Bq)**.

Questions

1 An alpha particle with a kinetic energy of 6.2 MeV travels a distance of 7.0 cm through a cloud chamber. Its track is visible because it ionises the vapour in the chamber. The energy required for each ion pair is 8.5 eV. Calculate the number of ion pairs formed per centimetre of the alpha-particle track.

2 From the list of energies at the start of this module, calculate:
  (a) the mean speed of an oxygen atom at 300 K
  (b) the speed of an electron in a cathode-ray tube
  (c) the wavelength of a gamma-ray photon of energy 400 000 eV.

3 **(a)** A small source of gamma radiation is placed at a distance of 160 mm from a detector of area 18 mm^2, as shown in Figure 4. The count recorded on the detector after 30 minutes was 15 804. Estimate the *activity* of the source.
  (b) State two factors that could result in your answer to **(a)** being incorrect.

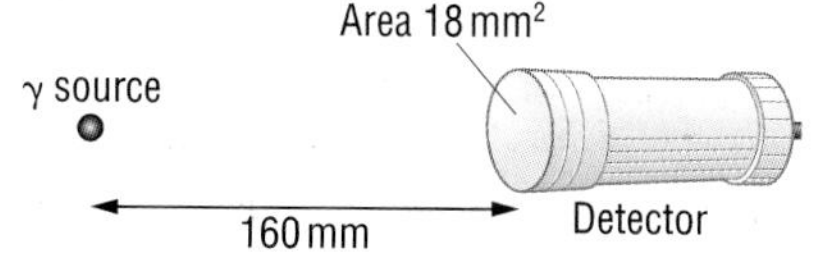

Figure 4 A gamma source is placed a distance of 160 mm from a gamma-ray detector

2.3 (9) Radioactive decay

Radioactive decay

By the end of this spread, you should be able to ...

* **Define and use the quantities decay constant and activity.**
* **Select and apply the equation for activity.**
* **Use the decay equations.**
* **Compare and contrast radioactive decay with decay of charge on a capacitor.**

Radioactive decay

Any radioactive source has nuclei that are unstable, which means there is a probability they will decay in the next unit of time. What causes the decay is not known. All attempts to find the cause of decay have been unsuccessful. Some uranium atoms have been in existence on Earth since it was formed and have been perfectly stable – but some of them will decay today, some more tomorrow. This gives some idea of just how many atoms there are in a piece of uranium. In uranium-238, 238 grams contains 6.02×10^{23} atoms; in contrast, the age of the Earth, 4 500 000 000 years, is (only) $4.5 \times 10^9 \times 365 \times 24 \times 3600 = 1.4 \times 10^{17}$ seconds. In other words, in just 238 grams of uranium, there are on average enough atoms for the nuclei of four million atoms to decay every second over the entire life of the Earth's existence.

Key definition

The **decay constant** λ relates activity A to the number of nuclei N by the equation $A = \lambda N$.

The decay constant

The relationship between N, the number of nuclei present in any radioactive source, and A, the activity of the source, is given by the **decay constant** λ. The equation defining the decay constant is

$$A = \lambda N$$

The number of nuclei present in any source will decrease over time. Assuming that activity is measured in becquerels (particles decaying per second), and since N is just a number, the unit of the decay constant will be s^{-1}. Be careful with this unit. From time to time you may see it given as $year^{-1}$ (y^{-1}). If you think of an answer using this, such as 'activity of 4.7×10^{10} per year', it is not difficult to see that it corresponds to $4.7 \times 10^{10}/(365 \times 24 \times 3600) = 1500$ Bq.

When this equation is written as

$$\frac{A}{N} = \lambda$$

you can see that λ also represents the fraction of nuclei that undergo decay in the next unit of time. For example, if the number of radioactive particles in a source is 5.6×10^6 and the present activity is 4.0×10^3 Bq, that is, 4000 decays per second, then 4000 out of 5 600 000 have decayed in the first second, or 1 in 1400. Note also that, by the time there are only 2 800 000 radioactive particles left, the average activity will have fallen to 2000 Bq. In this example the decay constant = 4000/5 600 000 = 1/1400 = 7.14×10^{-4} s^{-1}.

Decay equations

Compare these two statements. The first is for a number of nuclei of one nuclide, the second for the charge on a capacitor.

The rate at which the number of nuclei of a radioactive nuclide decreases is proportional to the number of nuclei present.

The rate at which charge leaves a capacitor (the current) is proportional to the charge on the capacitor.

The similarity of the two statements implies that the equations for the two systems will follow identical patterns. The two equations are

$$N = N_0\, e^{-\lambda t} \text{ and } Q = Q_0\, e^{-\frac{t}{CR}}$$

The first of these equations you have not met before. It shows the number of nuclei N present at any time t. N_0 is the number when $t = 0$. The second equation was used for capacitor discharge in spread 2.2.4. The discharge of a capacitor and radioactive decay follow identical patterns.

The difference between the mathematics of these equations is in the way the constant is entered. For the radioactive decay, the constant is the decay constant λ, whereas in the capacitor discharge equation it was $1/CR$. You can use these two equations in exactly the same way.

One further point is that, since the activity A is directly proportional to the number of nuclei N, the equation for activity A has exactly the same pattern as the one for N, namely

$$A = A_0\, e^{-\lambda t}$$

where A_0 is the activity when $t = 0$.

Worked example

A thorium-230 source has a mass of 6.35 mg. The nuclei in the source decay by emitting an alpha particle, and the decay constant is $2.75 \times 10^{-13}\ s^{-1}$. Calculate:

(a) the initial number of nuclei N_0 in the source
(b) the initial activity A_0 of the source
(c) the time taken before the activity falls to 1.00×10^6 Bq
(d) the number of undecayed nuclei at this time.

Answer

(a) 230 g of thorium-230 will have 6.02×10^{23} nuclei (the Avogadro constant), therefore 6.35 mg contains $6.02 \times 10^{23} \times 6.35/(230 \times 1000) = 1.66 \times 10^{19}$ nuclei.

(b) $A_0 = -\lambda N_0 = -2.75 \times 10^{-13} \times 1.66 \times 10^{19} = -4.57 \times 10^6$ Bq.

(c) Using the equation $A = A_0\, e^{-\lambda t}$ gives $1.00 \times 10^6 = 4.57 \times 10^6\, e^{-2.75 \times 10^{-13} t}$
Divide both sides by 4.57×10^6 to get

$$\frac{1.00 \times 10^6}{4.57 \times 10^6} = 0.2188 = e^{-2.75 \times 10^{-13} t}$$

Taking natural logs (ln on a calculator) gives $-1.5195 = -2.75 \times 10^{-13}\, t$

which gives $t = 1.5195/2.75 \times 10^{-13} = 5.526 \times 10^{12}$ s and this equals 1.75×10^5 years.

(d) Since A is directly proportional to N, if A decreases to 1/4.7 (= 0.213) of its previous value, then N will decrease to the same fraction, that is, 0.213×1.6 $6 \times 10^{19} = 3.53 \times 10^{18}$ nuclei.

Note: In almost all of these questions, extreme care must be taken with powers of 10. Remember, when putting a number such as 1.66×10^{19} into a calculator, you do so by entering 1.66 exp 19, *not* 1.66 × 10 exp 19.

Questions

1 Explain the difference between *activity* and *count rate*.

2 Uranium-238 has a decay constant of 4.88×10^{-18} s. One atom of uranium-238 has mass 3.95×10^{-25} kg.
(a) Calculate the number of uranium atoms that would have an activity of 16 000 Bq.
(b) What would be the mass of uranium-238 that would have this activity?

3 Potassium-40 is used for dating rock samples. Its decay constant is $9.15 \times 10^{-17}\ s^{-1}$.
(a) Calculate the mass of a potassium-40 atom.
(b) What is the activity of a sample of rock containing 0.0013 kg of potassium-40?

2.3 (10) Half-life

By the end of this spread, you should be able to ...

* **Define and apply the term half-life.**
* **Select and use the equation $\lambda t_{½} = 0.693$.**

Graphs of radioactive decay

Figure 1 shows how the activity of a radioactive source varies with time. The random nature of radioactivity results in a graph that is irregular. With a large activity, the amount of variation from the average is not too great, but if, for example, the background radiation is measured, a great deal of variation in activity is seen. In this case, with high activity, the background radiation is negligible. Figure 2 shows the same graph but with the irregularities removed. Figure 2 is an average of Figure 1.

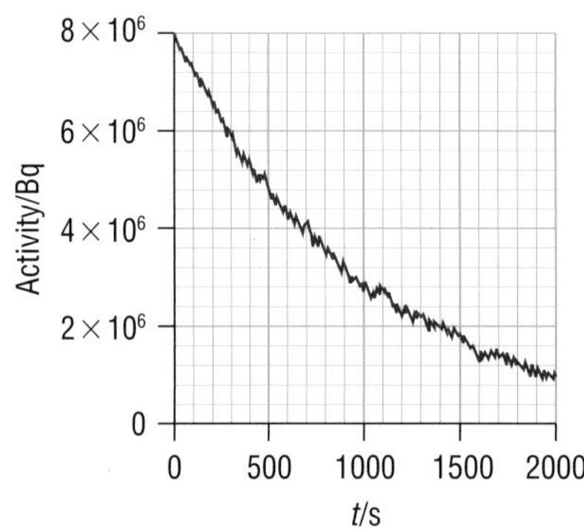

Figure 1 A graph of activity against time for a radioactive source

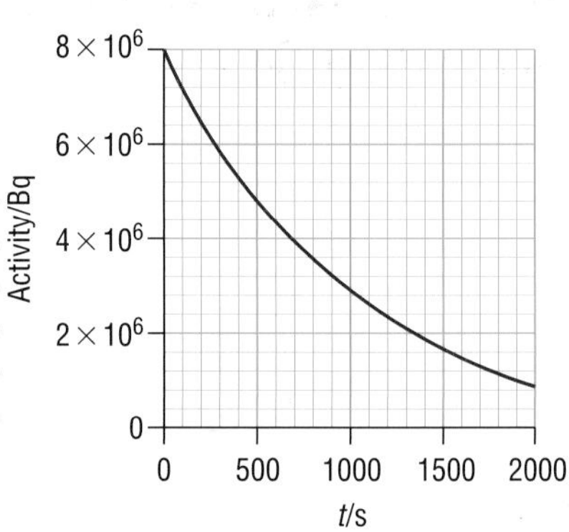

Figure 2 The graph of activity against time for the same radioactive source, with the irregularities removed

Figure 2 will be a graph of the equation

$$A = A_0 e^{-\lambda t}$$

From the graph, $A_0 = 8.00 \times 10^6$ Bq, and after 2000 s the activity falls to $A = 0.95 \times 10^6$ Bq. Putting these figures into the equation gives

$$0.95 \times 10^6 = 8.00 \times 10^6 \times e^{-\lambda \times 2000}$$

Taking natural logs gives $13.764 = 15.894 - \lambda \times 2000$, so $2000\,\lambda = 2.130$.

This gives $\lambda = 1.07 \times 10^{-3}\ s^{-1}$.

Half-life

Any exponential graph against time shows equal times for equal fractional falls. For a radioactive decay the fraction used is a half, and the time is called the **half-life**. The symbol used is $t_{½}$.

From Figure 2 the following data can be obtained.

Count at start/Bq	Count at finish/Bq	Time at start/s	Time at finish/s	Half-life/s
8.0×10^6	4.0×10^6	0	650	650
7.0×10^6	3.5×10^6	110	770	660
6.0×10^6	3.0×10^6	250	910	660
5.0×10^6	2.5×10^6	430	1100	670
4.0×10^6	2.0×10^6	650	1300	650

Examiner tip

Note how many significant figures have been kept in the expression after taking logs. This is necessary because the figure on a logarithm before the decimal point is an order of magnitude; it is only after the decimal point that you should start to count significant figures. This is clearer with an example using logs to base 10. Log 100 = 2. Any number between 100 and 999 will start with a figure 2, so to keep the calculation accurate to three significant figures on log 673, you need the 2 before the decimal point and three other figures, that is, 2.828.

Key definition

The **half-life** of a radioactive source is the time taken for the activity of the source to decrease by one half. It is also the time taken for the number of radioactive nuclei to decrease by one half.

The average half-life = 660 s to two sig. figs.

Figure 3 shows a decay in terms only of half-lives.

- After one half-life, the activity is half its initial value.
- After two half-lives, it is a quarter of its initial value.
- After three half-lives, it is an eighth of its original value, and so on.

It is easy to use half-lives when an activity or a number of nuclei happens to be halved or quartered, etc., but in the real world, this only happens infrequently.

If you measure half-life from a graph, it is more accurate to go from, say, A to $A/16$, a time equal to four half-lives, rather than measuring for just one half-life.

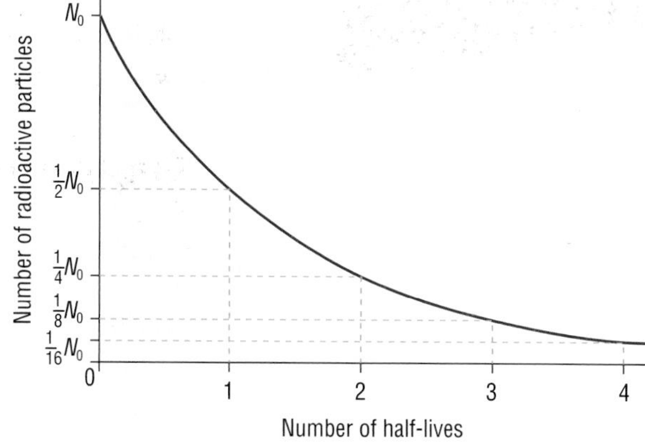

Figure 3 Radioactive decay measured in half-lives

The relationship between half-life, $t_{½}$, and the decay constant, λ

To find this relationship, it is necessary to use the decay equation

$$A = A_0\, e^{-\lambda t}$$

with $A = ½A_0$ and the time $t = t_{½}$. This makes the equation

$$½A_0 = A_0\, e^{-\lambda t_{½}}$$

Taking natural logs of this equation gives

$$\ln ½ + \ln A_0 = \ln A_0 - \lambda\, t_{½}$$

or

$$\ln ½ = -\lambda\, t_{½}$$

since $\ln ½ = -0.693$, we get $\lambda\, t_{½} = 0.693$. In words, this is

the decay constant × the half-life = 0.693

Examiner tip

Note that the correct sequence is 1, 1/2, 1/4, 1/8, 1/16, 1/32 .... But the (incorrect) sequence frequently given by candidates is 1, 1/2, 1/4, 1/16 ..., with the 1/8 term missing. Be careful you do not omit any terms.

Questions

1 How many half-lives are required for the activity of a radionuclide to decrease by a factor of **(a)**16, **(b)** 512, **(c)** 2048, **(d)** 2896?

2 A radioactive material is known to contain a mixture of two nuclides X and Y of different half-lives. Readings of activity, taken as the material decays, are given in the table together with the activity of nuclide X over the first 12 hours.

Time/hour	Activity of material/Bq	Activity of nuclide X/Bq	Activity of nuclide Y/Bq
0	4600	4200	
6	3713	3334	
12	3002	2646	
18	2436		
24	1984		
30	1619		
36	1333		

(a) The half-life of nuclide X is 18 hours. Draw and complete the last two columns in the table.

(b) Calculate the half-life of nuclide Y.

(c) Explain why the half-life of the mixture cannot be said to be about 19 hours.

Uses of radioactive isotopes

By the end of this spread, you should be able to ...

* **Describe the use of radioactive isotopes in smoke alarms.**
* **Describe the technique of radioactive dating.**

Introduction

There are thousands of uses of radioactive isotopes, so in this spread much will be omitted. The aim here is to give you some idea of the variety of uses to which radioactive materials are put, while at the same time to outline the two uses that you need to know for the examination.

Categories of uses

Radioactive materials can be used in many ways:

- archaeological dating, to find when an artefact was made
- ionisation, as in a smoke detector
- medical treatment and diagnosis, where radiation is required in a specific place
- penetration, to determine the thickness of a material
- power production, as in a nuclear reactor
- tracers, where the radioactivity in very small amount can be followed through a system.

Figure 1 An accelerator mass spectrometer being used to determine the ratio of C-14 to C-12 in a specimen

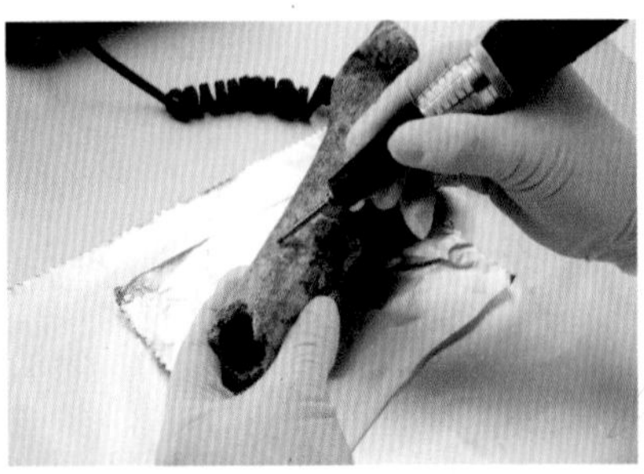

Figure 2 A sample being removed from a medieval bone. The sample taken is very small, so little damage is done to any specimen

Archaeological dating

While alive, a tree takes in carbon dioxide from the air to produce cellulose. A small fraction of the carbon atoms in atmospheric carbon dioxide is radioactive carbon-14. Once the tree dies, no more carbon-14 is absorbed, and the carbon-14 in the wood of the tree undergoes radioactive decay with a half-life of 5570 years. The ashes from an ancient fire taken from an archaeological site have fewer carbon-14 nuclei than the ashes from a new fire, so the count rate is less than the count rate from the same quantity of fresh ashes. The ratio of carbon-14 to non-radioactive carbon-12 decreases with time, so the ratio can be used for dating. Dating is accurate to the nearest 100 years. Because the quantity of carbon-14 is very small, count rates are correspondingly small. A technique is now available that allows all the carbon-14 to be obtained rather than just those nuclei that happen to decay. This is done using an accelerator mass spectrometer as shown in Figure 1. The same process can be used for dating artefacts such as bone, as shown in Figure 2.

Ionisation

There are many industries, such as the textile industry, the paper-making industry and the photographic industry, where static electricity is a real problem: pages of paper will stick together, dust will collect on a photo and dangerous voltages can build up and cause sparks. However, if a weak radioactive source emitting alpha particles is placed at key sites, the ionisation it causes makes the air conduct, thus limiting the build-up of static charge. Note that any object placed near a radioactive source does not itself become radioactive.

A *smoke detector* uses this process. The photo in Figure 3 shows the arrangement used. A battery powers the alarm itself, seen at the bottom of the photo. At the top of the detector is an ionisation chamber. It contains 0.2 μg of the radioactive nuclide americium-241, which is an alpha-emitter with a half-life of 432 years.

The source causes ionisation, and the battery causes a very small ionisation current through the chamber. When any smoke particles get into the chamber, they are charged by all the ions present, which reduces the ionisation current. The electronic circuitry detects the reduction in current and sounds the alarm.

Medical treatment and diagnosis

Several examples of medical treatment and diagnosis are given in spread 2.4.5.

Penetration

Keeping track of any continuous process is very difficult for manufacturers, so they prefer an automatic system. In making sheets of anything, such as plywood, steel or paper, the thickness needs to be controlled. Figure 4 shows a beta source being used to monitor the thickness of a piece of paper. By using a number of radioactive emitters it is possible to monitor sheets up to a thickness of several millimetres of steel. Whenever a detector under the sheet finds the count rate decreasing, it is because the sheet is too thick. An automatic system will then squeeze the forming rollers to reduce the thickness to the required amount.

Power production

Nuclear power will be dealt with in the next few spreads, but there are other uses of nuclear power on a much smaller scale. For example, polonium-210 discs are used as a heat source in order to produce electricity on space capsules sent far out in space where the Sun's radiation is weak. The discs stay hot as a result of decay, and the difference in temperature between them and the outside of the space capsule can be used to produce an electric current.

Tracers

The advantage of radioactive tracers is that they can be detected in extremely small quantities. If a plant is watered with a *very* weakly radioactive fertiliser, the rate at which the fertiliser is absorbed by the plant can be detected within minutes by monitoring the radioactivity of its leaves. Even if only a few thousand molecules have arrived at the leaf, some will decay and can therefore be detected.

Figure 3 A smoke detector

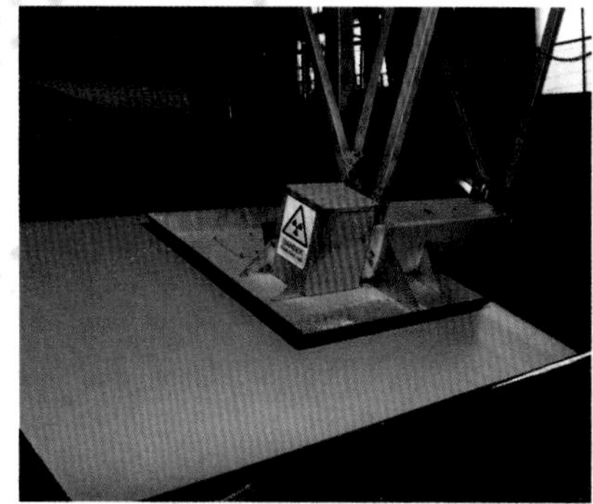

Figure 4 A beta source being used to monitor the thickness of a paper sheet

Questions

1 A polonium-210 atom has mass 3.5×10^{-25} kg, and each decay from one of these atoms produces an energy of 5.3 MeV.
 (a) How many decays per second are required to supply a power of 1000 W?
 (b) What mass of polonium-210 is required for this power? The decay constant of polonium-210 is 5.8×10^{-8} s^{-1}.

2 **(a)** What is the activity of the tiny piece of americium-241 described in the smoke detector in the section on ionisation?
 (b) Give two reasons why this source is not dangerous in normal use.

3 **(a)** A small piece of an archaeological specimen can now have all its radioactive carbon-14 atoms removed from it in a mass spectrometer. This gives much greater accuracy of carbon dating than just waiting for comparatively few carbon-14 atoms to decay. In one such investigation it was found that the ratio of carbon-14 to carbon-12 atoms was 2.74×10^{-13} compared with a ratio of carbon-14 to carbon-12 atoms in living matter of 1.30×10^{-12}. The decay constant of carbon-14 is 1.21×10^{-4} year^{-1}. How old is the archaeological specimen?
 (b) The most uncertain part of the above calculation is knowing whether the ratio of carbon-14 to carbon-12 atoms has remained constant over thousands of years. Originally, a value for the decay constant of carbon-14 was taken at its correct value of 1.24×10^{-4} year^{-1}. The value given in **(a)** is the value now used to account for variations in this ratio. How could this more reliable value be obtained?
 (c) Suggest why very little radiocarbon is found in fossil fuels.

2.3 (12) Binding energy

By the end of this spread, you should be able to ...

- **Select and use Einstein's mass–energy equation.**
- **Define binding energy and binding energy per nucleon.**
- **Use and interpret the graph of binding energy per nucleon against nucleon number.**
- **Determine the binding energy of nuclei.**

Einstein's principle of the equivalence of mass and energy

Einstein's theory of relativity concerned the relationship between one system and another. Whenever a velocity is measured, it is always a velocity relative to something else, usually the Earth. However, whenever the velocity of light is measured, the value obtained is always c. If you could move towards the light at some huge speed, you might expect the light you are approaching to be travelling faster than c, but it does not. One of Einstein's basic principles of relativity is that nothing can travel faster than c. This implies that anything moving with increasing speed becomes ever more difficult to accelerate. If something is getting more difficult to accelerate, this means its mass is increasing. Doing more work on an object increases its kinetic energy and hence increases its mass. This effect is not noticeable at low speeds. When you fly off to your next holiday destination, the plane will be travelling at around 250 m s^{-1}. At this speed, if your mass is 60 kg, the increase in your mass will only be about two hundredths of a microgram. On the other hand, a nuclear particle travelling at $0.99c$ will have a very different mass from when it is travelling at only $0.01c$. Mass changes with speed, so though you do not notice it, the extra energy you have on the plane does increase your mass. The relationship between mass and energy is given by the famous equation $E = mc^2$. However, it is better expressed using the Δ symbol, meaning 'the change in'.

$$\Delta E = \Delta mc^2$$

In words this could be read as 'the increase in energy equals the increase in mass multiplied by the speed of light squared' (or it could be a decrease).

If numerical values are put into this equation, we get

1 kg is equivalent to $1.0\text{ kg} \times (3.0 \times 10^8)^2\text{ m}^2\text{ s}^{-2} = 9.0 \times 10^{16}\text{ J}$

With atoms, it is more usual to work in the unified mass constant u. $1\text{ u} = 1.6605 \times 10^{-27}$ kg.

1 u is equivalent to $1.6605 \times 10^{-27}\text{ kg} \times (2.9979 \times 10^8)^2\text{ m}^2\text{ s}^{-2} = 1.4924 \times 10^{-10}\text{ J}$

Since $1\text{ eV} = 1.6022 \times 10^{-19}$ J, this energy, expressed in electronvolts, becomes

$$\frac{1.4924\text{ g} \times 10^{-10}\text{ J}}{1.6022 \times 10^{-19}\text{ J eV}^{-1}} = 9.3147 \times 10^8\text{ eV} = 931.47\text{ MeV}$$

These figures are given here to 5 significant figures because very small differences need to be measured. It is, however, worth trying to remember the mass–energy equivalence between mass in u and energy in MeV.

1 u is equivalent to 931 MeV

Binding energy

Imagine that you could handle an atom of calcium-40. Its mass is 39.9626 u. Calcium has a proton number of 20, so the atom contains 20 protons and therefore 20 electrons. It has 40 nucleons, so together with its 20 protons, it must have 20 neutrons in its nucleus. All the nucleons are bound together by the strong force. You now decide to separate the atom into 20 separate electrons, 20 separate protons and 20 separate neutrons and find their mass. Your mass spectrometer can find the mass of each of these particles very accurately, and the result you get is

mass of 20 protons = 20 × 1.00783 u = 20.1566 u
mass of 20 neutrons = 20 × 1.00867 u = 20.1734 u
mass of 20 electrons = 20 × 0.00055 u = 0.0110 u
total mass = 40.3410 u

The difference between the mass of the separate particles and the mass of the whole atom is because work has to be done to separate the particles, so the separate particles have more energy than the atom and therefore have more mass. The extra mass in this case is 0.3784 u. This corresponds to an energy of 0.3784 u × 931 MeV u^{-1} = 352 MeV. This energy is called the **binding energy** of the calcium-40 atom.

Key definition

Binding energy is the energy required to separate an atom into its constituent parts.

Be careful how you word a definition of binding energy. It is *not* the energy holding the atom together. Binding energy is the energy required to *separate* an atom into its constituent parts. In practice, the energy required to separate the electrons from the nucleus is negligible, so it is the act of dividing the nucleus into separate protons and neutrons that requires most of the binding energy.

To compare the binding energy of one atom with another, it is not so much the absolute size of the binding energy that matters but rather how large it is in comparison with the number of nucleons that need to be separated. For this reason the **binding energy per nucleon** is useful. For the given example of calcium-40, the binding energy per nucleon will be

352 MeV/40 nucleons = 8.8 MeV per nucleon

The graph of binding energy per nucleon against nucleon number

The binding energy per nucleon is not the same for all nuclei. When it is calculated for all 280 or so stable or nearly stable known nuclei, a chart of binding energy per nucleon plotted against nucleon number can be plotted as a series of points as shown in Figure 1. On this figure is drawn a graph showing the trend.

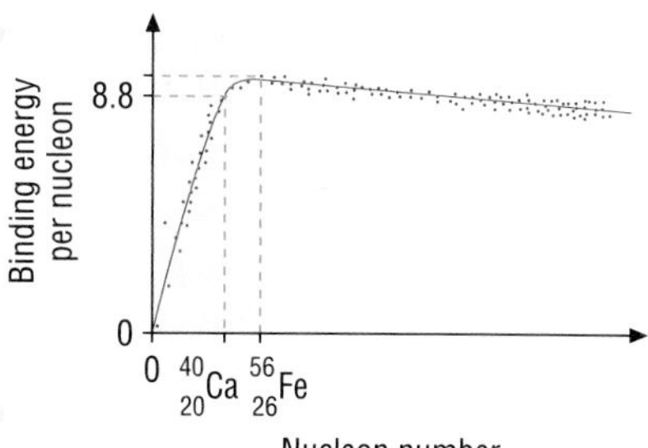

Figure 1 A chart plotting binding energy per nucleon against nucleon number. The graph shows the general trend

This graph has huge universal significance. It implies that nuclei of low nucleon number and also those of high nucleon number have smaller binding energy per nucleon than those nuclei with a nucleon number around 55. Any combining of the low nucleon elements into higher nucleon elements will result in a release of energy. This process is called **fusion** and is the process by which the Sun and other stars are supplied with energy. Similarly, if a heavy nucleus can be split into lighter nuclei, that too will result in a release of energy. All nuclear power stations use this process, which is called **fission**. These two processes are described in more detail in the next three spreads.

Questions

1 Explain why a nucleus at the top of the graph of Figure 1, with a nucleon number around 55, is the most stable of all nuclei. (This is why stars will cease to produce energy when their atoms are of about this nucleon number. It is also why there is a great deal of iron in the Earth left over from some cataclysmic event billions of years ago.)

2 A tin-120 atom has a mass of 119.902 u. It contains 50 protons.
 (a) How many neutrons and electrons does it contain?
 (b) Using the above values for the masses of the particles, calculate the extra mass that the particles have over the mass of the atom itself.
 (c) Calculate the binding energy of the atom in MeV and the binding energy per nucleon.

By the end of this spread, you should be able to ...

* **Describe the process of induced nuclear fission.**
* **Describe and explain the process of a nuclear chain reaction and its destructive use.**
* **Calculate the energy released in simple nuclear reactions.**

Induced fission

Several nuclei of heavy elements such as uranium will undergo fission in certain circumstances. Because uranium-235 has a half-life of 710 million years, it is the only heavy element found in any commercial abundance in the Earth's crust that is able to undergo fission.

Fission of a nucleus of U-235 can be caused by a slow neutron being absorbed into a U-235 nucleus, making the resulting nucleus unstable. The unstable nucleus quickly (in less than a microsecond) disintegrates, and particles fly off in all directions. One possible equation showing this is

$${}^{1}_{0}n + {}^{235}_{92}U \rightarrow {}^{236}_{92}U \rightarrow {}^{135}_{52}Te + {}^{97}_{40}Zr + 4\,{}^{1}_{0}n + \text{energy}$$

The energy–mass calculation for this becomes

	left-hand side		right-hand side	
	neutron	1.009 u	tellurium-135	134.941 u
	uranium-235	235.044 u	zirconium-97	96.911 u
			4 neutrons	4.034 u
totals		236.053 u		235.886 u

This gives a mass difference of 0.167 u. The mass has not vanished. It is the mass equivalent of the energy of the particles on the right-hand side and is the equivalent of 0.167 u × 931 MeV u^{-1} = 155 MeV.

The small amount of mass difference may not seem very significant, but

the energy released in the **fission products** from one nucleus is 155 000 000 eV.

Compare this with the energy released when one atom of carbon in a lump of coal combines with a molecule of oxygen in a coal-fired power station. The energy released this time is 4.1 eV.

The energy from one nucleus undergoing fission is nearly 40 million times larger than the energy from burning one atom of carbon – and there is no CO_2 produced from the nuclear reaction.

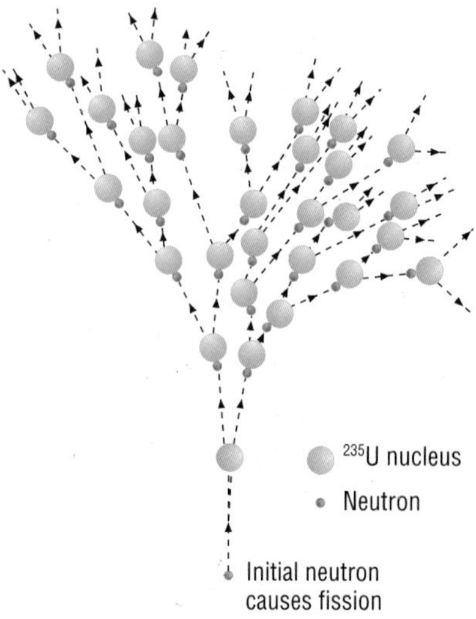

Figure 1 A diagrammatic sketch of a chain reaction

A chain reaction

You can see from the equation given as a possible fission reaction that four neutrons are emitted as the fission process takes place. The average number of neutrons emitted from the various possible reactions is 2.56, some of which are delayed for a few seconds before they are emitted. Conservation of momentum determines that the small particles, the neutrons, are likely to have about the same momentum as the larger particles. Since the neutrons have lower mass, they will have higher speed. If a neutron hits another uranium-235 nucleus, it can cause further fission to occur. If more than one neutron causes further fission, then the process can repeat itself, and the number of fissions can escalate very rapidly. This is in fact what happens in a nuclear bomb. In such a bomb, there is not much else present besides uranium-235 atoms, so many neutrons do indeed hit other nuclei. This is illustrated in Figure 1.

In a nuclear reactor, of the 2.56 neutrons that are produced per fission, only 1.0 of these neutrons is used to maintain the operation of the reactor. In practice, 0.9 neutrons are absorbed by some uranium-238, which does not undergo fission, and 0.58 are absorbed by materials in the reactor, leaving a small excess. Boron rods are used to absorb these neutrons and, by moving the rods in and out of the reactor, to control its rate of operation.

Uranium isotopes

It is thought that, when the Earth was formed 4.5 billion years ago, two isotopes of uranium were present in some rocks in about equal quantities. Uranium-235 has a half-life of 710 million years, and uranium-238 has a half-life of 4500 million years. As a result, most of the uranium-235 has now decayed, and when uranium ore is mined today, 99.3% of it is uranium-238 and only 0.7% is uranium-235. (When politicians and others talk about 'enriching' uranium, they are talking about increasing the percentage of uranium-235. Nuclear bombs can be made from uranium only if it is enriched considerably.) In reactors, natural uranium, or slightly enriched uranium, is the fuel normally used.

Slow neutrons

Whether or not a neutron causes fission of a uranium-235 nucleus depends on how fast it is travelling. If it is going too fast, it is far less likely to cause fission than if it is going slowly. (In this respect it is similar to a golf ball falling into a hole. The ball will always drop into the hole if it is going slowly across the hole, but will carry straight on if it is going fast.) The neutrons, when they emerge from a fission reaction, are always going fast. In fact, they have to be slowed down before they can cause a fission of another uranium-235 nucleus. In a reactor situation, the problem is made worse by the fact that neutrons can be absorbed by the uranium-238 nuclei present but not cause fission, and there are 140 of them present for every uranium-235 nucleus. The neutrons just bounce off uranium-238 nuclei once they are travelling slowly.

The mechanics of slowing neutrons down is illustrated in Figure 2. All the situations drawn can be shown to be valid by assuming the collisions are elastic collisions, so both momentum and kinetic energy are conserved. Some nuclear reactors use heavy water to moderate the speed of neutrons, but most reactors in the UK use carbon.

Figure 2 shows that a neutron can be slowed down most effectively by a hydrogen nucleus, but hydrogen nuclei absorb neutrons, so heavy water is often used. Heavier nuclei are, in order, helium, which is a gas, lithium, which is very reactive, beryllium, which is very expensive, boron, which absorbs neutrons, and carbon, which is what is used. Carbon is advantageous in that:

- it does not absorb neutrons
- it conducts heat well
- it is chemically stable
- is cheap and readily available.

Some carbon moderator material has been slowing down neutrons in reactors for over 40 years and has only now disintegrated to any appreciable extent.

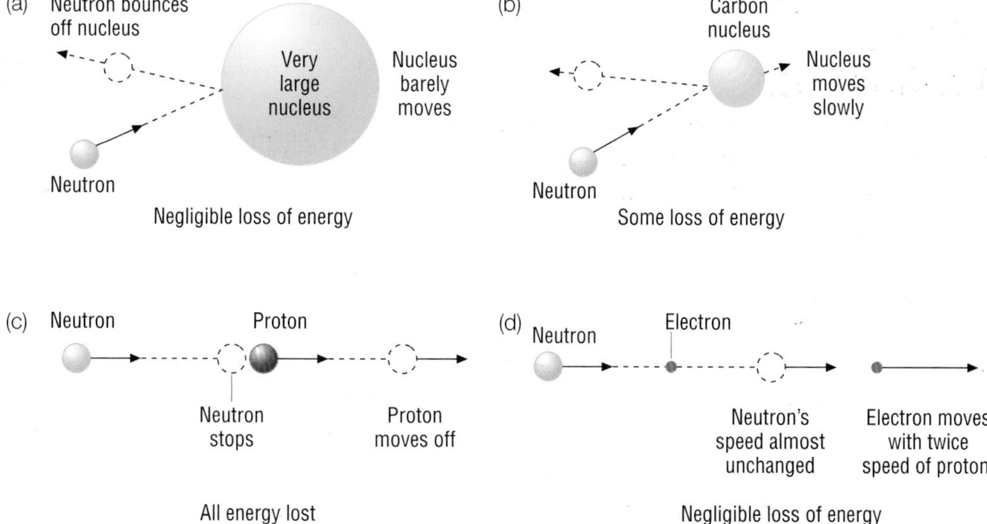

Figure 2 A neutron colliding with **(a)** a uranium nucleus, **(b)** a carbon nucleus, **(c)** a proton and **(d)** an electron. The neutron slows down the most when it collides with a particle that has a mass equal to its own mass

Questions

1 By writing equations showing conservation of kinetic energy and conservation of momentum, show that an elastic collision between neutron X travelling with velocity v directly towards neutron Y, which is stationary, will result in X stopping and Y moving off with velocity v.

2 One other possible fission reaction is

$$^{1}_{0}n + ^{235}_{92}U \rightarrow ^{236}_{92}U \rightarrow$$
$$^{143}_{56}Ba + ^{90}_{36}Kr + 3\,^{1}_{0}n + \text{energy}$$

Use details from the section on 'induced fission' on this spread together with the following data to find:

(a) the mass difference between the two sides of the above equation

(b) the energy equivalence of this mass.

Mass of barium-143 = 142.9365 u;
mass of krypton-90 = 89.9394 u.

2.3 (14)

The nuclear reactor

How Science Works

By the end of this spread, you should be able to ...

* **Describe the basic construction of a fission reactor.**
* **Explain the role of fuel rods, control rods and moderator.**
* **Describe the peaceful use of nuclear fission and its use as an energy source.**
* **Describe the environmental effects of nuclear waste.**

Reactor layout

The key parts of a nuclear reactor are the fuel elements, the moderator, the control rods and the coolant. The coolant circulates through the reactor and in the process heats up. It then passes through a heat exchanger, in which it loses heat in creating high-pressure steam. From this point onwards the passage of the steam through a steam turbine, its cooling system, the generator and the electrical distribution system are just like a conventional power station.

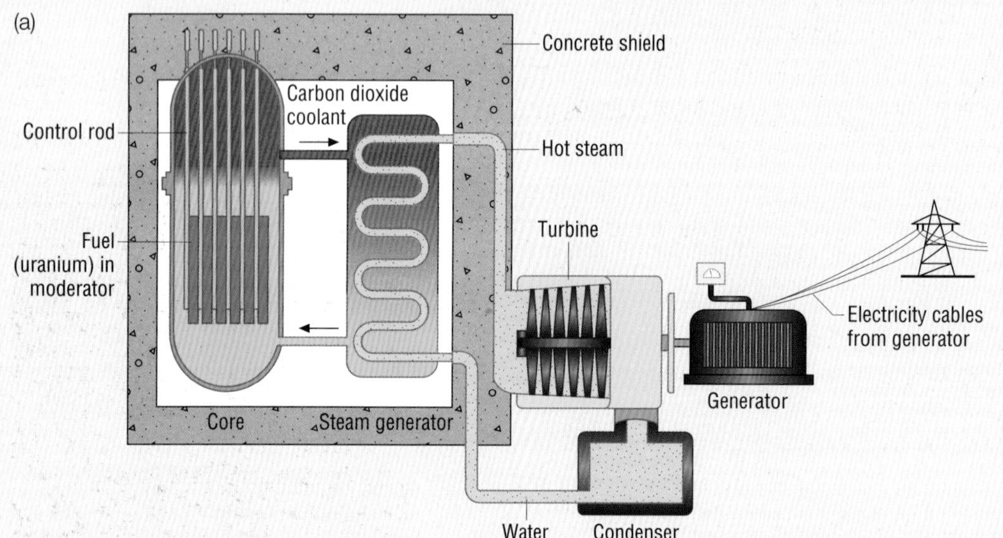

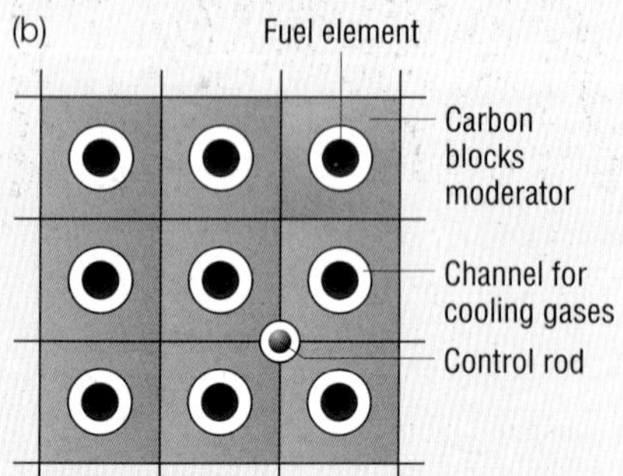

Figure 1 **(a)** A diagram showing the arrangement of components in an Advanced Gas Cooled Reactor and the shielding around the pressure vessel; **(b)** the arrangement of fuel elements, moderator and control rods inside the pressure vessel of an AGR

Figure 1(a) shows the arrangement of the components in an Advanced Gas Cooled Reactor (AGR), and Figure 1(b) is a cross-section of the arrangement inside the pressure vessel for a few of its fuel elements. The fuel elements are lowered into long vertical holes in the square blocks of carbon. These carbon blocks are the moderator. In the moderator, neutrons are slowed down to become so-called thermal neutrons, which then will drift back into the fuel elements to cause more fission reactions. Placed throughout the core are additional holes within which boron control rods can be raised or lowered. Boron has the ability to absorb neutrons, so the reactor output is dependent on how many control rods are present. The control rods are held by fail-safe systems that will automatically drop the rods and shut down the reactor should anything go wrong. The fuel elements themselves are inside cases made specially to allow carbon dioxide cooling gases to swirl through the spaces between the fuel elements and the carbon moderator. This carbon dioxide takes the energy output of the reactor to heat exchangers where the steam to power the turbines is heated.

The turbine in any power station is a heat engine; it transforms the thermal energy of high-pressure steam to do work on a generator on the other end of its axle (Figure 1(a)). The generator supplies electrical energy to the national grid. Any heat engine can have its efficiency increased by raising the inlet temperature and lowering the outlet temperature. Lowering the outlet temperature is done with lots of cooling water. That is one reason why nuclear reactors are near the coast.

Reactor design

There are many different designs of reactor. All but one of the commercial nuclear reactors in the UK were built 30 or more years ago and used carbon as a moderator and carbon dioxide as a coolant. Most of the early reactors have now been dismantled or shut down, and the operational ones now are AGRs. The one different type of reactor is the newest one, which is at Sizewell. This reactor uses enriched uranium, with water under pressure as its coolant and its moderator. Figure 2 is an aerial photo of the Sizewell Pressurised Water Reactor. The white dome is on top of the reactor, and the turbine hall is the building to the left of it. At the bottom of the photo are the transformers that connect the generators to the national grid.

As stated above, the efficiency of a heat engine is increased as the high temperature is raised. There are problems, however, with high inlet temperatures. In the first place, steam at a high temperature exerts a huge pressure, resulting in engineering problems. Additionally, metallic uranium cannot be used above about a temperature of 500 °C, because it burns. In the AGRs, the uranium is slightly enriched and is formed into a ceramic material better able to withstand a higher temperature. The size of the reactor can be gauged from the photo, Figure 3, of the floor above the reactor core. All replacement of fuel elements and control rods is done using the charge–discharge machine shown in the photo.

Figure 2 Sizewell nuclear power station. The reactor is directly beneath the white dome

The environmental effects of nuclear power generation

This is a divisive topic. Here, some important statements are made that should be kept in mind whenever the pros and cons of nuclear generation are considered.

- All types of power generation have an impact on the environment.
- All electrical power has to be generated at the same instant as it is used.
- Nuclear power produces radioactive waste. This waste undergoes radioactive decay: most of it fairly quickly, but some has a long half-life and will need to be contained for a very long time to avoid damage to plant and animal life.
- Nuclear power stations do not produce carbon dioxide emissions as a by-product of their process.
- Wind-generated electrical power cannot supply power on days when it is cold and windless.
- Tidal-generated electrical power will be supplied at predicted times that vary each day, so will often be unable to supply power at times of peak demand.
- All power stations produce a great deal of warm water that has been used for cooling. This could be used for central heating in houses or commercial buildings, but not only would the consumers need to be near the power station, no one would want warm water for heating during a summer heat wave.

Figure 3 The cap of an Advanced Gas Cooled reactor. The reactor itself is directly beneath the chequerboard pattern on the floor. The yellow and black machine is used to replace control rods and fuel elements while the reactor is running. This part of the building is 25 metres high, and the floor is 30 metres above the ground

Questions

1 A nuclear power station has an electrical power output of 400 MW. The components within the station have the following efficiencies:

(i)	heat exchanger from reactor to steam turbine	91%
(ii)	steam turbine	39%
(iii)	alternator	97%
(iv)	electrical supply to transformers	95%
(v)	transformers	98%

(a) Calculate the power that the reactor supplies.

(b) Describe briefly what is happening in stages **(i)**, **(ii)**, **(iii)** and **(v)**. (The figure in **(iv)** is only 95% because the power station itself needs electrical power for heating, lighting and control systems, as well as for all the pumping systems.)

(c) Suggest why the steam turbine has such a low efficiency, especially when compared with all the other systems.

2 The steam turbine in any power station requires a lot of cooling water. For the power station in Question 1 this is done using sea water with an inlet temperature of 15 °C. The power station is not allowed to discharge water back into the sea at a temperature greater than 21 °C. The power station will require 700 MW of power to be dissipated into the sea. Calculate the rate of flow of water required through the cooling system. The specific heat capacity of sea water is 3900 J kg^{-1} K^{-1}.

Fusion

By the end of this spread, you should be able to ...

- **Describe the process of nuclear fusion.**
- **Describe the conditions in the core of stars.**
- **Calculate the energy released in simple nuclear reactions.**

Nuclear fusion

In spread 2.3.12 a chart was drawn showing how heavy nuclei have less binding energy per nucleon than nuclei such as the iron-57 nucleus. This makes energy release possible when fission of a heavy nucleus takes place. That chart shows that energy release is also possible if light nuclei can be combined to make heavier nuclei. The combination of light nuclei into heavy nuclei is called fusion. Almost all of the power we rely on daily is, or has been, supplied by fusion taking place in the Sun. If not supplied directly by the Sun, it was the Sun's power millions of years ago that allowed plants and animals to live then and hence to provide the coal, oil and gas that we now burn. In the UK the only power that we currently use that the Sun has not provided is that from nuclear power stations.

One process of nuclear fusion looks deceptively simple. It can take place between two deuterons, which are the nuclei of an isotope of hydrogen called deuterium (or heavy hydrogen) and comprise one proton and one neutron. The process is

$$^{2}_{1}\mathrm{H} + ^{2}_{1}\mathrm{H} + 3.6\ \mathrm{MeV} = ^{3}_{2}\mathrm{He} + ^{1}_{0}\mathrm{n} + 6.9\ \mathrm{MeV}$$

The problem with this reaction is that it requires an energy input of 3.6 MeV per reaction. It is possible to get the output energy only if the input energy can be provided. The two deuterons repel one another very strongly at close range, so they will not normally fuse. So that an appreciable number of them will fuse, temperatures as high as the interior of the Sun are needed – around 20 000 000 K. Even then, many millions of close encounters of nuclei do not cause fusion, but there are a few that do.

Practical examples of fusion

Fusion in stars

Fusion powers all stars. The reaction is more complex than simply two high-speed deuterons colliding with one another. One possible sequence of reactions is:

$$^{1}_{1}\mathrm{H} + ^{1}_{1}\mathrm{H} \rightarrow ^{2}_{1}\mathrm{H} + ^{0}_{1}\mathrm{e} + ^{0}_{0}\nu$$

$$^{1}_{1}\mathrm{H} + ^{2}_{1}\mathrm{H} \rightarrow ^{3}_{2}\mathrm{He} + \gamma$$

$$^{3}_{2}\mathrm{He} + ^{3}_{2}\mathrm{He} \rightarrow ^{4}_{2}\mathrm{He} + ^{1}_{1}\mathrm{H} + ^{1}_{1}\mathrm{H}$$

The overall effect of these reactions is to convert four protons into one helium-4 nucleus and to supply 25 MeV of energy together with two positrons, two neutrinos and two gamma photons. Certainly the Sun is a source of vast numbers of neutrinos and gamma-ray photons. Positrons formed will be quickly annihilated by electrons to produce gamma-ray photons in the Sun's plasma, that is, the soup of nuclei, protons, neutrons and electrons of which the Sun is made.

Worked example

Use the data given to find:

(a) the power output of the Sun

(b) the decrease in mass of the Sun each second

(c) the number of fusion reactions taking place per second within the Sun

(d) the number of fusion reactions taking place per cubic metre of the Sun.

Data

- Earth–Sun distance 1.50×10^{11} m
- Power per unit area from the Sun at the top of the Earth's atmosphere (the solar constant) 1.4 kW
- The radius of the Sun 7.0×10^{8} m
- Energy of one fusion 3.3 MeV: 1 eV = 1.6×10^{-19} J

Answer

(a) A sphere of radius equal to the Earth–Sun distance has surface area $4\pi \times (1.50 \times 10^{11})^2 = 2.83 \times 10^{23}$ m^2.
Each of these square metres receives 1.4 kW of power from the Sun.
Total power output = 2.83×10^{23} m$^2 \times 1400$ W m^{-2} = 3.96×10^{26} W

(b) In one second the energy supplied by the Sun is 3.96×10^{26} J
Using $\Delta E = \Delta mc^2$ gives 3.96×10^{26} J $= \Delta m \times (3.0 \times 10^8)^2$
hence $\Delta m = 3.96 \times 10^{26}/(3.0 \times 10^8)^2 = 4.4 \times 10^9$ kg s^{-1}. Yes! The Sun is shrinking by over 4 million tonnes every second as a result of its radiation of electromagnetic waves out into space.

(c) Energy is supplied by a fusion reaction of 3.3×10^6 eV $= 3.3 \times 10^6 \times 1.6 \times 10^{-19}$
$= 5.28 \times 10^{-13}$ J
Number of fusion reactions per second = 3.96×10^{26} J s^{-1}/5.28×10^{-13} J
$= 7.5 \times 10^{38}$ s^{-1}

(d) Volume of the Sun = $4\pi r^3/3 = 4\pi \times (7.0 \times 10^8 \text{ m})^3/3 = 1.4 \times 10^{27}$ m^3
Number of fusion reactions per cubic metre per second
$= 7.5 \times 10^{38}$ s^{-1}/1.4×10^{27} m^3 = 5.3×10^{11} m^{-3} s^{-1}

Fusion on the Earth

Fusion can be caused experimentally on the Earth, but at present there is no commercial power station using fusion. Two big advantages of using fusion for power production would be that

- no radioactive waste products are formed by the fusion process
- there is a virtually unlimited supply of the raw materials. About 1% of sea water molecules have a deuterium atom in them.

The problem is to maintain a high enough temperature for long enough for sufficient fusion to take place. At present, any apparatus that can induce fusion requires much more electrical energy than it could produce.

Figure 1 is a computer artwork of the planned ITER tokamak device, which is to be built in France by joint cooperation between Canada, China, Europe, India, Japan, Korea, Russia and the USA. In the tokamak a huge discharge through a deuterium–tritium gas mixture from a bank of capacitors is compressed by magnetic fields into a doughnut-shaped ring, within which temperatures of perhaps as high as a hundred million degrees can be maintained for a few microseconds. The reaction that can take place is

$$^{3}_{1}\text{H} + ^{2}_{1}\text{H} \rightarrow ^{4}_{2}\text{He} + ^{1}_{0}\text{n} + 17.6 \text{ MeV}$$

The helium nucleus supplies 3.5 MeV of energy to the plasma, and the neutron escapes with 14.1 MeV of energy into a surrounding lithium blanket. Here it not only heats the lithium but also initiates a reaction that produces more tritium. The hope is that the efficiency of the device will allow enough energy to be produced to recharge the capacitors and to have some energy left over, eventually for sale.

Various other machines are attempting to harness fusion. All of them rely on huge powers for short times. For example, the Z machine in the USA may have reached a power of 10^{14} watts for a few billionths of a second, and there have been several attempts to fire an array of high-powered lasers all onto one tiny spot, with the resultant huge rise in temperature.

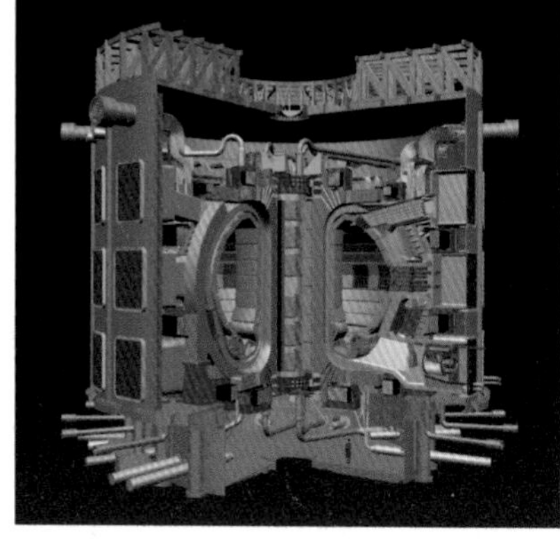

Figure 1 A diagram showing the planned ITER device

Questions

1 (a) It is possible, if the speed is high enough, to make two nuclei of heavy hydrogen fuse together to form a tritium nucleus and a proton. How much energy will be released in such a process? The masses of the relevant nuclei are $^{3}_{1}$H 3.01550 u; $^{2}_{1}$H 2.01355 u; $^{1}_{1}$H 1.00728 u.

(b) In your work on temperature and the energy of atoms, you used the equation $E = 3kT/2$, where k is the Boltzmann constant and has a value of 1.38×10^{-23} J K^{-1}. Use the equation here to find the order of magnitude of the temperature required for an atom to have a value of E equal to your answer to **(a)**.

2 A double-step reaction can produce a greater quantity of energy. One example of this is as follows.

$$^{2}_{1}\text{H} + ^{2}_{1}\text{H} \rightarrow ^{3}_{1}\text{H} + ^{1}_{1}\text{H} + 4.0 \text{ MeV}$$

$$^{3}_{1}\text{H} + ^{2}_{1}\text{H} \rightarrow ^{4}_{2}\text{He} + ^{1}_{0}\text{n} + 17.6 \text{ MeV}$$

Rewrite this as a single equation in order to see what particles are necessary for the reactions, what particles are produced and what the final energy output is.

2.3 Further questions D

Fundamental particles

(1) The π^0 meson has its mass quoted as 135.0 MeV/c^2. It decays into two gamma rays:

$$\pi^0 \rightarrow \gamma + \gamma$$

(a) Calculate the mass of the π^0 meson in kilograms.

(b) Assuming the π^0 meson to be initially at rest, calculate the energy and hence the wavelength of the two gamma rays.

Radioactivity

(2) Figure 1 shows a cross-section through a smoke detector mounted on the ceiling.

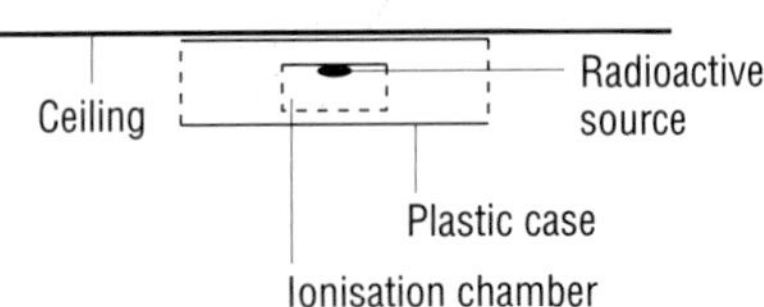

Figure 1

The radioactive source in the detector is americium-241, which emits α-particles. The air inside the chamber is ionised by the particles, allowing the air to conduct. Any smoke in the chamber absorbs the ions and reduces the conductivity of the air.

(a) A typical smoke detector contains 2.9×10^{-10} kg of americium-241.

(i) Show that the number N of americium nuclei in the source is about 7×10^{14}.

(ii) Americium has a half-life of about 450 y (1.5×10^{10} s). Show that its decay constant λ is about 5×10^{-11} s^{-1}.

(iii) Calculate the activity of the source.

(b) It is advised that the smoke detector be replaced after five years when about 5×10^{12} nuclei will have decayed.

(i) Use the equation $\Delta N = -\lambda N \Delta t$ to show that this is the number of nuclei which have decayed.

(ii) Explain why the equation in **(i)** will not give an accurate answer but only an adequate approximation to it.

(3) At the beginning of the twentieth century, Pierre and Marie Curie separated about 0.2 g of a radium salt from a ton of uranium ore called pitchblende. The radioactive radium nuclide $^{226}_{88}$Ra decays by alpha-particle emission with a half-life of 1600 years. 1 year = 3.16×10^7 s.

(a) This incredible feat led to the historic unit of radioactivity being called the curie. It is defined as the number of disintegrations per second from 1.0 g of $^{226}_{88}$Ra. Show that **(i)** the decay constant of the radium nuclide is 1.4×10^{-11} s^{-1} and **(ii)** 1 curie equals 3.7×10^{10} Bq.

(b) Use the data below to show that the energy release in the decay of a single nucleus of $^{226}_{88}$Ra by alpha-particle emission is 7.9×10^{-13} J.

nuclear mass of Ra-226 = 226.0254 u
nuclear mass of Rn-222 = 222.0175 u
nuclear mass of He = 4.0026 u

(c) Not knowing any of the physics in **(b)** above, the Curies and other famous scientists were mystified at first that the small sample of isolated radium self-heated. The phenomenon appeared to break the laws of thermodynamics.
Estimate the time it would take a freshly made sample of radium of mass 0.2 g to increase in temperature by 1.0 °C. Assume that 80% of the energy of the alpha particles is absorbed within the sample so that this is the energy which is heating the sample. Use data from **(a)** and **(b)**. Take the specific heat capacity of radium to equal 110 J kg^{-1} K^{-1}.

Fission and fusion

(4) This question is about the comparison of the energy released in typical fission and fusion reactions.

(a) Use data from Figure 5 on page 179 to show that the total binding energy of a single $^{235}_{92}U$ nucleus is about 2.8×10^{-10} J. [1]

(b) A typical nuclear fission reaction is

$$^{235}_{92}U + ^{1}_{0}n \rightarrow ^{141}_{56}Ba + ^{92}_{36}Kr + 3\,^{1}_{0}n$$

(i) Explain why the energy released in this reaction as kinetic energy of the fragments is only a small fraction of the energy calculated in **(a)**. [1]

(ii) Calculate the energy released per kilogram of $^{235}_{92}U$ assuming that the actual fraction is 1/6. [2]

(c) Real fusion reactions are complex. However, one sequence of reactions involving isotopes of hydrogen can be summarised by the single reaction equation:

$$4\,^{1}_{1}H \rightarrow ^{4}_{2}He + 2\,^{0}_{1}e$$

(i) Use Figure 5 to find the total energy released in this reaction. [2]

(ii) Calculate the energy released per kilogram of $^{1}_{1}H$ used. [2]

(d) Comment upon your answers to **(b) (ii)** and **(c) (ii)**. [1]

(5) This question is about a nuclear reactor used to power a submarine.

(a) In a nuclear reactor the process of nuclear fission is caused by neutron bombardment. The following equation summarises what may happen:

$$^{235}U + ^{1}n \rightarrow ^{139}Xe + ^{95}Sr + 2\,^{1}n + \text{energy}$$

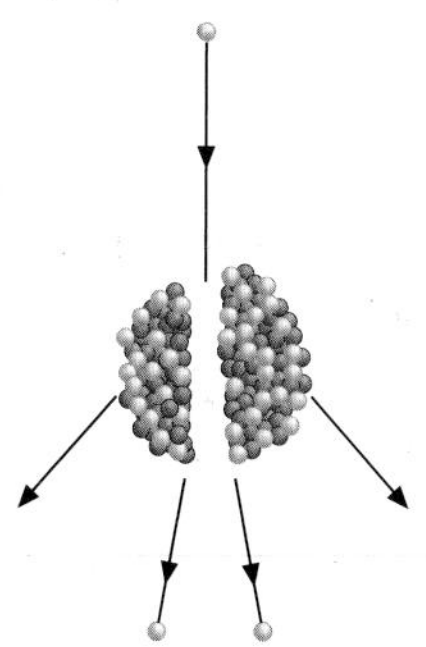

Figure 2

(i) Copy the diagram. Label all of the particles and then extend the diagram to illustrate how a chain reaction might develop. [2]

(ii) Use the data to show that the energy released in a single fission is about 3×10^{-11} J. [2]

particle	^{235}U	^{139}Xe	^{95}Sr	^{1}n
mass/u	235.0	138.9	94.89	1.009

$1\ u = 1.7 \times 10^{-27}$ kg

(b) Although the uranium fuel is enriched, only 3% of the uranium atoms in the fuel are the fissile ^{235}U isotope. The remaining 97% of the fuel is made up of ^{238}U.

(i) Show that there are approximately 8×10^{23} atoms of ^{235}U in 10 kg of fuel. [1]

(ii) Calculate how much energy is available if all of these atoms undergo fission. [1]

(c) The power needed for a submarine to travel at maximum speed is 750 kW. Show that 10 kg of fuel should last for at least one year (3.2×10^{7} s). [2]

2.3 Nuclear physics summary

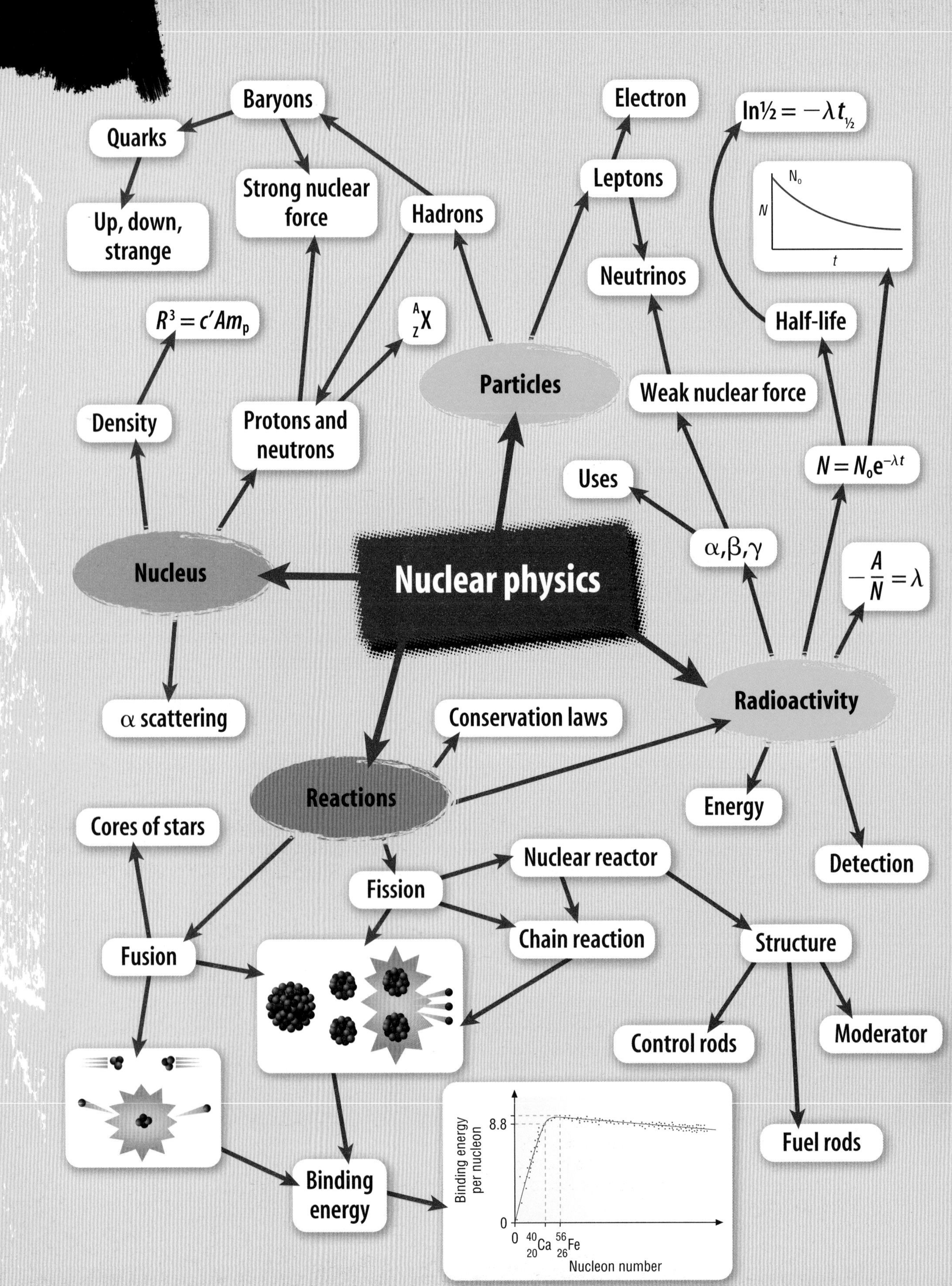

Practice questions

1 The radius r of a nucleus containing A nucleons is given by the equation $r = r_0A^{1/3}$.

(a) Explain what r_0 represents.

(b) Figure 1 is a graph of the relationship between A and r.

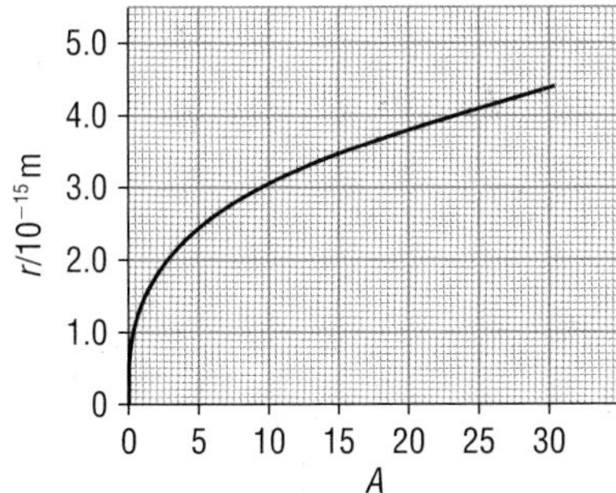

Figure 1

(i) Use Figure 1 to find the value of r when $A = 20$.

(ii) Hence show that r_0 is equal to 1.4×10^{-15} m.

(c) Use your answer to **(ii)** to estimate the density of the hydrogen nucleus, that is, the proton.

(d) Taking the distance between two protons in a nucleus to be $2r_0$, estimate the minimum value of the nuclear force holding them together. To do this, calculate the Coulomb repulsion force between the protons.

2 Figure 2 shows the path of an alpha particle ${}^4_2$He being deflected through an angle of 30° as it passes a nucleus N in a thin gold foil.

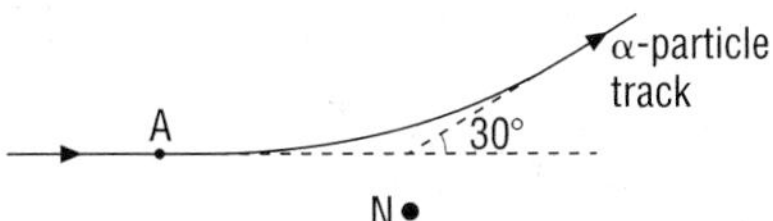

Figure 2

Copy Figure 2 and draw on it arrows to represent **(i)** the direction of the electrostatic force on the α-particle when it is at A, and **(ii)** the direction of the maximum electrostatic force on the nucleus N during the passage of the α-particle.

(b) The incident α-particle has kinetic energy 8.0×10^{-13} J and mass 6.7×10^{-27} kg. Show that **(i)** its initial speed is 1.5×10^7 m s^{-1} and **(ii)** the magnitude of its initial momentum is 1.0×10^{-19} kg m s^{-1}.

(c) Imagine a proton moving initially along the same path as the α-particle with the same kinetic energy.

(i) Show that the initial momentum of the proton is 5.0×10^{-20} kg m s^{-1}.

(ii) The proton is deflected through about 15° as it passes the gold nucleus. State qualitatively **two** ways in which the movement of the nucleus differs in this case from the movement caused by the α-particle.

(d) Calculate the magnitude in N of the electrostatic force between the proton at point A and the gold nucleus ${}^{197}_{79}$Au. The distance AN is 7.5×10^{-13} m.

3 The radioactive nuclide ${}^{238}_{92}$U decays by alpha-particle emission. The newly formed nuclide X is also unstable and decays by a different radioactive emission to a third nuclide Y. Y then decays to become another isotope of uranium, ${}^{234}_{92}$U.

(a) Explain the meaning of the term *isotope*.

(b) Write down suitable symbols in the form ${}^{238}_{92}$U for **(i)** an α-particle **(ii)** a β-particle.

(c) Show how ${}^{238}_{92}$U can become the isotope ${}^{234}_{92}$U after three decays.

4 **(a)** State the two classes of particle, each of which includes both the proton and the neutron.

(b) State the quark composition of **(i)** the proton and **(ii)** the neutron.

(c) The neutron can decay, producing particles that include a proton and an electron.

(i) Write a quark equation for this reaction.

(ii) Write number equations which show that charge and baryon number are conserved in this quark equation.

(d) Two other kinds of hadron are the π^0 and π^- particles. Each of these has a baryon number of zero and strangeness of zero. By writing number equations for the values of charge, baryon number and strangeness, explain whether the reaction

$$\pi^- + p^+ \rightarrow n^0 + \pi^0$$

may take place.

5 Uranium can change into other nuclides by two processes: *radioactive decay* and *fission*. For these processes describe **two** similarities and **two** differences between them.

1 Two adjacent protons, situated inside a certain nucleus, are acted upon by three forces. These are **(i)** electrostatic, **(ii)** gravitational and **(iii)** the strong interaction (i.e. strong force).

(a) State whether each of these forces is attractive or repulsive. [1]

(b) The average separation of the nucleons in this nucleus is 0.80×10^{-15} m. Calculate the magnitude of **(i)** the electrostatic force and **(ii)** the gravitational force. Give an appropriate unit in each case. [6]

(c) Use your answers to **(b)** to comment on the relative importance of electrostatic and gravitational forces inside the nucleus. [2]

(d) Figure 1 shows the variation with nucleon–nucleon separation of the strong interaction between two nucleons.

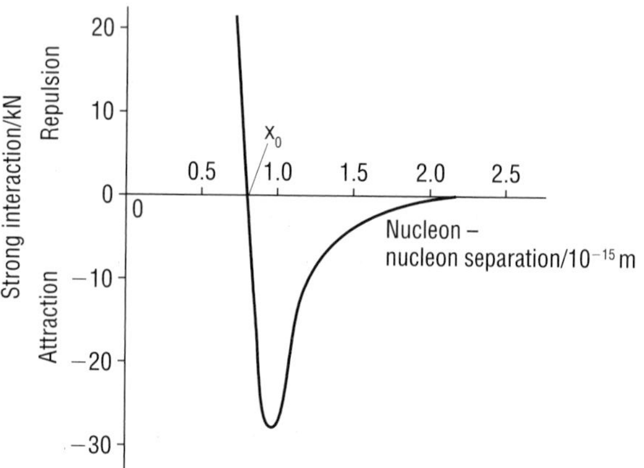

Figure 1

When both nucleons are *neutrons*, the equilibrium separation is x_0. Explain whether the equilibrium separation between two *protons* will be greater, less than or equal to x_0. [3]

(OCR 2825/04 Jun02)

2 **(a)** There are six quarks. Two are called *up* and *down*. Name the other four. [2]

(b) (i) Name the group of particles of which the electron and the positron are members. [1]

(ii) Name another member of this group. [1]

(iii) Nitrogen-14, $^{14}_{7}N$, can be formed as a result of the two types of β-decay:

1 β-decay of carbon-14, $^{14}_{6}C$.

2 β-decay of oxygen-14, $^{14}_{8}O$.

Write nuclear equations for these two reactions. [2]

(iv) In each of the reactions in **(iii)** state the name of the other particle which is produced. [2]

(c) (i) State the quark composition of the neutron. [1]

(ii) Write down the charge Q, baryon number B and strangeness S for each of the quarks in the neutron. [2]

(iii) Hence deduce the values of Q, B and S for the neutron. [1]

(d) It is suggested that a proton p^+ can react with a pi particle π^- to form a kaon K^0 and a neutron, thus:

$$p^+ + \pi^- \rightarrow K^0 + n^0$$

The quark composition of π^- is $d\,\bar{u}$ and of K^0 is $d\,\bar{s}$. Deduce whether the reaction is possible. [4]

(OCR 2825/04 Jan03 & Jun07)

3 **(a)** The charge and mass of the three types of ionising radiation emitted by radioactive substances can be given in terms of the fundamental charge e and the mass m_e of an electron or the mass m_p of a proton. Using these symbols, state the charge and mass of **(i)** α, **(ii)** β and **(iii)** γ radiation. [3]

(b) Alpha particles do not penetrate more than a few centimetres of air. Figure 2 shows how the mean range of alpha particles depends on their kinetic energy at emission.

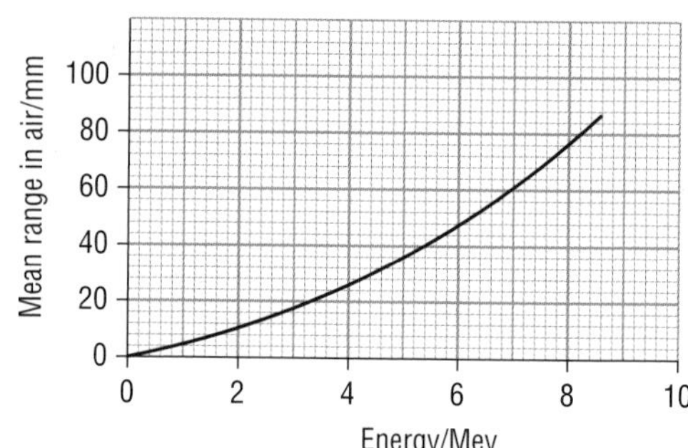

Figure 2

(i) Use the graph to find the range in mm of alpha particles emitted with an energy of 5.0 MeV. [1]

(ii) Calculate the initial speed in m s^{-1} of a 5 MeV alpha particle. [3]

1 MeV = 1.6×10^{-13} J

(iii) Explain how alpha particles lose kinetic energy as they travel through the air. [2]

(c) Figure 3 shows a film badge which is worn by people who work with ionising radiation, such as beta particles, X-rays and gamma rays. The film is wrapped in a light-tight paper wrapper. It is placed in a plastic holder which has a wide slot or 'window' cut through the plastic. The holder also contains a number of metallic and plastic filters. The amount of darkening in different regions of the film indicates the exposure to different types of radiation.

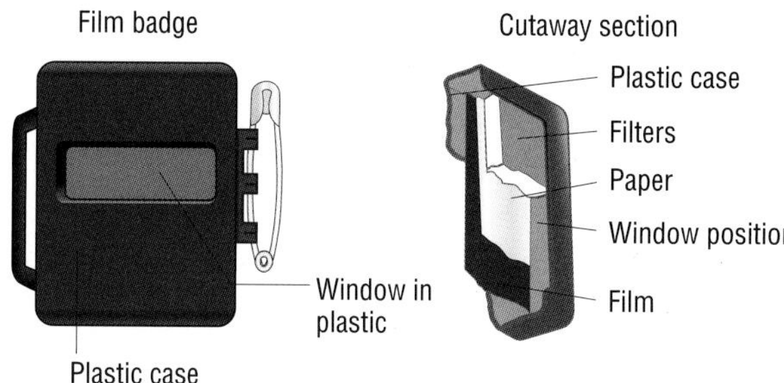

Figure 3

Suggest why film badges are not suitable for monitoring alpha radiation, and why the window and the different types of filter are provided. [4]

(OCR 2824 Jun04)

4 Two radioactive isotopes which are serious health hazards to human beings are strontium-90 and caesium-137. Both decay by β^- emission.

(a) The nuclear equations for each of the decays are shown below with letters substituted for some of the numbers.

$^{90}_{38}\text{Sr} \rightarrow {}^{90}_{Z}\text{Y} + \beta^-$

$^{137}_{55}\text{Cs} \rightarrow {}^{A}_{A-N}\text{Ba} + \beta^-$

Write down the numerical values of the two letters Z and N. State what each represents. [4]

(b) The radioactive decay law can be written in the form

$A = \lambda N$

where A is the activity, λ is the decay constant and N is the number of undecayed nuclei.

(i) Define the term *activity*. [1]

(ii) Caesium-137 has a half-life of 30 years. Calculate the decay constant λ in s^{-1}.
Take 1 year = 3.15×10^7 s [2]

(c) The radioactive dust cloud from the Chernobyl explosion in 1986 contained caesium-137. Figure 4 shows the graph of the number of undecayed nuclei of caesium-137 remaining in a dust particle against time after the explosion.

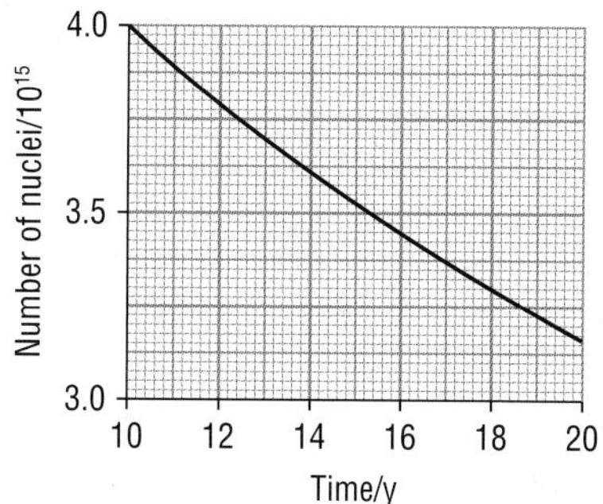

Figure 4

(i) Use Figure 4 to calculate the activity in Bq of the caesium dust particle after 15 years. [2]

(ii) Use data from the graph to show that the initial number of nuclei in the caesium-137 in the dust particle is about 5.0×10^{15}. [3]

(iii) Hence show that the original mass of caesium-137 in the dust particle is about 1 μg. [2]

(OCR 2824 Jan08)

5 Figure 5 shows the variation with nucleon number of the binding energy per nucleon for various nuclides.

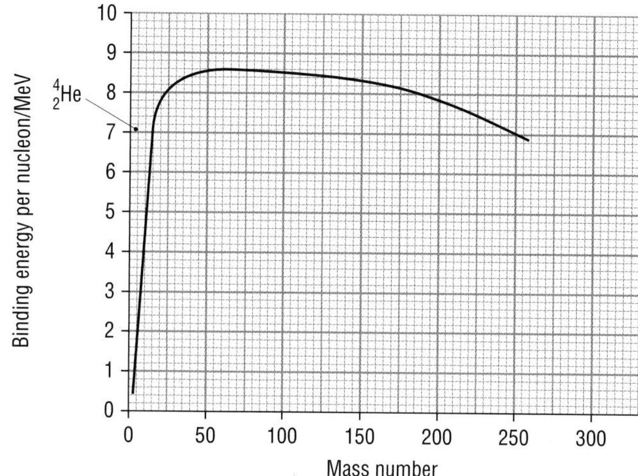

Figure 5

(a) State the number of nucleons in the nucleus of **(i)** $^{94}_{37}$Rb; **(ii)** $^{142}_{55}$Cs; **(iii)** $^{235}_{92}$U. [2]

(b) Use Figure 5 to calculate the energy in MeV released when a $^{235}_{92}$U nucleus undergoes fission, producing nuclei of $^{94}_{37}$Rb and $^{142}_{55}$Cs. [6]

(c) **(i)** Sketch a graph which shows the variation with nucleon number of the relative yield of fission products for a fissile material such as uranium-235. [2]

(ii) Mark possible positions for $^{94}_{37}$Rb and $^{142}_{55}$Cs on your graph and label them. [2]

(OCR 2825/04 Jun02)

2.3 Examination questions – 2

1 The radioactive nuclide $^{42}_{19}K$ decays by emission of a beta-particle. Figure 1 shows the apparatus used to measure the half-life of the nuclide. A Geiger-Müller (GM) tube connected to a counter is placed a short distance in front of the potassium source and the count per minute is recorded once every hour.

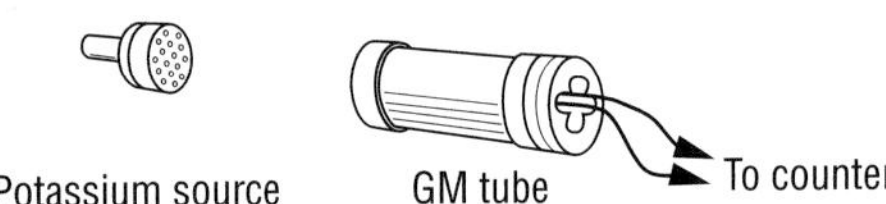

Figure 1

(a) The activity of the potassium source is proportional to the count rate minus the background count rate, that is

activity = constant × (count rate – background count rate).

(i) Explain the meaning of the terms *activity* and *background count rate*. [2]

(ii) Suggest, with a reason, **one** of the factors which affect the value of the **constant** in the equation above. [2]

(b) (i) The radioactive decay law in terms of the count rate C corrected for background can be written in the form

$$C = C_o e^{-\lambda t}$$

where λ is the decay constant.

Show how the law can be written in the linear form

$$\ln C = -\lambda t + \ln C_o$$ [2]

(ii) Figure 2 shows the graph of ln C against time t for the beta-decay of potassium.

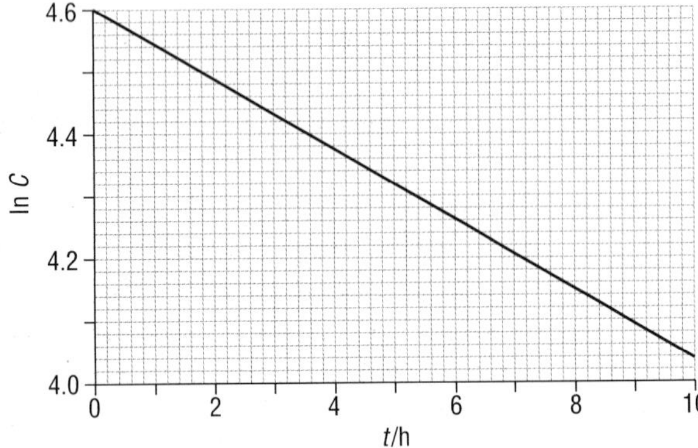

Figure 2

Use data from the graph to estimate the half-life in hours of the potassium nuclide. [3]

(c) State **three** ways in which decay by emission of an α-particle differs from decay by emission of a β-particle. [3]

(OCR 2824 Jan05)

2 The radioactive nuclide $^{239}_{94}Pu$ decays by alpha-particle emission with a half life of 2.4×10^4 y. The alpha-particle energy is 8.2×10^{-13} J.

(a) State the number of protons and neutrons

(i) in a $^{239}_{94}Pu$ nucleus [1]

(ii) in the nucleus produced as the result of the decay. [2]

(b) Calculate the decay constant in s^{-1} of the plutonium nuclide. Take 1 year = 3.2×10^7 s. [1]

(c) A small power source to generate 2.5 W is to be made from the plutonium isotope.

(i) Show that the rate of decay of the plutonium must be at least 3×10^{12} Bq. [2]

(ii) Calculate the number of plutonium atoms needed to provide this activity. [2]

(iii) Calculate the mass in kg of plutonium in the source. [2]

(d) Another isotope of plutonium, $^{238}_{94}Pu$, also decays by alpha-particle emission but with a half life of 86 y. The alpha-particle energy is 8.8×10^{-13} J.

State **one** advantage and **one** disadvantage of using ^{238}Pu instead of ^{239}Pu in the power source. [2]

(OCR 2824 Jan03)

3 This question is about using radioactive carbon-14 to date organic material. Carbon-14 has a half-life of about 5500 years.

Living matter has about 4×10^{10} atoms of carbon-14 in every gram of carbon. When an organism dies the carbon-14 is no longer replaced and so the number per gram falls as time passes.

(a) (i) Starting with 4×10^{10} atoms at time $t = 0$, calculate the number of carbon-14 atoms in one gram at times t of 5500, 11 000, 16 500 and 22 000 years. [2]

(ii) Use the data from **(i)** to plot a graph showing how the number of carbon-14 atoms per gram in a sample varies with time t in years. [2]

In 1983 a preserved body was discovered in a Cheshire bog. It has become known as the 'Lindow Man'.

The probability that a given atom of carbon-14 will decay in one second, λ, is 4.0×10^{-12} s^{-1}.

(b) (i) Show that 2.5×10^{11} atoms of carbon-14 are needed to produce an average decay rate of 1.0 decay s^{-1}. [1]

A sample containing 1.0 g of carbon was taken from the bog body. 65 atoms of carbon-14 in the sample were found to decay in 600 s.

(ii) Calculate the number of carbon-14 atoms present in the sample. [1]

(iii) Use your graph to estimate the age in years of the sample. [1]

(c) Suggest reasons why this technique is not used in measuring the age of each of the following samples:

(i) meteorites and other material found elsewhere in the Solar System;

(ii) samples more than 100 000 years old;

(iii) samples less than 100 years old. [3]

(OCR 2863 Jan02)

4 The age of the Solar System can be estimated by measuring the ratio of the isotopes of lead-206 and uranium-238 in rock samples. The method assumes that all of the lead-206 in the sample is due to the decay of uranium-238 which was present when the Solar system was formed. Lead-206 is a stable isotope.

(a) Uranium-238 decays into lead-206 by several stages. The overall decay can be represented with this equation:

$$^{238}_{92}\text{U} \rightarrow {}^{206}_{82}\text{Pb} + \text{decay products}$$

It is suggested that **all** of the decay products are alpha particles. Use the equation to show that this cannot be correct. [4]

(b) Describe and explain how the number of lead-206 nuclei changes with time after the creation of the uranium-238 nuclei, during two half lives of the decay sequence. [2]

(c) (i) Sketch a graph to show how the ratio

$$R = \frac{\text{number of lead-206 nuclei}}{\text{number of uranium-238 nuclei}}$$

in a sample of rock will change with time. Take $t = 0$ to be the instant of creation of the uranium-238. The half life of the decay sequence is 5×10^9 years. Plot your graph to $t = 10 \times 10^9$ years. [3]

(ii) Use the equation $N = N_0 e^{-\lambda t}$ to show that $R = e^{\lambda t} - 1$. [2]

(iii) A sample of rock which is analysed has a value of $R = 0.81$. Use $R = e^{\lambda t} - 1$ to calculate the age in s of the rock. $\lambda = 4.8 \times 10^{-18}\ \text{s}^{-1}$. [2]

(OCR 2864 Jun06)

5 This question is about nuclear fusion inside the Sun.

(a) (i) Explain what is meant by a plasma. [2]

(ii) Explain why the material in the interior of the Sun is in the form of a plasma. [2]

(b) (i) Explain how the high temperature inside the Sun aids the process of nuclear fusion. [1]

(ii) State **one** other condition inside the Sun which increases the likelihood of fusion. [1]

(c) Figure 3 is a flow diagram illustrating the stages in the carbon cycle, which occurs inside the Sun.

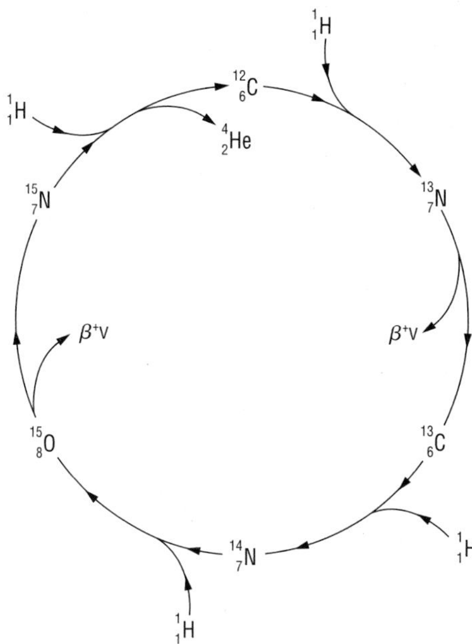

Figure 3

The following equations represent the reactions which make up this cycle.

$$^{12}_{6}\text{C} + {}^{1}_{1}\text{H} \rightarrow {}^{13}_{7}\text{N}$$
$$^{13}_{7}\text{N} + \rightarrow {}^{13}_{6}\text{C} + {}^{0}_{1}\text{e}$$
$$^{13}_{6}\text{C} + {}^{1}_{1}\text{H} \rightarrow {}^{14}_{7}\text{N}$$
$$^{14}_{7}\text{N} + {}^{1}_{1}\text{H} \rightarrow {}^{15}_{8}\text{O}$$
$$^{15}_{8}\text{O} + \rightarrow {}^{15}_{7}\text{N} + {}^{0}_{1}\text{e}$$
$$^{15}_{7}\text{N} + {}^{1}_{1}\text{H} \rightarrow {}^{12}_{6}\text{C} + {}^{4}_{2}\text{He}$$

(i) Why is this called the carbon cycle? [1]

(ii) Summarise the carbon cycle by reducing the six equations above to a single equation, in its simplest form. [2]

(iii) The binding energy per nucleon of $^{4}_{2}$He is 7.1 MeV. Show that the energy released in J when one $^{4}_{2}$He nucleus is formed is about 4.5×10^{-12} J. By referring to your answer to **(b) (ii)**, give **one** reason why this is only an approximation. [3]

(d) It is estimated that 8×10^{37} helium nuclei are formed per second inside the Sun. Assuming that this is the only energy-generating process, calculate the total power in W emitted by the Sun. [2]

(OCR 2825/04 Jun02 & 04)

UNIT 2

Module 4 Medical imaging

Introduction

In 1895, the year in which Marconi managed to send a radio signal a new record distance of one kilometre, Roentgen discovered some other electromagnetic waves that affected photographic film and could penetrate the human body. He called the new rays X-rays, because he did not know what they were, but a medical use was immediately apparent. An image of the bones within a patient made some diagnoses far more reliable. X-rays have become a standard technique of diagnosis after accidents and for many illnesses right up to the present, but problems have become apparent.

- They are high-energy electromagnetic waves, also called ionising radiation. Too high a dose of X-rays causes damage to cells. This is why your dentist goes out of the room when taking an X-ray of your teeth.
- X-rays penetrate body tissue, so soft organs do not show up well.

Many different types of imaging are now available. As well as X-rays, gamma cameras (which produced the image shown here), positron emission tomography, ultrasound and magnetic resonance imaging are now used. Computers have revolutionised imaging. If thousands of X-ray images, taken from different positions, are fed into a computer, a CAT (computerised axial tomography) scan is obtained. A 3-dimensional image can be obtained of a particular region of the body, even the brain.

In this module you will learn about:

- X-ray production and use
- diagnostic methods in medicine
- ultrasound.

Test yourself

1. What is a typical wavelength for X-rays?
2. Name two possible effects of ionising radiation on cells.
3. Sketch a ray diagram to show why a point source of X-rays gives a sharp shadow, but a wider source gives a fuzzy shadow.
4. Why is ultrasound scanning the preferred imaging method for pregnant women?

Module contents

2.4 (1) X-rays

By the end of this spread, you should be able to ...

* **Describe the nature of X-rays.**
* **Describe how X-rays are produced.**

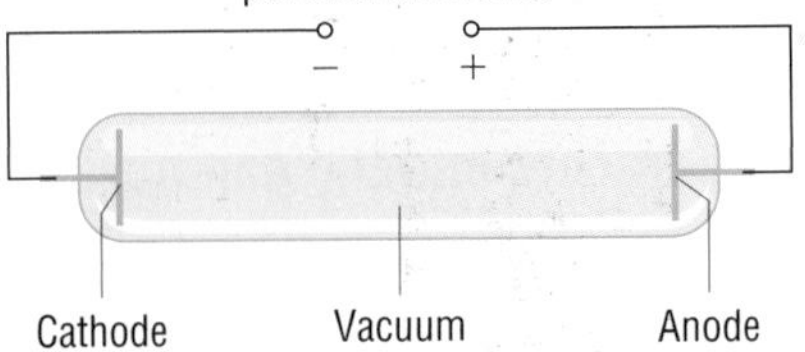

Figure 1 A discharge tube. The p.d. between the anode and the cathode can be varied. A good vacuum is needed for X-rays to be produced

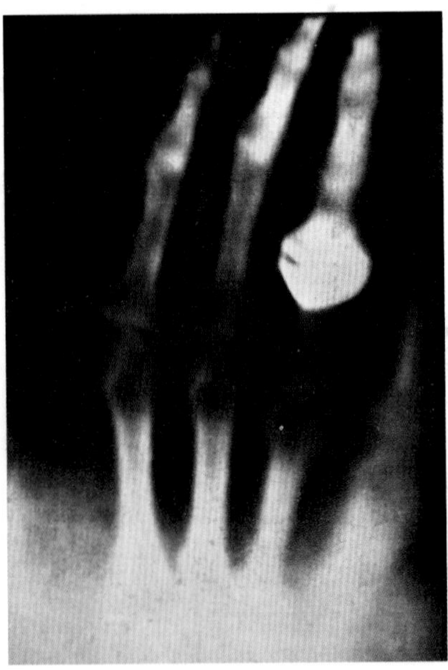

Figure 2 A reproduction of the first X-ray photo ever taken, an image of the hand of Mrs Röntgen

Introduction

X-rays were discovered by Wilhelm Röntgen in 1895. He was using the same type of apparatus as Thomson used in his discovery of the electron, namely an evacuated glass tube with a high voltage between a cathode and an anode, as shown in Figure 1. These tubes were called discharge tubes, and Röntgen was investigating the light that was given off with different gases at different pressures. With better high-voltage sources available to him and with better vacuum pumps, he was interested in what was happening once the pressure was so low that the tube went dark. At this stage he found that a fluorescent plate near his apparatus glowed. When he put his hand between the tube and the fluorescent plate he saw an image of his hand showing the bones inside. There were rays being emitted that clearly could pass through soft tissue but could not pass through bone. He soon put a photographic plate where the fluorescent plate had been and got his wife to put her hand in front of the plate. The photo he took is reproduced in Figure 2. These rays, called Röntgen rays in Germany, we know as X-rays.

The nature of X-rays

It took 17 years after their initial discovery for the nature of X-rays to be established. The question to be answered was 'Are X-rays waves or particles?' In 1906, Charles Barkla established that X-rays could be polarised, and in 1912, Arnold Sommerfeld estimated their wavelength. Finally, it was Max von Laue who reasoned that if X-rays were electromagnetic radiation of short wavelength they should cause diffraction if a grating with a small enough grating spacing could be found. He, and his students Friedrich and Knipping, used the regular array of atoms in a crystal as a diffraction grating and did indeed find a diffraction pattern that corresponded with wavelengths between 10^{-12} to 10^{-9} m. It was therefore established that X-rays are electromagnetic waves. Their spectrum covers a range from about a hundredth to a hundred thousandth of the wavelength of light.

Using X-rays to reveal structures

The early technique of measuring the wavelength of X-rays using crystals has subsequently been used in the reverse way. With X-rays of known wavelength, the father and son team of William and Lawrence Bragg used X-rays as a powerful tool to determine the arrangement of atoms in crystals. Later still, this was also the method used by Crick, Watson and their colleagues to determine the structure of the DNA molecule.

The production of X-rays

As stated above, the production of X-rays requires a high voltage and a good vacuum in a tube with an anode and a cathode. The reason for this is that electrons from the negative cathode need to be accelerated from the cathode and should not hit any gas molecules on their way to the positive anode. If they have enough energy when they hit the anode, some X-rays will be emitted. (The conditions for this mean that some weak X-rays are produced when the electrons hit the screen in a cathode-ray tube of an older television set. The voltage was kept comparatively low, and the thick glass screen of the television acted as an absorber of these X-rays.)

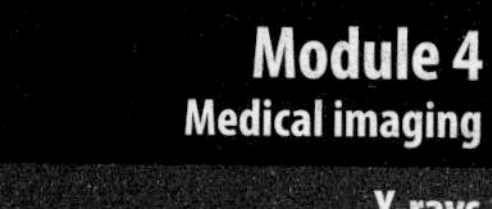

X-ray tubes are now manufactured in all sorts of shapes and sizes. The small ones in a dentist's surgery use voltages of around 100 000 V. A hospital radiography department will have some much larger and more powerful tubes with differing requirements of intensity of X-ray output and of their penetrating power. (Some X-rays are used for treatment as well as for diagnosis.) A modern X-ray tube is drawn in Figure 3, and its basic components are still a cathode and an anode in a good vacuum. The cathode is often heated to increase the output of electrons. The anode is usually shaped so that the X-rays come off in the desired direction through a window, and the tube is surrounded by a shield so that the radiographers themselves are not subjected to radiation. The energy output of X-rays is usually only about 1% of the energy of the electron beam. The 99% wasted energy heats up the anode, so in many X-ray tubes the anode has to be cooled by oil flowing through it.

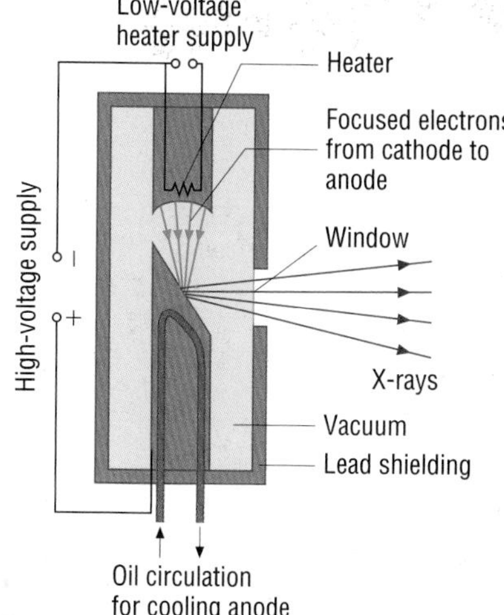

Figure 3 A modern X-ray tube

The energy of an X-ray photon

An electron, charge e, accelerated through a potential difference V gains energy eV. The energy of an X-ray photon cannot be more than this, so the maximum energy of an X-ray photon will also be eV. Since photon energy $E = hf$, we get

$E_{max} = hf_{max} = eV$, giving

$f_{max} = \frac{eV}{h}$ or, in terms of wavelength λ, $\lambda_{min} = \frac{hc}{eV}$ since maximum frequency occurs for minimum wavelength.

Worked example

Find the maximum frequency and the minimum wavelength for X-rays produced by a tube across which the p.d. is 90 000 V.

Answer

Maximum energy of electron = 1.6×10^{-19} C × 90 000 V = 1.44×10^{-14} J

Maximum frequency = 1.44×10^{-14} J/h = 1.44×10^{-14} J/6.6×10^{-34} J s

= 2.2×10^{19} Hz

Minimum wavelength = c/f_{max} = (3.0×10^8 m s^{-1})/(2.2×10^{19} Hz) = 1.38×10^{-11} m.

Questions

1 An X-ray tube has an efficiency of 0.60%. It uses a potential difference of 90 000 V, and the current through the tube is 24 mA. Calculate:
  (a) the electrical power supplied to the tube
  (b) the power of the X-ray beam.

2 An X-ray tube at a dentist's uses an accelerating potential difference of 70 000 V.
  (a) Calculate the kinetic energy of an electron accelerated through this potential difference in a vacuum.
  (b) If all of this energy is converted into a photon of X-radiation, what is the frequency of the radiation?
  (c) Calculate the corresponding wavelength of the radiation.

3 **(a)** A crystal is irradiated by X-rays of wavelength 2.7×10^{-11} m, and the first-order image is formed at an angle of 15°. Using the diffraction equation $n\lambda = d \sin \theta$, calculate the spacing of the atoms in the crystal.
  (b) Assuming that **(a)** is accurately answered, give two reasons why it would be difficult to rely on your answer.

2.4 The interaction of X-rays with matter

By the end of this spread, you should be able to …

* **Describe how X-rays interact with matter using the photoelectric effect, Compton effect and pair production.**

The variation of intensity of X-rays with wavelength

In the previous spread the minimum wavelength of X-rays from an X-ray tube with a fixed p.d. across it was calculated. Not all the electrons arriving at the anode produce X-rays with this wavelength, so there is a variation of intensity with different, longer wavelengths. A graph of intensity against wavelength is shown in Figure 1.

The graph is not as expected. While it shows no intensity below a minimum value and a falling away at large wavelengths, it has some sharp peaks showing particularly strong emissions at certain wavelengths. These characteristics are similar to line spectra in light. Just like these spectra, the wavelengths of X-ray line spectra are characteristic of the elements in the anode. The high-speed electrons hitting the anode dislodge electrons from atoms in the anode. When other electrons fall back into the spaces left behind, they emit X-rays of these characteristic wavelengths.

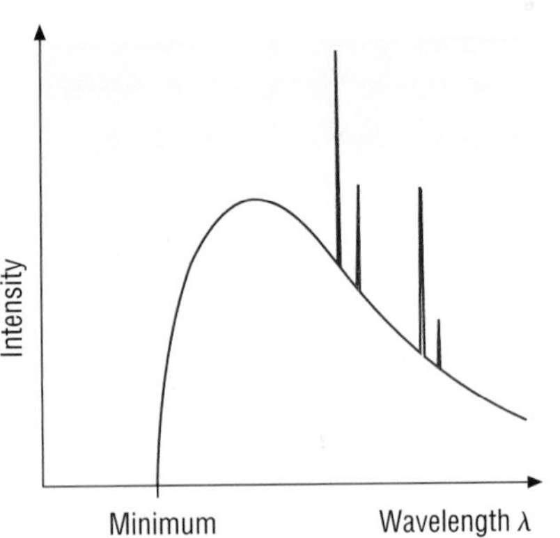

Figure 1 A graph showing how the intensity of X-rays varies with wavelength for a particular anode and accelerating p.d.

X-rays as particles

At AS level, when we looked at with the photoelectric effect, the idea of wave–particle duality was introduced. Indeed, it was the discovery of the photoelectric effect that led to waves being considered as particles and vice versa. With X-rays, the same principle holds true. When using the idea of an X-ray photon in the previous spread, we simply took the idea as given. Here, three examples of X-rays being regarded as particles are given. They are the familiar photoelectric effect, a process called pair production and the Compton effect.

X-rays and the photoelectric effect

Just as with ultraviolet radiation, X-rays are capable of causing emission of photoelectrons. From the work you did at AS, you may remember the equation that comes from applying the conservation of energy to the photoelectric effect, namely

energy of incoming UV photon = work function + kinetic energy of photoelectron

where the work function is the energy required to liberate an electron from the photocathode. Typical values there were 4.6 eV = 2.9 eV + 1.7 eV.

This equation looks very different when dealing with X-ray photons. The worked example on the previous spread showed an X-ray photon having an energy of 1.44×10^{-14} J or 90 000 eV, so the equation, while still valid, becomes 90 000 eV = 2.9 eV + 89 997.1 eV. In practice, therefore, the work function is so small it can be ignored. The emitted photoelectrons, when produced using X-rays, have a maximum kinetic energy equal to the photon energy of the X-rays. These emitted electrons cause ionisation in the same way as beta particles do. Measuring the energy of the electrons is a method of detecting and measuring the energy of X-rays.

Pair production

In a beam of high-frequency X-rays, it is possible for a photon of X-rays to collide with a particle and spontaneously produce a positron and an electron. The equation for this process is

$$\text{energy of X-ray photon} = {}^{0}_{-1}e + {}^{0}_{+1}e$$

From the information that the mass of both an electron and a positron is 0.00055 u, and that 1 u is equivalent to 931 MeV, we know the energy of the X-ray photon must be at least

$$2 \times 0.00055 \text{ u} \times 931 \text{ MeV u}^{-1} = 1.02 \text{ MeV}.$$

Ordinary X-ray tubes will not be working at a p.d. of over a million volts, so the effect is seen only in particularly high-voltage systems (or with high-energy gamma rays).

The Compton effect

Compton carried out some experiments using X-rays of just one wavelength (monochromatic X-rays). He obtained these by filtering out all the wavelengths except those corresponding to the strongest sharp peaks in Figure 1. The work he did was on the scattering properties of different materials, and he employed a graphite (carbon) target. He used an X-ray spectrometer to measure the wavelength of the scattered radiation and found that some deflected X-rays had a longer wavelength than the initial wavelength. He explained this by using the quantum theory. He regarded the X-rays as a stream of particles (photons) colliding with free electrons in the carbon and bouncing off them, as shown in Figure 2. The laws of conservation of momentum and of energy can be applied to this collision. Any photon deflected through a large angle will have lost more energy and so will have a longer wavelength, and any deflected through a small angle will not have lost much energy, and so its wavelength will have shown little increase. This was precisely what Compton found, and it was regarded at the time as strong evidence for the correctness of the quantum theory.

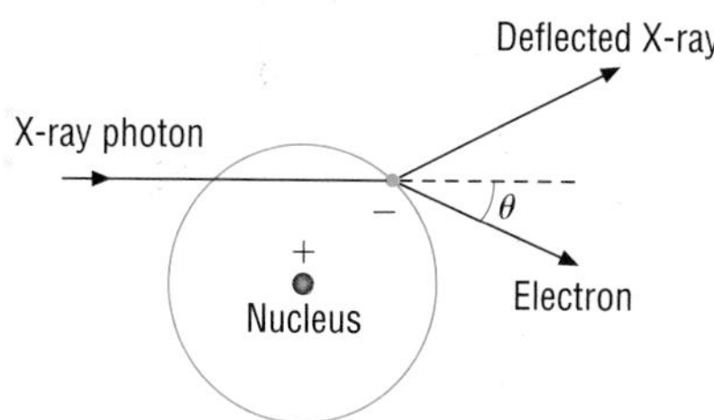

Figure 2 An X-ray photon hitting a free electron and being deflected by it. The greater the deflection, the greater the loss of energy of the photon, and hence the bigger its wavelength becomes

Worked example

When a photon of wavelength λ is deflected through an angle θ by a stationary electron, as shown in Figure 2, the change in the wavelength $\Delta\lambda$ of the photon is given by

$$\Delta\lambda = \frac{h}{m_e c}(1 - \cos\theta)$$

where m_e is the mass of the electron, h is the Planck constant and c the speed of light.

Calculate the wavelength of the emerging photon at an angle of 30° when the incident photon is gamma radiation from cobalt-60 with an energy of 1.3 MeV.

Answer

Substituting the values into the equation gives

$$\Delta\lambda = \frac{6.63 \times 10^{-34}}{9.11 \times 10^{-31} \times 3.00 \times 10^{8}}(1 - \cos 30) = 3.25 \times 10^{-13} \text{ m} = 0.325 \text{ pm}$$

The original wavelength can be obtained by using Planck's equation, $E = hc/\lambda$. This gives

$$1.3 \times 10^{6} \times 1.6 \times 10^{-19} = \frac{6.63 \times 10^{-34} \times 3 \times 10^{8}}{\lambda}, \text{ so } \lambda = 9.56 \times 10^{-13} \text{ m} = 0.956 \text{ pm}.$$

Since the wavelength increases when the energy of a photon decreases, the emerging wavelength will be 0.956 pm + 0.325 pm = 1.281 pm.

Questions

1 (a) An X-ray photon of energy 1.22 MeV generates an electron–positron pair. As can be seen above, the energy required for this is 1.02 MeV. How will the law of conservation of energy apply? What becomes of the 0.20 MeV difference between the two values?

(b) If the X-ray photon is of even higher energy, say 1.62 MeV, how does it require modification to your answer to **(a)**?

2 Calculate the loss of energy of the photon in the worked example on the Compton effect. Put this energy into electronvolts. What happens to this energy?

2.4 (3) X-ray intensity

By the end of this spread, you should be able to …

* **Define intensity and use the intensity and absorption equation.**
* **Describe ways of obtaining better X-ray images.**
* **Explain how soft tissue such as the intestines can be imaged using a barium meal.**

Key definition

The **intensity** *I* of a beam of X-rays is defined as the power per unit cross-sectional area.

Intensity

The intensity of X-rays, as for any other electromagnetic radiation, is defined as the power per unit cross-sectional area.

You need to be careful with the term for X-rays as the beam itself may be spreading out as from a point source, in which case the normal inverse square law applies. That is, if for example the intensity is found at a distance of 3*x* and compared with the intensity at a distance *x*, then the intensity will be one-ninth of its original value. On the other hand, the X-ray beam may be **collimated**. This implies a parallel beam of X-rays, in which case the intensity hardly changes with distance. The difference between these two situations is shown by comparing Figures 1(a) and 1(b).

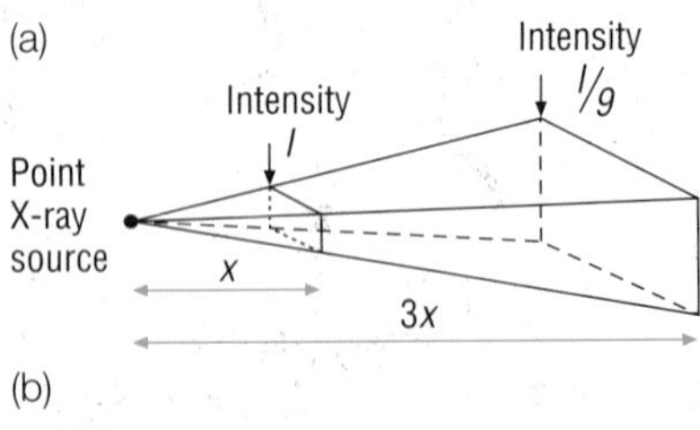

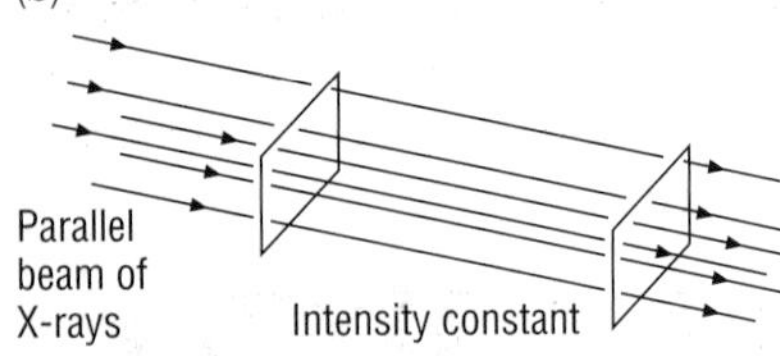

Figure 1 **(a)** An X-ray beam from a point source obeying the inverse square law for intensity; **(b)** a collimated X-ray beam whose intensity remains constant

High-energy electromagnetic radiation, ultraviolet, X-rays and gamma rays are dangerous. They can cause cancers. For this reason it is important to limit the exposure to both patients and radiographers whenever X-rays are used. To do this reliably, any dose of X-rays needs to be assessed. This can be done only if the intensity of the radiation, the amount of absorption and the time of the exposure are known.

X-ray absorption

When a collimated beam of X-rays is passed through any substance, the intensity decreases with distance. The amount of absorption varies considerably with the frequency of the X-rays. Low-frequency (low-energy) X-rays are mostly absorbed by causing photoelectrons. At higher frequencies, the Compton effect is the main method of absorption, and at very high frequencies, pair-production is the most important. As with many problems of decreasing activity, such as radioactive decay and capacitor discharge, the fall-off in intensity is exponential. The equation for intensity *I* is

$$I = I_0 e^{-\mu x}$$

where I_0 is the initial intensity, μ is a constant called the **attenuation coefficient** for the medium through which the X-rays are passing, and *x* is the distance through the medium, as illustrated by Figure 2.

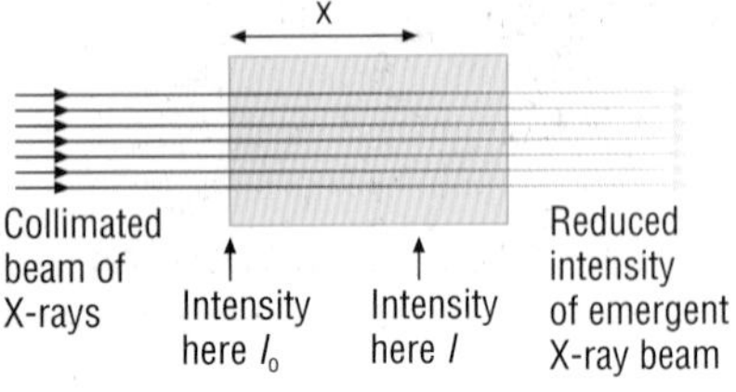

Figure 2 The intensity of X-rays decreases as they pass through any substance

Attenuation coefficients for various materials vary with the wavelength of the X-rays being used.

Typical values of μ for medical X-rays are:

- for a vacuum, 0
- for flesh, 100 m^{-1}
- for bone, 300 m^{-1}
- for lead, 600 m^{-1}.

As with other exponential decays, the equation determines that there is a distance at which the intensity falls to half its initial value. Twice this distance will result in the intensity being one quarter the initial value, and so on. The distance for halving the intensity is called the **half-value thickness**.

Worked example

Using the values given above for the attenuation coefficient, calculate:

(a) the percentage of the intensity of X-rays not absorbed after passing through 1.0 cm of flesh, bone and lead

(b) the half-value thickness for bone.

Answer

(a) Reorganising the equation,

$$\frac{I}{I_0} = e^{-\mu x} = e^{-(100 \times 0.01)} = e^{-1} = 0.37 \text{ for flesh, or } 37\%$$

$$\frac{I}{I_0} = e^{-\mu x} = e^{-(300 \times 0.01)} = e^{-3} = 0.050 \text{ for bone, or } 5.0\%$$

$$\frac{I}{I_0} = e^{-\mu x} = e^{-(800 \times 0.01)} = e^{-6} = 0.0025 \text{ for lead, or } 0.25\%$$

(b) For $I = ½I_0$, $½ = e^{-300x}$ for bone

therefore by taking natural logs, $\ln ½ = -0.693 = -300x$

This gives $x = 0.693/300 = 0.00231$ m = 2.3 mm to 2 sig. figs.

As mentioned above, attenuation coefficients are very dependent on the voltage being used to produce the X-rays, and the basic equation becomes more complicated when Compton scattering is involved.

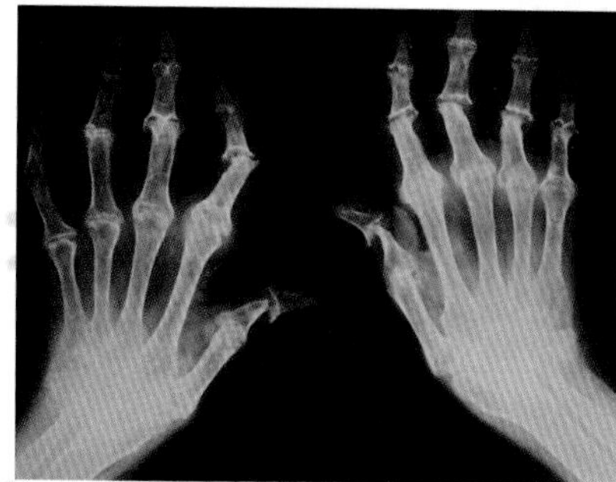

Figure 3 A traditional X-ray photo of the hands of someone who has rheumatoid arthritis

Image enhancement

Photographic X-ray film is the traditional way of making an X-ray image. It does, however, require considerable exposure and produces only a still image. Figures 3 and 4 show the improvement in the images that has taken place, from Figure 3, which is a shadow of a hand, to the false-colour image of Figure 4. Notice how, in Figure 4, the image of the intestine is enhanced. The image of the spine and pelvis is present, but much less clear. Various methods are used to obtain better quality images and at the same time reduce the exposure to the patient. The following are some of the methods used.

- Use photographic film that is more sensitive to X-rays, or put a fluorescent plate behind the X-ray film. Both these methods result in less exposure.
- Use an X-ray-absorbing substance as a contrast medium. Patients are given a barium meal before having an X-ray taken of the digestive tract. This improves the contrast of the image (Figure 4).
- Use an image intensifier. Many radiography departments now use digital methods. In place of film, a screen, somewhat like a television screen, is placed under the patient. Each tiny dot on the screen is a phosphor that glows under X-rays. This can be recorded with a high-quality digital camera and used to give a moving picture of the organ being examined, or be printed out electronically.

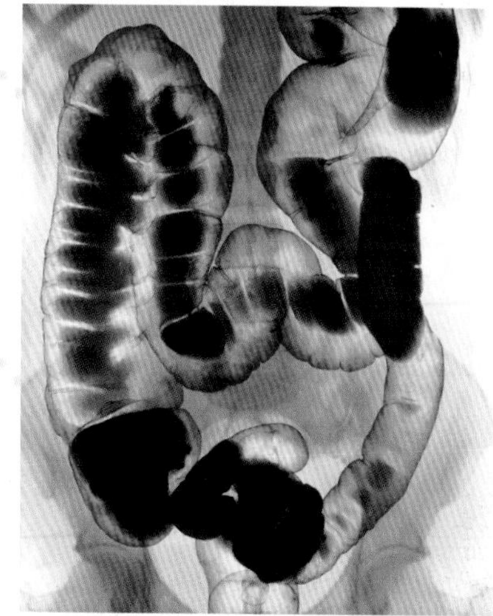

Figure 4 A false-colour X-ray of a healthy large intestine; barium sulfate has been swallowed to enhance the image

Questions

1 Suggest a typical value for the intensity of an X-ray beam. Use values given in previous spreads for the power supplied to an X-ray tube and for its efficiency in producing X-rays. Then consider the likely area over which this X-ray power is distributed. A wide range of answers will be acceptable.

2 As mentioned above, attenuation coefficients are very dependent on the wavelength of the X-rays being used. The table in the margin gives attenuation coefficients for one X-ray source.
Calculate, separately, for this source, the intensity on an X-ray plate beneath 3.0 cm of bone, 15 cm of muscle and 2.0 cm of lead. The initial intensity $I_0 = 4.8 \times 10^3$ W m^{-2}.

Material	Attenuation coefficient/m^{-1}
Lead	90
Bone	53
Muscle	6.9

4 3D X-ray images

By the end of this spread, you should be able to ...

- **Describe the use of X-rays in imaging internal body structures.**
- **Describe the operation of a CAT scanner.**
- **Describe the advantages of a CAT scan compared with an X-ray image.**

2D X-rays

Traditional X-rays show a shadow of the part of the body through which the X-rays have passed. If the reason for taking the X-ray is a broken bone, the position of the break can be established from an X-ray shadow. The shadow will be reasonably sharp provided the X-rays come from a point, as shown in Figure 1(a), and not from an extended source, as in Figure 1(b). It will be more difficult if the break is a hairline break or if the radiographer has not positioned the patient well and if, for example, the tibia obscures the fibula. All of these problems get worse if the X-ray required is of part of the chest or abdomen, as inevitably there will be overlap of different parts of the body.

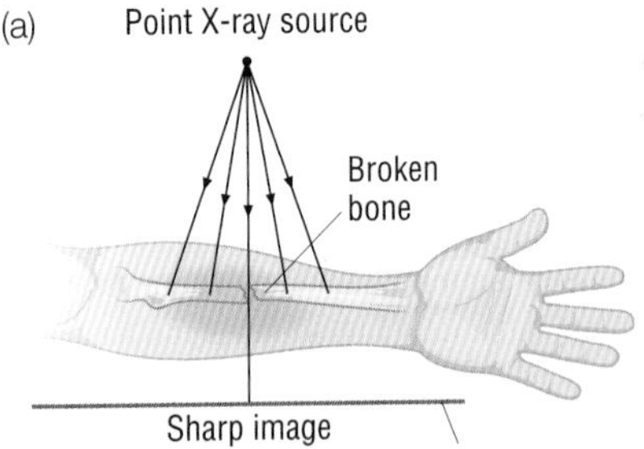

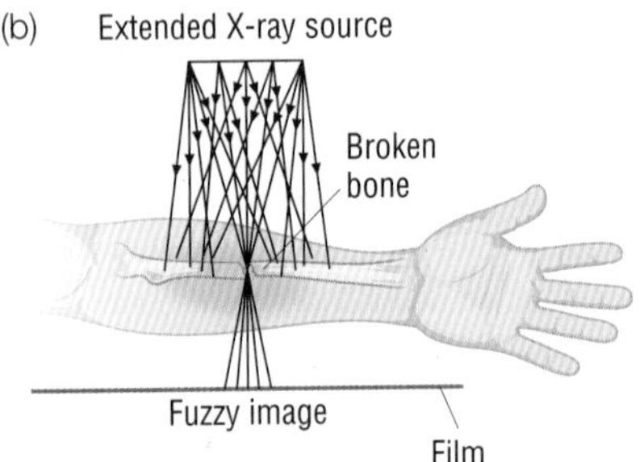

Figure 1 (a) A point source of X-rays will display a sharp shadow of a break in an arm bone; **(b)** an extended source of X-rays will show only a blurred shadow of the same break

Angiograms

Figure 2 is a false-colour X-ray image of the arteries that supply blood from the heart muscle. The patient's arteries are dangerously narrowed. This angiogram has been obtained by a method called a subtraction technique. An X-ray was taken and digitised. A contrast medium was then injected into the bloodstream, and a second X-ray was taken and digitised. The computer images were then subtracted from one another so that only differences show on the final photo. This eliminates all the detail that is not required and concentrates on the contrast medium in the heart arteries. The computer can be programmed to eliminate any small movement of the patient.

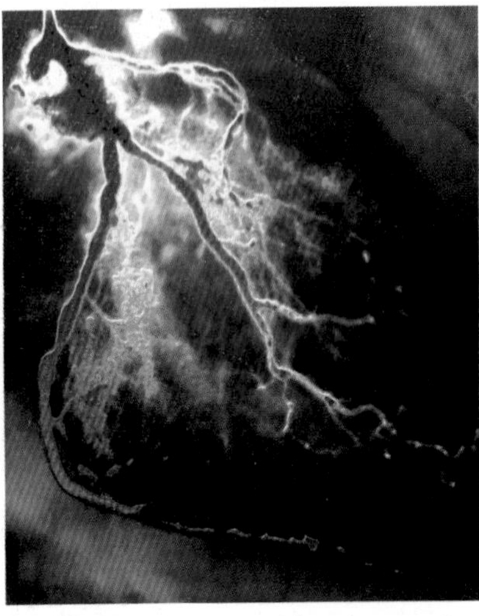

Figure 2 A false-colour X-ray image of the arteries carrying blood from the heart

Computerised axial tomography (CAT) scan

Computers can now be used in conjunction with X-ray machines to give 3D images of the body. In order to get a true 3D view of any part of the body, images must be taken from various viewpoints. The final image is usually of a 'slice' of the body taken horizontally. The quality of CAT scans, often called just CT scans, is shown in Figures 3(a) and 3(b).

(a)

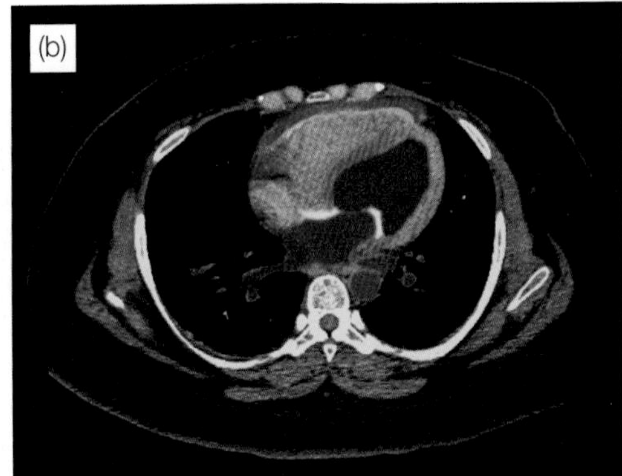

Figure 3 (a) A colour-enhanced CT scan of the head at the level of the ears; **(b)** a colour-enhanced cross-sectional CT scan through the chest at the level of the heart chambers. Blue is used to show un-oxygenated blood, red for oxygenated blood, yellow for bone, and the black spaces next to the heart are air in the lungs

As its name implies, CAT depends on a complex computer analysis. The shape of the X-ray beam is shown in Figure 4(a). The source is shielded so that the rays emerge from a point and spread out through the patient. The X-ray beam is fan-shaped: it has very little thickness, so the X-rays irradiate only a thin slice of the patient at any one time. ('Tomos' is Greek for 'slice'.) Having passed through the patient, the X-rays are detected by a ring of up to a thousand detectors, as shown in Figure 4(b). The X-ray source is rotated around the patient, and by the time it has moved round one complete revolution, both it and the detectors have moved up about a centimetre, which means that on the next revolution it looks at the next slice of the body. The computer takes all the images formed and constructs from them pictures such as those in Figures 3(a) and 3(b). It can also construct a 3D image of an organ on the computer screen. A doctor can rotate this image in order to view it from any desired angle and zoom in on it.

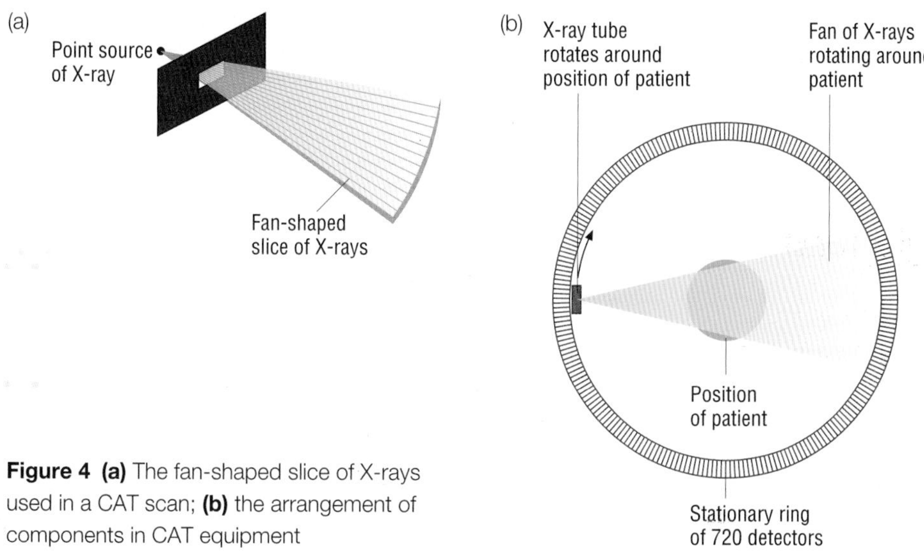

Figure 4 **(a)** The fan-shaped slice of X-rays used in a CAT scan; **(b)** the arrangement of components in CAT equipment

CAT scans do involve a dose of radiation for the patient, but the dose is less now than it used to be, because of increased sensitivity of the sensors.

One big advantage of CAT scans is that they can be taken quickly, so a large number of patients can be scanned per day. This is in contrast to MRI scans (see spread 2.4.7) that can often take up to ¾ of an hour per patient. In addition, the initial cost of CAT systems is less than the cost of MRI systems.

Questions

1 With a conventional X-ray photo, small detail, such as a crack in a bone, is often invisible. Consider the situation shown in Figure 5, where the X-ray source has width x and is a distance y from the detail of size d to be observed. X-rays are spread out over an area. An X-ray film is placed a distance z behind the crack where the full shadow of the bone ends. If the film is any further away from the bone than z, the photo will not show the detail clearly, even if it shows it at all.

(a) When $x = 2$ cm, $y = 15$ cm and $z = 5$ cm, what is the size of d the smallest detail that can be seen clearly?

(b) z cannot be changed. How should x and y be changed to give a sharper image?

2 Sketch a diagram to show how, from a conventional X-ray tube, a fan-shaped beam of X-rays could be obtained for a CAT scan machine.

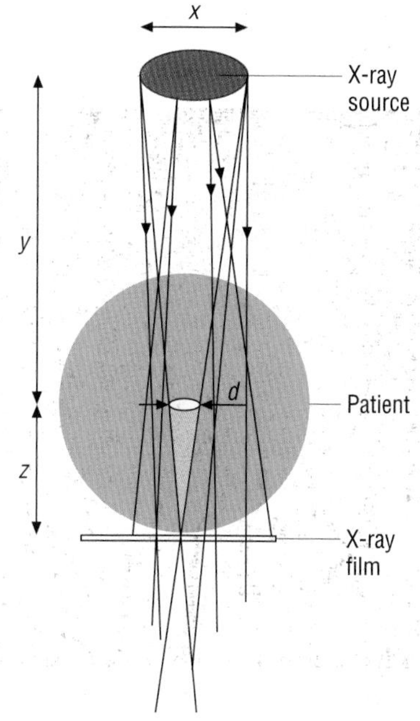

Figure 5

2.4 ⑤

Radioactive tracers and the gamma camera

By the end of this spread, you should be able to

* **Describe the use of medical tracers.**
* **Describe the gamma camera.**
* **Describe the principles of positron emission tomography (PET).**

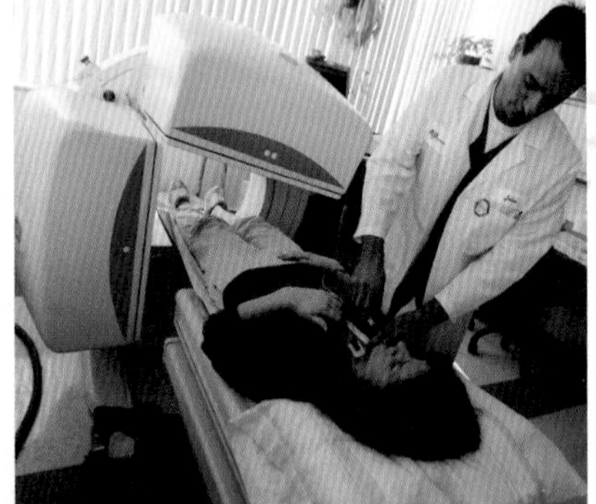

Figure 1 A patient being positioned to undergo a gamma camera scan

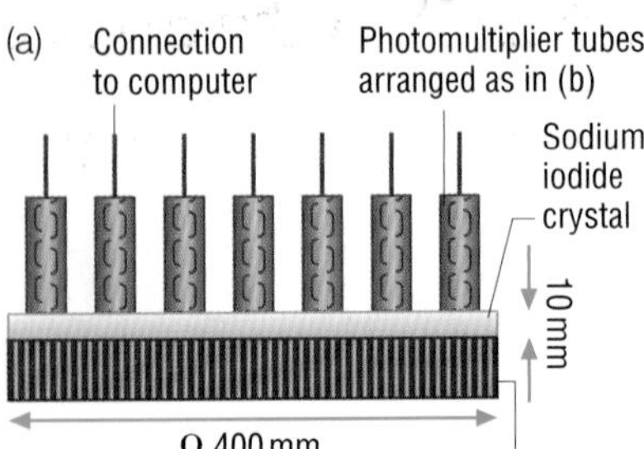

(b)

Plan view of photomultiplier tubes

Figure 2 **(a)** A horizontal section through the gamma camera shown in Figure 1; **(b)** a vertical section through the camera showing the arrangement of photomultiplier tubes

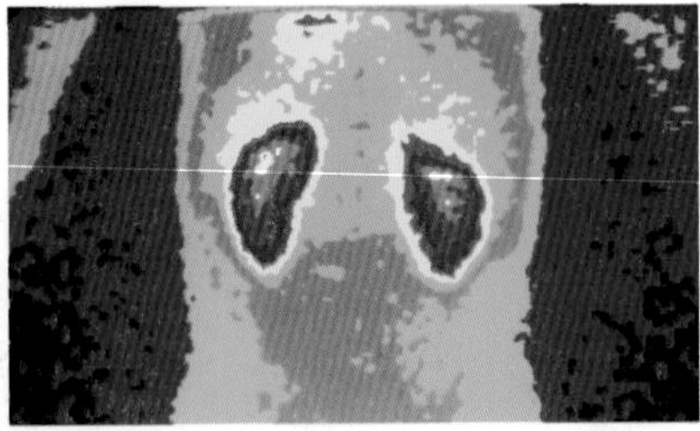

Figure 3 A gamma camera photograph showing healthy human kidneys

Radioactive medical tracers

Radioactive materials may be put into a patient's body for one of two reasons: to diagnose or to treat illness. There are differences between the methods used for diagnosis and those for treatment, but in both cases several things must be considered. These are:

- gamma-ray sources must be used, because alpha and beta rays would be absorbed by (and damage) the body
- gamma-ray sources do cause some ionisation, and so the patient will be exposed to some radioactivity, as may be the patient's family and nurses
- the half-life of the source must be long enough to carry out the investigation, but no longer
- time must be allowed for the source to be brought from its manufacturing site to the hospital
- the source must not be chemically poisonous
- it must be possible to get the radioactive material to the part of the body where it is needed
- once the tracer is in the body it must be possible to monitor it.

Specific examples of the use of radioactive tracers will be given later in the spread, but first we will describe the system used for detecting the gamma radiation.

The gamma camera

The gamma camera is basically a detector of gamma photons emitted by a source inside a patient. Figure 1 shows a patient being positioned in front of a gamma camera. A block of lead with tens of thousands of vertical holes is close to the patient. These parallel holes collimate the beam so only photons travelling vertically can pass through the lead block. Any photons going sideways will be absorbed by the lead, so it is simple to know where any gamma photon has come from. This is shown in Figure 2(a). Once through the collimator, the gamma photons enter a large crystal of sodium iodide. Typically it is 400 mm in diameter and 10 mm thick. Sodium iodide is a fluorescent material and it scintillates when it absorbs a gamma photon – that is, it emits a tiny pinprick of visible light. Behind the sodium iodide crystal is an array of photomultiplier tubes. Photomultiplier tubes, as their name suggests, multiply the effect of this tiny flash of light and give an electrical pulse output for every flash. These tubes are arranged in a hexagonal pattern. Figure 2(b) shows an array of 37 photomultiplier tubes, but there can be 61 for very good resolution of detail. The output of each one of them is connected to a computer. For one flash, all the photomultiplier tubes will respond with an output, not just the one closest to the flash. The tubes furthest from the flash will only produce a weak output, and the computer,from all the outputs, calculates where the actual flash occurred and gradually builds up an image on a screen. One advantage of the gamma camera is that there is no radiation from the parts of the body where there is no radioactive material, so a doctor can look at a specific part of the body. Figure 3 shows a false-colour image from a gamma camera of healthy human kidneys.

The gamma camera in use

Gamma cameras are used to diagnose diseases of the thyroid, liver, brain, kidneys, lungs, spleen, heart and circulatory system. For most of these organs the radioactive nuclide technetium-99 is used. Its nucleus decays from its excited state to its ground state with the emission of a 140 keV gamma photon, with a half-life of 6.0 hours. Its chemical properties enable a small quantity to be incorporated into many kinds of molecules, so it can be directed at a large number of organs. For example, an iodine compound containing some technetium can be administered to test the function of the thyroid gland. If the thyroid does not absorb the compound, little radioactivity will show on the gamma camera, indicating poor thyroid function.

Some modern gamma cameras have more than one scintillating crystal. With two crystals at right angles to one another around the patient it is possible to use this method to obtain a three-dimensional image of an organ.

Methods are being developed for administering radioactive material with a longer half-life to people with certain cancers. The idea is to attach the radioactive material to cancerous cells in a tumour, thereby destroying them without giving dangerous doses of radiation to healthy tissue.

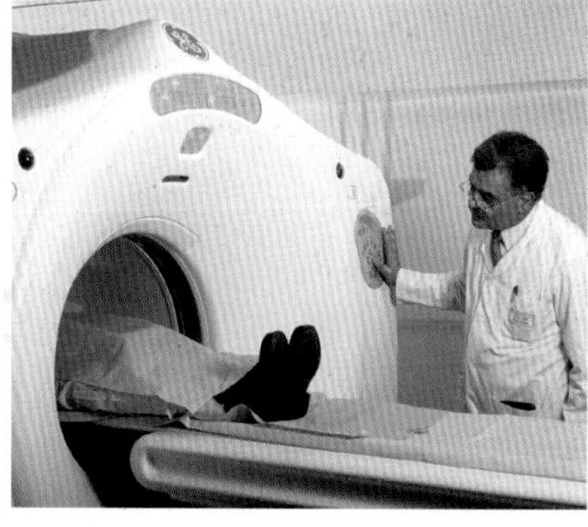

Figure 4 A patient with most of his body inside a PET scanner

Positron emission tomography, PET

This is an extension of gamma-ray photography, and is used to detect abnormal metabolic or chemical activity within the body. In this case radiolabelled glucose is injected into the patient's bloodstream, from which it is absorbed into the tissues, which need glucose for respiration. When a positron is emitted, it and an electron are annihilated and two gamma photons, each of energy of 511 keV, are emitted in opposite directions simultaneously. If two detectors receive two photons simultaneously then the position of the annihilation must be along the line between the points where the photons were detected. A ring of detectors surrounds the patient, as can be seen in Figure 4. The signals from the detectors are analysed by a computer to give an image of the organ. Figure 5 shows the type of image a PET scan can produce. It shows different brain activity for a person listening to four different types of auditory stimulus.

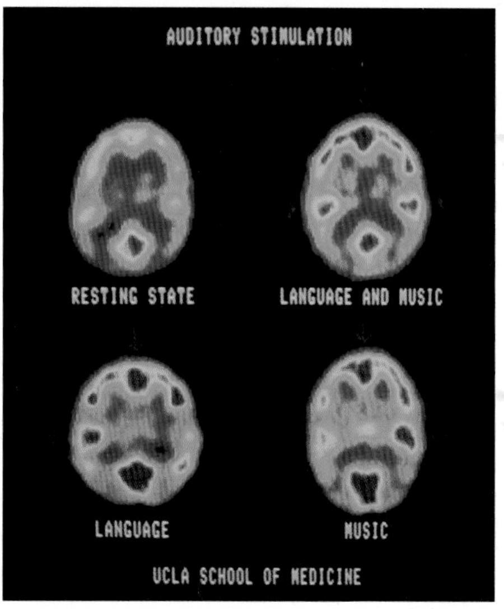

Figure 5 A series of four images taken in a PET scanner, showing different brain activity for four different types of auditory stimulation: resting, language and music, language only, music only; the most active parts of the brain need most energy and so absorb more of the radiolabelled glucose than tissues at rest

Questions

1 A technetium-99 source, for use in conjunction with a gamma camera, has a half-life of 6.0 hours and an activity, when prepared, of 500 Bq. Transport to a hospital and administration to a patient take 6 hours.
   (a) Calculate the activity in the patient a day after the gamma scan.
   (b) Calculate the time taken before the activity of the technetium is lower than 1 Bq.

2 The principle of the gamma camera can be illustrated using just two sensors. (The mathematics gets more complicated with every extra photomultiplier tube.) Figure 6 shows two photomultiplier tubes, a distance 7.0 cm apart. They receive light from a flash in the crystal directly between the two tubes and send electrical signals to a computer. The computer receives the signals a time of 0.10×10^{-9} s apart. The speed of light in the crystal is 2.0×10^8 m s^{-1}. Calculate x, the distance of the flash from the left-hand photomultiplier tube.

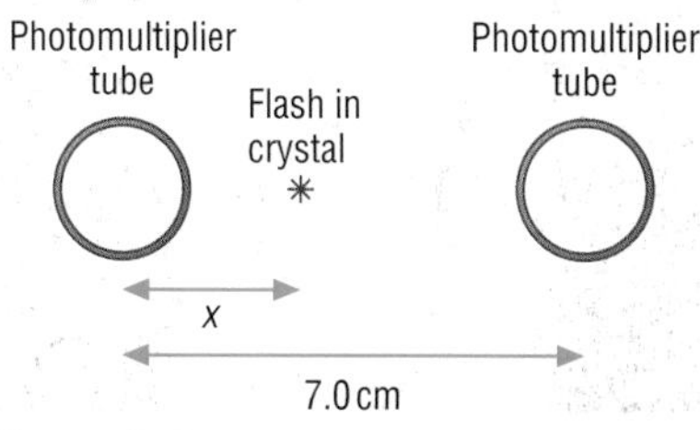

Figure 6 Question 2. The arrangement of two photomultiplier tubes

2.4 (6) Magnetic resonance

By the end of this spread, you should be able to …

*** Outline the principles of magnetic resonance.**

Spin and precession

Magnetic resonance imaging (MRI) depends on a property of nuclei called **spin**. This is a mechanical quantity that has not been covered by the mechanics section of this course. As its name implies, it is connected with rotation. A large-scale device that demonstrates spin is a gyroscope. Figure 1 shows a toy gyroscope balanced on a piece of string. The principle of the gyroscope is that as long as its disc remains spinning rapidly the direction of the spin axis will stay pointing in the same direction independently of any movement of its support.

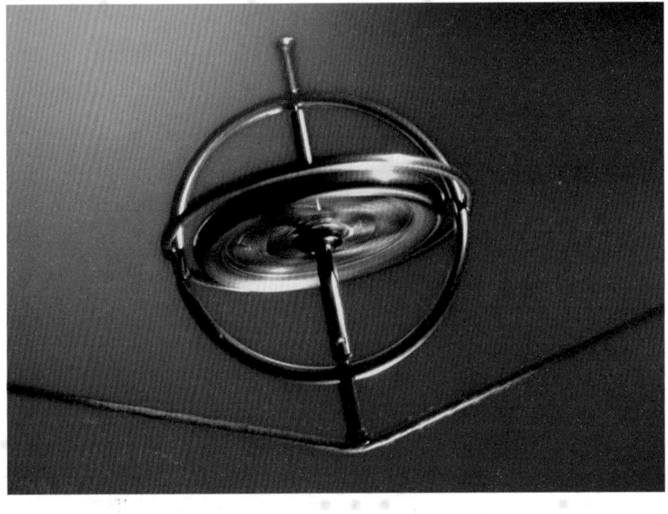

Figure 1 A toy gyroscope. A gyroscope is a heavy, spinning disc mounted on an axle that is free to move

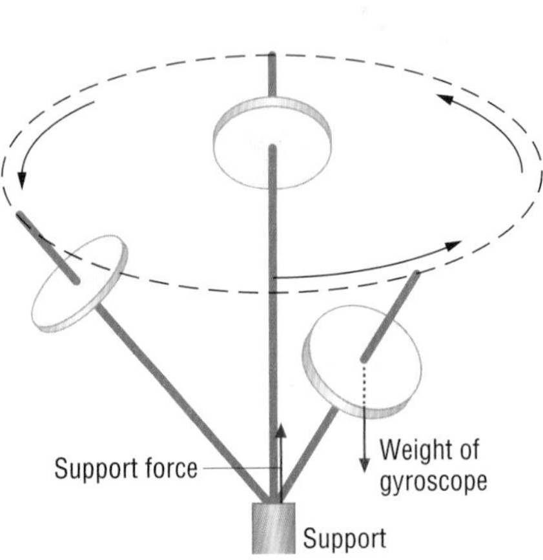

Figure 2 The effect of a torque applied to a gyroscope is to make it precess. The top of the axle moves round in a horizontal circle

The direction of the spin axis of a gyroscope can be altered by applying a torque to it. The effect of a torque on a gyroscope is to make the gyroscope **precess**. This motion is shown in Figure 2. The torque is supplied by the support force and the weight of the gyroscope. The gyroscope does not fall, and the top end of the spin axis moves round in a horizontal plane. This is called precession.

Nuclear precession

The spinning of a gyroscope has the same mechanical properties as the spinning of a nucleus. Most biological molecules have hydrogen atoms within them. The hydrogen atom has in its nucleus a single proton, which spins on its axis. This spinning gives the proton a very small magnetic property called its **magnetic moment**. When in a magnetic field, the proton experiences a torque and so it precesses just like a gyroscope. The frequency of precession is called the **Larmor frequency**.

The value of the Larmor frequency is $4.25 \times 10^7 \times B$, where B is the total magnetic flux density.

In a magnetic field of flux density 1.40 T, the Larmor frequency $f_L = 1.40 \times 4.25 \times 10^7$ Hz = 59.5 MHz. Electromagnetic radiation of this frequency is a radio wave.

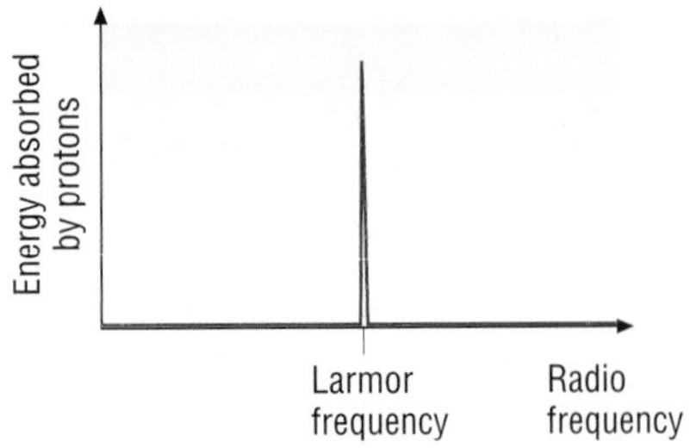

Energy absorbed by protons

Larmor frequency

Radio frequency

Figure 3 A graph showing how the energy absorbed by a proton varies with the applied radio frequency

Nuclear resonance

When the applied magnetic flux density is altered, an interesting example of resonance occurs. (See spread 1.2.15.) The magnetic field is altered by using an alternating current of radio frequency, f_R, in coils placed in the magnetic field. The graph in Figure 3 shows the effect of applying various frequencies to these coils. When the radio frequency equals the Larmor frequency, a relatively large amount of energy is absorbed by the proton. The proton actually flips its axis over to this higher energy state, as shown in Figure 4.

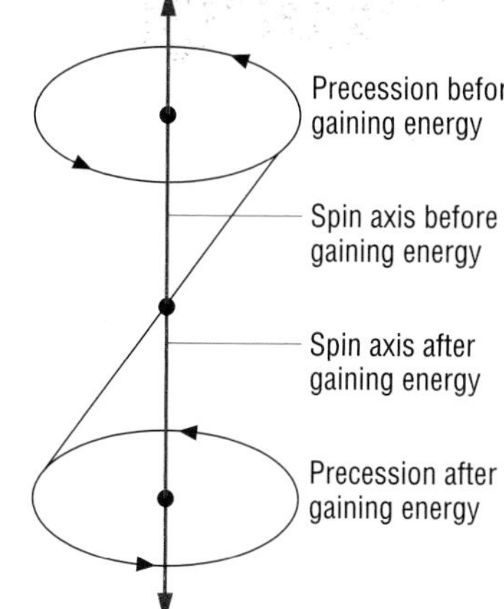

Figure 4 The axis of spin is tipped over when the proton gains energy at the resonant frequency

Relaxation

Once a proton has gained this energy from a pulse of the radio waves at the Larmor frequency, it is in a semi-stable state. It will not remain in that state for long, but will relax back to the lower energy state. Relaxation is the key to MRI. Relaxation times depend on the magnetic field at the position of any proton. In different chemicals, the magnetic field strength at the proton differs because all the other atoms around it have their own magnetic field due to all the electrons moving about. (Any moving charge causes a magnetic field.) Relaxation times for hydrogen nuclei in water are long, about 2 seconds, whereas relaxation times for brain tissue are much shorter, around 200 ms. Tumour tissue has a relaxation time midway between these two.

Another important fact about relaxation is that the energy gained when the spin axis flips now has to be lost. It is lost as radio waves, which can be detected, amplified and interpreted.

Why use MRI scans?

The quality of the information gained from MRI scans is very high. You should also be able to see from the discussion so far that another advantage is that no ionising radiation is required. Because the radio frequency used is no higher than that used for normal radio, there are no concerns about electromagnetic waves.

On the other hand, the magnetic field used is about a hundred thousand times the value of the Earth's magnetic field, and some people worry that this may have an adverse effect, although there is no evidence that it does.

Two more problems are the cost of the equipment in the first place and that a scan can take 45 minutes, so comparatively few patients can be scanned in a day. Since the patient has to keep still for this length of time, the procedure is not suitable for young children.

The apparatus necessary for an MRI scan is the subject of the next spread.

Questions

1 A spinning disc (also known as a wheel) is used in a bicycle. You can balance a bicycle only when the wheels are rotating. Use a force diagram for the front wheel to show how a torque is produced on the wheel when the wheel leans over. Deduce what the precession caused by the torque enables you to do.

2 This question deals with the design problem for the main magnet of a MRI scanner. The magnetic field to be produced inside a long coil of wire is 1.40 T.
The equation for the magnetic field B inside a long coil (called a solenoid) is related to N the number of turns in the coil, the length L of the coil and the current I in the coil. The equation is

$$B = \frac{4\pi \times 10^{-7} \times N \times I}{L}$$

(a) Show that the value this gives for a coil 0.50 m long is $N \times I = 557\,000$ ampere turns.

(b) What problems arise with each of the following suggestions for obtaining this large value?

(i) $I = 10$ A.

(ii) $I = 500$ A.

(c) Why is a superconducting magnet needed?

2.4 (7) Magnetic resonance imaging

By the end of this spread, you should be able to ...

* **Describe the main components of an MRI scanner.**
* **Outline the use of magnetic resonance imaging.**
* **Describe the advantages and disadvantages of using MRI scans.**

The MRI scanner

The main magnet

Figure 1 A patient ready to undergo a full body scan by magnetic resonance imaging (MRI)

A photo of an MRI scanner is shown in Figure 1. As you can see, it is a large piece of equipment within which a patient has to keep still for up to 45 minutes if a full body scan is to take place.

The large part of the apparatus is the main magnets, which have to produce a magnetic field with a very large field strength of 1.4 T. Since this field strength must be over the whole part of the patient undergoing the scan, the magnetic field is produced by coils carrying huge currents in wires kept at temperatures near absolute zero. This uses the principle of superconductivity, whereby the resistance of a wire is zero provided the temperature is low enough. Elaborate cooling systems using liquid helium at 4.2 K are needed to keep the wires of the electromagnets cold enough. Not only does the magnetic field strength have to be very large, but its value must also be constant across a central imaging section 90 cm long.

Additional magnets

In the previous spread it was stated that radio waves were emitted when protons lost energy after the relaxation time. If all the radio waves from all the protons were at exactly the same frequency, it would be impossible to know where any particular relaxation took place. Very accurately calibrated additional magnets are therefore positioned to alter the strength of the magnetic field of the main magnet very slightly from place to place. The arrangement of these magnets is shown in Figure 2. The field needs to be known at all points in a 3D space. A scan is done point by point. For any point being scanned, the field strength and hence the Larmor frequency are known. The transmitter and receiver are tuned to the Larmor frequency emitted by a nucleus at the point. Then the scanning of the next point is carried out at a slightly different frequency. It is because of these slight alterations at each point that a scan takes a long time.

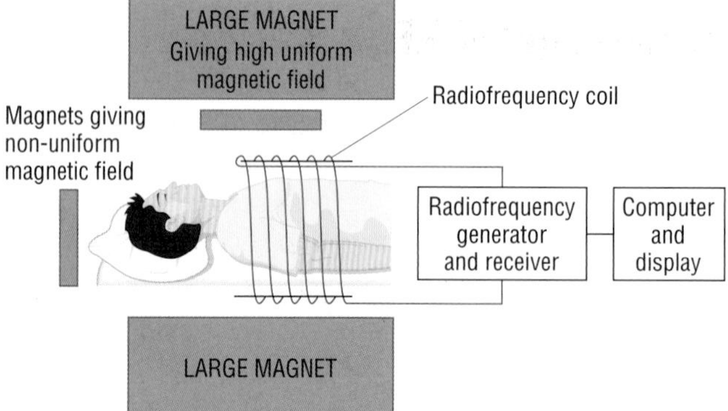

Figure 2 The arrangement of components in an MRI scanner

Radiofrequency coil

If the radiofrequency (RF) electromagnetic waves were continuous, there would be no possibility of measuring the relaxation time, because the start of the relaxation time would not be known. Therefore the RF waves are emitted from a coil in pulses. After each pulse, a coil picks up the emitted RF waves from the patient. In practice, two coils are not necessary. The same coil can be used first as a transmitter and then as a receiver. Since relaxation times are up to a few seconds, the frequency of the pulses is very slow by electronic standards.

Computer

The amount of data that the computer need to process is huge – but computers are now well able to handle this. Programming the computer is complex because of the need to isolate slightly different radio frequencies and link them to a point in 3D space. This can be done only if the magnetic field strength is known very accurately at all points within the volume being scanned. Then the relaxation time for that point needs to be measured, relative to the type of material at the point, and the whole used to provide a display.

Display

The display is normally on a computer screen, and printouts can be made. The type of display can be altered to give a view that is a 'slice' through a patient or a 3D view of an organ, with the organ's view able to be rotated by the operator. False colours can be attached to the display. Areas with short relaxation times could be red, with areas of intermediate relaxation times being green, and areas of long relaxation times being blue. Figure 3 is a photo showing a thrombosis (blockage of an artery) of a patient's legs. In this case the thrombosis is just above the knee on the left of the photo. Figure 4 shows twins in the womb.

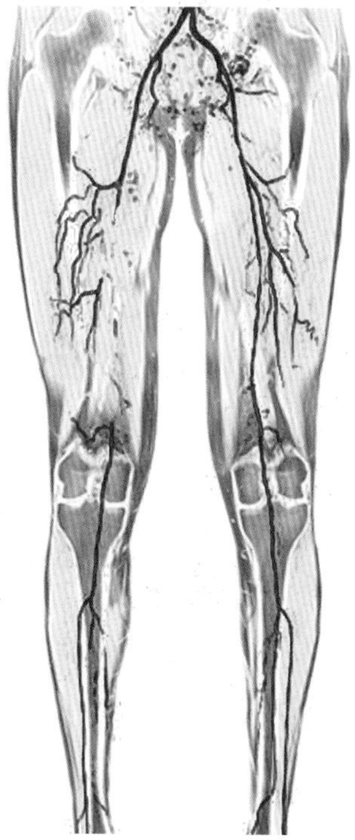

Figure 3 This photo, from an MRI scan photo, shows a thrombosis of a leg artery causing an interruption of the blood supply

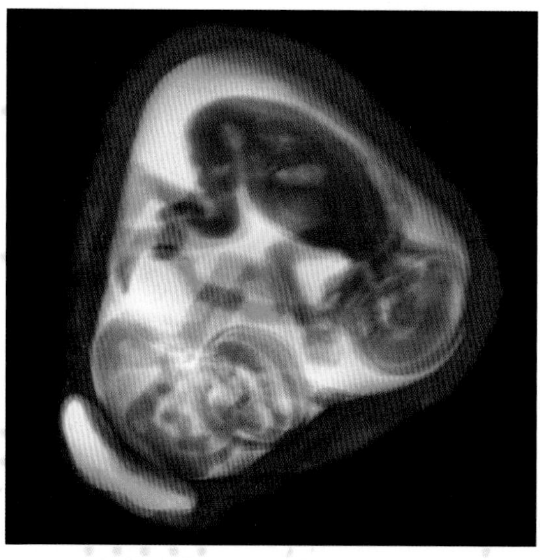

Figure 4 An MRI scan of 32-week twin male fetuses; the placenta is pink and is seen at the lower left

The advantages and disadvantages of MRI scanning

Advantages

- There is no ionising radiation involved, so neither patient nor staff receive any radiation dose.
- The quality of the image is high.
- There is good distinction between different types of soft tissue.
- Bone provides no barrier to the radio waves, so pictures inside the brain, for example, are clear.
- There are no side effects from having a scan.

Disadvantages

- No metallic objects can be scanned, or they heat up. Patients cannot be scanned if they have pacemakers or surgical pins in bones in place.
- The equipment must not have any radio waves from external sources within it. It can be screened to eliminate stray fields.
- The machines are very expensive and cannot have a fast throughput of patients since they take a relatively long time for each scan.

Question

1 The magnetic field due to the main magnet in an MRI scanner is 1.400 T. Using subsidiary magnets, the total field is increased linearly from 1.400 T at point X to 1.440 T at point Y a distance of 0.500 m along the length of the patient.

(a) At what distance from X is the Larmor frequency **(i)** 59.5 MHz, **(ii)** 61.2 MHz and **(iii)** 60.0 MHz?

(b) What is the advantage in having different radio wave frequencies at different places along XY?

2.4 (8) # Non-invasive techniques in diagnosis

By the end of this spread, you should be able to ...

* **Give reasons why non-invasive techniques are needed for diagnosis.**
* **Describe the properties of ultrasound.**
* **Explain what is meant by the Doppler effect.**

Non-invasive techniques for diagnosis

Fifty years ago, the only images of the inside of a living person that were available for diagnosis were taken using X-rays. As you have seen from preceding spreads, there are now many different ways of producing high-quality images of any body part. It is important, however, that any procedure does not have undue adverse effects on the patient, and several new techniques are available that do not involve ionising radiation. These are called non-invasive techniques.

One non-invasive technique is MRI scanning, but it is expensive and time-consuming. For routine diagnosis, a straightforward procedure that can be done easily is necessary. One of these situations is when examining fetuses in the womb. A simple technique frequently used in this situation is ultrasound scanning, covered in the next few spreads. One version of this procedure uses an effect called the Doppler effect, which we will look at in this spread.

Another simple and quick method is the use of endoscopes. Endoscopy and ultrasound will be described in this and the following spreads.

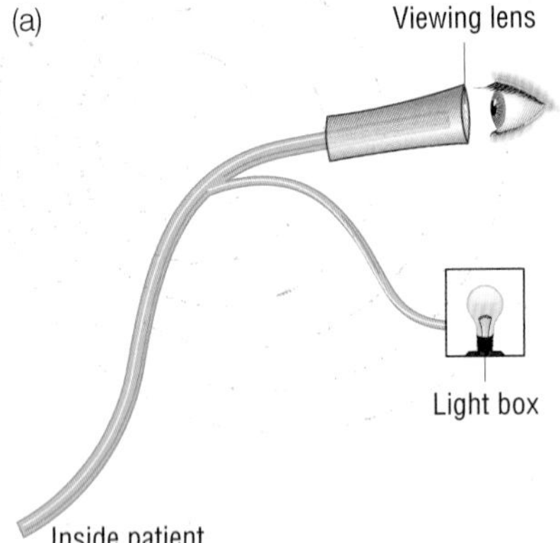

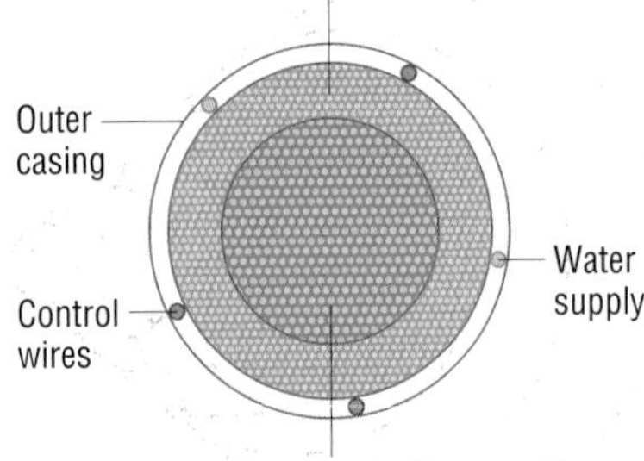

Figure 1 **(a)** The arrangement of components in an endoscope; **(b)** a cross-section view of the tube

The endoscope

Figure 1 shows a diagram of an endoscope. These use optic fibres that can be inserted into body openings. Light is passed down one set of optic fibres, say to the lungs, and reflected light passes back up a different set of optic fibres that are arranged so that they have exactly the same arrangement in the bundle at the bottom as at the top. This allows the pattern of light from, say, the lungs to be seen by a doctor through a viewing eyepiece. In addition to the optic fibres, control wires are incorporated into the endoscope so that its tip can be manipulated to guide it down into the body and then to view various parts of the organ.

Ultrasound in diagnosis

Audible sound has a frequency range of around 20 Hz to 20000 Hz. Any waves of the same type that have a frequency above the audible range are called **ultrasound**. In medical applications the frequencies are not just above the audible range, but are usually of the order of a few megahertz. Ultrasound scans cause no ionisation so are safe to use on women during pregnancy. They also have an additional advantage over X-rays in that X-rays of the heart show it as just a shape, while an ultrasound scan distinguishes between muscle and blood and can also show blood movement (spread 2.4.11). Nevertheless, care must be taken to keep the intensity of the ultrasound as low as possible, as the energy of the waves is absorbed by tissue. If it is too intense, it can be destructive.

The Doppler effect in sound

The Doppler effect is used in Doppler ultrasound scanning (spread 2.4.11). We can best understand it by thinking about sounds we hear every day. When sound is emitted from a stationary source, the sound waves spread out in concentric circles, and the distance between the waves is the wavelength λ. When the frequency of the waves is f, the speed of travel of the waves, c, is given by the usual formula, namely

speed = frequency × wavelength, or $c = f \times \lambda$

However, if you move towards a stationary source of sound, as in Figure 2, you will not hear the same frequency as when you were stationary, because extra waves will have passed into your ears. This change of frequency that takes place whenever the person hearing the sound wave is moving is known as the Doppler effect.

A numerical example shows the change in frequency more clearly. Assume a source of sound is stationary and emitting a frequency of 200 Hz. The sound is travelling at 340 m s^{-1}, so the wavefronts are 1.7 metres apart. If you are stationary, wavefronts go past you at a rate of 200 per second. Now imagine you are in a car moving towards the source of sound at a speed of 30 m s^{-1}. In 1 second you will have travelled 30 m, so you will have passed an extra 30/1.7 = 17.6 wavefronts. Altogether, 217.6 wavefronts will have passed your ears; you will hear a frequency of 217.6 Hz. A higher frequency is a higher pitch.

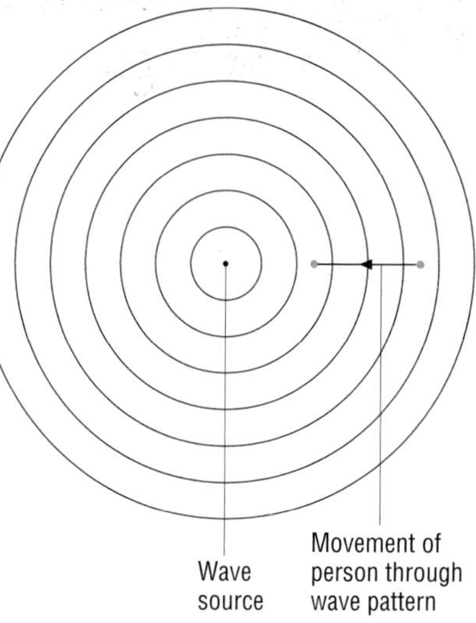

Figure 2 When a person moves through a wave pattern towards the source, there will be an increase in the number of wavefronts passed per second. The frequency heard therefore increases

The situation is slightly different when the movement is movement of the source of sound rather than movement of the observer. This is illustrated in Figure 3. Each wavefront is still circular, but each is produced from a slightly different point as the source moves. The overall effect is to increase the wavelength behind the moving source and to reduce the wavelength in front. This is what happens with ultrasound scans.

Consider a wave of frequency *f* travelling with speed *c*. The time *t* between one wave and the next is 1/*f*. In this time a wave has moved *c*/*f*. If the speed of the source is *v*, the source has moved *v*/*f*. This gives the new wavelength, λ', in front of the source as

$$\lambda' = \frac{c}{f} - \frac{v}{f} = \frac{(c - v)}{f}$$

The new frequency f' will therefore become $f' = \frac{c}{\lambda'} = \frac{c}{(c - v)} \times f$

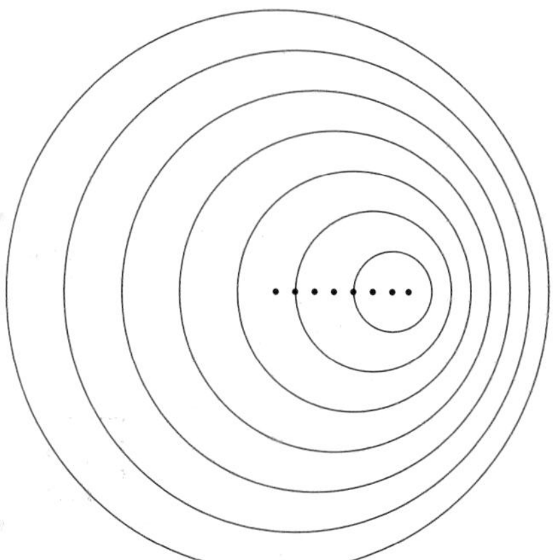
Figure 3 The effect on sound wave patterns when the sound originates from a moving source

The Doppler effect is very clear when listening to motorcycles going past if you are standing on a pavement. As the motorcycle approaches, the sound it produces is a high-frequency noise that gets louder on approach. It is not a note of just one frequency but has a fairly obvious high-sounding note. As the motorcycle passes you, the frequency of the note drops markedly, and as it moves away from you, the note remains low-pitched as the volume of the sound decreases. The pitch (frequency) of the note changing is due to the Doppler effect. A graph is shown in Figure 4 to show this characteristic drop in frequency. If you imagine the sound of the motorcycle, you should be able to relate it to the graph drawn.

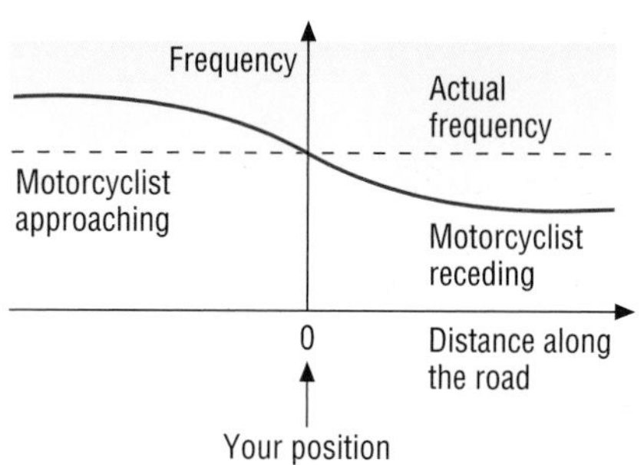

Figure 4 When a motorcycle passes you, the frequency of the sound you hear changes from above to below the actual frequency

Questions

1 Figure 5 is a wave diagram showing the wave pattern produced when a wave source is moving faster than the wave itself. The scale used shows the wavelength to be 3.0 mm, and the source is moving 5.0 mm between producing two adjacent crests.
State two situations where a pattern of this kind will be produced.

2 Calculate the frequency heard when a train, travelling towards you with a speed of 60 m s^{-1}, sounds its whistle, of frequency 400 Hz. The velocity of sound is 340 m s^{-1}.

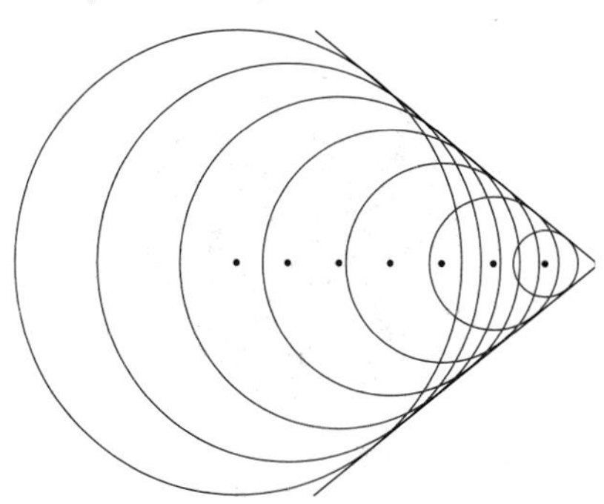
Figure 5

Ultrasound

By the end of this spread, you should be able to ...

* **Describe the piezoelectric effect.**
* **Explain how ultrasound transducers can both transmit and receive high-frequency sound.**
* **Describe the principles of ultrasound scanning and explain why a gel is required.**

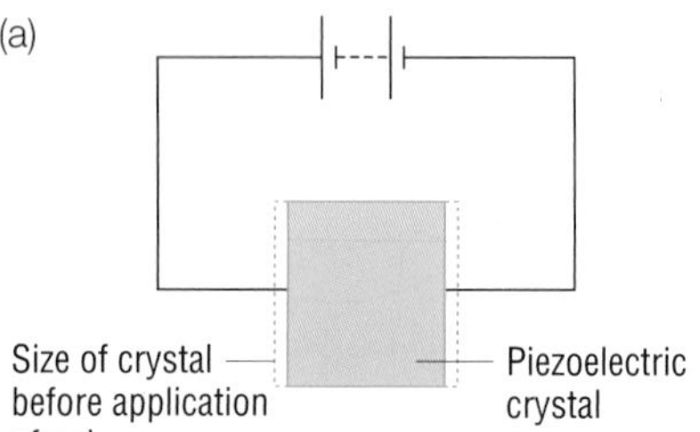

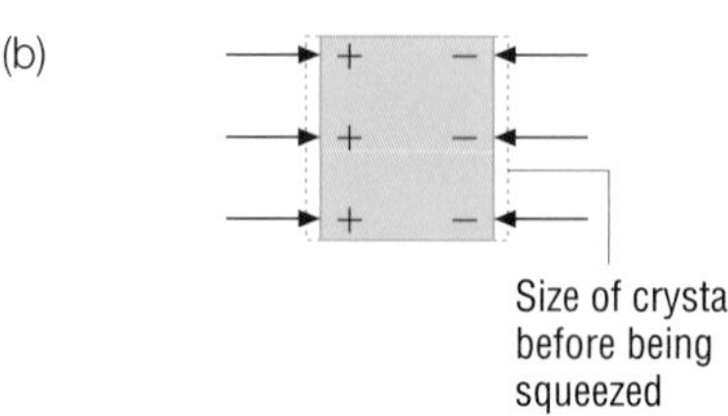

Figure 1 **(a)** A crystal with a p.d. across it contracts by a very small amount; **(b)** the same crystal forced to contract by ultrasound induces a p.d. across the crystal

The piezoelectric effect

The methods used to produce sound, with microphones, amplifiers and loudspeakers, cannot be used to produce ultrasound. Instead, a completely different system is used that depends on a physical effect called the piezoelectric effect. When certain crystals (for example lead zirconate titanate) have a potential difference (p.d.) applied to them, they contract a little. When a high-frequency alternating p.d. is applied, called a signal, the crystals oscillate at the frequency of the signal and send out ultrasound waves. Because the process can work in reverse, the same crystal can also act as a receiver of ultrasound. (In practice, to increase the vibration, particularly when it is receiving ultrasound, the crystal is cut so that its thickness is a whole number of wavelengths. This gives a resonance effect.) If a compression from an ultrasound wave arrives at the crystal, a p.d. is created across it. This can be amplified electronically. Figure 1(a) shows the principle of the creation of ultrasound, and Figure 1(b) illustrates the creation of a p.d. from a compression caused by an ultrasound wave.

The ultrasound transducer

Figure 2 is a photo of a sonographer giving a pregnant woman an ultrasound scan. The item of equipment in the sonographer's right hand is called a transducer. It contains the piezoelectric crystal and acts as both a transmitter and a receiver of ultrasound (Figure 3). Its curved faceplate shapes the ultrasound waves into a narrow beam. The tuning device controls the frequency of the ultrasound waves. To ensure that the ultrasound enters the body, a gel is applied between the transducer and the skin.

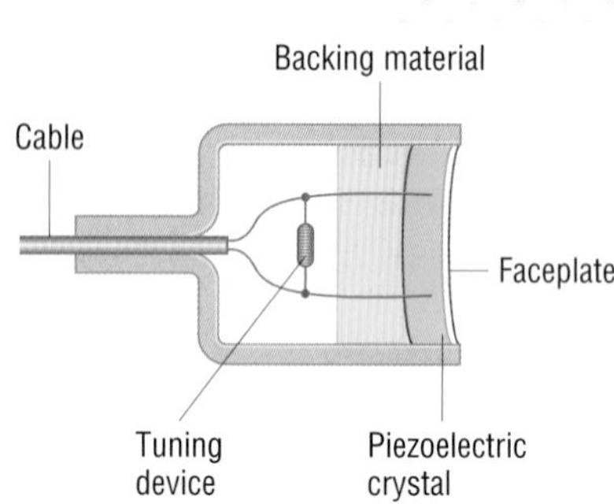

Figure 3 The structure of an ultrasound transducer

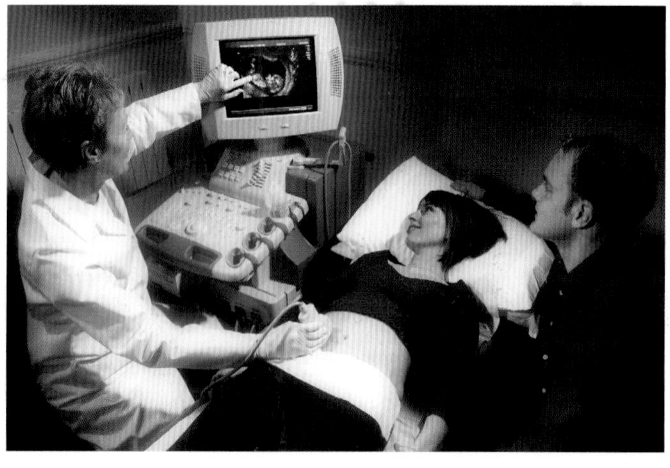

Figure 2 A sonographer gives a pregnant woman an ultrasound scan. The transducer is held in her right hand

The principles of ultrasound scanning

Apart from the obvious fact that ultrasound scanning uses ultrasound rather than electromagnetic radiation such as X-rays, there are two key facts about ultrasound scanning that make it very different from other types of scanning. These are:

- Ultrasound is *reflected* from surfaces rather than going right through a body. Echoes are used. A boundary between tissue and liquid, or tissue and bone, or air and skin, etc., reflects the waves.

- Ultrasound sent into a body must be *pulsed*. After a pulse of ultrasound is sent into the body from the transducer, there is a pause while reflected echoes come back to be picked up by the transducer. (In this respect an ultrasound scan is similar to both a bat's echo-location system and the sonar system used by boats for the detection of solid objects under water.)

Some typical numerical values are required to see how the system functions:

Speed of ultrasound waves in muscle: 1600 m s^{-1}
Speed of ultrasound in air: 340 m s^{-1}
Frequency of ultrasound: 1 MHz

The time taken for an ultrasound wave to travel through, say, 20 cm of muscle and back to the transducer will be 0.40 m/1600 m s^{-1} = 0.00025 s, or 0.25 ms. During this time the transducer must not be transmitting. If a maximum time of 1 ms is allowed for a reflection to be received, it means that the transmission of pulses cannot be at a frequency any greater than 1000 Hz. This is the **pulse repetition frequency**. The minimum time for a reflected echo to be received may be much smaller than this for boundaries near the transducer, so most of the time between pulses needs to be spent receiving.

It is important that the pulse itself has a sharp start. If it is not, then timing becomes difficult for its reflected echo. An outgoing pulse, therefore, will have only a few ultrasound waves in it. The shape is shown in Figure 4(a).

A reflected echo will have a lot of different pulses of different heights from surfaces at different distances from the transducer. A typical reflected pattern is shown in Figure 4(b).

(a)

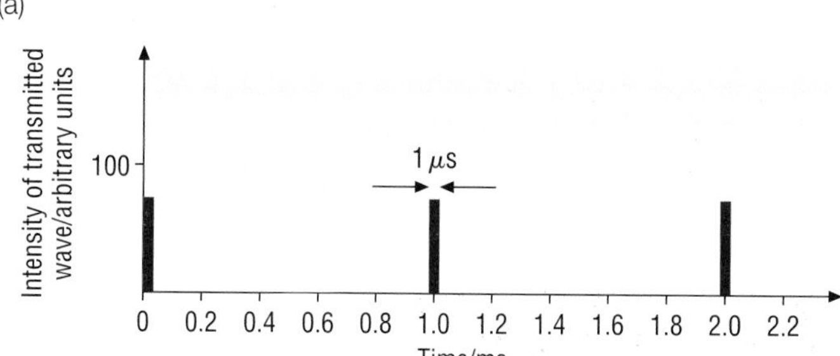

(b)

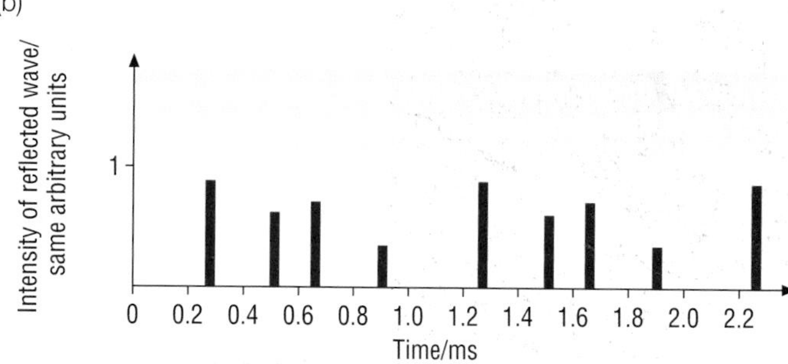

Figure 4 **(a)** A graph showing how the intensity of the transmitted ultrasound wave varies with time, and **(b)** the corresponding reflected wave. The amplitude of the reflected wave is much less than that of the wave transmitted

Questions

1 At a frequency of 1.0 MHz the intensity of any ultrasound falls by 50% in 70 mm of soft tissue. Deduce the percentage reduction in intensity of 1.0 MHz ultrasound after travelling 28 cm through soft tissue.

2 An ultrasound system sends out pulses of ultrasound of duration 40 μs. It has a pulse repetition frequency of 500 Hz and an ultrasound frequency of 1.2 MHz. The speed of the ultrasound in the patient is 1600 m s^{-1}. Sketch the *shape* of the outgoing and returning pulses (not the waves themselves) and then calculate:
(a) the number of waves within one pulse of ultrasound
(b) the range within which echoes can be detected.

2.4 (10) Acoustic impedance

By the end of this spread, you should be able to …

- **Describe the difference between A-scan and B-scan.**
- **Calculate acoustic impedance.**
- **Calculate the fraction of intensity reflected.**
- **Explain why impedance matching is important.**

Different types of scanning

An A-scan gives an output on a cathode-ray tube that looks like one cycle of the pattern shown in Figure 4(b) on the previous spread. No photo is produced, but measurements can be taken from it to determine dimensions. One example of its use is in measuring the diameter of a duct from the gall bladder. Sufficient accuracy can be obtained to find the diameter of the duct to the nearest millimetre. A healthy duct will have a diameter of 6 mm, a blockage to the duct will increase its diameter and a cancer will decrease it.

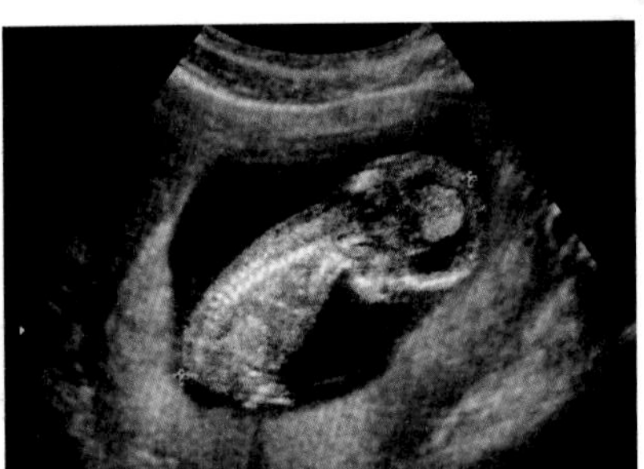

Figure 1 A 13-week-old fetus in an ultrasound scan; the length of the fetus from top to bottom is only 78 mm

The B-scan is much more common and is shown in Figure 1 of this spread. Fetal scanning is now routine during pregnancy. For a B-scan, an array of transducers is used together with a fanning out of the ultrasonic beam across the body. Many returning echoes are recorded, and the information is used to build up a picture on the computer's monitor or is printed out.

Acoustic impedance

Any ultrasound scan depends on ultrasound being reflected at a boundary between two materials. Of course, if at the first boundary it encounters all the ultrasound is reflected, then there will be no ultrasound left to be reflected at any further boundary. The key to being able to get multiple reflections from different boundaries depends on the fraction of the intensity of reflected ultrasound to the fraction transmitted. A term called the **acoustic impedance**, Z, is used in determining the fraction of the intensity that is refracted at a boundary between two materials of different acoustic impedances. Acoustic impedance is defined by the equation

$$Z = \rho c$$

where ρ is the density of the material and c is the speed of sound in the material. Some typical values for various materials are given in the table.

Consider a beam of ultrasound travelling in one material and meeting a boundary with another material. Some of the ultrasound is reflected, and some is transmitted, as shown in Figure 2.

Key definition

Acoustic impedance, Z, is used to determine the fraction of the intensity refracted at a boundary between two materials of different acoustic impedances. Acoustic impedance is defined by the equation

$$Z = \rho c$$

where ρ is the density of the material and c is the speed of sound in the material.

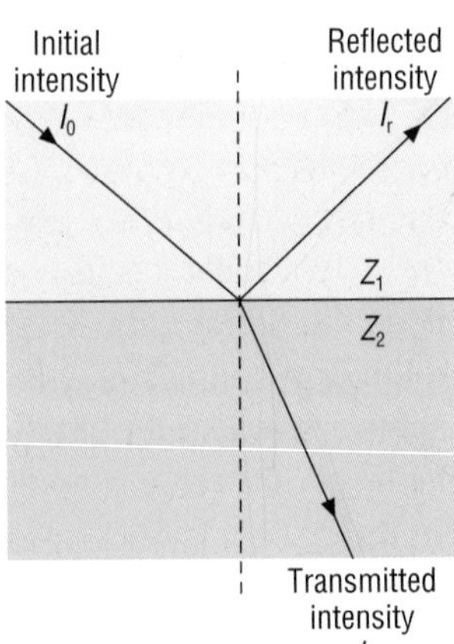

Figure 2 At a boundary, part of the initial intensity is transmitted, and part is reflected

Material	c/m s^{-1}	ρ/kg m^{-3}	Z/kg m^{-2} s^{-1}
Air	340	1.3	440
Bone	3500	1600	5.6×10^6
Muscle	1600	1000	1.6×10^6
Soft tissue	1500	1000	1.5×10^6
Fat	1400	1000	1.4×10^6
Blood	1600	1000	1.6×10^6

The equation for the ratio of the intensity reflected, I_r, against the incident intensity, I_0, when ultrasound is at a boundary and leaving one material of acoustic impedance Z_1 and entering another of acoustic impedance Z_2 is

$$\frac{I_r}{I_0} = \left(\frac{Z_2 - Z_1}{Z_2 + Z_1}\right)^2$$

Note what this means for ultrasound entering the body from air. The equation becomes

$$\frac{I_r}{I_0} = \left(\frac{1.6 \times 10^6 - 440}{1.6 \times 10^6 + 440}\right)^2 = \left(\frac{1\,599\,566}{1\,600\,440}\right)^2 = 0.9995$$

This means that at an air-to-skin boundary very little ultrasound is refracted; most is reflected.

Impedance matching

The very high value of the fraction of incident ultrasound waves that are reflected when ultrasound has to be passed between two very different materials is the reason why a gel must be used to couple the transducer straight to the skin. If the gel is not used, most of the ultrasound will be reflected and never enter the body at all. The need to match up similar impedances to get good transmission/reflection values is called **impedance matching**.

Similar calculations to the one above show that little reflection takes place at a muscle–tissue boundary. At any boundary with a bone, a good proportion of the ultrasound is reflected, so if, for example, the heart is to be scanned, the transducer needs to be placed so that it is above a space in the ribcage.

Questions

1 (a) Show that the unit of acoustic impedance is kg m^2 s^{-1}.

(b) Explain why the term

$$\left(\frac{Z_2 - Z_1}{Z_2 + Z_1}\right)^2$$

has no units and why the term in brackets needs to be squared.

2 A transducer is sending out ultrasound pulses into the materials shown in Figure 3. You are to consider the part of each pulse X that travels through fat and muscle before being reflected by the front surface of bone and the part Y that additionally travels through the bone before being reflected. The thickness of fat, muscle and bone are 10 mm, 30 mm and 20 mm respectively, as shown on the diagram. Use data from the above table. You are advised to tabulate all your answers.

(a) Calculate the time for both the X and the Y part of the pulse.

(b) Calculate the value of I_r/I_0 for each of the four boundary crossings involved, namely fat to muscle, muscle to bone, bone to muscle and muscle to fat.

(c) Assuming that intensity only falls on reflection, calculate, as a percentage of the initial intensity, the percentage of X and the percentage of Y that return to the transducer. Assume that there is more muscle behind the bone.

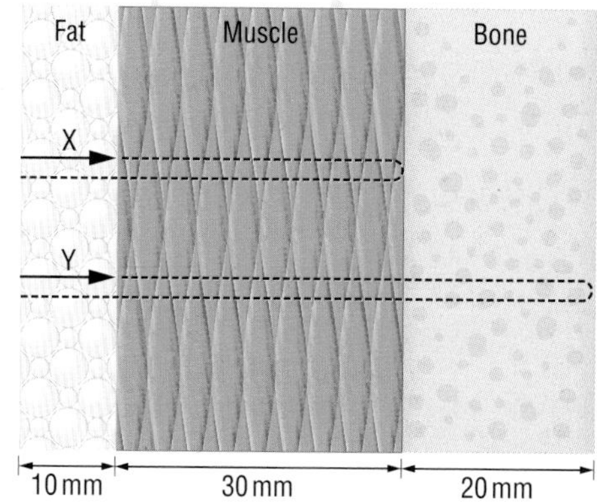

Figure 3

2.4 (11) Doppler scans

By the end of this spread, you should be able to ...

*** Explain qualitatively how the Doppler effect can be used to measure the speed of blood.**

The use of the Doppler effect to measure speed

In spread 2.4.8 it was shown that the apparent frequency of a wave increased when the source of the waves is moving towards you. This process is used in police speed guns. Electromagnetic waves are emitted from the gun and are reflected from a vehicle back to the receiver in the gun. The vehicle acts as a mirror to the waves, and the image of the source is formed behind the vehicle. As can be seen in Figure 1, the image moves at twice the speed v of the vehicle. The frequency f' at the receiver is given by

$$f' = \frac{c}{(c - 2v)} \times f$$

where c is the velocity of electromagnetic waves and f is the frequency of the transmitted waves.

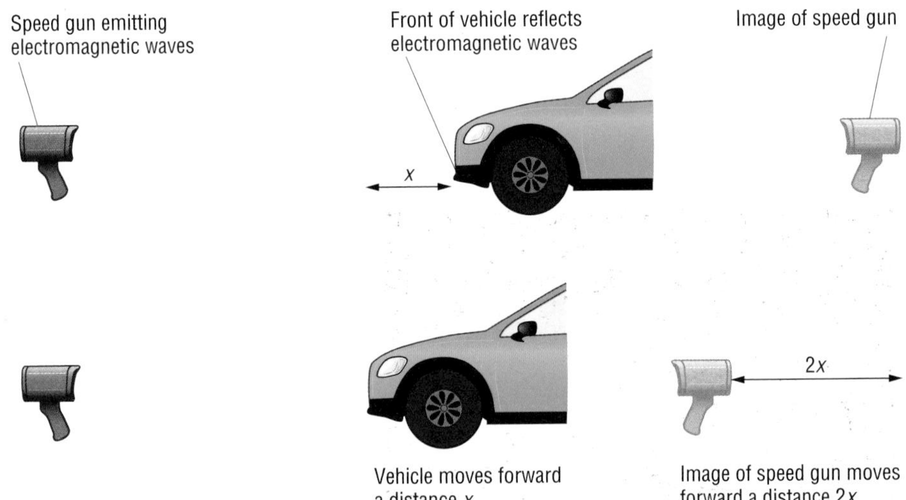

Figure 1 The image of a stationary object moves at twice the speed of the mirror in which it is being reflected

STRETCH and CHALLENGE

Writing this equation as

$$\frac{f'}{f} = \frac{c}{(c-2v)} = \frac{1}{(1-2v/c)} = \left(1 - \frac{2v}{c}\right)^{-1}$$ enables the binomial theorem to be applied.

Question

Apply the binomial theorem to get Δf in terms of f, v and c, where Δf is the change in the frequency.

Measurement of blood flow

It is of critical importance that blood flow through the heart of a fetus is sufficient and in the correct direction. If valves in the heart are not formed correctly, blood tends to flow backwards in some part of the pumping cycle. It is also possible for the blood to take a short cut rather than being directed around the whole body. The process that will be described can be used with children and adults as well as with fetuses.

The principle described above for a speed gun can be used with ultrasound instead of electromagnetic waves. For a moving object, extra information has to be extracted from the reflected signal. As usual, the time at which a pulse is reflected from the blood needs to be measured so that its position can be determined. Additionally, the new frequency of the reflected pulse has to be obtained in order to measure the speed of blood flow. To get enough information for the computer to produce a readable image, the frequency of the ultrasound waves is increased up to around 8 MHz. The greater the difference between the frequency of the transmitted and received signal, the greater the speed of the blood. It requires an even more elaborate computer program to produce an image of the moving blood on the computer screen. Figure 2 is a still photo of a heart. Moving photos would be needed to show blood moving within the heart. The moving pictures do take some interpretation, but doctors who are used to examining such photos can gain a huge amount of information from watching the screen. They can quickly establish whether or not a heart is functioning correctly.

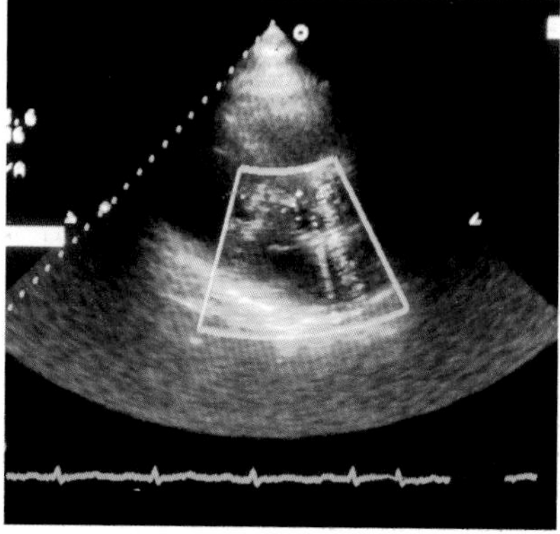

Figure 2 A still from a moving picture of blood flowing through the heart

Coloured ultrasound scans

The difference in frequency of a Doppler scan can be colour-coded. For example, if a vein and an artery are close to one another, then the blood will be flowing in opposite directions within them. A flow of blood towards the source of ultrasound waves will result in an increase in the frequency of the received wave. This could be colour-coded red. Blood flowing in the opposite direction will result in a decrease in the frequency. This could be colour-coded blue. On the screen, this would give arterial, oxygenated blood a red colour, and blood in veins a blue colour. Stationary tissue could be coloured green or left as black and white, as Figure 3 shows.

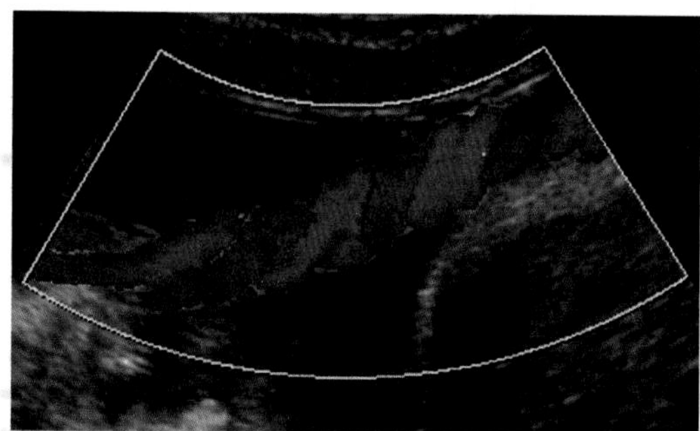

Figure 3 Coloured ultrasound scans can distinguish between blood flowing in opposite directions, here in the umbilical cord

Worked example

Blood is moving through an artery with a speed of 0.13 m s^{-1}. The artery is being examined with ultrasound waves of frequency 6.0 MHz, and the blood in the artery is travelling directly towards the transducer. The speed of the waves in the blood is 1600 m s^{-1}. What is the change in frequency caused by the Doppler effect?

Answer

Using the equation

$$f' = \frac{c}{(c - 2v)} \times f \text{ gives } f' = \frac{1600}{1600 - (2 \times 0.13)} \times 6.0 \times 10^6$$

$$= \frac{1600 \times 6.0 \times 10^6}{1599.74} = 6\,000\,975 \text{ Hz}$$

The change in the frequency is therefore +980 Hz to 2 sig. figs.
(If the blood had been flowing in the opposite direction, there would have been the same change in frequency, but it would have been negative, that is, –980 Hz to 2 sig. figs.)

Questions

1 Calculate the volume of blood moving past any point in 1 second through an artery of internal diameter 5.0 mm when its speed is 0.13 m s^{-1}. Give your answer in cm^3.

2 (a) Sketch a wave pattern of five waves across a piece of paper. Now superimpose another wave pattern of four waves of the same amplitude covering the distance of the five waves. You should notice that the waves are in phase with one another at the start and the finish but in antiphase in the middle.

(b) What does the resultant wave pattern look like if you add the two wave patterns together?

(c) In the worked example on the left, waves emitted from the transducer have a frequency of 6 000 000 Hz and those received by the transducer have a frequency of 6 000 975 Hz. In practice, waves of the same amplitude of these two frequencies are added together so that they interfere with one another. With what frequency will the amplitude of the resultant wave change?

2.4 Medical imaging summary

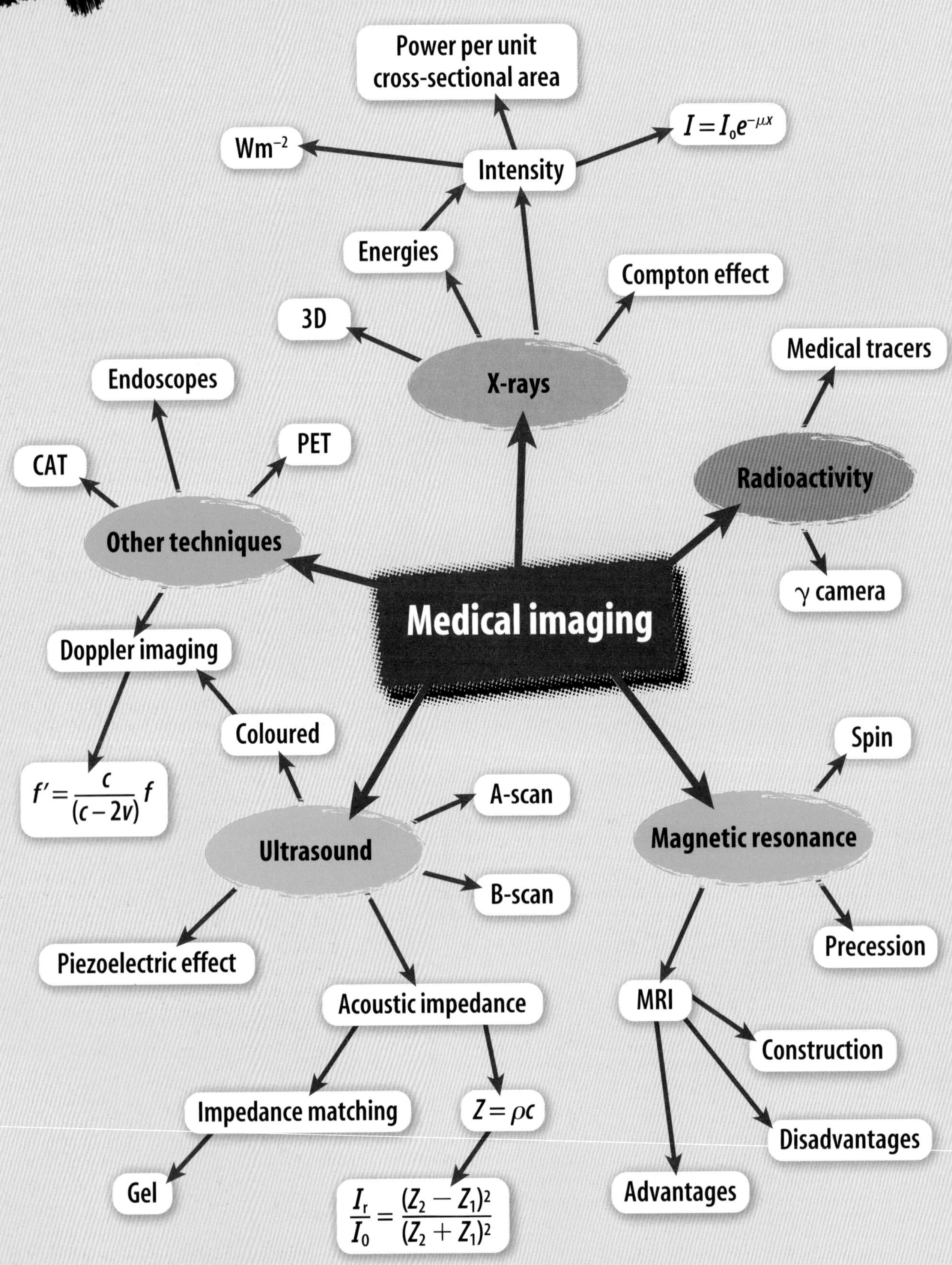

Practice questions

1 In an X-ray tube, electrons accelerated to high speeds impact with a tungsten target, losing their energy to produce high-energy electromagnetic radiation, or X-rays.

(a) For a tube voltage of 100 kV, calculate:

(i) the maximum energy E_{max} in J of the X-ray photons produced.

(ii) the minimum wavelength λ_{min} of these photons.

(b) Figure 1 shows the relative distribution of photon energies from the X-ray tube.

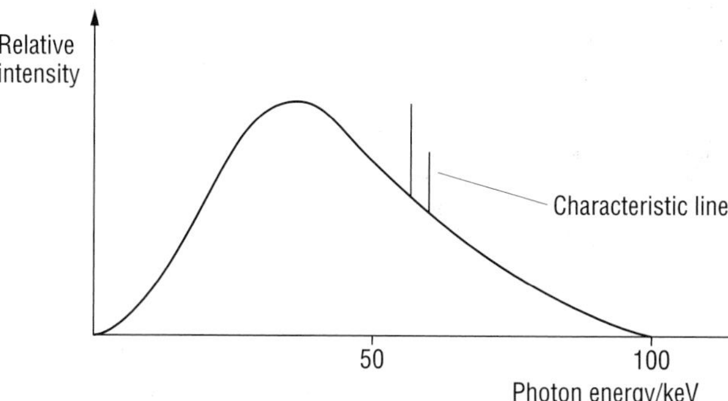

Figure 1

(i) Explain the origin of the characteristic lines at about 60 keV.

(ii) State the changes, if any, to E_{max}, λ_{min} and the shape of the intensity curve, Figure 1, when each of the following is increased independently:

1 the tube voltage

2 the tube current.

2 **(a)** The intensity I of a parallel mono-energetic X-ray beam after passing through a thickness x of a medium is given by the equation $I = I_0 e^{-\mu x}$ where I_0 is the incident X-ray beam intensity and μ is a constant.

(i) Define the term *intensity*.

(ii) State the name of the constant μ.

(iii) Give two factors that determine the value of μ.

(b) A parallel mono-energetic X-ray beam passes through 25 mm of a material. The emerging X-ray beam has an intensity of 0.37 of its initial value. Calculate the value of μ for this situation.

3 Non-invasive medical techniques often involve endoscopy. Figure 2 shows a cross-section through the probe of a typical fibre-optic endoscope. The two light channels both contain fibre-optic bundles, only one of which is a coherent bundle.

(a) **(i)** Explain how the fibres are positioned in a coherent bundle.

(ii) State which of the light channels in Figure 2 contains the non-coherent bundle in the endoscope. Explain why this bundle satisfactorily fulfils its task.

(iii) State the function of the coherent fibre-optic bundle in Figure 2 and explain why a coherent bundle is required.

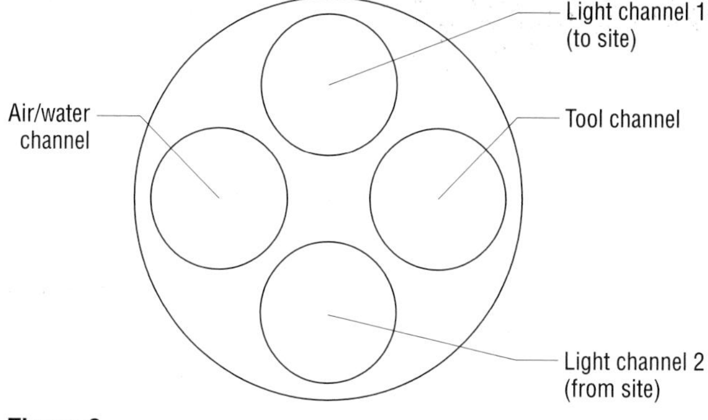

Figure 2

(b) Explain the factors that affect the brightness of the image seen in a fibre-optic endoscope.

(c) Give two medical uses of a fibre-optic endoscope.

(d) A neodymium–yttrium aluminium garnet (Nd-YAG) laser may be pulsed along an endoscope to 'burn' cancerous tissue found in the oesophagus. The water of the cells in the tissue is vaporised, and the cells shrivel. During a single pulse from the laser, 0.12 J of energy is delivered to an area of 1.2 mm^2 of tissue in a time interval of 0.75 ms.

Calculate **(i)** the intensity of the laser at the tissue and **(ii)** the number of photons in the pulse for the wavelength of laser light of 1060 nm.

4 One system that measures blood flow non-invasively uses a beam of ultrasound with a frequency f between 2 and 10 MHz. Moving red corpuscles reflect the sound, with a change in frequency, a Doppler shift, given by $\Delta f = 2vf\cos\theta/c$ where v is the speed of the blood corpuscles along the direction of the blood vessel, c is the speed of sound in the tissue and θ is the angle between the direction of the ultrasound beam and the blood vessel.

(a) Explain the distinction between invasive and non-invasive methods.

(b) As flesh is mostly water, the speed c of sound is 1500 m s^{-1}. Use this information to estimate an upper limit to the wavelength used in this technique.

(c) Taking the speed v of blood flow to be 0.3 m s^{-1}, calculate the maximum possible change in frequency Δf that an ultrasound device using this range of frequencies might have to detect.

2.4 Examination questions

1 This question is about X-ray photography.

(a) The intensity pattern of a beam of diagnostic X-rays, transmitted through a human body, is recorded on a photographic film. Explain why the intensity will vary where materials of different proton number are encountered within the body. See Figure 1. [2]

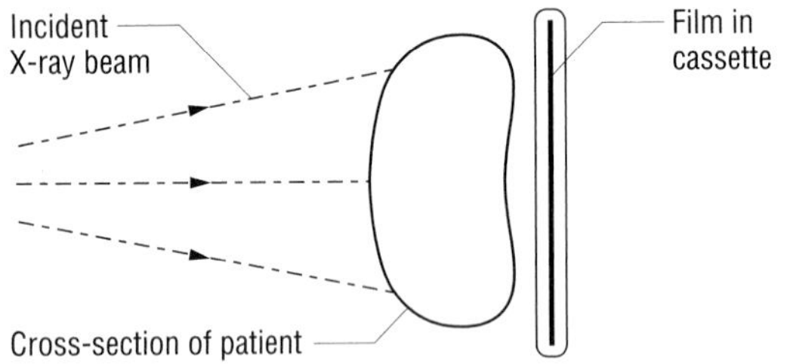

Figure 1

(b) (i) An image-intensifying screen is sometimes placed between the body and the X-ray film. Explain how the screen works and what effect it has on the film. [3]

(ii) State the chief advantage of image intensification to the patient. [1]

(c) (i) Explain why contrast media are sometimes used in diagnostic X-rays. [2]

(ii) Explain how the use of a contrast medium improves the quality of an X-ray photo. [2]

(OCR 5634 Jun98)

2 A student wishes to explain the principles involved in a CT scan. She draws nine boxes, each representing a unit volume of soft tissue or bone. She draws X-ray beams that pulse units of energy in the way shown in Figure 2 and writes down the energy outputs after they have passed through three boxes.

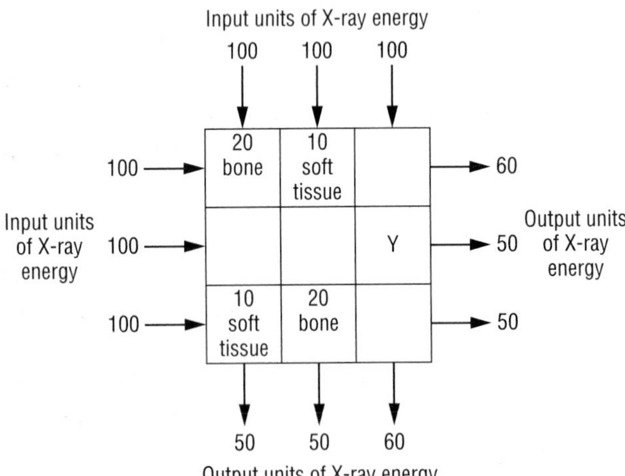

Figure 2

(a) Suggest what the numbers 20 and 10, in the first two boxes of the top row, represent. [2]

(b) Explain why the student has put the larger number in a box that represents a unit volume of bone. [1]

(c) Copy Figure 2 and fill in the values for the remaining five boxes and hence determine the material contained in box **Y**. [4]

(OCR 2825/02 Jan05)

3 This question is about the collision of an electron e^- and its antiparticle, a positron, e^+.

In the collision, the particles annihilate each other, creating two gamma rays, γ. Provided the electron and positron can be considered to be at rest, the two γ-ray photons are produced with equal energy and travel in opposite directions to each other (Figure 3).

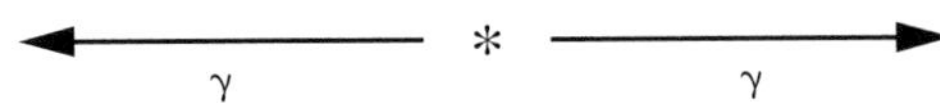

Figure 3

The table contains some information about electrons and positrons.

Particle	Mass/kg	Charge/C
Electron	9.1×10^{-31}	-1.6×10^{-19}
Positron	9.1×10^{-31}	$+1.6 \times 10^{-19}$

(a) (i) Use the equation $\Delta E = c^2 \Delta m$ to calculate the energy in J released when the electron and positron annihilate each other. [2]

(ii) Hence show that the energy of each γ-ray is about 0.5 MeV. [2]

(b) Calculate the frequency of the emitted γ-radiation. [2]

(c) In medical diagnosis, positrons can be used to find the position of a tumour. A material which emits positrons is absorbed by the tumour. When positrons are emitted, they almost immediately collide with electrons, causing annihilation and the production of γ-ray pairs.

If the tumour is on one side of the body, the time difference between the arrival of the γ-rays at each of the two detectors equidistant from the centre of the body can be used to locate the tumour. See Figure 4.

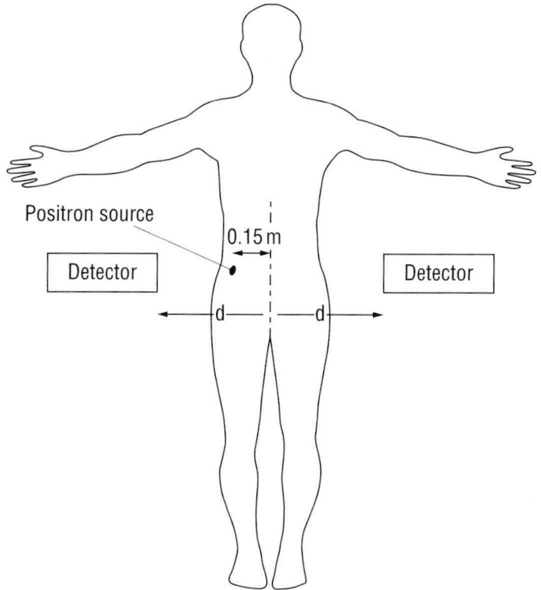

Figure 4

Suppose the tumour is 0.15 m from the centre of the body. Will it be possible to locate the tumour when the detectors are used with a counter which can detect time differences as small as 0.5 nanoseconds?
Show the working needed to justify your answer. [3]

(OCR 9661/2 Jun95)

4 Figure 5 shows a cross-section through an ultrasound transducer.

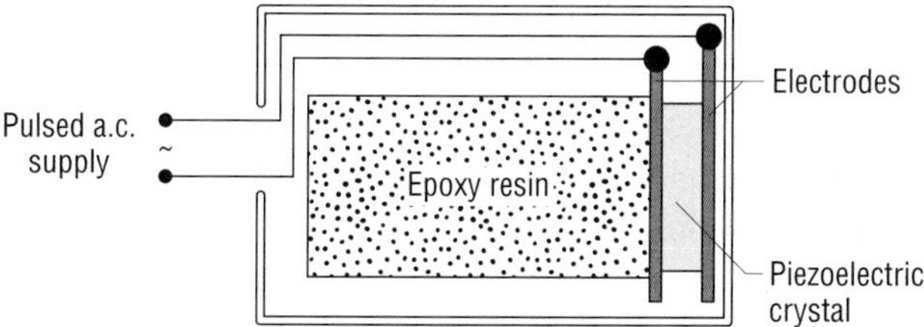

Figure 5

The piezoelectric crystal is backed by a slab of epoxy resin, and the power supply to the electrodes either side of the crystal is pulsed.

(a) Describe the generation and detection of ultrasound by a piezoelectric crystal. Explain why the epoxy resin is needed and give reasons for pulsing the ultrasound. [8]

(b) Figure 6 shows a cross-section through a part of the body. Ultrasound is pulsed through the centre of the section so that it passes first through an organ and then through a bone. Figure 7 is an oscilloscope trace of the reflected ultrasound signal received from the gel–skin boundary and then from the front and back edges of first the organ and then the bone.

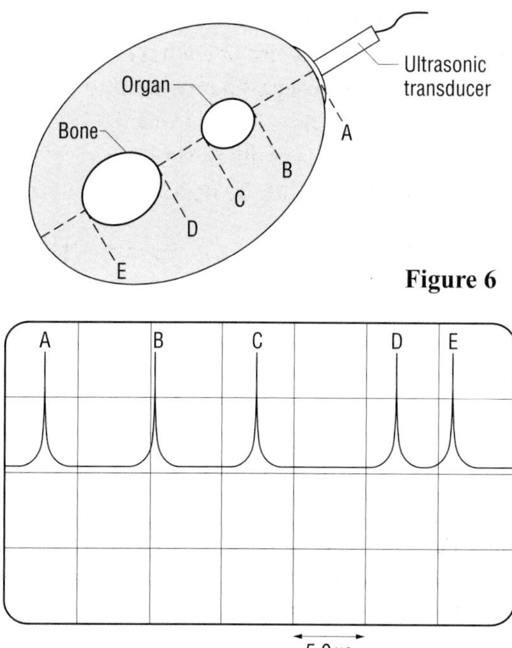

Figure 6

Figure 7

Data:

Material	Speed of ultrasound/10^3 m s^{-1}
Organ	1.6
Bone	4.1
Soft-tissue	1.1

(i) Deduce from Figure 7 the time interval in s during which the ultrasound travels in the organ. The time-base setting on the oscilloscope is 5.0 μs cm^{-1}. [1]

(ii) Calculate the distance in m travelled by ultrasound through the organ. [1]

(iii) Calculate the thickness in m of the organ. [2]

(iv) Calculate the thickness in m of the bone. [3]

(c) Explain one example where ultrasound is used rather than X-rays for medical imaging. [2]

(OCR 2825/02 Jan04)

5 **(a)** Explain briefly why ultrasound is suitable for medical echo-sounding. [3]

(b) Explain the limitations in the medical application of the A-scan technique. Do **not** describe the method in detail. [3]

(c) Describe a B-scan technique and show how it helps to overcome the difficulties which you described in part **(b)**. [6]

(d) Explain in what ways the choice of frequency of the ultrasound beam is affected by resolution and attenuation. [4]

(OCR 5634 Jun99)

UNIT 2

Module 5 Modelling the universe

Introduction

This module demonstrates how scientific theories develop as more experimental evidence becomes available. Star maps were drawn in ancient times, and in 905 a Persian astronomer recorded the Andromeda galaxy for the first time. He could see it as a patch of light rather than a point star. In 1054 Chinese and Japanese astronomers were the first to record a supernova. The Crab nebula, its remnants, can still be seen using modern telescopes, as in the photograph on this page.

When Galileo used the first telescope in 1509 he saw the moons of Jupiter for the first time. Newton improved telescopes by using mirrors rather than lenses, and this led to the discovery of millions more stars than could previously be seen. Large modern telescopes can see around a trillion (10^{12}) stars in the Andromeda galaxy alone.

The use of methods to detect electromagnetic radiation other than light has spurred further huge developments in astronomy. X-rays can be detected from many regions of the sky, often in pulses, and may come from neutron stars or black holes. Other objects at a great distance can be detected with radio telescopes. Some are intense radio sources called quasars and pulsars. You will learn how background radio waves have contributed to our knowledge of the universe. Infrared photographs, too, provide information, particularly about nebulae, large gas clouds in space.

In addition to the discovery and description of the different types of body in the universe, astronomers have discovered that the universe itself is expanding. By working backwards in time we can conclude there must have been a 'big bang'. This is when time began!

In this module you will learn about:

- the structure of the solar system and the universe
- Olbers' paradox and Hubble's law
- the life history of stars
- the evolution of the universe.

Module contents

1. The structure of the universe
2. The development of a star
3. Other bodies in the universe
4. Astronomical distances
5. The redshift
6. The expanding universe
7. The evolution of the universe
8. The future of the universe
9. Critical density

Test yourself

1 Why are reflecting telescopes able to give clearer images than refracting telescopes?

2 What is the numerical value of the speed of light? How far does light travel in one year? (This is a distance called a light-year.)

3 List the following objects in order of increasing mass.

Sun Moon meteorite galaxy comet Earth

4 What is your estimate of the order of magnitude of the age of the Earth?

10^{17} s 10^{21} s 10^{29} s 10^{33} s

5 What happens to the frequency of light from an object moving away from you?

2.5 (1) The structure of the universe

By the end of this spread, you should be able to …

* **Describe the principal components of the universe.**
* **Describe the Solar System in terms of the Sun, planets and planetary satellites.**

The scale of the universe

Everything about the size of the universe is vast. One might say, correctly, it is 'astronomical'. The word 'astronomical' is used in everyday speech for something very big. The only way of dealing with masses, times and distances when dealing with the universe is by using standard forms. For example, the order of magnitude of:

- the time since the Big Bang is 10^{17} seconds
- the mass of the Sun is 10^{30} kilograms
- the distance to the furthest galaxy is 10^{23} metres.

When you think of sums of money, just one order of magnitude seems a big jump. £1 is almost trivial, £10 is affordable, £100 makes you think, and £1000 is out of range. All of these are covered by just 3 orders of magnitude, yet in the list above, a jump of 30 orders of magnitude is necessary to go from the mass of a bag of sugar to the mass of the Sun.

The components that make the universe

Here we will look at only the main features of the universe. There are several groups of bodies that will be omitted from this initial list, and there is a large quantity of matter in the universe, called dark matter, about which little is known. The arrangement here is starting from the largest components and working down in size. Any numerical values given in this section are typical values to give you an idea of size only.

Figure 1 A spiral galaxy seen through a cloud of stars in our own galaxy, the Milky Way

Figure 2 The Andromeda Galaxy, seen with two other smaller galaxies, one of them bottom left, and the other, appearing like a star, directly above the nucleus of the Andromeda Galaxy

Galaxy

A **galaxy** is a cluster of many billions of stars rotating slowly around its own centre of gravity. Two galaxies are shown in Figures 1 and 2. Figure 1 is a spiral galaxy similar to our own galaxy, the Milky Way. In this photo, ignore all the white dots. The spiral galaxy is way beyond all of those stars. The photo had to be taken through the curtain of stars that is the Milky Way. Figure 2 is a photo of the closest galaxy to the Milky Way, named the Andromeda Galaxy. Two other galaxies are shown in the photo. One is the star-like dot directly above Andromeda's nucleus, and the other is the blurred smudge to the lower left of the Andromeda Galaxy.

Galaxies usually have a nucleus where the concentration of stars is greatest. Near the nucleus, there is a bulge in the galaxy (Figure 3). All the stars in a galaxy rotate around its nucleus. The stars further away from the nucleus take longer to complete one orbit than those near to the core. The Sun takes about 230 million years to complete one revolution.

In the universe, there are thought to be at least 100 million galaxies.

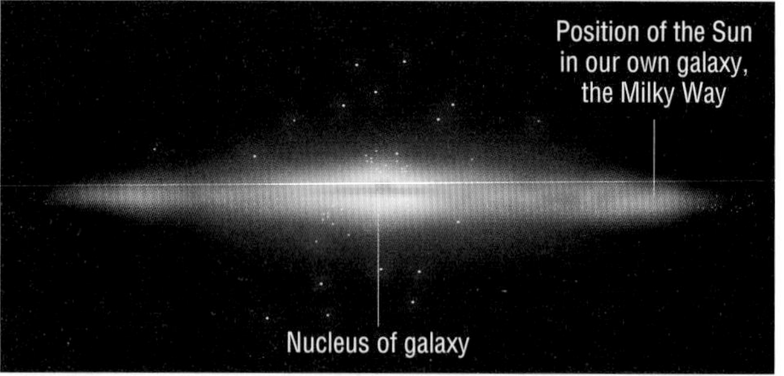

Figure 3 A spiral galaxy seen edge-on shows increased thickness towards the nucleus

Star

The stars are the powerhouses of the universe. They emit electromagnetic radiation, which is how we know about them. Their energy supply is from fusion. As you will find in later spreads, there are many different types of star. They are categorised by their brightness and their colour, but brightness can be misleading. An extremely bright star a long way away may appear much fainter than a star much less bright but closer to the Earth. The stars visible from Earth with the naked eye number a few thousand. When viewed through a telescope, that number increases to billions. To get a good view of the stars without a telescope, a few things are necessary. They are worth doing, as the panorama of the night sky is then quite startling.

- First you need to have a good, clear, night sky with no Moon.
- Second, you need to be somewhere it is really dark. Street lights limit visibility.
- Third, you need to wait at least a quarter of an hour in complete darkness. This gives your eye a chance to form a substance called visual purple. This increases the sensitivity of your eye considerably. You will have noticed this effect frequently when, in the middle of the night, you switch on an ordinary lamp. It seems unduly bright because, while you were asleep in the dark, your eye becomes more than usually sensitive.

Figure 4 A collection of photos showing the planets of the Solar System

Planet

A planet is a relatively cold object in a nearly circular orbit around a star. Very little is known about planets other than the planets that orbit around our own star, the Sun. Telescopes only now have sufficient accuracy to detect the slight wobble of some stars as a result of planets rotating around them. All the stars apart from the Sun are too far away for their planets, if they have any, to be seen. Size and distance are two problems with trying to see planets. Another major difficulty is that they are not hot enough to radiate any visible radiation, though the infrared of a few planets around distant stars has been detected. Even the planets in orbit around the Sun, the Solar System, are in many cases difficult to see. When they are visible, it is only because they reflect light from the Sun.

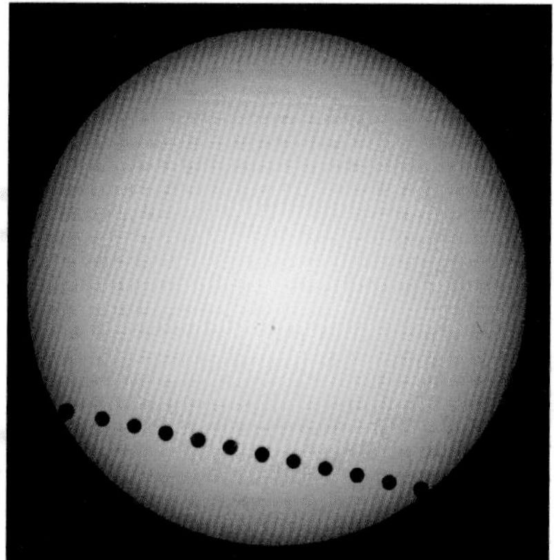

Figure 5 A composite image of the transit of Venus that took place on 8 June 2004. The first image was taken at 05:41 GMT and the last at 11:04 GMT. This was the first transit since 1882

Figure 4 shows a collection of photos of the planets in the Solar System. Mercury is small and close to the Sun. It is possible to see it only just after sunset or just before dawn. Venus, Mars, Jupiter and Saturn are readily visible if you look in the right place at the right time. Occasionally, Venus and Mercury line up between the Earth and the Sun. This is known as a transit. The photo in Figure 5 shows Venus moving across the face of the Sun in June 2004. Uranus and Neptune are a long way away and so are only dimly lit by sunlight. A telescope and its accurate positioning are needed to see them. Pluto is not now regarded as a planet, as it is too small. There are actually many millions of lumps of rock, some large, some small, in orbit around the Sun. Most of these are between the orbits of Mars and Jupiter in a region called the asteroid belt.

Moon

A moon is a satellite of a planet. It does not radiate any visible radiation. A moon, when visible, is seen by reflected radiation from a star – in the case of the Earth's Moon, the Sun (Figure 6). The phase of the Moon depends on how much of the Moon's illuminated surface is visible from the Earth, as the Moon rotates around the Earth each month.

Figure 6 A telephoto picture of the Moon rising over the city of Vancouver, Canada

Questions

1 Why are transits of planets across the Sun possible only with Venus and Mercury?

2 Why are eclipses of the Sun from any point on Earth rare events but eclipses of the Moon from the same point more frequent?

3 The mass of the Sun is 2.0×10^{30} kg; its radius is 7.0×10^{8} m. What is its mean density? Give one reason for this value being much smaller than the mean density of the Earth.

4 The radii of the orbits of Venus and the Earth are 1.08×10^{11} and 1.50×10^{11} m respectively.

  (a) Calculate the ratio of the maximum angular size of Venus to its minimum angular size when viewed from Earth.

  (b) Using data from Question 3 and Figure 5, estimate the diameter of Venus.

2.5 (2) The development of a star

By the end of this spread, you should be able to ...

* **Describe the formation of a star.**
* **Describe the probable evolution of a star such as the Sun.**

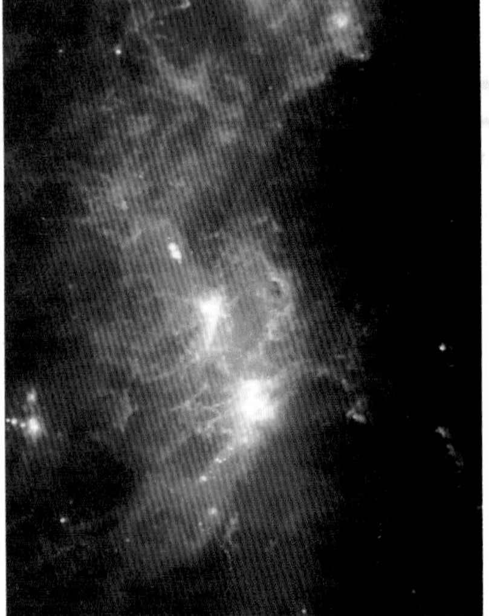

Figure 1 The Orion Nebula. This photo was taken using a telescope designed to take photos in the infrared spectrum

The formation of a star

Most of the universe is space. In places, the density of the universe is such that, unlike in a solid, where atoms are likely to be about 10^{-10} metres apart, in much of space the distance between atoms may be as much as 10^{2} metres. Since the ratio between these two terms is 10^{-12}, the ratio of the density of space to the density of a solid is 10^{-36}. Put another way, an atom in space has 10^{36} times more space to move in than an atom has in a solid. However, the density of space is not constant; there are some regions where the density is larger, and these regions therefore have a greater gravitational attraction towards themselves than the regions where the density is very low. Given enough time, these areas will very gradually become more dense, and the density will rise at an ever increasing rate until some of the gases in the area become hot enough to glow. This means that they can be detected through telescopes designed to observe infrared radiation. The regions are called **nebulae**, and two well-known ones are shown in Figures 1 and 2. The first is the Orion Nebula, the photo of which was taken using infrared radiation. The second is the Horsehead Nebula, and this image was taken using visible light. In this case, the nebula glows because it is ionised by radiation from comparatively near hot stars. Nebulae are the birthplace of stars.

Figure 2 The Horsehead Nebula seen in the visible spectrum. The gases in the nebula are ionised by comparatively near hot stars

As the density of the gases in a nebula increases, the atoms in them, attracted towards each other, lose potential energy and so gain kinetic energy. This results in an increase in temperature. The sequence of attraction, concentration and increasing internal energy results in a large core of material known as a protostar. The protostar continues to attract material and so increases in mass and surface temperature until it is large enough to emit light. Once the core of any star becomes sufficiently dense, the pressure becomes very large as well as the temperature. Under these conditions, fusion of nuclei becomes possible. During this process, hydrogen fuses into helium with the release of energy, as explained in spread 2.3.15.

The process of forming a star is relatively short. The time taken varies from star to star, because some stars form in denser parts of the universe and are very massive once formed; others have less material in their vicinity and will be smaller. The time of formation for a small star can be as little as 10 000 years; larger stars can take around a million years to form. During this process, some of the material that does not form into the protostar remains circling around the star and eventually becomes the planets of the star.

The formation of the Sun

The Sun and its planets were formed from a dust cloud around 5000 million years ago. The Sun has a core temperature of about 100 million kelvin, in comparison with a surface temperature of 6000 kelvin. During the last 4500 million years, during which Earth has existed as a planet, the Sun will have been a remarkably stable **main sequence star**. It remains stable because it has reached thermal equilibrium. It radiates electromagnetic energy out into space at a rate determined by the rate at which fusion reactions occur. At the present size and temperature of the Sun, the power generated by fusion is about 4×10^{26} W – so the power of the emitted radiation at the existing temperature of the surface is also 4×10^{26} W. This massive power is reducing the mass of the Sun only by a fraction, a mere 6×10^{-8} every million years. Since it will stay around the same size for any million-year period, it will keep the same rate of fusion – and the same output power. (There is no way the hydrogen itself will run out, since the Sun is mostly hydrogen.) The Sun will therefore stay as a main sequence star for at least another 5000 million years.

The eventual fate of the Sun

Eventually the rate of hydrogen fusion will decrease in the core of the Sun as much of it will then be fusion products, mostly helium. Some hydrogen fusion will continue in a shell around the core, but the core itself will contract. This is expected to have a strange effect. The loss of potential energy on contraction will mean an increase in kinetic energy and hence an increase in temperature and therefore pressure of the core. The huge pressure in the core will cause the entire Sun to grow. It will gradually absorb into itself Mercury, Venus and, in time, Earth. The surface temperature of this massive star will be much lower than now. It will become a **red giant**. During this stage of its evolution, some fusion of helium will take place in the very high-temperature core.

The entire red-giant stage will last only about 15% of the time it spends as a main sequence star. Once the fusion of helium finishes, the star becomes unstable, and much of its mass is radiated outwards in huge ion sprays. (This is the effect referred to above that causes the Horsehead Nebula to be visible.) The rest of the Sun will shrink to become a **white dwarf**. Its diameter will then be only 1% of its present diameter, and its density will increase from its present value of 1400 kg m^{-3} to about 700 million kg m^{-3}. As a result of loss of potential energy, its surface temperature will rise again, perhaps to as high as 20 000 kelvin. After the white dwarf stage, the Sun will gradually cool. The changes across the development of the Sun are shown, not to scale, in the sequence of diagrams, Figures 3 (a)–(d). The Sun is not big enough to become a neutron star, or a black hole, or a supernova. It will just fade away to a lump of cold, very dense, matter.

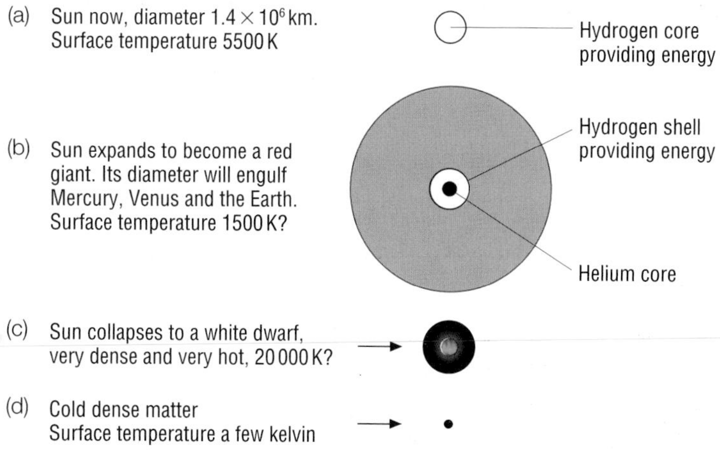

Figure 3 The probable development of the Sun from its present size until several billion years from now

Questions

1 (a) In one region of a nebula, the mean separation of atoms is 2.3×10^{-3} m. What volume of the nebula contains enough atoms to make a star, similar to the Sun, of radius 7.0×10^{8} m within which the mean distance between atoms is 1.0×10^{-10} m?

(b) Use the data from **(a)** and the Sun's density, 1400 kg m^{-3}, to estimate the mass of the Sun.

2 (a) Use $E = mc^2$ to estimate the rate of loss of mass of the Sun, given that its power output equals 4×10^{26} W.

(b) How long will it take for the mass of the Sun to fall to 99% of its present value, assuming a constant rate of loss of mass? (Use the answer from Question 1 for the mass of the Sun.)

2.5 ③ Other bodies in the universe

By the end of this spread, you should be able to …

* **Describe comets.**
* **Describe the formation of neutron stars and black holes.**

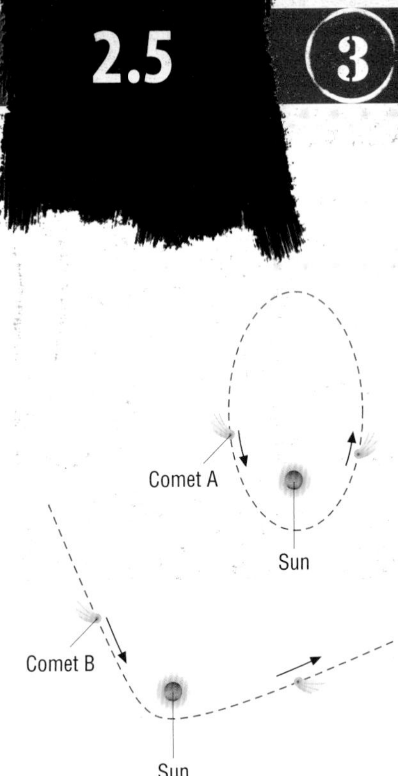

Figure 1 The paths of comets around the Sun. Comet A is on an elliptical path and will pass the Sun at regular intervals. The tail of the comet always points away from the Sun. Comet B is on a hyperbolic path. After passing the Sun, it will disappear for good

Figure 2 Halley's Comet. The tail is only faintly visible. Notice that all the stars seen in the photo appear as short lines because a time exposure was necessary for the photo, and during that time the rotation of the Earth seemed to make the stars move

Introduction

The main categories of objects in the universe were listed in spread 2.5.1. There are other objects in the universe, however, and this spread will describe some of them.

Comets

Comets are fragmented bodies consisting of ice and rock together with a cloud of gas, and originate in a region of rock and ice called the Kuiper Belt outside the orbit of Neptune. Some comets travel around the Sun along elongated elliptical paths and others along a hyperbolic path. As can be seen in Figure 1, only those travelling in an ellipse move around the Sun at regular intervals. Those on hyperbolic paths appear once and are never seen again. Halley's Comet is shown in Figure 2. It returns to the Sun every 76 years and can then be seen from the Earth. It last appeared in 1985 and will next appear in 2061. The faint tail of a comet appears only when it is near the Sun. The solar wind, an emission of ions from the Sun's surface, causes the gases associated with the comet to spread out, to become ionised and hence to glow.

Meteorites and meteors

Meteorites are commonly called shooting stars. In fact, this could not be more incorrect. They are usually tiny fragments of rock from interplanetary space that happen to enter the Earth's atmosphere and heat up as a result of friction with the atmosphere. They are visible for a second or so when at a high temperature. Figure 3 is a time exposure of the night sky showing their tracks. Most vaporise, so they never reach the ground, but occasionally a large meteorite collides with the Earth. The surface of the Moon shows the effect of large meteor collisions that have taken place over the last 4000 million years.

Binary stars

Photographs cannot show stars as anything other than points of light, because they are too far away. Any width to an image of a star is a diffraction pattern, with the width dependent on such things as the focal length and the quality of the lens. The photo of the binary star in Figure 4(a) is an image taken by the Faint Object Camera on board the Hubble Space Telescope. Mira A, on the right, is a variable (unstable) red giant with a diameter about 700 times that of the Sun. It rotates around its companion star, which is a hot white dwarf. They are 70 times further apart than the Earth and Sun are. Figure 4(b) shows two stars of Alpha Centauri, part of the nearest star system to the Earth, at a distance of only 4.3 light years. These two stars rotate around each other once every 80 years.

Figure 3 On 17 November each year, the Earth, in its orbit around the Sun, passes through the debris from a comet, giving rise to a shower of meteorites, as shown

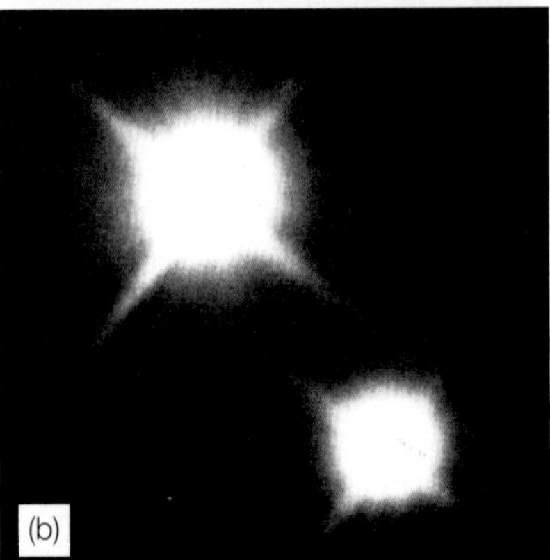

Figure 4 **(a)** The binary star Mira – the star on the right is a red giant; the one on the left is a white dwarf, and the two stars rotate around one another; **(b)** the binary star Alpha Centauri

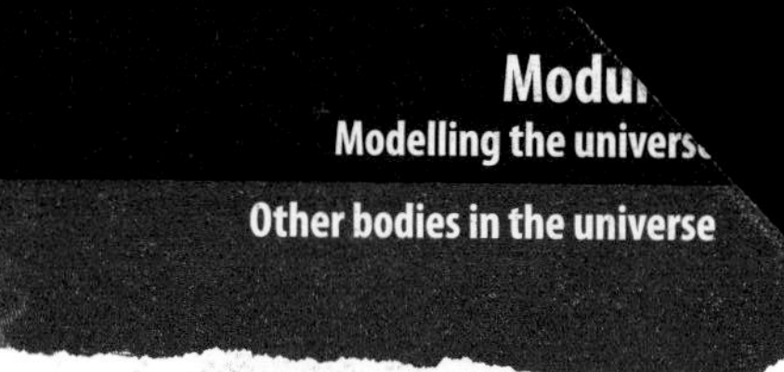

Supernovae and neutron stars

If a star is big enough, it reaches a stage at the end of its red-giant phase when further nuclear fusion reactions in its core can occur at temperatures rising in stages, as it collapses, to billions of kelvin. During this stage the immense pressure causes protons to absorb electrons to become neutrons. When the final collapse takes place, it may take only a few days. The collapse produces intense heating followed by an explosive blowing out of the outer shell and compression of the core. The huge release of energy is called a **supernova**. In a supernova, particle energies are high enough to create all the elements in the Periodic Table. The Earth and all the elements in it are the remains of a supernova explosion. One such explosion, seen on Earth in 1054 AD, formed the Crab Nebula. Its remains, which can be seen today in powerful telescopes, will become the birthplace of future stars after more of the hydrogen in space is attracted to it (Figure 5).

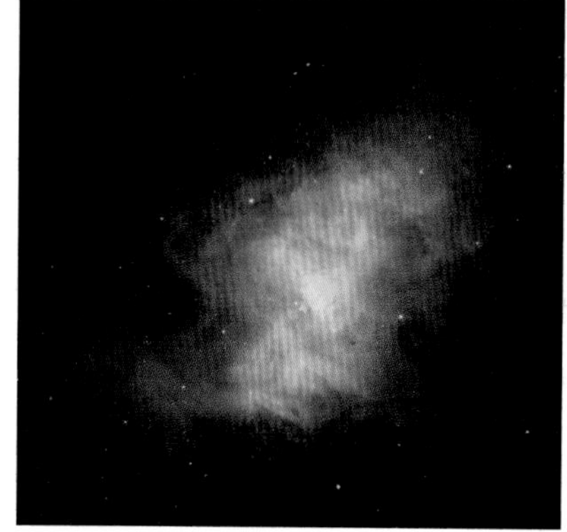
Figure 5 The Crab Nebula

Under certain conditions the nucleus of a supernova explosion can remain intact. This is a **neutron star**. Its density will be such that a neutron star of mass equal to that of the Sun would have a diameter of only 30 km. These stars rotate rapidly and emit very accurately defined electromagnetic waves. There is one in the Crab Nebula that emits electromagnetic radiation over a broad spectrum from gamma rays to radio waves and with a spin frequency of 30.2 Hz. The magnetic field of the neutron star must be large, and the frequency at which the pulses of radiation are emitted is assumed to be the rate at which the star, and its associated magnetic field, rotates. The star sends out this radiation somewhat like the revolving beam of a lighthouse. Such neutron stars are **pulsars**.

Black holes

A further stage of development is possible in the case of supergiant stars. Theoretically, the pressure on the core could become so large that the neutron star would collapse to a point at which the density would become infinite. Whether normal laws of physics apply at this stage is debatable, but if the density is high enough, the gravitational field in a region around the point will be so large that nothing, not even light, can escape it. This region is known as a **black hole**. Work on certain stars suggests that their centripetal movement makes them one of a binary pair – but the other one of the pair cannot be seen. Perhaps the other star is a black hole. This seems likely for a star in the Milky Way called Cygnus X-1. It emits X-rays and could be a binary star with a black hole. Gases from it would be accelerated towards a black hole and would gain sufficient energy to emit the high-frequency X-rays observed.

Quasars

Quasars are very distant objects with phenomenal brightness – perhaps as much power output as a trillion (10^{12}) Suns. They have black holes at their centre and are probably forming galaxies.

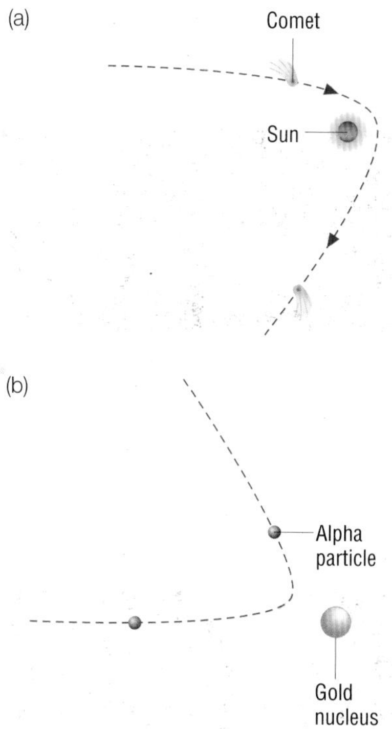

Figure 6 **(a)** A comet in its hyperbolic orbit around the Sun; **(b)** an alpha particle being deflected by a gold nucleus

Questions

1 The path of a comet in a hyperbolic path around the Sun is shown in Figure 6(a). The path of an alpha particle being deflected by a gold nucleus is shown, on a vastly larger scale, in Figure 6(b).
   (a) On sketches of the two figures, show the forces acting on the comet and on the alpha particle in both of the positions shown.
   (b) State one similarity and one difference between the two situations.

2 A binary star consists of one star of mass M and another of mass m a distance d apart. They both rotate in circles around their common centre of mass C as shown in Figure 7.
   (a) State the force acting on each star in terms of M, m, d and G, the gravitational constant.
   (b) Deduce the values of R and r in terms of M, m and d.
   (c) Explain why the two stars must have the same period of rotation T.
   (d) Deduce the value of T in terms of M, m, d and G.

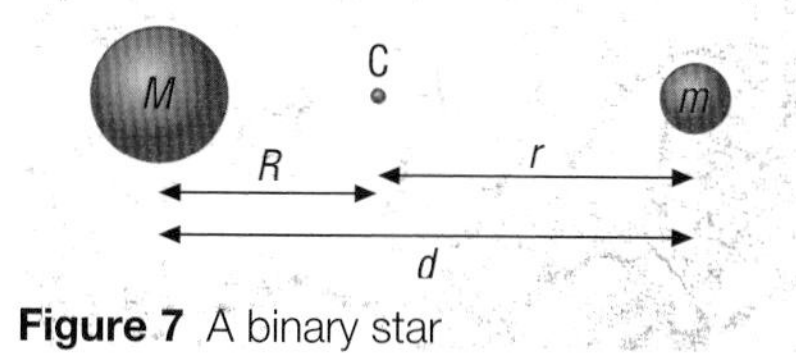

Figure 7 A binary star

4 Astronomical distances

By the end of this spread, you should be able to ...

* **Define distances measured in astronomical units (AU), parsecs (pc) and light years (ly).**
* **State the approximate values of these units in metres in standard form.**
* **State and interpret Olbers' paradox.**

Introduction to distance units

The problem of units for measurements of astronomical distances has resulted in four different units being currently used by astronomers. You will need to know what these units are and approximate conversion factors from one to the other. (Astronomers are inclined not to use standard form. Instead they tend to use multiplying factors such as k, for kilo, and M, for mega. This just adds to the danger of making mistakes. As always with arithmetic of this kind, answers need to be double-checked.)

The astronomical unit of distance (AU)

The astronomical unit of distance is the mean distance from the centre of the Earth to the centre of the Sun. The astronomical unit is used for studies of the Solar System. Its value has been measured to 8 significant figures and is given in standard form to 4 significant figures as

1 astronomical unit (AU) = 1.496×10^{11} metres

The Earth's orbit around the Sun is elliptical. In January the Earth is 1.471×10^{11} m from the Sun, and in July it is slightly further away at a distance of 1.521×10^{11} m. The average of these two is 1.496×10^{11} m, 1 AU. (Note that summer and winter have nothing to do with these distances. The seasons are in fact determined by the angle of the Earth's axis to the plane of the Earth's orbit.)

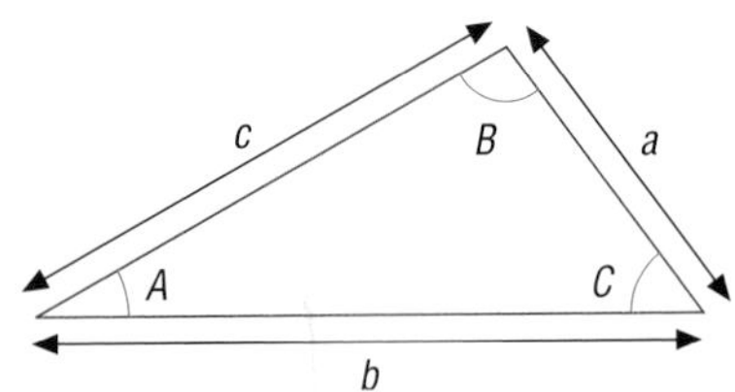

Figure 1 Triangulation

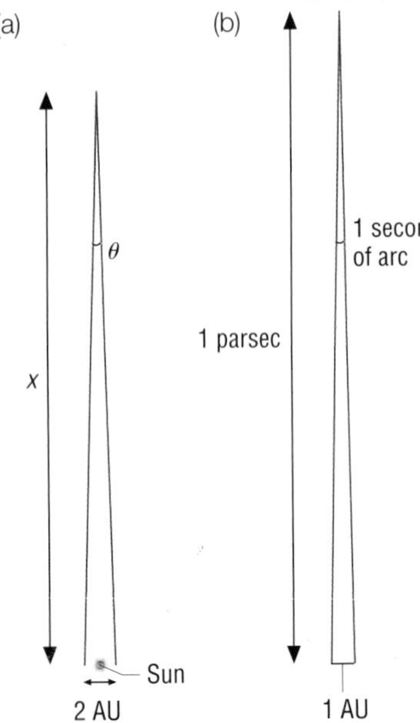

Figure 2 **(a)** and **(b)** Determining distances to stars using a triangulation method over periods of time

The parsec (pc)

Distances to stars were first measured using triangulation, which is a method similar to the one first used for mapping. It is illustrated in Figure 1. In this, a base line of known length b is taken, and the angles A and C are measured. This enables the distances a and c to be obtained. Unfortunately, when the process is repeated for stars, using a base line on the Earth, the angles A and C are always both 90°. This gives the distance to the star as infinity. However, if, having taken one reading of the position of a star against the background of distant stars, you wait for six months before taking the second reading, you will effectively have a base line that is 2 AU long. This is just long enough to be able to get two different readings for the angles for stars comparatively close to the Earth and hence to calculate their distances from Earth. This method is illustrated in Figure 2(a). The angle θ will always be small, so the distance x to a star in this position will be given by

$$\sin\theta = \frac{2\text{ AU}}{x} \approx \theta \text{ in radians for small angles. This gives } x = \frac{2\text{ AU}}{\theta}.$$

The **parsec** is a unit related directly to this method of measuring astronomical distances.

One parsec is the distance from a baseline of length one astronomical unit (1 AU) when the angle is one second of arc (Figure 2(b)). That angle is 1/3600 of a degree. Measured in radians, the angle is 4.848×10^{-6} radians.

The conversion to the astronomical unit is therefore given by 1 AU/1pc = 4.848×10^{-6} rad.

This gives 1 pc = 2.063×10^5 AU to 4 sig. figs.

Conversion to metres in standard form gives 1 pc = $2.063 \times 10^5 \times 1.496 \times 10^{11}$
$= 3.086 \times 10^{16}$ m

The light year (ly)
One light year is the distance light will travel through a vacuum in one year. Note that a light year is a *distance*. It is *not* a time.

To obtain an answer to 4 significant figures, an Earth year is $365.25 \times 24 \times 60 \times 60 = 3.1558 \times 10^7$ s, and the speed of light is 2.9979×10^8 m s^{-1}. This gives a light year as 9.461×10^{15} m.

Key definition

1 astronomical unit (AU) $= 1.496 \times 10^{11}$ m
1 parsec (pc) $= 3.086 \times 10^{16}$ m
1 light year (ly) $= 9.461 \times 10^{15}$ m

Olbers' paradox

Once measurements to find the distance to close stars had succeeded, astronomers began to wonder how much further the distant stars were. Many thought that the universe was infinite, arguing that, if it were finite, gravitational forces would cause its collapse.

Figure 3 is needed for the explanation of Olbers' paradox, together with the facts that we are dealing with spheres rather than circles and that the surface area of a sphere is $4\pi r^2$. Olbers' reasoning went like this:

- The universe is infinite.
- On a large enough scale, stars are spread evenly throughout the universe, with n stars per unit volume.
- The thin shell A of stars has volume $4\pi r^2 t$ (surface area × thickness) and contains $4\pi r^2 tn$ stars.
- The thin shell B of stars has volume $4\pi(2r)^2 t$ and contains $16\pi r^2 tn$ stars.
- The brightness of any star is inversely proportional to its distance squared.
- The brightness at the Earth due to the stars in shell A $= k4\pi r^2 tn/r^2 = k4\pi tn$ where k is a constant.
- The brightness at the Earth due to the stars in shell B $= k16\pi r^2 tn/(2r)^2 = k4\pi tn$.
- Every shell produces the same brightness at the Earth, and there are an infinite number of shells.
- The Earth is infinitely bright because of starlight.

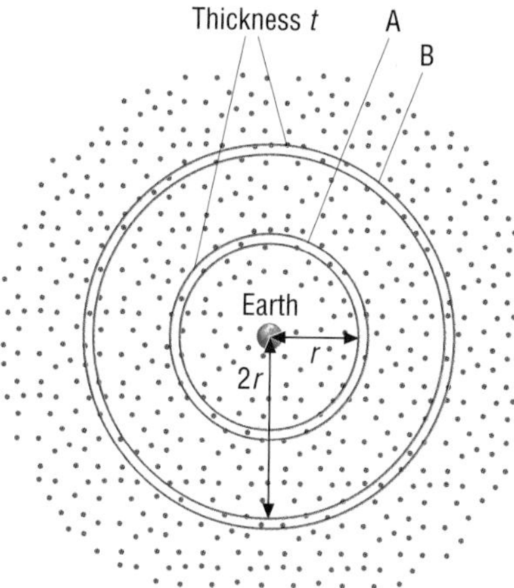

Figure 3 The Earth is considered at the centre of two spherical shells of equal thickness t: one of radius r and the other of radius $2r$. Earth receives light from stars within both shells

The paradox is that, from a seemingly correct starting point and correct mathematics throughout, the result is obviously not true.

Olbers' deduction from his paradox was that the universe is not infinite.

Olbers' paradox is sometimes written as follows:

> With an infinite number of stars in an infinite universe, it does not matter what direction you look in – you will always see a star along the line of sight. Therefore, the night sky will be as bright as the day sky.

However, this statement misses out much of Olbers' original deduction, which caused much scientific argument when it was published in 1826. More detail about the uniformity of the universe will be given in spread 2.5.6.

Questions

1 (a) (i) What defines a year?
   (ii) If you had lived in Roman times, how could you have measured a year accurately?
 (b) (i) What defines a day?
   (ii) Using an accurate watch, could you now measure a day by observing the apparent movement of stars?

2 What is the distance of the Earth from the Sun, in terms of light years (ly)?

3 The nearest star to the Earth (apart from the Sun) is Proxima Centauri. It is approx. 4.5 ly from the Earth, as shown in Figure 4. As viewed from the Earth when in position A and six months later from position B, the parallax angle, $\frac{1}{2}\theta$, is as shown. Calculate the value of θ.

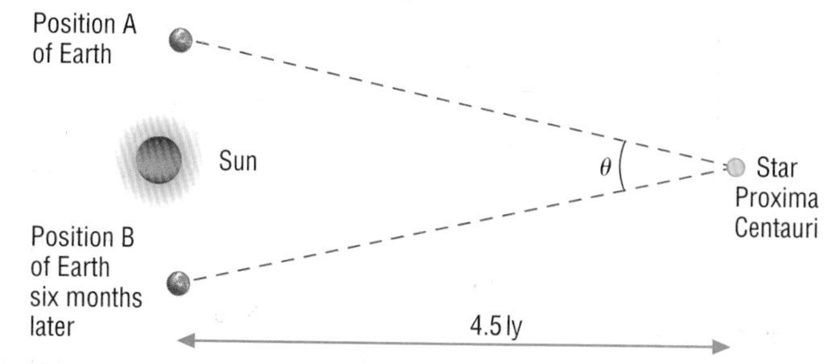

Figure 4 The sighting of Proxima Centauri from two positions of the Earth (not to scale)

2.5 (5) The redshift

By the end of this spread, you should be able to …

- **Select and use the equations $\Delta\lambda \neq \lambda = v \neq c$.**
- **Describe and interpret Hubble's redshift observations.**
- **State and interpret Hubble's law.**
- **Convert the Hubble constant H_0 from its conventional units to SI.**

Worked example

In the laboratory the wavelength of the blue line in the hydrogen spectrum is 434.0 nm. The light from a distant quasar shows that the corresponding line has a wavelength of 616.3 nm. How fast is the quasar receding?

Answer

The change in wavelength
= 616.3 nm – 434.0 nm
= 182.3 nm.
$\Delta\lambda/\lambda$ = 182.3 nm/434.0 nm
= 0.420.
This is a fraction; the units cancel out.
Therefore, v/c = 0.420 and
$v = 0.420 \times 3.00 \times 10^8\ \text{m s}^{-1}$ =
126 million metres per second.

The Doppler effect

In spreads 2.4.8 and 2.4.11 the Doppler effect was explained for ultrasound, and we saw how the effect could be used for measuring the speed of blood flow in a baby's heart. Exactly the same effect can be used for electromagnetic waves from stars. The original frequency f of a wave from a source moving towards an observer with velocity v has a higher frequency f' at the observer. The relationship was shown to be

$$\frac{f'}{f} = \frac{f + \Delta f}{f} = 1 + \frac{\Delta f}{f} = 1 + \frac{v}{c}$$

where c is the speed of the wave. This gives

$$1 + \frac{\Delta f}{f} = 1 + \frac{v}{c} \text{ or } \frac{\Delta f}{f} = \frac{v}{c}$$

Since $c = f\lambda$, the expression can be given in wavelength terms rather than frequency. It then becomes

$$\frac{\Delta\lambda}{\lambda} = \frac{v}{c}$$

where $\Delta\lambda$ is the change in wavelength and λ is the original wavelength. Note that, for an approaching source, the frequency rises and the wavelength falls. The opposite is true for a receding source – in this case, the wavelength increases and the frequency falls.

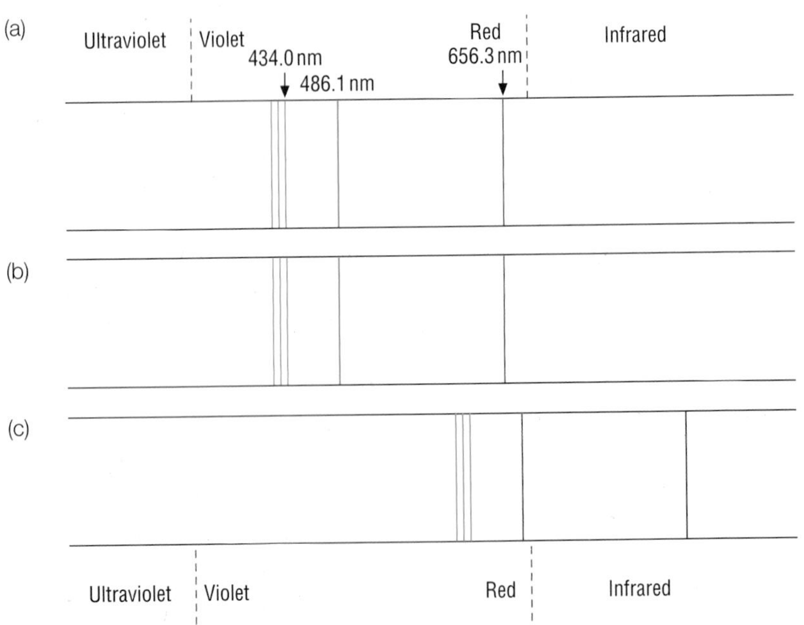

Figure 1 **(a)** shows the spectrum of hydrogen as seen in a laboratory; **(b)** shows the same spectrum from a star in the Milky Way, our own galaxy; **(c)** shows a large redshift in the same spectrum from a distant galaxy

The redshift of stars

A sketch of a photo taken in a laboratory of a hydrogen spectrum is shown in Figure 1(a). When the hydrogen spectrum from a star in the Milky Way is observed, it looks the same as it was in the laboratory – see Figure 1(b). However, careful measuring showing a very slight movement towards the red end of the spectrum had been noticed as early as 1868. When Hubble looked at data for some galaxies, he found the spectrum for one of them like that shown in Figure 1(c). This did not fit any known element, but the pattern was the same as that for hydrogen but shifted a large distance towards the red end of the spectrum. One of the lines even became invisible in the infrared. Hubble was convinced that the shift was due to the Doppler effect. The shift corresponded to the galaxy having a speed of recession much larger than anything found previously. Since then, over 100 000 quasars have been discovered. These quasars are receding even faster.

Hubble's law

Hubble knew the distances to some comparatively close galaxies. He found the small redshift for these galaxies and calculated their corresponding speed of recession. When he plotted a graph of speed of recession against distance from the Earth, he obtained a straight line graph (Figure 2).

Hubble's law summarises his findings. It states:

> The speed of the recession of a galaxy is directly proportional to its distance from the Earth.

The law can be expressed mathematically as

$$\frac{\text{speed of recession}}{\text{distance from Earth}} = H_0$$ where H_0 is a constant known as the Hubble constant.

Key definition

Hubble's law states that the speed of the recession of a galaxy is directly proportional to its distance from the Earth.

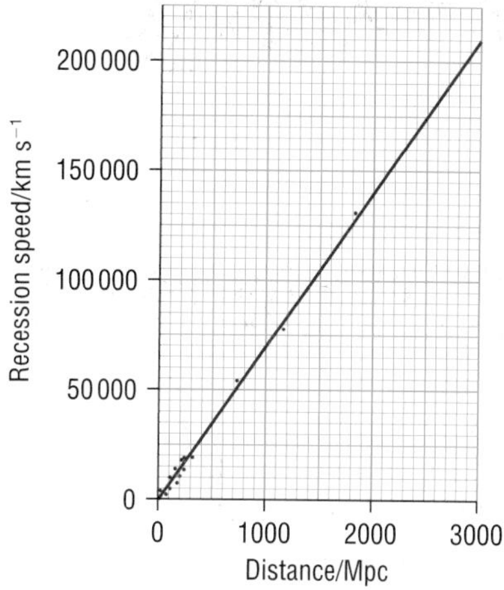

Figure 2 A graph showing how the speed of recession of a galaxy is proportional to its distance from the Earth

The Hubble constant

The gradient of the graph of speed of recession against distance from the Earth, Figure 2, gives the Hubble constant.

Its value is $H_0 = \frac{\text{speed of recession}}{\text{distance from Earth}} = \frac{175\,000 \text{ km s}^{-1}}{2500 \text{ Mpc}} = 70 \text{ km s}^{-1} \text{ Mpc}^{-1}$.

There are several problems with this constant. One of them is about its units; the more fundamental problem concerns what its value actually is. The unit problem stems from its historical use. It was originally, and often still is, given in terms of km s^{-1} Mpc^{-1}, that is, kilometres per second (the unit of speed of recession) per megaparsec (the unit of distance from Earth). This can be converted into SI units as follows:

$1 \text{ km s}^{-1} = 1000 \text{ m s}^{-1}$
$1 \text{ Mpc} = 10^6 \text{ pc} \times 3.09 \times 10^{16} \text{ m/pc} = 3.09 \times 10^{22} \text{ m}$

Therefore

$$H_0 = 70 \text{ km s}^{-1} \text{ Mpc}^{-1} = \frac{70 \times 1000 \text{ m s}^{-1}}{3.09 \times 10^{22} \text{ m}} = 2.3 \times 10^{-18} \text{ s}^{-1}$$

The other problem with the Hubble constant is that it is very difficult to obtain an accurate value of it. The problem is that the most accurate values of distance and recession speeds are those obtained from close stars and galaxies. Even here the problem is complicated by the fact that both stars and galaxies are rotating as well as receding. Near galaxies are in a cluster of galaxies, of which the Milky Way is one. The value of H_0 above, (70 ± 2) km s^{-1} Mpc^{-1}, is the latest value, but over the last 50 years, values between 50 and 100 km s^{-1} Mpc^{-1} have also been given. It is hoped that a more accurate value can be achieved using the Hubble Space Telescope. The Hubble Telescope can provide images from distant galaxies that are millions of times clearer than even the best ground-based telescope.

Hubble showed that the whole universe is expanding. This means that the distance between any point in the universe is getting further away from every other point as a result of this expansion. This automatically means that the speed of recession between any two points must be directly proportional to their separation, with the constant of proportionality being the Hubble constant. The Hubble constant is a property of the expansion and has the same value at every point in the universe. There is therefore nothing special about the position of the Earth.

Hubble's law is now used to calculate the distance to galaxies at the edge of the observable universe. Since the speed of light puts a limit on the speed of recession of a galaxy, it also means that the universe is not infinite in size. This then resolves Olbers' paradox. Put simply, the sky is dark at night because the universe is expanding. The next spread will go into more detail about the expansion of the universe.

Examiner tip

Put the units into conversion equations as shown in the text here. If the units are correct after cancelling, this will ensure not only that the conversion factors are correct but also that they are used the right way around. You will not then get nonsense such as 500 kg m^{-3} = 0.500 g m^{-3} because you divided rather than multiplied.

Questions

1 Explain why stars in the Milky Way show little or no redshift.

2 A distant galaxy shows a different redshift from one edge of the galaxy to the redshift from its opposite edge. What could be deduced from:

(a) the mean redshift?

(b) the difference between the two values from opposite edges?

3 The wavelength of a particular calcium absorption line in a spectrum when measured in a laboratory is 3.969×10^{-7} m. When the same line is viewed in a spectrum of light from the galaxy known as the Boötes Cluster, its wavelength is found to be 4.485×10^{-7} m. Calculate the speed of recession of the Boötes Cluster.

2.5 (6)
The expanding universe

By the end of this spread, you should be able to ...

- **State the cosmological principle.**
- **Describe and explain the significance of the 3 K microwave background radiation.**
- **Explain that the big bang model implies a finite age for the universe, and use the expression age of universe $\approx 1 \neq H_0$.**

The cosmological principle

From the viewpoint of Earth, it seems obvious that Earth itself is the largest object in the universe, with the Sun as the dominant object in the sky, followed by the Moon and then the planets and a large number of stars circling around us. Since all the stars appear to travel around us at the same rate, it is not surprising that all ancient writings stated these ideas as facts. No one understood that the apparent movement of the Sun and stars was because the Earth was slowly rotating. The Earth seemed to them to be fixed. Gradually, though, over the years, each of these so-called facts has been found to be false.

The following principle is the modern view of the universe.

The **cosmological principle** states that on a large scale the universe is uniform.

Key definition

The **cosmological principle** states that on a large scale the universe is uniform.

That is, the universe is
- isotropic – the same in all directions
- homogeneous – of uniform density

as long as a large enough volume is used.

In effect, the principle states the opposite of all the ancient writings. It says that nowhere is special – every galaxy is moving away from every other galaxy, and there is no preferred direction along which all matter is concentrated or rotating. This is not to say that there are no local concentrations of matter or centres of rotation. The Sun is the centre of the Solar System, about which the planets rotate. There is a point at the centre of our Galaxy, the Milky Way, about which the Galaxy rotates. What there is *not*, however, is a point where, if you look one way you will see the universe, and if you look in the opposite direction you will see nothing. Our view of the universe is, basically, exactly the same as it would be from anywhere else in the universe. The density of the universe is constant everywhere, provided you use a large enough unit of volume. That is, the universe is **isotropic** and **homogeneous**.

The background radiation

In 1965, Penzias and Wilson used a radio telescope to examine the radio spectrum of various parts of the sky. Wherever their radio telescope pointed, they picked up unwanted noise. But the strange thing about this noise was that it had the same frequency peak from all points in the sky where there seemed to be nothing. It did not vary from day to night or winter to summer. Not only did the frequency not vary, but neither did the amplitude. It was not, therefore, associated with just the Solar System, but pervaded all space. They made a calculation to find the temperature of the source of the radio waves, which had a maximum intensity at wavelength of 1.1 cm, and found it to be 2.7 K.

The significance of this background radiation was that it settled a scientific argument that had lasted for some time. Some astrophysicists thought that the universe was static and had existed for ever and that matter was continually being generated from nothing to account for the expansion of the universe. This is the steady-state theory. (One person went as far as to suggest that the universe would need only one hydrogen atom to be formed in a space equivalent to the volume of St. Paul's Cathedral per year.) Other astrophysicists proposed the 'big bang' theory. They calculated that from the big bang the universe would expand and cool and that a background radiation would exist at a few degrees kelvin. Thus, the eternally old steady-state universe would be cold, and there would be no background radiation. Penzias and Wilson's discovery of the so-called cosmic microwave background (CMB) radiation, at just the right temperature, therefore confirmed the big bang theory.

STRETCH and CHALLENGE

Radiation from hot bodies is well understood. When the ring on an electric cooker is switched on, you can feel the infrared radiation from it before you can see any light. Once the ring is emitting light, it is long-wavelength, deep red light. As the temperature rises, the ring turns more orange as shorter wavelength light is emitted. Filament bulbs at a temperature of 2000 K do not emit much violet light, so they seem rather yellow compared with light from the Sun, emitted at a temperature of 5600 K. This is shown in Figure 1. The wavelength of peak emission λ_{max} is inversely proportional to the Kelvin temperature.

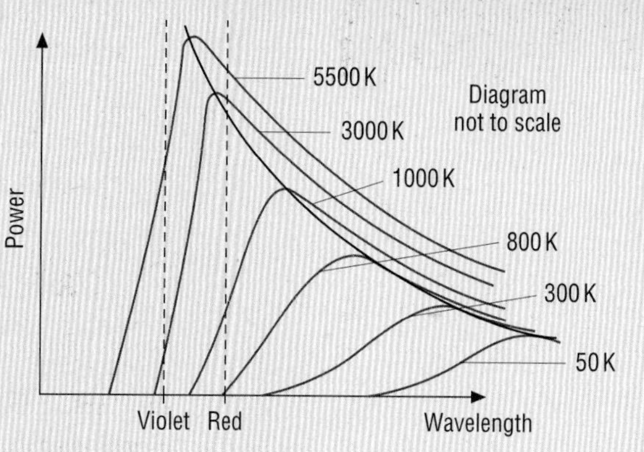

Figure 1 Radiation emitted from hot bodies

Question

At a temperature of 5600 K, the peak of the graph occurs at a wavelength of 5.2×10^{-7} m. What will be the wavelength at the peak of the graph for a temperature of 2.7 K?

The age of the universe

The acceptance of the big bang theory of the universe poses the immediate question 'How long ago did it happen?' The Hubble graph, Figure 2 on spread 2.5.5, gives information about this. Look at the graph. Note that more readings are available for comparatively close galaxies. Values for the distant galaxies are less certain, so the reliability of the gradient of the graph is poor.

A galaxy at a distance of 2000 Mpc has a recession speed of 140000 km s^{-1}. The time it would take for the galaxy to reach this position at this speed from the time of the big bang is the distance divided by the speed, which is therefore the reciprocal of the Hubble constant. Working from first principles gives

$$\text{time} = \frac{\text{distance}}{\text{speed}} = \frac{2000\ \text{Mpc}}{140000\ \text{km s}^{-1}} = \frac{2000\ \text{Mpc} \times 3.09 \times 10^{22}\ \text{m Mpc}^{-1}}{1.4 \times 10^{8}\ \text{m s}^{-1}}$$

$$= 4.4 \times 10^{17}\ \text{s}$$

$$= \frac{4.4 \times 10^{17}\ \text{s}}{3.15 \times 10^{7}\ \text{s year}^{-1}} = 1.4 \times 10^{10}\ \text{year}$$

This value of the age of the universe, 14 billion years, is somewhat on the high side. It is therefore preferable to write

$$\text{age of universe} \approx \frac{1}{H_0}$$

The approximate value comes from realising that several approximations have been made during the deduction. These are as follows:

- The major approximation is to assume that the galaxy in question has been travelling at the same speed throughout its existence. In practice, it must have gained some gravitational potential energy during its lifetime, which will mean it has lost some kinetic energy. This has the effect of slowing down the rate of expansion of the universe. The present speed of a galaxy is therefore below its average speed. If the average speed is used in the above calculation, therefore, the time since the big bang will be lower.
- The uncertainty in the value of the Hubble constant itself will make the age of the universe uncertain.
- There is a problem at the time of the big bang itself. The galaxies did not form all at once. Any time delay at this stage has been ignored.

The best value to date (2008) for the age of the universe is 13 ± 1 billion years.

Questions

1. Calculate the value, in SI units, for the age of the universe from the following data.
   A galaxy at a distance of 1.0×10^{10} ly recedes from the Earth with a speed of 2.0×10^{8} m s^{-1}.
2. A star at a distance of 11 ly from the Earth provides us with a power per unit area of 1.7×10^{-12} W m^{-2}. Calculate the power output of the star and suggest how such a small rate of supply of energy might be measured.
3. The star Sirius is a bright white star whose surface temperature is in the region of 20000 K. Using information from the Stretch and Challenge box, deduce its wavelength of peak emission. In what region of the electromagnetic spectrum does this wavelength lie?

2.5 (7) The evolution of the universe

By the end of this spread, you should be able to ...

* **Describe the evolution of the universe from 10^{-43} s after the big bang to the present.**

Introduction

The universe as we know it today has been examined in great detail. Way back in 781 BC, the Chinese were recording eclipses. In the time of the classical Greeks and Romans, calculations of the position of stars, of the length of a year and the radius of the Earth were being made. These data were needed for navigational and agricultural reasons. Later, in the Middle Ages, the detailed work carried out by scientists such as Copernicus, Brahe, Kepler, Galileo and Newton laid the framework for the current understanding of the Solar System. It is worth pointing out that throughout this course you have assumed all orbits to be circular. All these scientists did not make this simplification. They worked with the ellipses that are actually the shape of the orbits.

A great leap forward was made when Galileo realised the importance of the telescope. This greatly enlarged the range of knowledge, and further advances have taken place as bigger and better telescopes have been constructed. Major advances during the twentieth century have been Einstein's theory of relativity, the development of the quantum theory, the vastly greater understanding of atomic and nuclear structure, and the ability to view the universe from space, where the absence of obscuring atmosphere has led to much greater detailed knowledge. Not only is there now a wealth of detail, but powerful computers are also able to manipulate the mass of data that is now produced from any experiment. The twenty-first century promises to start well, with results on particle physics from the new CERN accelerator about to be published.

The sequence of events after the big bang

Figure 1 A somewhat problematic imaginary view of the big bang (see text)

The standard model of the universe depends on two fundamental features. The first is that there was a big bang. The second concerns what we know about the present-day universe. In practice the theoretical development of the standard model was worked backwards in time from the present phase of the universe until the big bang. Calculations using the full theory have now reached the stage where the earliest time used in the theory is within a very small fraction of a second of the big bang itself. At this stage, there is doubt as to whether the usual laws of physics hold. An illustration of the big bang is shown in Figure 1. It is, of course, an image from the imagination of the artist. There is a fundamental flaw in this type of sketch. It presumes that the whole process can be viewed from outside the universe – but because the universe is everything, in reality there is no 'outside'. The universe expanded from a point at the time of the big bang and has been expanding ever since. Everything is therefore the universe. There is no need to use the words 'inside' and 'outside'. They give an erroneous mental image.

The sequence of events from the big bang to the present follows. The timings and temperatures are all typical values and do not represent sudden changes except at the very start.

Temperature infinite; time zero

The big bang. All matter and energy concentrated at a single point.

Temperature 10^{27} K; time 10^{-43} s

All four types of force (gravitation, electromagnetic, strong and weak) are unified: rapid expansion occurring.

Temperature 10^{22} K; time 10^{-34} s
Gravitation force separating from the other three forces: the primordial quark soup stage plus photons.

Temperature 10^{16} K; time 10^{-16} s
Strong force separates from electromagnetic force and weak force: leptons form from photons. For some unknown reason, there is already more matter than antimatter in the minuscule universe.

Temperature 10^{10} K; time 10^{-3} s
The weak and the electromagnetic forces separate: quarks exist only in particles such as protons and neutrons. The ratio of protons to neutrons is about 4 to 1. Much combination of matter and antimatter occurring, increasing the ratio of matter to antimatter still further, until all antimatter disappears, at least from the region that becomes our galaxy.

Temperature 10^{7} K; time 100 s
Helium and lithium nuclei being formed, but the temperature is becoming too low for further fusion to occur. The matter in the universe is in **plasma** form. This is a state in which protons and electrons are not bound to one another, because the temperature is too high. (In the present, the concentration of elements in the universe is 70% hydrogen, 27% helium and 3% everything else. Clearly, just after the big bang, there has to be more than 70% hydrogen to allow for all the fusion that has taken place in stars ever since.)

Temperature 10^{4} K; time 100 000 years
The temperature is low enough for atoms to be formed. Gradually, as the temperature falls, more of the electrons will become attached to the protons present: photons travel freely, the universe is transparent. This is when the cosmic microwave background (CMB) was formed.

Temperature 6000 K; time 1 million years
Density fluctuations result in the first structure of the universe.

Temperature 17 K; time 1 billion years
More structures formed: heavy elements formed as a result of the gravitational collapse of stars.

Temperature 2.7 K; 13 billion years
The present time: life on Earth. The ratio of protons to neutrons is still about 4 to 1.

Figure 2 is also artwork but with more scientific facts shown. It is a pictorial graph. Time began at a point about 12 billion years ago. As you look across the picture, time is increasing, and you can see both the size of the universe, shown by the height of the pattern, and the gradual formation of the galaxies from simpler clouds of matter.

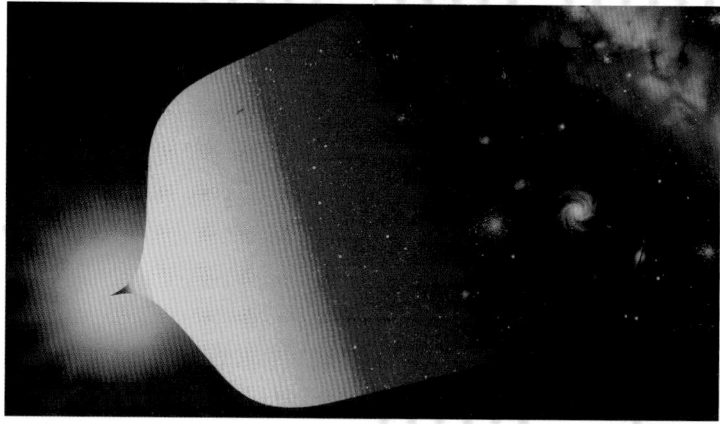

Figure 2 The history of the universe in a pictorial graph

Questions

1 Draw a time line using the data given in this spread and showing the development of the universe from just after the big bang until the present. Since the line will cover about 60 orders of magnitude, you will need to make the timescale logarithmic. Start at log 10^{-43} and finish at log 10^{18}.

2 Use the time line you have drawn in Question 1 to sketch a graph of log T against log t, where T is the kelvin temperature and t is the time. Is there a simple relationship between time and temperature?

2.5 (8) The future of the universe

By the end of this spread, you should be able to ...

- **Explain that the ultimate fate of the universe depends on its density.**
- **Define the term critical density and explain that the density of the universe is currently believed to be close to it.**
- **Select and use the expression for critical density of the universe $\rho_c = 3H_0^2/8\pi G$.**
- **Explain that the universe may be 'open', 'flat' or 'closed', depending on its density.**

Introduction

Consider a rocket taking off from the Earth and rising vertically. It fires its engines for a few minutes and reaches a high speed. What can happen to it? If it is going too slowly (less than 11.2 km s^{-1}) it will lose all its kinetic energy in gaining potential energy and will stop and fall back to Earth. A rocket going faster than this will have some kinetic energy left over after gaining all its potential energy in leaving the Earth's gravitational well, and it will continue out into space, albeit at a lower speed than its initial speed.

The question for the universe is essentially the same. Are the galaxies going fast enough now to go on for ever, or if they do not have enough kinetic energy, will they fall back to a 'big crunch' at some time in the future?

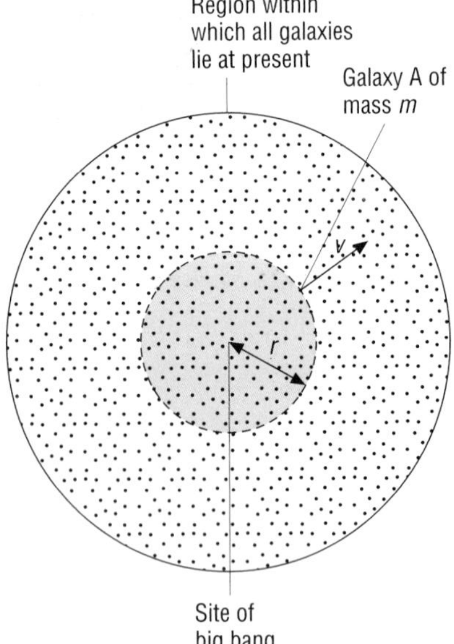

Figure 1 A galaxy of mass *m* at a distance *r* from an arbitrary point in space. It is travelling directly away from that point. The expansion of space following the big bang means that *v* is directly proportional to *r*. The shaded circle shows the area containing all the galaxies with a smaller value of *r*

STRETCH and CHALLENGE

You should be able to work through the following proof. It will not be tested, but you should be able to see where the final equation comes from.

Figure 1 shows a galaxy A of mass m at a distance r from a point in the universe. The mass of all the other galaxies with a smaller distance from the point is M. For A to travel outwards for ever, it needs to overcome the attractive forces of the galaxies of mass M. It needs to gain potential energy E given by

$$E_p = GMm/r$$

(The proof of this equation requires calculus.)

When A is travelling with velocity v, its kinetic energy $E_k = ½mv^2$.

Using the Hubble constant H_0, its velocity $v = H_0 r$, and so its kinetic energy is

$$E_k = ½m\,H_0^2 r^2$$

If the kinetic energy is greater than the potential energy, it will travel on for ever. If it is less than the required amount of potential energy, it will stop and fall back into a big crunch.

The calculation can be continued by realising that

$$M = V\rho = \frac{4}{3}\pi r^3 \rho \quad \text{so } E_p \frac{4\pi G r^3 \rho m}{3r} = \frac{4\pi G r^2 \rho m}{3}$$

where ρ is the present mean density of the universe.

The limiting condition therefore is when $E_p = E_k$, giving

$$\frac{4\pi G r^3 \rho m}{3} = \frac{m H_0^2 r^2}{2} \text{ which for this limiting condition gives } \rho_c = \frac{3H_0^2}{8\pi G}$$

where ρ_c is the critical density.

The mean density of the universe

Using the cosmological principle that the universe is homogeneous, we consider that the total mass of all the matter in all the galaxies divided by the current volume of the universe to be the mean density ρ of the universe. Its value is given, very approximately, as 10^{-27} kg m^{-3}.

The equation deduced above gives the critical mean density of the universe. If the present density of the universe is less than ρ_c, the universe will go on expanding for ever. If it is greater than ρ_c, the universe will at some time stop expanding and collapse, eventually producing the big crunch.

Using the equation for the critical density, we find its value as

$$\rho_c = \frac{3H_0^2}{8\pi G} = \frac{3 \times (2.3 \times 10^{-18})^2}{8\pi \times 6.67 \times 10^{-11}} = 9.5 \times 10^{-27} \text{ kg m}^{-3}$$

As you can see, the critical density and the actual density have the same order of magnitude. Since neither the actual density nor the critical density is known very accurately, at present it is not possible to say which is larger. Some think that the two figures may be identical.

Possible fates of the universe

Figure 2 shows three possible outcomes for the universe over the next 20 billion years or so. The graph shows the present time as zero on the x-axis, so the future is positive x and the past negative x.

Some facts are now known to within about 10%. These are:

- the average separation of any two galaxies
- the rate of expansion of the universe.

This means that the position where each line crosses the y-axis is known and that the gradient at that point is the same for all three graphs.

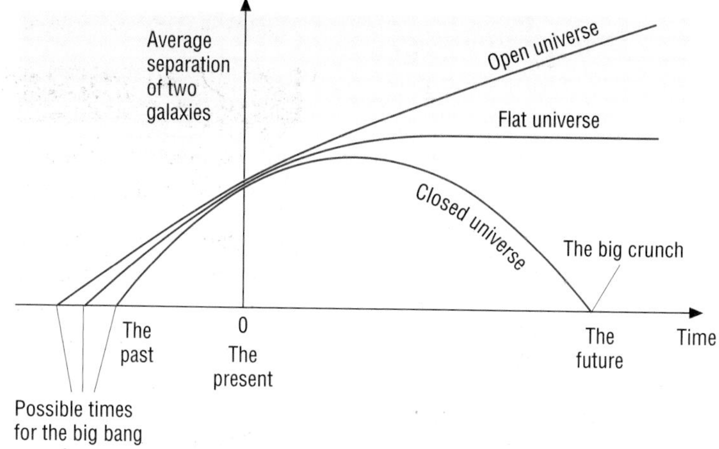

Figure 2 Three possible outcomes for the future of the universe

The graph for the **closed universe** outcome shows the situation where ρ is *greater* than ρ_c. This would mean that the actual density of the universe is so high that gravitational forces will prevent galaxies going on out into space for ever. Instead, they will slow down, stop and then return to a big crunch, after more additional time than the universe has already existed.

The graph for the **open universe** outcome represents the situation where ρ is *less* than ρ_c. This would mean that the actual density of the universe is *not* high enough for gravitational forces to prevent galaxies from going out into space for ever. Each galaxy will reach a constant velocity when sufficiently far apart from one another for the gravitational force on each to be negligible. At these velocities, galaxies will continue to separate from each other for ever.

The graph for the **flat universe** is the situation where ρ is equal to ρ_c. This boundary condition is unlikely, because it implies that the galaxies will gradually slow down over a very long time but never quite stop.

You can see from the graph that each possibility implies a different time in the past for the big bang. When greater accuracy of measurement is possible for this time and for H_0, the fate of the universe could be determined.

As always in physics, the solution of one problem leads to many other questions. There is always plenty to discover, and there is no end of possible questions.

Questions

1 What is the average amount of space available for each atom in the universe?

2 Why does the text say that a flat universe, in which the galaxies will slow down but never quite stop, is 'unlikely'?

2.5 Modelling the universe summary

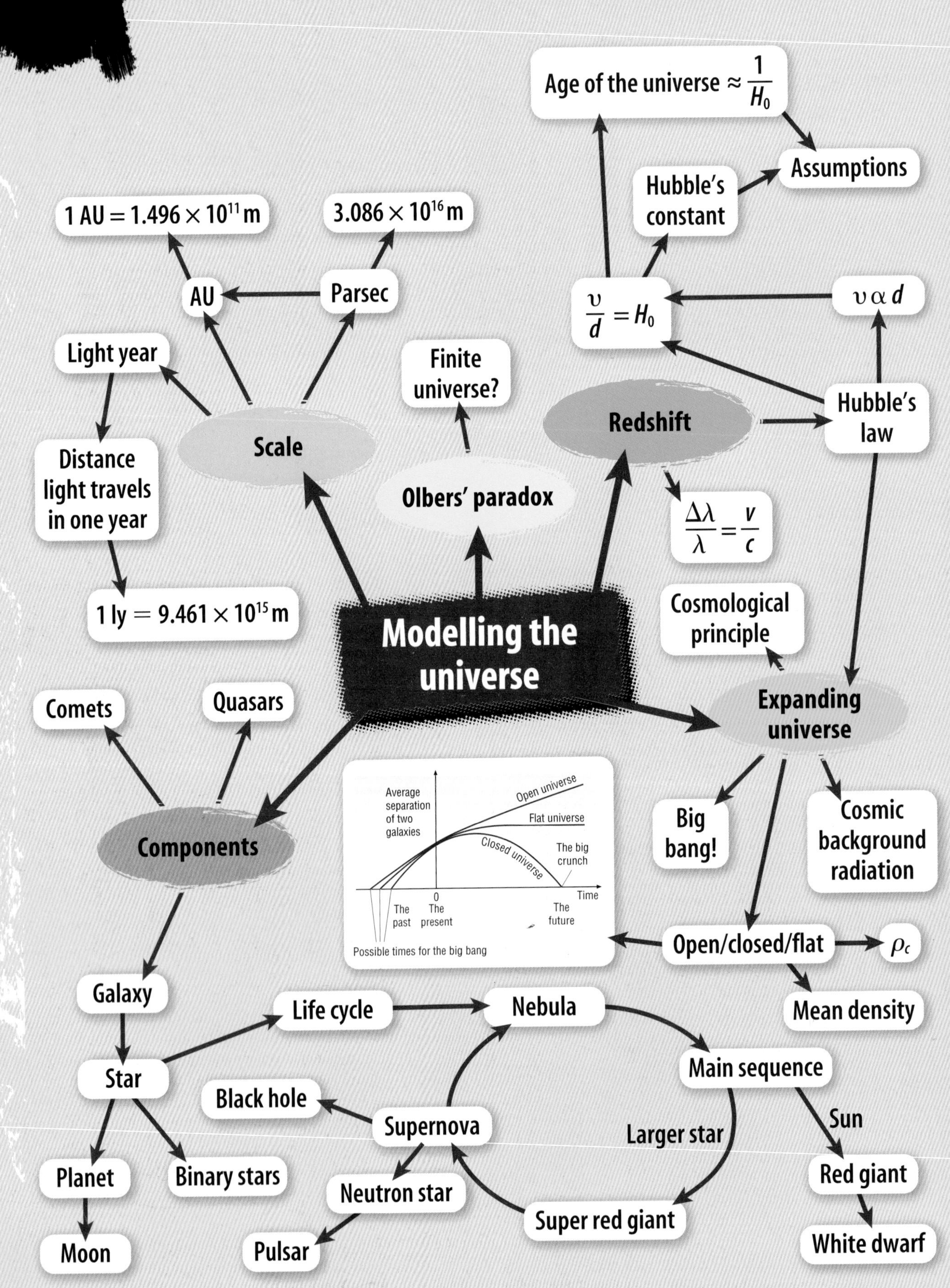

Practice questions

1. The nearest star, Proxima Centauri, is at a distance of 4.3 light years from the Earth.

   Calculate the distance to Proxima Centauri in:

   (a) metres

   (b) AU

   (c) parsecs.

2. Hydrogen gas in a discharge tube in the laboratory can be excited to emit a line spectrum. The strongest wavelength in the visible spectrum is at a wavelength of 660 nm.

   (a) Light from the discharge tube is viewed through a diffraction grating that has 600 lines per mm. Show that the 660 nm line will appear at an angle of about 23° from the zero order.

   (b) The zero and first-order lines at 660 nm seen through the grating are shown in Figure 1.

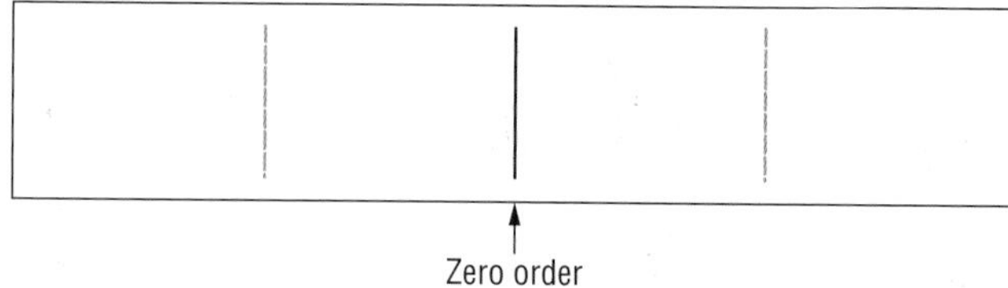

Figure 1

The light from a star, moving away from the Earth, is redshifted. Copy Figure 1 and draw on it possible positions of the same spectral lines from the star seen through the grating.

   (c) The wavelengths of light from the star Regulus are found to be redshifted by 0.0020%. Calculate the velocity of recession of Regulus relative to the Earth.

3. Hubble's law states that the velocity of recession of a galaxy is proportional to the distance to the galaxy as measured from the Earth. The constant of proportionality is called Hubble's constant, H_0.

   (a) State the observational evidence that supports Hubble's law.

   (b) Figure 2 shows a graph for the observed speed of recession v of a number of distant galaxies against their distance d from our galaxy.

   (i) Explain how the graph illustrates Hubble's law.

   (ii) Calculate the value of H_0 given by the graph. Give your answer in units of s^{-1}.

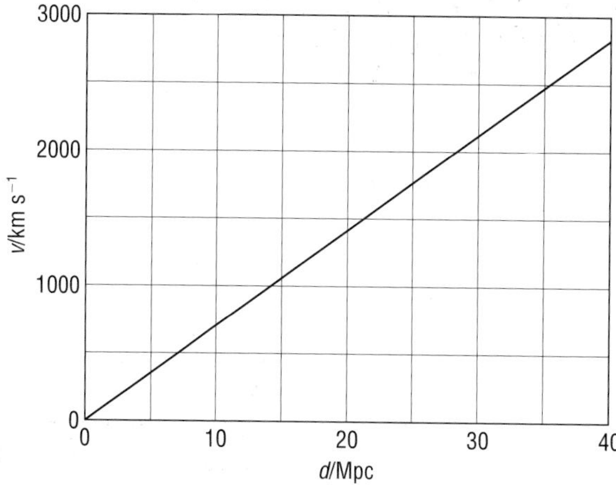

Figure 2

   (c) The value of $1/H_0$ gives an estimate of the time passed since all the galaxies were close together, that is, an estimate of the age of the universe.

   (i) Use your value of H_0 to estimate the age of the universe in years.

   (ii) Suggest one reason that the age of the universe may be larger than your answer to **(c) (i)**.

4. The age of an old star can be calculated using the radioactive decay of uranium-238. By observing the spectra in the star's light, astronomers can determine how much uranium-238 it contains. This is compared with the amount of uranium-238 present in a young star of the same type. The half-life of uranium-238 is 4.5×10^9 y.

   (a) The old star has only 1/8 of the amount of uranium compared to the young star. Calculate the age of the old star.

   (b) This method of finding the age of a star gives a minimum age for the universe. Explain why this age:

   (i) is the least possible age of the universe

   (ii) helps to give an upper limit to Hubble's constant H_0.

5. An object of mass m travels from outer space and falls down onto the surface of the Earth. In doing so, it is said to have fallen into the Earth's gravitational well, and its loss in potential energy in joules is given by $6.26 \times 10^7\ m$.

   (a) What minimum speed must a rocket have near ground level if it is to be able to escape from the Earth's gravitational well without firing its engines again?

   (b) A rocket near the Earth's surface is travelling directly away from the Earth with speed 17.0 km s^{-1}. With what speed will it be travelling when it is a long way from the Earth? Assume that it is not under the influence of any other body and that its engines are switched off.

2.5 Examination questions

1 This question is about a method of measuring the mass of the planet Saturn.

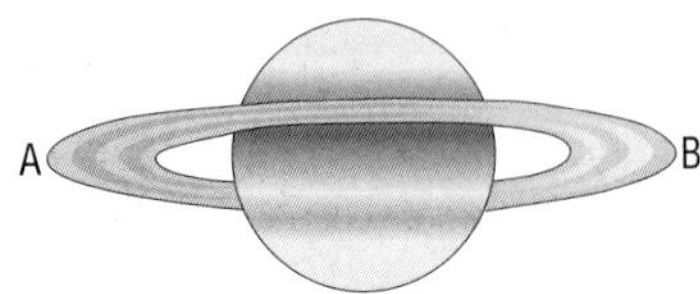

Figure 1

Saturn has a system of rings that orbit the planet. The rings are composed of ice and rocks varying in diameter from about one centimetre to ten metres.

(a) Observations from Earth show that the wavelengths of the light from point A are stretched by a very small amount. The wavelengths from point B are reduced by a very small amount. Suggest a reason for these observations. [1]

(b) Consider a piece of rock of mass 3000 kg in a ring at a distance of 1.8×10^8 m from the centre of the planet. The rock orbits the planet at a speed of 1.5×10^4 m s^{-1}.

(i) Show that it takes the rock about 21 hours to orbit the planet at this distance. [2]

(ii) Show that the centripetal force on the rock is about 3800 N. Write down the equation you use to calculate your result. [2]

(iii) The centripetal force is the force on the rock due to the gravitational attraction of Saturn. Show that the mass of Saturn is about 6×10^{26} kg. Write down the equation you use in your calculation. [2]

(c) Show that the speed of a rock in a ring is given by

$$v = \sqrt{GM/r}$$

where M is the mass of Saturn and r is the distance between the rock and the centre of Saturn. [2]

(d) A rock at a distance of 1.8×10^8 m from the centre of Saturn orbits the planet at a speed of about 1.5×10^4 m s^{-1}. Explain why a rock four times the distance from the centre of the planet orbits at half this speed. [2]

(OCR 2863 Jun07)

2 This question is about neutron stars.
Neutron stars are the remnants of huge stars that have exploded as supernovae. One such star has about the same mass as the sun but its radius is only of the order of 10 km. Such a dense object has a very high gravitational field strength at its surface.

(a) (i) Write down an expression for g, the gravitational field strength at the surface of a star of mass M and radius r. [1]

(ii) For a spherical star of average density ρ, the magnitude of g at its surface is given by

$$g = 4/3\ G\pi r\rho$$

Use this expression to show that the units of g are N kg^{-1}. [2]

(iii) Show that the gravitational field strength at the surface of the star is about 1×10^9 N kg^{-1}. The density of the star is 4.0×10^{14} kg m^{-3}. [2]

(b) A remarkable property of neutron stars is that they spin about their axes at a very great rate. The radiation from these starts is observed as regular pulses. This particular neutron star of radius 10 km rotates 50 times every second.

(i) Show that the speed of a point on the equator of the star is about 1% of the speed of light. [3]

(ii) Calculate the magnitude of the centripetal acceleration at a point on the equator of the star. [2]

(c) Neutron stars can spin at a great rate without flying apart, because the gravitational field strength is high enough to keep material on the surface of the star. Explain how this statement is supported by your answers to **(a) (iii)** and **(b) (ii)**.

(OCR 2863 Jun03)

3 The first stars were not formed until some time after the big bang.

(a) Outline how the first main sequence stars formed from clouds of gas. [3]

(b) The first stars are believed to have consisted solely of hydrogen and helium.

(i) State the origin of the helium. [1]

(ii) State one major difference in chemical composition between the 'first' stars and the Sun. [1]

(OCR 2825/01 Jan02)

4 The critical density of the universe can be shown to be given by the equation

$$\rho_0 = 3H_0^2/8\pi G$$

(a) State two assumptions made in the derivation of this equation. [2]

(b) Calculate the critical density of the universe, giving your answer in hydrogen atoms per cubic metre. Hubble constant = 1.6×10^{-18} s^{-1}, and the mass of a hydrogen atom = 1.7×10^{-27} kg. [4]

(c) Theory suggests that the universe may have three possible fates, referred to as *open*, *flat* and *closed*. Describe each of these and illustrate the evolution of the universe in each case by a suitable sketch graph with 'size' on the y-axis and time on the x-axis. [6]

(OCR 2825/01 Jan02)

5 The Sun produces its energy mainly by a series of nuclear fusion reactions in which hydrogen is converted to helium. For each 1.000 kg of hydrogen consumed in the fusion reactions, the rest mass of the products is only 0.993 kg. This change in mass is associated with the production of energy.

(a) Calculate the energy in J produced from 1.000 kg of hydrogen. [4]

(b) The Sun's power output is 3.9×10^{26} W. Calculate the rate in kg s^{-1} at which the Sun is using up its hydrogen. [2]

(c) The mass of the Sun is 2.0×10^{30} kg, and it is expected to leave the main sequence when approximately 10% of its hydrogen has been used up.

(i) Estimate the main sequence lifetime of the Sun. [3]

(ii) State one assumption you have made in carrying out this calculation. [1]

(OCR 2825/01 Jun02)

6 **(a)** State three properties of the cosmic microwave background radiation. [3]

(b) Describe how the microwave background radiation is thought to have arisen in standard big bang cosmology. [5]

(c) The cosmological principle states that 'on a sufficiently large scale, the universe is *homogeneous* and *isotropic*'.

(i) Explain the meaning of the terms *homogeneous* and *isotropic*. [2]

(ii) State how the microwave background radiation supports the cosmological principle. [1]

(OCR 2825/01 Jun02)

7 **(a)** Outline the assumptions and arguments leading to Olbers' paradox. Explain how it may be resolved in big bang cosmology. [6]

(b) A certain galaxy at a distance of 300 Mpc is observed to be receding from Earth at a velocity of 2.1×10^4 km s^{-1}.

(i) Calculate a value for the Hubble constant in km s^{-1} Mpc^{-1} based on these data. [1]

(ii) Estimate the age in s of the universe using your answer to **(b) (i)**. [3]

(iii) Explain why the Hubble constant is not really a constant at all. [2]

(OCR 2825/01 Jan03)

8 In a binary star system, two stars orbit each other, held together by their mutual gravitational attraction. A line in the spectrum of calcium has wavelength 393.40 nm when measured from a source in the laboratory.
The wavelength of the same line from one of the stars of a binary star system was measured over a period of time, and the results are recorded in the table.

Time/hour	Wavelength/nm
0	393.40
10	393.63
20	393.69
30	393.53
40	393.27
50	393.11
60	393.17
70	393.40
80	393.63
90	393.69
100	393.53

(a) Plot a graph of wavelength against time. [3]

(b) Suggest why the wavelength changes. [2]

(c) Calculate the orbital speed in m s^{-1} of the star. [3]

(d) **(i)** Use your graph to show that the orbital period of the star is 2.5×10^5 s. [2]

(ii) Calculate the radius of the orbit, assuming that it is circular. [3]

(OCR 2825/01 Jun02)

Answers

Spread answers

1.1.1

1 (a) Weight, 9.8 N downwards; tension in spring, 9.8 N upwards.
  (b) Tension in spring and weight; tension is greater than weight, causing a resultant (net) upward force to accelerate mass.
  (c) Steady motion is the same as at rest, so answer as **(a)**.
  (d) No; mass is an inherent property of the object, and weight is the gravitational attraction of the mass to the Earth, which varies only with the inverse square of the distance between their centres of mass.

2 (a) With no friction, there are no horizontal forces. As soon as your weight acting vertically downwards through your centre of mass is no longer in a vertical line with the contact force of the ice, there is a couple acting, and you will rotate, falling flat to the ice.
  (b) To produce a horizontal force, remove a piece of clothing and throw it away from you horizontally. The reaction force will propel you in the opposite direction to the garment. If you are naked in your dream then all you can do is blow hard!

3 A wheel rolls because there is a horizontal push from the ground on the wheel when it pushes horizontally on the ground. Without friction, there is no mechanism to produce horizontal forces. The wheel slides if already moving.

1.1.2

3 (a) 8.0 kg m s^{-1}; (b) 40 m s^{-1};
  (c) 50%.
4 (a) 25 m s^{-1}; (b) 1.25 kg m s^{-1}.
5 (a) 0.40 kg m s^{-1} or N s; (b) 2.0 N.

1.1.3

1 (a) 2.0 kg m s^{-1}; (b) 10 N.
2 (a) Two vertical arrows passing through the centre of mass of the balloon, the upward one longer than the downward one; labelled 1.4×10^5 N and Mg or weight.
  (b) 4.0×10^3 kg

1.1.4

2 (a) Contact force from the floor (upwards); contact force from the suitcase (downwards); gravitational force (weight) (downwards); no overall turning moment.
  (b) Contact force from arm (upwards); equal and opposite gravitational force (weight) (downwards).
  (c) Gravitational force (weight).
  (d) Gravitational force (weight) (downwards); much larger contact force from the floor (Upwards).

3 (a) 19.9 kg m s^{-1}
  (b) The force on the clown = rate of change of momentum of the water; the water is pushed forwards, and by Newton's third law the clown, through the pistol, experiences an equal and opposite force backwards.
  (c) The water bounces off the clown, so its change in velocity is greater than 7.1 m s^{-1}; the change in momentum per second of the water is greater than 20 N, so the force on the clown is greater too.

4 (a) 13 500 kg m s^{-1}
  (b) 54 000 N
  (c) Using Newton's third law or the conservation of momentum the plane experiences a force downwards, and hence its undercarriage suspension will contract slightly.

1.1.5

1 Assuming that there are no horizontal forces between the boat and the water, the centre of mass of the boat plus occupants, etc., cannot move. There are no external forces. When the ball is passed to the left, the boat must move to the right and vice versa, such that the centre of mass of the system remains at rest in the same place. Thus the observers see the boat oscillate back and forth when the ball is moving.

2 (a) 0.1 m s^{-1}
  (b) 8 N
  (c) Some of the gas escapes at very high velocity in the opposite direction to the motion of the bullet, with equal and opposite momentum to that of the bullet. The rifle therefore does not need to 'take up' any of the momentum to conserve momentum of the system of rifle, gas and bullet.

3 (a) There are no external forces, so momentum is conserved and the centre of mass of the system cannot move. A mass of gas moves to the right, so the astronaut must move to the left, albeit slowly, to maintain the centre of mass of the system in the same place.
  (b) 16 kg m s^{-1}
  (c) 0.13 m s^{-1}

4 (a) The pucks move together until the spring is compressed and slows them to a halt. They then move apart to their original separation. The oscillation continues about their common centre of mass, assuming there is no dissipation of energy.
  (b) The system must move with constant momentum equal to the mass of a puck multiplied by the velocity

of puck B when puck A is released. Initially, puck B will slow and puck A accelerate. Will puck A take all of the momentum so that puck B comes to rest, stretching the spring, and then puck A slows with puck B regaining the momentum, etc.? Or will both pucks come to half of the initial speed of puck B with the spring unstretched? Or something else? To answer, remember that both momentum and kinetic energy must be conserved. You might find it helpful to consider two coupled pendulums or a Newton's cradle for comparison.

1.1.6

1 **(a)** Each 1 cm^2 square is an impulse of 0.13 N s. The area is approximately 15 squares, giving a total of 1.9 N s.
(b) 42 m s^{-1} (using 1.9 Ns)
(c) 1200 N (using 1.9 Ns)
(d) Yes. The area under the curve or under the line to 1.55 ms with the *x*-axis is equal to the impulse, i.e. both areas are equal.

1.1.7

1 **(b)** 9. (As most collisions are not head-on, in fact on average about 25 are needed to reduce the speed sufficiently.)
2 **(a)** The total momentum before and after is *mv* to the left.
(b) 12 mv^2
(c) 1.2×10^7 m s^{-1}

1.2.1

1 **(a)** 115°;
(b) triangular shape per cycle;
(c) square wave equally above and below zero axis per cycle;
(d) graph (c) is the gradient of graph (b).
2 **(a)** 60°, $\pi/3$; 180°, π; 270°, $3\pi/2$; 360°, 2π;
(b) 3 s; **(c)** 80°, 0.44π or 1.4 rad.

1.2.2

1 **(a)** 30° s^{-1} or $\pi/6$ rad s^{-1}; **(b)** 2.1 m s^{-1};
(c) 1.1 m s^{-2} towards centre.
2 **(a)** 1.0 km s^{-1}; **(b)** 2.7×10^{-3} m s^{-2}
3 **(a)** 28 m s^{-1}; **(b)** 89 m s^{-2}; 9.1 *g*.
4 2.1×10^{13} m s^{-2}

1.2.3

1 **(a)** 70 N;
(b) frictional force between roundabout surface and child
2 **(a)** 2.4 N;
(b) reduction in measured weight as some of the gravitational force is pulling you to the surface, i.e. the reaction force is less than your weight as you are accelerating downwards.
3 **(a)** 190 N;
(b) Taking moments about the contact point of the tyre, there must be a turning moment towards the centre of the arc as a centripetal force must be created through the centre of mass of cyclist plus bicycle. This is provided by leaning inwards.

1.2.4

1 **(a)** 0.99 m s^{-1}; **(b)** 0.99 ms^{-2} upwards;
(c) 2.2 N.
2 2300 N
3 **(c)** 33°; **(d)** 940 N

1.2.5

1 There must be a neutral point in the centre between the discs. The field will be at right angles towards each disc, so overall it will be like the magnetic field between two South poles.
2 At the crossing point, the pull on the mass could be in either of two different directions.
3 27 N kg^{-1}.
4 **(a)** 2.6×10^6 m; **(b)** 6.4×10^6 m.

1.2.6

1 6.0×10^{-10} N
2 2.0×10^{27} kg
3 1.8×10^{27} kg
4 $g/2$, $g/4$, where $g = 9.8$ N kg^{-1}; $g = 9.8\, r/R$ where $R = 6.4 \times 10^6$ m at distance *r* from the centre

1.2.7

1 It passes over the same points on the Earth's surface at the same times every day.
2 87 minutes
3 **(a)** 8.2×10^5 N; **(b)** 8.7 N kg^{-1}; **(c)** 9.5×10^4 kg.
4 When the rocket motors are fired the spacecraft accelerates but the astronaut remains at constant speed until the inner surface of the spacecraft itself pushes the astronaut – sometimes very forcefully. The astronaut then experiences 'artificial gravity'.

1.2.8

1 87 minutes
2 **(a)** 165 y; **(b)** 1.1×10^{11} m
4 **(a)** 3.2×10^{16} s, 10^9 y;
(b) *T* and *r* will both be larger.

1.2.9

1 **(c)** 1.7×10^{-10} W m^{-2}

1.2.10

1 In a wave all points are oscillating. At each instant of time we see the positions of every oscillator – all x at one t. In an oscillation we see how the position of one oscillator changes over time – one x at all t. A wave can be pictured as a series of coupled oscillators which pass energy along the line… and so on.

2 **(b)** The displacement–time graph looks like the mirror (in the y–z plane) image of the displacement–position graph, i.e. back to front for $t = 0$ to $t = 0.5$ s, then $y = 0$ to $t = 1.0$ s.

3 **(a)** **(i)** V; **(ii)** UY; **(iii)** UY; **(iv)** UW, WY, XZ
(b) **(i)** 160 Hz; **(ii)** 1000 radians s^{-1}
(c) **(i)** $3\pi/2$; **(ii)** $\pi/4$

1.2.11

1 **(a)** A, B; **(b)** O; **(c)** O; **(d)** O; **(e)** A.

2 **(a)** s^{-2} or radians s^{-2};
(b) The second oscillates at twice the frequency of the first, which is 0.8 Hz.

3 **(a)** **(i)** 0.050 m; **(ii)** 0.50 Hz; **(iii)** 2.0 s
(b) **(i)** 0, 0.035 m up, 0, 0.040 m down;
(ii) 0, 0.35 m s^{-2} down, 0, 0.40 m s^{-2} up.
(c) **(i)** 0.16 m s^{-1} up; **(ii)** 0

1.2.12

1 **(a)** S; **(b)** R.

2 **(a)** **(i)** 0.11 m; **(ii)** 1.43 Hz; **(iii)** 9.3 m s^{-1}

3 **(a)** **(i)** 2.5 m;
(ii) 2.5 m;
(iii) 0.08 tides per hour
(b) 8 hours 30 mins to 10 hours depending on the day
(c) Depth = $c + A \sin 2\pi ft$, where c is a constant, A the amplitude and f the frequency.

1.2.13

1 **(b)** **(i)** $E - \frac{1}{2}kx^2$; **(ii)** $A\sqrt{(k/m)}$ or $\sqrt{(2E/m)}$

2 **(a)** 12.5 mJ, 0, 6.25 mJ, 6.25 mJ;
(b) 0, 12.5 mJ, 6.25 mJ, 6.25 mJ

3 Reduced to one quarter, as total energy is proportional to amplitude squared.

4 **(a)** 0.50 m s^{-1}; **(b)** 0.16 m

1.2.14

1 **(a)** Yes; yes; by approximately 0.62.
(b) The gradient of the line crossing the x-axis decreases at each crossing.

2 There is greater damping because of increased air resistance on wings. This will cause greater energy loss per oscillation; the amplitude dies away more quickly, so the plane stops oscillating in a shorter time. With greater mass, there is greater inertia in the system, so the frequency of oscillation will decrease and the period increase.

1.2.15

1 **(a)** Resonance occurs when the natural frequency of oscillation of the mirror equals the driving frequency of the engine; maximum energy is transferred between the engine and the mirror, giving it a large amplitude.
(b) **(i)** Resonance of the mirror will occur at lower frequency because of its greater inertia, causing a reduced natural frequency. With the engine at the original frequency, the mirror motion will be smaller.
(ii) Resonance of the mirror will occur at a higher frequency as there is now a larger restoring force causing an increase in the natural frequency. With the engine at the original frequency, the mirror motion will be smaller.

2 Resonance occurs at or close to the natural frequency of the oscillating plane caused by driving force at this frequency, when maximum energy transfer between oscillator and plane enables maximum amplitude to be achieved.
The amplitude of oscillation of the plane is approximately equal to that of driver at low frequencies; the amplitude rises to maximum at resonance; before reducing to a smaller and smaller amplitude at high frequencies.

1.3.1

1 **(a)** 9.4×10^{24};
(b) 8.4×10^{28};
(c) 1.2×10^{-29} m^3, 2.3×10^{-10} m;
(d) 10%.

2 **(a)** 3.73×10^{-26} m^3;
(b) 3.34×10^{-9} m;
(c) 3.34×10^{-9} m, more than 10 times the atomic diameter.

1.3.2

1 450 m s^{-1}

2 **(a)** 0.013 s
(b) The molecules travel a much greater distance because they make so many collisions, causing their movement to be random.
(c) The scent molecules are much more massive but have the same energy, so their velocities are small, hence

the rate of diffusion is lower. An alternative argument: scent molecules are much larger, so more likely to make collisions with more changes in direction (shorter mean free path), hence the rate of diffusion is slower.

1.3.3

1 (a) 1.8×10^3 m s^{-1};
  (b) 3.3×10^3 J
2 1.7×10^2 m s^{-1}
3 5.5×10^{-21} J
4 (a) (i) 425 m s^{-1};
   (ii) 8.3 m s^{-1} to the right;
   (iii) 430 m s^{-1}
  (b) (i) 3.9×10^{-25} kg m s^{-1};
   (ii) 4.4×10^{-21} J

1.3.4

1 (a) all sections from A to F;
  (b) AB, CD, EF;
  (c) AB, CD, EF
3 (a) Any situation where friction slows the motion of an object; the external kinetic energy becomes randomised in the molecules of the object.
  (b) e.g. The internal energy of the exploding air–vapour mixture in the cylinder of an internal combustion engine results in the external energy of the piston motion.

1.3.5

1 (a) −268.9 °C; (b) −183.0 °C; (c) −39.2 °C;
  (d) 444.9 °C; (e) 1066.8 °C

1.3.6

1 13 K
2 (a) 46 K.
  (b) Number of vapour molecules will increase and their average speed will increase; therefore there will be more and harder collisions with the lid per second; both factors increase the pressure.
3 330 s, 5.5 minutes; it will take much longer as the convector heater will transfer only a fraction of its input power to the air passing through it. Another small effect, for example, will be the energy transfer to the walls and objects within the room by the air.

1.3.7

1 (a) (i) 2.5×10^6 J kg^{-1};
   (ii) 4.5×10^4 J mol^{-1}
   (accepted value is 4.07×10^5 J mol^{-1})
  (b) Thermal energy transfer to the surroundings
2 (b) When p doubles ln p increases by 0.69, so the increase in temperature is about 22 K.
3 The tea is at 0 °C, as there was not enough thermal energy in the tea to melt all of the ice.

1.3.8

1 (a) 2.6 mm;
  (b) the temperature at 40 m will be lower than at the surface, so the bubble will expand further.
2 0.4 m^3
3 760.5 mmHg

1.3.9

1 12 m^3
2 39 °C
3 6.0×10^6 Pa or 6.0 MPa
4 $1.2(1) \times 10^5$ Pa

1.3.10

1 (a) 0.029 kg mol^{-1}; (b) 2.1×10^{25}
2 (a) 58; (b) 1.6 kg;
  (c) 1.4 m^3; (d) 58
3 (a) 7.2×10^{19}; (b) 1.7×10^{-3} kg m^{-3}
4 (a) 4.8×10^{22}; (b) 1.3×10^5 Pa;
  (c) 3.6×10^{22}

1.3.11

1 (a) 8.3×10^{-3} m^3;
  (b) 3.0×10^5 Pa, 3.0 atm;
  (c) Yes, the pressure, double the value
2 (a) (i) 5.65×10^{-21} J;
   (ii) 4.7×10^{-26} kg
  (b) (i) 5.65×10^{-21} J, 1.70×10^{-20} J;
   (ii) 1300 m s^{-1}, 2250 m s^{-1}
3 (a) 2.1×10^{-20} J;
  (b) (i) 3.53 km s^{-1} (ii) 2.50 km s^{-1};
  (c) No, because r.m.s. speed > 2.2 km s^{-1} for both.
4 530 K

Further questions A

1 (a) (i) $mu = mv_1 + mv_2$
   $\frac{1}{2}mu^2 = \frac{1}{2}mv_1^2 + \frac{1}{2}mv_2^2$
   (ii) The equations reduce to $u = v_2$ and $u^2 = v_2^2$.
  (b) (i) Ball 1 gives its momentum to ball 2 and stops; ball 2 passes its momentum to ball 3, etc.; ball 5 receives all the momentum and moves away with speed u.
   (ii) Ball 2 passes its momentum to ball 3 and stops; this momentum is passed to ball 5, which moves away. Ball 1 passes its momentum to ball 2 and stops; this momentum reaches ball 4, which moves away. So balls 4 and 5 move away with speed u apparently together.

(iii) Ball 1 bounces back; and balls 2 to 5 move slowly towards the right

2 (a) (i) 48 N; 0.25 s
(ii) estimating area under graph or mean Ft gives 7 ± 1 N s
(b) (i) 96 m s^{-2}
(ii) 14 m s^{-1}
(iii) 49 J
(c) 61 N

3 The pointer moves to the angle θ more quickly than at critical damping, and the oscillations are sufficiently small that they will have died away by the time the eye has focused on the scale to read the value.

4 (a) (i) $g = (-)\, GM/R^2$
(ii) $g = 9.8 = 6.67 \times 10^{-11}M/(6.4 \times 10^6)^2$ giving $M = 6.0 \times 10^{24}$ kg
(iii) $g_m = M_m/M_e.R_e^2/R_m^2.g_e$ or gR^2/M = constant; so $g_m = 3.7^2/81 \times 9.8 = 1.66$ N kg^{-1}
(b) $a = v^2/r = GM/r^2$ or $F = mv^2/r = GMm/r^2$; use $a = 4\pi^2r/T^2$ to give $T^2 = 4\pi^2r^3/GM$; substitute values to find T = 27 days

5 (a) (i) 25 cm; 2.5 Hz
(ii) $a = -4\pi^2f^2A = 6.2$ m s^{-2}
(b) (i) 0.1/0.3/0.5 s, etc.
(ii) 0/0.2/0.4 s, etc.
(c) Inverted or 180° phase shift graph of Figure 5, so has same period amplitude on y-axis: 6.2 m s^{-2}

6 (a) (i) Fig. 7(a): x and a in opposite directions/ acceleration towards equilibrium point; Fig. 7(b): proportional graph between x and a
(ii) $a = 4\pi^2f^2x$; $50 = 4\pi^2f^2 \times 50 \times 10^{-3}$; giving $f^2 = 25$ and $f = 5.0$ Hz
(iii) cosine wave with initial amplitude 25 mm; decreasing amplitude; correct period of 0.2 s
(b) (i) The acceleration towards A/centripetal acceleration or force is constant
(ii) $a = v^2/r$; so $50 = v^2/10$; $v^2 = 500$ giving $v = 22.4$ m s^{-1}

7 (a) The sum of the random kinetic and potential energies of the atoms/molecules/particles of the gas.
(b) (i) $n = pV/RT = 2.8 \times 10^5 \times 2.1 \times 10^{-3}/(8.3 \times 288) = 0.246$ mol
(ii) p/T = constant gives $T = (290/280) \times 288 = 298$ K = 25°C
(iii) ratio = T_2/T_1 = 1.03 or 1.04 as internal energy $\propto T$

2.1.1

1 (a) 2.8×10^4 N C^{-1}
(b) 1.4×10^{-4} N towards the positive sphere

2 (a) Top plate negative, bottom positive
(b) Vertical downward arrows of equal length
(c) 1.3×10^{-14} N

3

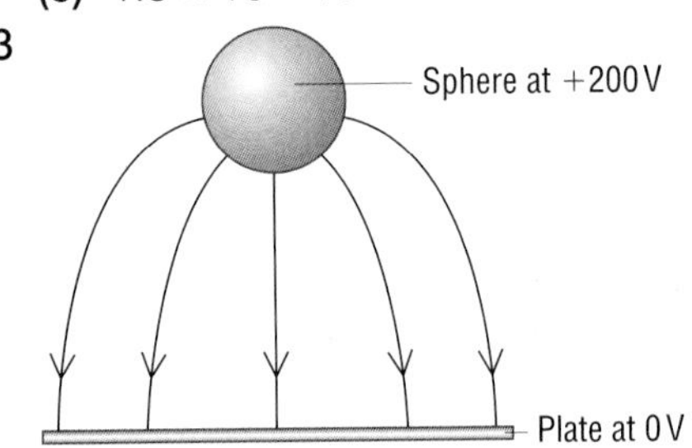

2.1.2

1 (a) (i) 6.0×10^{-9} N; (ii) 2.25×10^{-9} N;
(b) 670 N C^{-1}

2.1.3

1 (a) 5.0×10^4 N C^{-1};
(b) (i) 3.3×10^{-14} N upwards;
(ii) $6.6. \times 10^{-19}$ C;
(iii) accelerates upwards until it hits the top plate.

2.1.4

1 (a) Field lines become twice as far apart.
(b) Density of lines (flux density) doubles.

2 (a) Uniform field, weak to the left.
(b) Uniform field at 45° down to the right (and stronger than either original field).
(c) Neutral point at top centre, strong field at bottom centre. (Field as in motor effect, sometimes called the catapult field.)

3 (a) at B, 2.0 mT; at C, 2.0 mT; at D, 1.0 mT;
(b) 4.0 mT; density of lines doubles; (c) north.

2.1.5

2 The rod is in a non-uniform field, so the induced S-pole will experience a greater attraction than the repulsion of the induced N-pole in the rod. The rod is pulled into the solenoid. The forces on the induced poles are equal and opposite when the rod is at A; resultant force zero.

3 The armature is attracted to the coil (electromagnet) when there is a current. This movement breaks the circuit. The magnetic field collapses, so the armature springs back to remake the circuit and the process is repeated.

2.1.6

2 (a) DF; (b) DF; (c) 4.3×10^{-4} N;
(d) (i) Rotate the wire clockwise (viewed in the direction DF) through 60° in the plane CGEH;
(ii) Rotate another 30° to make the wire lie in the direction CE.

2.1.7

1 (a) B; (b) C; (c) A.
2 (a) 1.6×10^{-14} N;
(b) 1.8×10^{16} m s^{-2}, 2.2 cm
3 (a) Parabolic path bending downwards.
(b) Circular path bending upwards initially.
(c) Sum of forces exerted by magnetic and electric forces on proton is 0; no net force on proton so it moves at constant velocity.
4 (a) Same velocity but greater mass;
(b) Circle of larger radius, so passes beneath collector trap;
(c) Collisions with air molecules could change the velocity or charge of the ions, causing some to enter the collecting trap.

2.1.8

1 0.0414 s
2 (a) The force is always at right angles to the motion.
(b) Centripetal.
(c) 0.50 T.
(d) Neon-22 ions have greater mass and momentum, so greater radius in the field, so the detector must be moved down.
3 (a) use $eV = ½mv^2$ and $p = mv$ to find $p = 4.7 \times 10^{-21}$ N s
(b) 0.25 m;
(c) Uranium ions have greater mass and momentum, so increasing m or mv in $r = mv/Be$ shows that r is bigger.

2.1.9

2 (a) (i) 2.0×10^{-6} Wb; (ii) 5.0×10^{-2} T
(b) For a wooden or air core some of the flux passes through the sides of the solenoid; almost all of the flux stays in an iron rod to its ends.

Further questions B

1 (a) 1.25×10^{6} N C^{-1}; (b) 6.25×10^{-3} N
2 (b) 8.219 g
3 (a) (i) 9.6×10^{-17} J; (ii) 1.5×10^{7} m s^{-1};
(b) (i) 1.25×10^{4} N C^{-1};
(iii) Parabolic path curving upwards between plates and then straight path to screen; constant horizontal speed as no horizontal force; vertical acceleration caused by force between plates due to electric field; no force outside field region.
4 (a) (i) 9.6×10^{-13} N; (ii) 1.5×10^{14} m s^{-2};
(b) (i) It moves in a horizontal circle while in the field;
(ii) constant speed.
5 No. The current required is 3000 A. The wire fuses at a much lower current.

6 The needle will move one way when the magnetic flux of the magnet linking the coil is increasing (as the coil enters the space between the poles) and will move the other way when the flux is decreasing (the coil leaves the space between the poles). When the flux through the coil has a constant value (including zero) the needle is at zero. The needle only moves when there is a rate of change of flux through the coil.

2.1.10

1 4.0 V
2 (a) (i) 0.4 V; (ii) 12.5 mA;
(b) Clockwise; the current in the coil will try to keep the magnetic field in existence, from Lenz's law.
3 (a) maximum gradient = 7.5 ± 0.1 mWb per ms giving 7.5 V;
(b) cosine curve with amplitude 7.5 V, period 8 ms;
(c) 1500 V;
(d) Insert an iron core; increase area of coil; rotate the coil faster or in a stronger field.
4 (a) (i) 6.4 mWb;
(ii) 6.4 mV;
(iii) These sides are moving parallel to the field;
(b) (i) 3.2 mA; (ii) 20 μW;
(c) (i) 100 μN; (ii) 20 μW.

2.1.11

1 (a) (i) 0; (ii) −0.4 V;
(iii) 0; (iv) +0.4 V;
(b) 3 cycles of a cosine curve of amplitude 0.4 V and period 1.0 s;
(c) (i) amplitude becomes 0.8 V, period unchanged;
(ii) amplitude becomes 0.2 V, period unchanged;
(iii) amplitude becomes 0.6 V, period becomes 0.67 s.
2 (a) (ii) A larger magnetic field is produced as the magnetic domains line up easily; easily demagnetised too; iron conducts flux lines through coil, so provides magnetic circuit for flux;
(b) The flux linkage of the coil changes as the magnet rotates, so by Faraday's law an e.m.f. is generated.
(c) When the rotor is **(i)** horizontal and **(ii)** vertical.
(d) Increasing the number of coils, cross-sectional area of core, strength of the magnet will increase the flux linkage; decreasing the air gap to increase the field; laminating the core will reduce eddy currents and increase the flux through the coil.

2.1.12

1 (b) 5000 A; (c) 170 W m^{-1}; (d) 118 km
2 (a) Power dissipated $P = I^2R = \rho I/\pi r^2$ per metre.
(b) Graph has shape k/r^2 as cost ∝ power loss.

3 (a) Mass = volume × density, and as mass ∝ cost, then cost ∝ r^2 since length and density are constant; curve is $k\,r^2$ passing through (0,0).
(b) (i) Capital costs too high;
(ii) power losses too high.

2.1.13

1 (a) 50 Hz; (b) 1840.
2 (a) 21; (b) 10 A.
3 (a) Magnetic flux;
(b) Every cross-section of the core, if solid, would act as a single-turn secondary coil and draw a large current, called *eddy currents*; the transformer would be very inefficient and become very hot.

2.2.1

2 4.5 V.
3 (a) 8.0 C;
(b) (i) 8.0×10^4 A; (ii) 1 6 MW

2.2.2

1 (a) (i) 3.0 μF;
(ii) 180 μC, 90 μC, 90 μC;
(iii) 30 V across each
(b) 9.0 μF
(c) (i) 6.0 μF: 240 μC; 3.0 μF: 60 μC; 9.0 μF: 180 μC;
(ii) 6.0 μF: 40 V; 3.0 μF: 20 V; 9.0 μF: 20 V
2 (a) (i) 15 mC; (ii) 10 mC
(b) 10 V
(c) (i) 0.11 J; (ii) 0.075 J

2.2.3

1 The ratios are about 1.61 ± 0.05

2.2.4

1 (a) 0.65 mA;
(b) (i) 6.5 V; (ii) 0.16 mA;
(c) (i) 9.6 V; (ii) 0.24 mA;
(e) 26 s.

2.2.5

1 See text.

Further questions C

1 (c) 2.7 V, 1.0 V, 0.37 V;
(d) 0.13 s;
(e) make the value of *RC* 100 times smaller.
2 (a) 14 mJ; (b) 440 μF
3 Series: 4.0 μF: 32 μC, 8.0 V; 8.0 μF: 32 μC, 4.0 V; parallel: 4.0 μF: 48 μC, 12 V; 8.0 μF: 96 μC, 12 V
4 2, 3, 4, 6, 9, 12, 18 μF

5 Taking ratios of *p* values at 2 km intervals gives 1.30 ± 0.02.
6 Line 1 of table: 2.4×10^{-3}, 4.8×10^{-3}; line 2: 2.2×10^{-3}, 4.4×10^{-3}, 4.7×10^{-2}.
7 (a) (i) $C_p = 2C + C = 3C$;
(ii) $1/C_s = 1(2C) + 1/C; = 3/(2C)$, giving $C_s = 2C/3$
(b) (i) V; (ii) $Q = C_pV; = 3CV$
(c) $E = \frac{1}{2} C_sV^2; = {}^1/_3CV^2$
(d) (i) Discharge circuit made through voltmeter; voltmeter behaves as a (large) resistor, so plates will discharge; rate of discharge depends on size of voltmeter's resistance;
(ii) capacitors in series as capacitance is smaller; rate of discharge depends on value of *RC*, i.e. time constant.

2.3.1

1 8.1×10^{-8} N
2 (a) electron: $-1840\ e/u = 1.77 \times 10^{11}$ C kg^{-1}
(b) proton: $1\ e/u = 9.64 \times 10^7$ C kg^{-1}
(c) helium nucleus: $2e/4u = 4.82 \times 10^7$ C kg^{-1}

2.3.2

1 (a) 2.4×10^{-15} m
(b) 39.7 N
(c) Almost no difference from the value for two neutrons in equilibrium. Just very slightly larger than 2.4×10^{-15} m.
2 (a) It changes from negative to positive
(b) Attraction
(c) $Ax^4 = B$

2.3.3

1 (a) 6p, 8n, 6e
(b) 8p, 11n, 8e
(c) 20p, 24n, 20e
(d) 8p, 8n, 9e
(e) 10p, 8n, 10e
2 (a) 10^{-15} m
(b) radius = 7.4×10^{-15} m; volume = 1.7×10^{-42} m^3
(c) 2.3×10^{17} kg m^{-3}

2.3.4

1 An electron travelling in a vacuum at right angles to a magnetic field will travel in a circle. The radius of the circle will be smaller for a particle of low mass, such as an electron, than for the other particles that have greater mass. The electron in the photograph must be slowing down (as a result of collisions), so the radius of its orbit decreases.
2 In terms of *e* the fundamental charge, Left: 2*e*; Right: $e + 7e - 7e + e + 0 = 2e$

3 (a) ${}^{240}_{94}Pu \rightarrow {}^{236}_{92}U + {}^{4}_{2}He$
(b) 0.0056 u = 9.3×10^{-30} kg
(c) 8.37×10^{-13} J
(d) 1.6×10^{7} m s^{-1}
(e) At these speeds relativistic considerations are not needed.

2.3.5

1 (a) up + ⅔e, down – ⅓e;
(b) proton uud, neutron udd
2 (a) u → d + π^+;
(b) 2;
(c) $u\bar{d}$

2.3.6

1 Particle equation $p^+ \rightarrow n + e^+ + \nu$
quark equation $uud \rightarrow udd + e^+ + \nu$
that simplifies to $u \rightarrow d + e^+ + \nu$
giving charge + ⅔ = – ⅓ + 1 + 0
baryon number ⅓ = ⅓ + 0 + 0
and lepton number 0 = 0 – 1 + 1
2 (a) Particle equation $n \rightarrow p^+ + e^- + \bar{\nu}$
quark equation $udd \rightarrow uud + e^- + \bar{\nu}$
that simplifies to $d \rightarrow u + e^- + \bar{\nu}$
(b) 0.16 MeV
(c) The antineutrino will not take any of the energy released, but the recoil nitrogen nucleus will have a very small amount (it is about 25 000 times more massive than the electron so has very little k.e.)

2.3.7

1 *Random* implies irregularity of emission; it is impossible to predict when any particular nucleus will decay. *Spontaneous* implies that there is no known cause of emission.
2 (a) 4.7 MeV.
(b) Relativistic effects are considerable at this speed.
3 (a) 26.984 343 u;
(b) The difference can be obtained to 4 sig. figs provided u, *c* and *e* are used to 4 sig. figs. This will give an answer to 8 sig. figs, with the last one unreliable. If u, *c* and *e* are used to only 3 sig. figs, then there can only be a maximum of 7 sig. figs.

2.3.8

1 104 000 cm^{-1}
2 (a) 694 m s^{-1};
(b) 4.6×10^{7} m s^{-1};
(c) 3.1×10^{-12} m
3 (a) 1.57×10^{5} Bq;
(b) e.g. Some of the gamma radiation may be absorbed by the source itself, the detector may not detect all of the gamma radiation emitted, background count has not been considered (though with this level of activity it is not likely to make an appreciable difference), the activity of the gamma source may not be a constant over 30 minutes.

2.3.9

1 *Activity* is the rate at which a radioactive source decays; *count rate* is the figure recorded by a scaler, a counter of radioactive particles received.
2 (a) 3.28×10^{21}
(b) 0.0013 kg
3 (a) 6.64×10^{-26} kg
(b) 1.79×10^{6} Bq

2.3.10

1 (a) 4;
(b) 9;
(c) 11;
(d) 11½; the figure is $2048 \times \sqrt{2}$
2 (b) 72.1 hours;
(c) The combined graph is the sum of two exponential decays. This is not an exponential decay. It is because the half-life of X dominates at the start and that of Y after a long time.

2.3.11

1 (a) 1.2×10^{15};
(b) 7.2 g
2 (a) 2.5×10^{5} Bq;
(b) It emits alpha particles within an enclosed space and alpha particles cannot penetrate the case. Even if they did, they would be absorbed by 7 cm of air. They do not make their surroundings radioactive.
3 (a) 12 900 years.
(b) Use a specimen from an accurately dated event, e.g. some piece of wood from Pompeii, then work backwards to find the decay constant.
(c) Fossil fuels are too old.

2.3.12

1 All the other nuclei have a smaller binding energy per nucleon, so these nuclei cannot release any energy by fusion with other nuclei or by fission into small nuclei.
2 (a) 70 neutrons and 50 electrons;
(b) 1.124 u;
(c) 1046 MeV, 8.7 MeV per nucleon

2.3.13

1 Start with $mu - mv = mV$ and $\frac{1}{2}mu^2 - \frac{1}{2}mv^2 = \frac{1}{2}mV^2$ then cancel ½ and m and divide one equation by the other to show that $V = u$ and hence $v = 0$.

2 **(a)** 0.150 u;

(b) 140 MeV. Note: In this problem and the similar one in the spread, all the masses given are for the atoms, not just the nuclei. Be careful, when doing such problems, either to include all the electrons throughout or to exclude them throughout. The difference in mass between the nucleus and the atom is not large, but when you are trying to find a mass difference, electron masses are significant.

2.3.14

1 **(a)** 1250 MW

(b) **(i)** Heat loss in circulating steam from reactor to turbines,

(ii) steam causing rotation of alternator,

(iii) alternator producing electrical power,

(v) output high voltage supplied for transmission.

(c) All conversions from heat to work depend on temperature differences. To get greater efficiency a higher input temperature and a lower output temperature are needed, but input temperature is high already and output temperature cannot be any lower than surroundings (~ 300 K)

2 30000 kg s^{-1} (or 30 m^3). All power stations produce a lot of tepid water – hence the cooling towers at inland coal-fired power stations.

2.3.15

1 **(a)** 4.0 MeV; **(b)** 3×10^{10} K

2 3 deuterons produce a helium-4 nucleus together with a proton and a neutron and 21.6 MeV of energy

Further questions D

1 **(a)** 2.40×10^{-28} kg; **(b)** 1.98×10^{-14} m

2 **(a)** **(i)** 7.1×10^{14};

(ii) 4.6×10^{-11} s^{-1};

(iii) 3.3×10^4 Bq

(b) **(i)** 5.2×10^{12};

(ii) N will not change much over a five-year period as this is much less than the half-life of 450 y; $\Delta N/\Delta t$ is approximately constant over the five-year period so there will be hardly any difference in activity; for an accurate answer the area under the decay curve for the first five years must be calculated, e.g. by integration, counting squares on a graph or $N = N_0e^{-\lambda t}$

3 **(a)** **(i)** $\lambda = 0.693/1600 \times 3.16 \times 10^7 = 1.4 \times 10^{-11}$ s^{-1}

(ii) $A = \lambda N$ so $N = 6.02 \times 10^{23}/226 = 3.7 \times 10^{10}$ Bq

(b) $\Delta m = 0.0053$ u $= 8.8 \times 10^{-30}$ kg;
$E = c^2\Delta m$; $= 9 \times 8.8 \times 10^{-14} = 7.9 \times 10^{-13}$ J

(c) $Q = mc\theta$; so $0.8 \times 7.4 \times 10^9 \times 7.9 \times 10^{-13}$
$= 2.0 \times 10^{-4} \times 110\ \theta$:
giving $\theta = 0.2126$ K s^{-1}; and $t = 1/\theta = 4.7$ s

4 **(a)** 1739 MeV $= 1.6 \times 10^{-13} \times 1739 = 2.78 \times 10^{-10}$ J

(b) **(i)** energy release is the difference in the binding energies; **(ii)** 1.2×10^{14} J

(c) **(i)** 4.5×10^{-12} J; **(ii)** 6.8×10^{14} J

(d) Fusion provides more than 5 times as much energy as fission.

5 **(a)** **(ii)** mass defect = 0.20 u, giving energy = 3.1×10^{-11} J

(b) **(i)** $300/235 \times 6 \times 10^{23} = 7.7 \times 10^{23}$ atoms;

(ii) 2.4×10^{13} J

(c) time $= 2.4 \times 10^{13}/7.5 \times 10^5 = 3.2 \times 10^7$ s

2.4.1

1 **(a)** 2160 W **(b)** 13 W

2 **(a)** 1.12×10^{-14} J **(b)** 1.7×10^{19} Hz

(c) 1.8×10^{-11} m

3 **(a)** 1.04×10^{-10} m

(b) e.g. The equation applies to parallel slits; the surfaces of crystals have hexagonal or square patterns of atoms. X-rays can penetrate crystals where there are many different separations of planes of atoms. The diffraction pattern will be a series of spots, not lines, so it is difficult to know what order is being used. The X-rays might well have a variety of wavelengths rather than just one value.

2.4.2

1 **(a)** It becomes kinetic energy of the positron and electron.

(b) This would give the electron and positron a speed greater than the speed of light. The theory of relativity forbids this. The masses of the electron and positron increase as their speed increases.

2 330 keV; it becomes extra kinetic energy of the scattered electron.

2.4.3

1 X-ray tube electrical powers can vary from a few hundred watts to several thousand watts. Most are about 0.5% efficient, so X-ray output, for machines used for taking photos, might vary from 0.5 W to 100 W. The smaller machines will be used for small areas, say 20 cm^2, the larger ones for say 200 cm^2. Combining this information gives intensities from 250 W m^{-2} to 5000 W m^{-2}.

2 Intensity through lead = 790 W m^{-2}: through bone = 980 W m^{-2}: through muscle = 1.7 kW m^{-2}

2.4.4

1 (a) 0.5 cm
(b) reduce x, increase y

2 Use a slit in a block of lead, with the block near to the X-ray source.

2.4.5

1 (a) 15.6 Bq;
(b) 54 hours

2 2.5 cm

2.4.6

1 When leaning over, the weight of the rider is not in line with the support force from the road. A torque is therefore formed. The precession caused results in a change in direction. Leaning over is how you steer.

2 (b) (i) The wire is far too long. It will have huge resistance, so a very high voltage would be needed and there would (probably) be enough heating effect to melt the wire.
(ii) The wire is a more manageable length, but it would have to be very thick to take this current and so would occupy a huge amount of space. Heating would still be a problem
(c) With superconducting wires very large currents are possible with no heating effect whatsoever, because the resistance is exactly zero. The special wires do have to be cooled down. A liquid nitrogen outer blanket contains within it the wires of the magnet it surrounds, which are themselves cooled further by liquid helium at 4.2 K.

2.4.7

1 (a) (i) 0; (ii) 0.50 m; (iii) 0.147 m
(b) The different frequencies reveal the different places along the body from which each signal has originated, so each frequency represents a 'slice' of the body.

2.4.8

1 e.g. The wash of a boat, an aircraft going faster than the speed of sound

2 486 Hz

2.4.9

1 Reduced by 94%

2 (a) 48 waves

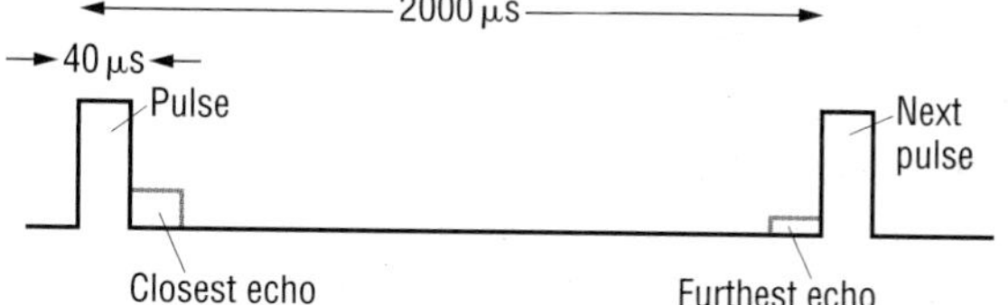

(b) shortest distance = 32 mm,
longest distance = 1600 mm

2.4.10

1 (b) The units on the top of the expression are divided by the same units on the bottom. By squaring the expression, negative values are eliminated.

2 (a) X: (0.007 ms + 0.019 ms) × 2 = 0.052 ms. Y: (0.007 ms + 0.019 ms + 0.006 ms) × 2 = 0.064 ms
(b) I_r/I_0 values are fat–muscle = muscle–fat = 0.0044 ≈ 0: muscle–bone = bone–muscle = 0.31
(c) X 31% returns, Y 14% returns

2.4.11

1 2.6 cm^3

2 (b) A variation from maximum to minimum and back to maximum over 5 cycles of one wave and four of the other.
(c) The frequency of this oscillation equals the difference in the frequency of the two waves. The same happens with the ultrasound waves. A so-called beat frequency of 975 Hz is obtained. This will vary with the speed of the blood and so can be monitored.

2.5.1

1 Mars, and the rest of the planets apart from Venus and Mercury, are further from the Sun than the Earth is, so they can never pass between the Earth and the Sun.

2 An eclipse of the Moon can be seen from anywhere on the dark side of the Earth, but eclipses of the Sun can be seen only from comparatively small areas of the Earth, because the Moon is smaller than the Earth.

3 1400 kg m^{-3}; e.g. there is a far smaller proportion of heavy elements in the Sun, the core of the Earth is largely iron.

4 (a) 6.1 (b) 1.1×10^7 m

2.5.2

1 (a) 1.8×10^{49} m^3 (b) 2×10^{30} kg

2 (a) 4.4×10^9 kg s^{-1} (= 4.4 million tonnes per second)
(b) For present mass of 2.0×10^{30} kg, time = 4.5×10^{18} s (= 140 billion years).

2.5.3

1 (a) The forces on the comet are directly towards the Sun, with a larger force when closer to the Sun; the forces on the alpha particle are directly away from the gold nucleus, with a larger force when closer to the nucleus.
(b) Both paths are hyperbolic. Both forces vary as inverse squares of distance. Attraction in one case and repulsion in the othher produce the same effect.

(If a particle with the opposite charge to the gold nucleus had been used in Rutherford's scattering experiment, the scattering effect would have been exactly the same.)

2 (a) GmM/d^2

(b) $R = dm/(m + M)$; $r = dM/(m + M)$

(c) The force on M is towards m and vice versa. Both forces go through C, on a straight line between M and m. This can only be true if both have the same period.

(d) $T = 2\pi \sqrt{\dfrac{d^3}{G(M + m)}}$

2.5.4

1 (a) (i) The time taken for the Earth to complete one revolution around the Sun.

(ii) Watch the position of the Sun on the horizon at sunset. Count the number of days it takes for this point to move from furthest north of west to furthest south of west and back to furthest north of west. The Romans did this with sufficient accuracy to get 365¼. This is not quite correct. It is 3 days too many in 400 years, so, by 1752, March 10 was the date when it should have been the spring equinox, March 21. When a correction was then applied, people grumbled that they had lost 11 days of their life! This is the reason why Christmas is celebrated on January 6 in the Russian Orthodox Church.

(b) (i) The time for the Sun to appear to move from its position due south to the next time it appears to be due south.

(ii) The simple answer is to use the Sun as the star and measure this time directly. The problem is that, because the Sun is a large, bright object, it ought to be easier to use a point of light, namely a star. This, however, gives a different answer. The Sun moves across background star patterns once a year – Aries, Taurus, Gemini…, Pisces. A so-called sidereal day is different from a solar day by 24 hours divided by 365¼, about 4 minutes.

2 1.58×10^{-5} ly

3 7.0×10^{-6} rad (= 0.0004°)

2.5.5

1 'Little' because the speed of recession of other stars in the galaxy is very small; 'none' because the galaxy is rotating, and for one star it could be that it is moving towards the Earth by rotation at the same speed as recession.

2 (a) The speed of recession.

(b) The rate of rotation of the galaxy.

3 3.90×10^7 m s^{-1}.

2.5.6

1 4.7×10^{17} s

2 2.3×10^{23} W. Use a large reflecting telescope to concentrate the beam of light on to a tiny, accurately calibrated, insulated, sensitive thermometer, e.g. a thermocouple with a very small heat capacity. Knowing the heat capacity of the thermometer and the temperature rise, the energy input over a period of time can be determined. (These values are known for very many stars.)

3 $\lambda_{max} \propto 1/T$; for the Sun, λ_{max} is 520 nm and T is 5600. This gives the wavelength of maximum emission from Sirius as 146 nm. This is ultraviolet radiation.

2.5.7

2 The line is (surprisingly) straight. Its gradient is about –0.42.

2.5.8

1 Very approximately 2 m^3. (Most of the atoms in the universe are hydrogen atoms. If you take the average mass of an atom to be larger than the mass of a hydrogen atom, you will get a slightly higher value.)

2 The condition for a flat universe is a boundary condition between enough k.e. for everlasting expansion and too little k.e., resulting in a big crunch. Of all the vast range of k.e. values possible, there is no reason it should have this particular exact value.

Stretch and challenge answers

1.1.3

$m\,dv/dt + v\,dm/dt = kF$

1.2.6

The gravitational force will be towards the bulge in the Earth's shape, but this is not the same as the direction of the hole.

The surface of the Earth is accelerating. Part of the gravitational force will provide this acceleration towards Earth's axis. The rest of the force is not in the direction of the hole.

1.2.11

The ratio is unchanged at $-(2\pi f)^2$.

1.3.2

(a) 1/5 mile per second,
(b) because sound is molecular vibration, **(c)** because of multiple collisions between the molecules causing the smell and molecules in the air.

1.3.11

332 m s^{-1}.

2.1.2

3.0 units.

2.2.3

There is no other component in the circuit so $V_C + V_R$ must equal zero.

2.4.11

$\frac{f'}{f} = \frac{f + \Delta f}{f} = 1 + \frac{\Delta f}{f} = 1 + \frac{2v}{c} + \ldots$ Since v/c is small, other terms in the binomial expansion will be even smaller, and hence $\Delta f = 2fv/c$. The change in frequency is directly proportional to the speed, since f and c are constant.

2.5.6

This wavelength is strongly absorbed by the Earth's atmosphere so could not be studied directly, but the shape of the graph of the background radiation corresponded to a temperature of 2.7 K.

Practice answers

1.1 Newton's law and momentum

1 **(a)** 65–70 m s^{-2}
(b) Mass and hence the weight of the rocket are less at 0.25 s than at 0.15 s. Thrust is the same, so resultant force (= thrust – weight) is greater. Acceleration (= resultant force/mass) is greater.
(c) Constant velocity means that using Newton's first law there is no resultant force on the rocket. Therefore thrust equals weight.
(d) Straight line means constant acceleration and constant force. No thrust, so weight is the only force. Gradient of line is $-g$.

2 **(a)** 3.8 ± 0.3 N s
(b) Change in momentum of the ball or the impulse on the ball.
(c) 24 m s^{-1}
(d) 150 m s^{-2}

3 **(a)** **(i)** Use $E = \frac{1}{2}mv^2$ to show $v = 1.9 \times 10^6$ m s^{-1}
(ii) 1.3×10^{-20} kg m s^{-1}
(iii) $v = 3.2 \times 10^4$ m s^{-1}
(b) **(i)** X is about 15 mm from P.
(ii) XP arrow direction is a straight line through P.
(iii) about 0.3 mm

4 **(a)** Using $F = ma$ gives P = 5ma, hence a = P/5m
(b) P/5
(c) **(i)** P/5m
(ii) P/5
(d) **(i)** 3P/5 to the right
(ii) 2P/5 to the left

1.2 Circular motion and oscillations

1 **(a)** **(i)** $v = 2\pi rf = 2\pi \times 0.015 \times 50$; = 4.7 m s^{-1}
(ii) $a = v^2/r = 4.7^2/0.015$; = 1.5×10^3 m s^{-2}
(b) Resonance occurs when the natural frequency of vibration of the panel = rotational frequency of the motor.

2 **(a)** **(i)** 9.0×10^9 J
(ii) larger as g decreases with height
(iii) 5.9 or 6.0×10^{11} J
(b) **(i)** 4.4 or 4.5 N kg^{-1}
(ii) $g = GM/r^2$
(iii) $g \propto 1/r^2$; so value is 40/9 = 4.4 N kg^{-1}

3 **(a)** **(i)** $g = GM/R^2$ so $g_O/g = R^2/16R^2$ giving g_O = 40/16 = 2.5 N kg^{-1};
$g_P/g = R^2/25R^2$ so g_P = 1.6 N kg^{-1}
(ii) average g = (2.5 + 1.6)/2 = 2.(05) so Δp.e. (= $mg_{av}R$) = $4.0 \times 10^3 \times 2.(05) \times 2.0 \times 10^7$; = 1.6×10^{11} J
(b) $g = v^2/r$; = $4\pi^2(4R)/T^2$
$1.6 = 4 \times \pi^2 \times 10.0 \times 10^7/T^2$ giving $T^2 = 24.0 \times 10^8$ and $T = 4.9 \times 10^4$ s

4 **(a)** Newton's second law gives $F_H = m_H a_H$ and $F_I = m_I a_I$;
Newton's third law gives $F_H = F_I$
SHM gives a ∝ –x; hence $x_H/x_I = a_H/a_I = m_I/m_H = 127$
(b) **(i)** A sine or cosine curve with amplitude 8.0×10^{-12} m and period = 1.5×10^{-14} s
(ii) A resonance situation, since the driving frequency of radiation is approximately equal to the natural frequency of oscillation of the molecule.

1.3 Thermal physics

1 2.6×10^7 J or 26 MJ

2 **(a)** **(i)** 410 m s^{-1}; **(ii)** 460 m s^{-1}
(c) **(i)** 420 m s^{-1}; **(ii)** 4.1×10^{-21} J

3 **(a)** When pressure or volume of an ideal gas tends to zero, the temperature must tend to zero; the temperature scale with this zero of temperature is the kelvin scale.

(b) pV/T = constant, so $V/290 = 0.01 \times 10^6/230$ giving $V = 1.26 \times 10^4\,m^3$

(c) (i) $n = pV/RT = 1.0 \times 10^5 \times 1.26 \times 10^4/(8.31 \times 290)$ $= 5.2 \times 10^5$

(ii) $4.0 \times 10^{-3} \times 5.2 \times 10^5 = 2.1 \times 10^3\,kg$

(d) internal energy $\propto T$ so $E = 1.9 \times 230/290 = 1500$ MJ

4 $Q = mc\theta$ so $0.8 \times 3.7 \times 10^{10} \times 7.9 \times 10^{-13}\,t = 0.001 \times 110 \times 1$ giving $= 4.7$ s
or $Q = mc\theta$; $Q/K = 0.001 \times 110 = 0.11\,J\,K^{-1}$ and $Q/s = 0.0234$ J so $t = 0.11/0.0234 = 4.7$ s

5 Combine $pV = nRT$ and $U = 3/2nRT$ to give $U = 3/2\,pV = 3/2 \times 1.0 \times 10^5 \times 24 = 3.6 \times 10^6$ J or 3.6 MJ
or $n = m/M$ where $m = \rho V$; $n = 1.2 \times 24/0.03 = 960$; $U = 3/2nRT = 3/2 \times 960 \times 8.31 \times 300 = 3.6 \times 10^6$ J or 3.9 MJ
or using $pV = nRT$ to find n gives $n = 986$ with $U = 3.6 \times 10^6$ J or 3.6 MJ

6 (a) Using $½Mv^2 = mc\theta$, $\theta = 8°C$

(b) Not all of the energy goes into heating the brake blocks, e.g. bicycle wheel rims; mass of the brake blocks is too big as rubber is a poor conductor and the heating will be much more local; the wheels are rotating as well as moving along, so this rotational energy has to be dissipated. Thus the temperature rise is likely to be greater.

2.1 Electric and magnetic fields

1 (a) 5.0 mm s^{-1};

(b) The magnetic force is at right angles to the electron motion, pushing them to the bottom edge of the strip, leaving positive ions at the top edge of the strip (or holes are pushed to the top edge of the strip).

(c) E-field from plus to minus charge; $1.0 \times 10^{-3}\,V\,m^{-1}$.

2 (a) Circular motion caused by a force in plane perpendicular to the B-field and at right angles to the motion of the charged particle at all points.

(b) (i) $F = mv^2/r = 9.1 \times 10^{-31} \times 10^{16}/0.04 = 2.3 \times 10^{-13}$ N

(ii) Perpendicular to path towards centre of circle

(c) $F = BQv = 2.3 \times 10^{-13}$
so $B = 2.3 \times 10^{-13}/1.6 \times 10^{-19} \times 10^8 = 1.4 \times 10^{-2}$ T

3 (a) (ii) Soft iron; causes a larger magnetic field; conducts flux better; magnetic domains line up easily

(b) (i) There is a continuously changing flux where the disc enters or leaves the magnetic field. This induces an e.m.f. (Faraday's law) in the disc, and because of the low resistance a current is generated in a loop as shown.

(ii) The currents in the disc interact with the field so as to oppose the change of flux (Lenz's law), causing the braking.

(iii) The slowing down of the disc results in a decrease in the rate of change of flux and hence a lower e.m.f. and current. The force decreases, so the force will become zero as the disc slows to a halt – the electromagnetic force cannot stop the vehicle; conventional brakes are required.

2.2 Capacitors and exponential decay

1 (a) The power supply pumps electrons onto one plate, repelling them from the other until the imbalance of charge on the plates gives a p.d. of 600 V between the plates. Charge is stored on the plates.

(b) (i) 7.2×10^{-10} C; **(ii)** 2.2×10^{-7} J

2 (a) 1.2 nC, 200 pF, 6.0 V, 3.6 nJ

(b) V; 0.6 nC, 100 pF, 6.0 V, 1.8 nJ

(c) Q; 0.6 nC, 200 pF, 3.0 V, 0.9 nJ

3 (a) $Q = VC$; $W = ½\,VC \times V = ½\,CV^2$

(b) curve of parabolic shape passing through origin; plotted accurately is $W = 1.1\,V^2$

4 (a) $Q = CV = 1.2 \times 10^{-12} \times 90 = 1.1 \times 10^{-10}$ C

(b) $n = Q/e = 1.1 \times 10^{-10}/1.6 \times 10^{-19} = 6.9 \times 10^8$

(c) $N = 6.9 \times 10^8/1.8 \times 10^{-10} = 3.8 \times 10^{18}$

(d) (i) $W = ½\,QV = ½\,CV^2 = 0.5 \times 1.1 \times 10^{-10} \times 90$ $= 4.95$ nJ

(ii) $t = 5 \times 10^{-7}$ s;

(iii) the flash will be of longer duration and much lower power, or as the human eye needs about 0.05 s to register the flash, at 5×10^{-7} s it will not be seen; a much larger capacitor and radioactive source are needed to achieve a flash of sufficient power and duration.

5 (a) $T = RC$; $= 6.8 \times 10^3 \times 2.2 = 1.5 \times 10^4$ s = 4.16 h

(b) $\Delta W = ½\,C(V_1^2 - V_2^2) = 1.1(25 - 16)$; = 9.9 J

(c) $4 = 5\exp(-t/1.5 \times 10^4)$;
giving $t = 1.5 \times 10^4 \times \ln 1.25 = 3.3 \times 10^3$ s

(d) $P = \Delta W/\Delta t = 9.9/3.3 \times 10^3 = 3.0$ mW or
$P = V_{av}^2/R = 4.5^2/6.8 \times 10^3 = 2.98$ mW

2.3 Nuclear physics

1 (a) Radius of one nucleon, e.g. proton or neutron

(b) (i) 3.8×10^{-15} m; **(ii)** $3.8 \times 10^{-15}/20^{1/3}$

(c) $1.5 \times 10^{17}\,kg\,m^{-3}$

(d) $F = (1/4\pi\varepsilon_0)\,Q_1Q_2/r^2$; $Q_1 = e$, $Q_2 = e$ giving $F = 29.4$ N

2 (a) (i) Line in direction NA;

(ii) line passing perpendicular to the tangent at the point of closest approach to N

(b) (i) k.e. = $½\,mv^2$ ($= 8 \times 10^{-13}$) giving $v = 1.5 \times 10^7\,m\,s^{-1}$

(ii) $mv = 6.7 \times 10^{-27} \times 1.5 \times 10^7 = 1.0 \times 10^{-19}\,kg\,m\,s^{-1}$

(c) (i) proton has $m_\alpha/4$, so v must be doubled to give same energy;
so mv = **(b) (ii)** value/2, i.e. $5 \times 10^{-20}\,kg\,m\,s^{-1}$

(ii) average force is smaller, recoil slower, momentum less, interaction time shorter, angle of recoil different

(d) $F = (1/4\pi\varepsilon_0)\, Q_1Q_2/r^2$; $Q_1 = e$, $Q_2 = 79\,e$ giving $F = 0.032$ N

3 (a) An element can exist in more than one form, having a different number of neutrons, that is, can have different mass but same proton number

(b) (i) ${}^{4}_{2}\text{He}$ or ${}^{4}_{2}\alpha$; (ii) (–)${}^{0}_{-1}\text{e}$ or ${}^{0}_{-1}\beta$

(c) ${}^{238}_{92}\text{U} \rightarrow {}^{234}_{90}\text{X} + {}^{4}_{2}\alpha$ then ${}^{234}_{90}\text{X} \rightarrow {}^{234}_{91}\text{Y} + {}^{0}_{-1}\beta$ then ${}^{234}_{91}\text{Y} \rightarrow {}^{234}_{92}\text{U} + {}^{0}_{-1}\beta$

4 (a) hadron, baryon

(b) (i) uud; (ii) udd

(c) (i) udd $\rightarrow$ uud + e^- + $\bar{\nu}$;

(ii) charge $+\frac{2}{3} - \frac{1}{3} - \frac{1}{3} \rightarrow +\frac{2}{3} + \frac{2}{3} - \frac{1}{3} - 1 + 0$;
baryon number $+\frac{1}{3} + \frac{1}{3} + \frac{1}{3} \rightarrow +\frac{1}{3} + \frac{1}{3} + \frac{1}{3} + 0 + 0$

(d) charge $-1 + 1 = 0 + 0$; baryon number $0 + 1 = 1 + 0$; strangeness $0 + 0 = 0 + 0$; showing that reaction may take place

5 *Similarities*: both release energy in process; rest mass of fragments less than original; conservation of charge/mass–energy, etc.
Differences: decay into two particles; fission into more particles/4 or 5;
decay energy release is small compared to fission;
decay cannot be initiated by any known process/random/spontaneous/obeys laws of probability; fission can be initiated by incident neutron/fission rate can be varied/controlled;
energies and masses in decay always the same; fission can be into many different combinations with different energies;
most of energy in decay carried away by small particle; in fission by massive particles/fragments.

2.4 Medical imaging

1 (a) (i) 1.6×10^{-14} J; (ii) 1.24×10^{-11} m

(b) (i) Electrons are removed from inner shells; outer electrons fill vacancies; emitted photon has energy equal to the difference in levels.

(ii) **1** E_{max} increases, λ_{min} decreases, peak intensity move to higher energy and area under graph increases; **2** only the area under graph (the total intensity) increases

2 (a) (i) Energy transmitted per second (or power) per unit cross-sectional area of the beam;

(ii) (total linear) attenuation coefficient;

(iii) energy or frequency of the X-ray photons; density or proton number of the material through which the beam passes.

(b) 40 m^{-1}

3 (a) (i) The relative positions of the fibres within the bundle at one end are the same as the positions at the other end;

(ii) light channel 1 as the light transmitted is used purely to illuminate site, no image is necessary;

(iii) light channel 2 transmits light to form an image for the observer; a coherent bundle is necessary for an unmuddled clear image.

(b) Power of light source, i.e. energy input; length of probe as signal is attenuated along the fibres; end losses due to partial reflection; a high refractive index of fibre leads to greater absorption; excessive bending of fibre leads to some light escaping from its sides.

(c) Diagnostic, e.g. investigating possible tumour or ulcer, etc.; therapeutic, e.g. microsurgery, removal of foreign body, etc.

(d) (i) 1.33×10^{8} W m^{-2}; (ii) 6.4×10^{17}

4 (a) An invasive method would require the exposure of the blood vessel with the help of *surgery*, i.e. with the use of the knife; no surgery is necessary in non-invasive techniques.

(b) Longest λ has lowest f so use $f = 2$ MHz giving $\lambda = 7.5 \times 10^{-4}$ m

(c) Use highest $f = 10$ MHz and $\theta = 0$ to obtain $\Delta f = 4$ kHz.

2.5 Modelling the universe

1 (a) taking 1 year = 3.2×10^{7} s, 4.1×10^{16} m;

(b) taking 1 AU = 1.5×10^{11} m, 2.7×10^{5} AU; **(c)** 1.3 pc

2 (a) 23.1°;

(b) Both lines are moved the same distance away from the centre.

(c) 6.0 km s^{-1}

3 (a) Redshift of light from galaxies increasing with distance

(b) (i) Straight line through the origin means $v = H_0 d$;

(ii) 70 km s^{-1} Mpc^{-1} = 2.3×10^{-18} s^{-1}

(c) (i) 4.3×10^{17} s, 1.4×10^{10} y;

(ii) the universe did not begin with galaxies, so time must be added for their formation.

4 (a) 3 half-lives, 1.35×10^{10} y;

(b) (i) stars were formed some time after the big bang;

(ii) the age of the universe is given by $1/H_0$, so the smallest age gives the upper limit.

5 (a) 11.1 km s^{-1} **(b)** 12.8 km s^{-1}

Examination answers

1.1 Newton's law and momentum

1 (a) (i) Two vertical arrows of equal length and opposite direction in the same vertical line passing through the ball labelled weight/gravity/*mg*/0.49 N and (normal) reaction/string tension/0.49 N

(ii) one pair of forces is the gravitational force; acts on ball and Earth; the other pair is the contact or reaction force acting between the ball and the strings of the racket.

(iii) 0.1 N

(b) (i) Use $v^2 = u^2 + 2gh$ or $\frac{1}{2}mv^2 = mgh$ to give $v^2 = 2gh$ and hence $v = 4.0$ m s^{-1}

(ii) 0.20 kg m s^{-1}

(iii) 0.40 kg m s^{-1}

(iv) 8.0 N

2 (a) (Electrostatic) repulsion between charged particles slows alpha and accelerates nucleus.
The momentum of system is conserved as there are no external forces.
The sum of the momenta of alpha and nucleus must always equal initial momentum of alpha, that is, be a constant, so speed of nucleus can be calculated as momentum = *mv*

(b) 3.3×10^5 m s^{-1}

(c) 2.2×10^{-20} s

3 (a) 300 kg m s^{-1} or N s

(b) (i) The speed of the bar increases, so it is accelerated forwards; this requires a resultant forward force using $F = ma$

(ii) arrow in the direction of motion, i.e. to the right

(iii) 5.0 s

(iv) 120 N

4 (a) (i) mass × velocity

(ii) $0 = m_A v_A \pm m_B v_B$ or $m_A v_A = m_B v_B$, so $v_A/v_B = \pm m_B/m_A$

(b) (i) $v_A = 2.0$ m s^{-1} and $v_B = 1.0$ m s^{-1}

(ii) $t_1 = 1.5$ s

(iii) $x = 0.6$ (m)

(iv) $v = v_B + (5/50)v_A = 1.0 + 0.2 = 1.2$ m s^{-1}

(v) $t_2 = t_1 + 0.6/1.2 = 2.0$ s

(vi) at collision the container (and fragments) stop since by conservation of momentum, total momentum is still zero

(vii) straight lines from (0,0) to (1.5,0); (1.5,0) to (2.0,0.1); (x,0.1) for all $x > 2$

5 (a) 825 kg m s^{-1};

(b) $F = 5890$ N, giving 7.8 times body weight.

(c) deceleration is less as takes longer time or distance; therefore force is less; head will not bounce.

(d) (i) graph shows that the maximum force is lower.

(ii) graph shows same area under line.

6 (a) Momentum of a particle = mass × velocity; linear momentum is constant in every collision; because there are no external forces. Total energy is constant in every collision; k.e. is (only) conserved in elastic collisions; otherwise some k.e. is lost/dissipated/randomised/turned to heat, etc.

(b) The neatest and possibly shortest answer is in terms of constant steady motion of the centre of mass of the system. Here are the points you could make in note form:
small particle incident on large one
Analogy with ball bouncing off wall; energy transfer to massive particle is very small; as *v* of massive particle is so small; because momentum conserved;
large particle incident on small one
Massive particle can only transfer a small fraction of its momentum; so keeps most of its k.e.; small particle hardly needs any k.e.; *alternative wording could be:* Small particle moves off at roughly twice velocity of massive particle; massive particle hardly slowed;
common features
Constant (steady) motion of centre of mass of system; incident momentum very small in first case compared to second; ratio of masses to inverse ratio of velocities/distances moved; k.e. depends on v^2, so *v* ratio has more effect than mass ratio on energy transfer.

1.2 Circular motion and oscillations

1 (a) Equal vertical arrows in opposite directions, in correct positions, labelled weight or *mg* and tension or *T*

(b) Two forces, one vertical, the other along string, correctly labelled.
Resultant force/vector sum of the tension and weight/forces is a horizontal force/(component of) tension; provides horizontal force; acting towards centre of rotation/axis.

(c) (i) 0.38 m s^{-1} (ii) 0.057 N

(d) Moves in circle of larger diameter/longer path; larger centripetal force/acceleration is required at higher speed; provided by larger horizontal component of tension/greater angle of string to axis

2 (a) (i) Force per unit mass (placed at that point)

(ii) $g = GM/R^2$

(iii) Choosing a correct pair of values from the graph, e.g. 6.4×10^6 & 9.8,10 × 10^6 & 4.0; substitute, $9.8 = 6.67 \times 10^{-11} \times M/(6.4 \times 10^6)^2$ to show $M = 6.0 \times 10^{24}$ kg
(iv) linear graph through origin/from 0 to R
(v) 64 km; 1/100 of R as linear graph under Earth; 64000 km; $g \propto 1/r^2$ so for 1/100 g $r = 10R$
(b) $GM_e/R_1^2 = GM_m/R_2^2$; $M_e = 81\ M_m$; $R_1 = 0.9\ R_2$; $M_m = 6.0 \times 10^{24}/81 = 7.4 \times 10^{22}$ kg

3 (a) (i) 120 mJ
(ii) 120 – 70; = 50 mJ
(b) (i) k.e. = $\frac{1}{2}mv^2 = 50 \times 10^{-3} = 0.2\ v^2$; $v^2 = 0.25$; $v = 0.5$ m s^{-1}
(ii) Reasoning, e.g. max energy = $\frac{1}{2}mv_m^2 = \frac{1}{2}kA^2$ so $A \propto v_m$; or max k.e. = 12.5 mJ, so total energy = 82.5 mJ, read x from graph; giving $A = 0.025$ m
(c) (i) $a = -4\pi^2f^2x$;
$f^2 = 110/4\pi^2 = 2.786/f = 10.5/2\pi = 1.67$, so $f = 1/T = 0.6$ s
(ii) sinusoidal wave with correct period, 0.6 s; correct amplitude, 0.05 m; correct phase, A or $-A$ at 0 and 0 at 0.15 s

4 (a) (i) Acceleration ∝ displacement (from a fixed point); directed towards that point.
(ii) amplitude is decreasing; follows sine wave (of decreasing amplitude)/has constant period/frequency/period/frequency independent of amplitude
(b) 6 oscillations in 4 s; $f = 1/T = 1.5$ Hz
(c) (i) 5 mm
(ii) e.g. 0 to 3 in 0.5 steps
(iii) approx. same (or slightly lower) resonance frequency; smaller amplitude/broader peak but curves must not cross; passes through (0, 5 mm)

5 (a) Resonance occurs at/close to the natural frequency of an oscillating object/system; caused by driving force (at this frequency); when maximum amplitude of driven achieved/maximum energy transfer between driver and driven
Examples:
(good) microwaves, watch (quartz), pendulum clock, open and closed pipes, electrical resonance/tuning, etc.
(bad) Tacoma Narrows or Millennium bridge, wine glass fracture, vibration of building/earthquake, motorcar wing mirror, rattles/steering wheel vibration at different speeds, etc.
Practical significance of each choice given in a meaningful manner can score 2 marks.
Nature of driving force clearly stated for each example can score 2 marks.
(b) Possible marking points: Resonance over wider frequency range; energy stored/amplitude of resonance decreased; shift down of resonance frequency with increased damping; critically or overdamped system will not oscillate/no resonance; resonance oscillation die away quickly/exponential decay of amplitude with damping etc. when driving force removed, etc.
A correctly annotated amplitude vs. frequency diagram can score up to 3 marks.
A suitable example of a real vibrating system including any sensible laboratory demonstration relating real system to features described can score up to 2 marks.

1.3 Thermal physics

1 (a) Celsius and kelvin scales have same increment; temperature scales differ numerically by 273; so at 500 000, 273 is a negligible difference.
(b) (i) V/T = constant or p/T = constant or pV/T = constant = nR; at absolute zero, $p = 0$ or $V = 0$ or $pV = 0$.
(ii) Temperature is proportional to the (kinetic) energy of molecules or atoms; at absolute zero, k.e. is zero, i.e. molecules stop moving.
(c) (i) p/T = constant, so $p/p_o = T_1/T_o = 400/300$, giving $p = 1.33\ p_o$.
(ii) use of $n = pV/RT$ or $N \propto p$ shows $f = (N_B/N_A) = n_B/n_A = p_o/p = 0.75$

2 (a) p is the pressure, V the volume, n is the number of moles or amount of gas, R is (universal) gas constant, T is the absolute temperature in K
(b) (i) $pV = m/M\ RT$
so $1.0 \times 10^5 \times 0.1 = m/0.03 \times 8.31 \times 300$;
$n = 4.0$ mol; $m = nM$; $m = 0.12$ kg
(ii) V/T = constant or ρT = constant;
$x = \rho_1/\rho_2 = T_2/T_1 = 300/500 = 0.6$
or calculate mass = 0.072 kg at 500 K;
using $pV = m/M\ RT$; ratio with **(b)(i)**
(iii) molecules have more k.e., or k.e.$\propto T$; $v \propto \sqrt{T}$ or $\frac{1}{2}mv^2 \propto T$, so $f = \sqrt{(500/300)} = 1.29$ or 1.3

3 (a) Internal energy is the sum of the (random) kinetic and potential energies of the molecules/atoms in the system/gas.
An ideal gas has no attraction between molecules/atoms; so its internal energy is only kinetic/internal energy of ideal gas, tends to zero at 0 K; but internal energy of real gas does not.

(b) Gas changes to liquid; and then solid; as temperature falls, internal energy decreases.
Absolute zero is the temperature for minimum internal energy.
At a change in phase, there is no temperature change.
Arrangement/packing of particles: in liquid free to move within body of liquid; in solid fixed in position but free to vibrate; statement about increase in order of particle arrangement across one change of phase.
At phase change: large change of p.e.; little or no change in k.e.
Between phases: major change in k.e.; little or no change in p.e.

4 (a) Internal energy is the sum of the random kinetic and potential energies of the particles or molecules or atoms in the system or body; s.h.c. is the change in (internal) energy per unit mass or the energy required to heat unit mass or kg per unit rise in temperature, i.e. °C or K.

(b) Suitable description of apparatus for electrical heating of body for given time so that energy input = VIt; measurement of mass of body and temperature rise hence $VIt = mc\theta$ with c found; need some comment on heat loss and how it can be minimised or compensated for.

(c) (i) $Q = 2.0 \times 920 \times 293 = 540$ kJ

(ii) 2 kg contains 2/0.027 = 74 moles so no. of atoms in 2 kg = $74 \times 6.02 \times 10^{23} = 4.46 \times 10^{25}$; energy per atom = $5.4 \times 10^5/4.46 \times 10^{25}$
$= 1.2 \times 10^{-20}$ J

(iii) there are several methods
e.g. $2 \times 920/74 = 24.9$ J mol^{-1} K^{-1}

5 (a) $n = m/M$; $\rho = m/V$; $p = nRT/V = (m/V)RT/M = \rho RT/M$

(b) A ratio or half-height test is suitable.

(c) $p/p_o = \rho/\rho_o$; p at 8 km $= 3.5 \pm 0.3 \times 10^4$ Pa
so $\rho = 0.35 \times 1.3 = 0.46$ kg m^{-3}

(d) $p/\rho T$ = constant so $10^5/1.3 \times 293 = 3 \times 10^4/\rho \times 250$
giving $\rho = 0.46$ kg m^{-3}

6 (a) r.m.s. speed = $(3kT/m)^{1/2}$; as T and k are constant
$\sqrt{c^2} \propto m^{-1/2}$

(b) Show $\sqrt{c^2}\, m^{1/2}$ = constant for three pairs of data

(c) (i) Range of energies; colliding with each other; exchanging energy or changing speed or momentum;

(ii) there is only a small probability that the molecules will gain above average energy from a large number of collisions

(d) (i) 2.3×10^5 m^{2}s^{-2}; **(ii)** 290 K

2.1 Electric and magnetic fields – 1

1 (a) (i) Horizontal arrows outwards

(ii) $F_e = Q^2/4\pi\varepsilon_o r^2 = 9 \times 10^{-16} \times 9 \times 10^9/36 \times 10^{-4}$
$= 2.25 \times 10^{-3}$ N

(b) Arrows for weight (down) and tension (along string)

(c) (moments about suspension) $mgl \sin\theta = F_e l \cos\theta$ or (resolution) $T \sin\theta = F_e$ and $T \cos\theta = mg$ hence $\tan q = F_e/mg = 2.25 \times 10^{-3}/8.0 \times 9.8 \times 10^{-4}$ giving $\theta = 15.7°$ or $16°$ so $2\theta = 31°$ or $32°$

(d) $F_g = Gm^2/r^2$; calculation to give 1.2×10^{-14} N or
$F_g/F_e = Gm^2 4\pi\varepsilon_o/Q^2$
$F_g/F_e = 1.2 \times 10^{-14}/2.25 \times 10^{-3} = 5.3 \times 10^{-12}$

2 (a) Force on unit positive charge at that point

(b) (i) Suitable pattern around not just between the charges; symmetry, spacing, lines joined to charges required; arrows towards B on some lines

(ii) use of $E = (1/4\pi\varepsilon_0)\, Q/r^2$; use of $r = 4.0 \times 10^{-10}$; sum of two equal terms, so $E = 2 \times 9 \times 10^9 \times 1.6 \times 10^{-19}/(4.0 \times 10^{-10})^2 = 1.8 \times 10^{10}$ N C^{-1}

(c) Equal and opposite forces or suitable E-field patterns drawn on each figure in correct directions

(i) the dipole rotates to or oscillates about the position in figure; because a couple is formed causing rotation clockwise

(ii) no motion, as electric forces on charges are equal and opposite

3 (a) Equally spaced horizontal parallel lines from plate to plate; arrows towards B

(b) $E = V/d = 600/0.04 = 1.5 \times 10^4$ V m^{-1}

(c) $F = QE = 1.6 \times 10^{-19} \times 1.2 \times 10^4 = 2.4 \times 10^{-15}$ N

(d) $1/2mv^2 = Fd = 2.4 \times 10^{-15} \times 0.04$ or
$QV = 1.6 \times 10^{-19} \times 600$ so $v = 1.45 \times 10^7$ m s^{-1}

(e) 2.9×10^7 or 3.0×10^7 m s^{-1}

(f) Fewer electrons will reach grid **C** as higher initial speed required so current will fall (to zero if beam is taken to be mono-energetic)

4 (a) Appropriate shape with lines perpendicular to and touching plate and sphere and arrows towards negative sphere

(b) (i) Use moments or triangle of forces or resolution of forces to show $F = 1.0 \times 10^{-5} \tan 20$
$= 3.64 \times 10^{-6}$ N

(ii) $E = F/Q = 3.64 \times 10^{-6}/1.2 \times 10^{-9} = 3.0 \times 10^3$ N C^{-1}

(c) $E = (1/4\pi\varepsilon_o)Q/r^2$ so $3.0 \times 10^3 = 9 \times 10^9 \times 1.2 \times 10^{-9}/r^2$;
$r^2 = 3.6 \times 10^{-3}$ giving $r = 6 \times 10^{-2}$ m

(d) Field line sketch must have a minimum of five lines symmetrical about line joining centres with arrows; Figure 6 sketch matches RHS of Figure 7 or argue that plate in Figure 6 is analogous to mirror with other sphere being mirror image

5 (a) Positive as E-field is downwards or top plate is positive and like charges repel

(b) (i) k.e. = $QV = 300 \times 1.6 \times 10^{-19} = 4.80 \times 10^{-17}$ J

(ii) $\frac{1}{2}mv^2 = 4.8 \times 10^{-17} = 0.5 \times 2.3 \times 10^{-26} \times v^2$ giving $v = 6.46 \times 10^4$ m s^{-1}

(c) $d = V/E = 600/4 \times 10^4 = 0.015$ m

(d) (i) Semicircle to right of hole

(ii) mv^2/r; $= BQv$ giving $r = mv/BQ = 2.3 \times 10^{-26} \times 6.5 \times 10^4/(0.17 \times 1.6 \times 10^{-19}) = 55$ mm so distance = $2r = 0.11$ m

6 (a) (i) Equally spaced horizontal parallel lines from plate to plate with arrows towards cathode

(ii) $\frac{1}{2}mv^2 = qV$; $v = \sqrt{(2eV/m)} = \sqrt{(2 \times 1.6 \times 10^{-19} \times 7000/9.1 \times 10^{-31})}$ so $v = 4.96 \times 10^7$ m s^{-1}

(b) (i) Perpendicular to path towards centre of arc

(ii) out of paper, decided using Fleming's LH rule for conventional current

(iii) $mv^2/r = Bqv$ so $r = mv/Bq = 9.1 \times 10^{-31} \times 4.96 \times 10^7/(3.0 \times 10^{-3} \times 1.6 \times 10^{-19}) = 9.4 \times 10^{-2}$ m

(c) change magnitude of current in coils to change field; change field to change deflection; reverse field, i.e. current, to change deflection from up to down.

2.1 Electric and magnetic fields – 2

1 (a) (i) Arrow through P towards centre of circle

(ii) Fleming's LHR for conventional current, i.e. positive charge movement

(iii) force of constant magnitude on moving charge or ion caused by perpendicular *B*-field; direction perpendicular to path at all times, i.e. towards centre of circle

(b) Larger semicircle, i.e. less curvature as force same but mass larger so less acceleration (Newton's 2nd law)

(c) (i) $F = BQv = 0.60 \times 1.6 \times 10^{-19} \times 3.0 \times 10^5 = 2.9 \times 10^{-14}$ N

(ii) use $F = mv^2/r$ to give $r = 0.125$ m

2 (a) (i) Flux = $B \times A$ (normal to B) with symbols explained

(ii) Linkage = $N \times$ flux; $A = x^2$ so linkage = NBx^2

(b) (i) Statement of Faraday's law or indication e.g. $V = \mathrm{d}(NBx^2)/\mathrm{d}t$ from **a(ii)**; $V = NBx\mathrm{d}x/\mathrm{d}t$ or $V = NBxv$ or argue area swept out per second is xv giving $V = 1250 \times 0.032 \times 0.02 \times 0.1 = 0.08$ V or 80 mV

(ii) equal positive and negative regions; equal positive and negative values of 'maxima' on *y*-axis; value changes at times, t = 0.2, 0.4, 0.6, 0.8 s; 'square pulse' shape

3 (a) (i) F is towards 'open' end of tube; using Fleming's LH rule

(ii) $F = BIw$

(iii) $F = 0.15 \times 800 \times 0.0025 = 3.0$ N

(b) (i) A voltage is induced across moving metal as it cuts lines of flux; voltage is proportional to flux change per second; the flux change per second is Bwv, that is, it is proportional to the area of metal moving through the field per second or is proportional to v

(ii) flux (linkage) doubles, so using Faraday's law, V doubles

4 (a) (i) $E = V/d = 325/1.25 = 260$ V m^{-1}

(ii) atomic electrons are removed from atoms because electrons and nuclei are forced apart by the field as they have opposite charges; free electrons are accelerated by the field and collide with atoms, ionising them and producing more free electrons

(b) (i) Take gradient at 0, 10 ms or 20 ms to give 250 V

(ii) the voltage is a cosine curve with zero at 5, 15, 25 ms, i.e. 90° out of phase

(c) The changing flux in the iron induces an opposing e.m.f. which reduces the p.d. across the tube, effectively putting an extra 'resistance' in the circuit.

2.2 Capacitors and exponential decay

1 (a) (i) $E = V/d = 2000/4 \times 10^{-3} = 5 \times 10^5$ N C^{-1}/V m^{-1}

(ii) $Q = CV$;$= 200 \times 10^{-12} \times 2000 = 4 \times 10^{-7} = 0.40$ μC

(iii) $W = \frac{1}{2}CV^2 = \frac{1}{2}QV = 0.5 \times 200 \times 10^{-12} \times 4 \times 10^6 = 400$ μJ

(b) (i) 4000 V

(ii) 100 pF

(iii) 800 μJ

(c) The mechanism pulling the plates apart/force working against attraction between charged plates/opposite charges/work done in separating plates.

2 (a) (i) $C = Q/V$ or gradient of graph = 24 μC/3V = 8.0 μF

(ii) $E = \frac{1}{2}CV^2 = \frac{1}{2} \times 8 \times 3^2 = 36$ μJ or $\frac{1}{2}QV = \frac{1}{2} \times 24 \times 3 = 36$ μJ

(iii) $T = RC = 0.04$; $C = 0.04/8.0\mu = 5.0 \times 10^3\ \Omega$

(iv) Idea of exponential/constant ratio in equal times, which is independent of initial value, or can be argued mathematically in terms of $Q/Q_0 = e^{-t/RC}$

(b) (i) $C_p = C + C = 6$ μF; $1/C_s = 1/2C + 1/C = 3/2C$ giving $C_s = 2C/3 = 2$ μF

(ii) 2 sets of (3 in series) in parallel or 3 sets of (2 in parallel) in series

3 (a) (i) 5.0 V

(ii) 10.0 V

(b) (i) $Q = CV = 1.0 \times 10^{-3}$ C

(ii) The total capacitance of each circuit is the same (namely 100 μF) because capacitors in series add as reciprocals; in parallel add; supply voltage is the same and $Q = VC$, etc.

(c) (i) A1 will give the same reading as A2 because the two ammeters are connected in series.

(ii) A4 will show the same reading as A2 at all times; A3 will show half the reading of A2 initially and at all subsequent times.

4 (a) $C = Q/V$ with symbols explained or charge per unit potential difference.

(b) (i) **1** $Q = CV = 4.7 \times 10^{-7} \times 11 = 5.2 \times 10^{-6}$ C or 5.2 μC

2 $E = ½ QV$ or $½ CV^2 = 2\ 84 \times 10^{-5}$ J or 28.4 μJ

(ii) **1** $V = IR$; $I = 11/2200 = 5$ mA or 0.005 A

2 $T = RC = 2200 \times 4.7 \times 10^{-7} = 1.0 \times 10^{-3}$ s

(c) (i) Show constant ratio for equal time intervals or log linear graph is a straight line.

(ii) $\Delta Q = I \times \Delta t$; estimate area under graph between $t = 1$ ms and $t = 2$ ms; $\Delta Q = 1.20 \pm 0.1 \times 10^{-6}$ C; or can use $Q = Q_0 e^{-t/RC}$.

5 (a) (i) Electrons/negative charge are/is moved from upper plate of C to lower plate by the action of the battery, or equivalent statement in terms of conventional positive charges

(ii) $Q = CV = 500 \times 12 = 6000$ μC

(b) (i) Initial current = 6 mA; $R = V/I = 2$ k or 2×10^3 Ω or use $RC = 1.0$ s

(ii) $RC = 1.0$ s

(iii) $I = 6\ (\times 10^{-3})e^{-t}$

(iv) Area under curve is the integral of current against time/sum of $I \times \Delta t$ at all t; charge = current × time

(v) Initial current = 12 mA; curve with time constant = 0.5 s.

2.3 Nuclear physics – 1

1 (a) (i) repulsive; (ii) attractive; (iii) attractive

(b) (i) 360 N; (ii) 2.9×10^{-34} N

(c) Gravitational force is about 10^{-36} times smaller than the electrostatic force.

(d) For protons equilibrium at separation greater than x_0; strong force must be attractive to balance repulsive electrostatic force; only a small change in separation is needed to produce 360 N, so equilibrium separation still close to x_0.

2 (a) Strange, charm, top and bottom

(b) (i) Leptons;

(ii) neutrino, muon, tau(on);

(iii) **1** ${}^{14}_{6}C \rightarrow {}^{14}_{7}N + {}^{0}_{-1}e + \bar{\nu}$; **2** ${}^{14}_{8}O \rightarrow {}^{14}_{7}N + {}^{0}_{1}e + \nu$;

(iv) **1** anti-neutrino; **2** neutrino

(c) (i) udd;

(ii) u: Q ⅔, B ⅓, S 0; d: Q –⅓, B ⅓, S 0;

(iii) n: Q 0, B 1, S 0.

(d) not possible; expressing both sides of equation in quarks: u's balance, d's do not nor do s's; looking at Q, B and S: Q and B balance but S does not.

3 (a) (i) α: +2e, $4m_p$; (ii) β: –e, m_e; (iii) γ: 0, 0

(b) (i) 36 mm

(ii) $E = ½ mv^2 = 5 \times 1.6 \times 10^{-13}$
$= 0.5 \times 4 \times 1.67 \times 10^{-27} \times v^2$
so $v = 1.53 \times 10^7$ m s^{-1}

(iii) collision with air molecules; alpha particles ionise air; collision is inelastic mechanism for energy transfer during collision

(c) α radiation cannot penetrate air or paper or plastic, so the film is not exposed to α radiation
β will penetrate thin plastic, i.e. window;
γ radiation is much more penetrating than β; only γ passes through the metal, thicker and denser filters. Different thicknesses of plastic for β filter and metal for γ filter will discriminate strength.

4 (a) 39; number of protons in Y-90 nucleus. 81; number of neutrons in the Ba-137 nucleus

(b) (i) The number of nuclei which decay per second or number of nuclear decays per second

(ii) $0.693/(30 \times 3.15 \times 10^7) = 7.3(3) \times 10^{-10}$ s^{-1}

(c) (i) $A = \lambda N = 7.33 \times 10^{-10} \times 3.525 \times 10^{15}$
$= 2.58 \times 10^6$ Bq or 2.60 MBq
or can take the gradient of the tangent to the curve at (15, 3.525)

(ii) e.g. take N at $t = 15$ y then $N = N_0 \sqrt{2}$ giving $3.525 \times 10^{15} = 0.707\ N_0$ hence $N_0 = 4.99 \times 10^{15}$ or use $N = N_0 e^{-\lambda t}$ with appropriate substitution for N and t

(iii) $N = (m/M)N_A$ giving
$4.99 \times 10^{15} = (m/137) \times 6.02 \times 10^{23}$ hence
$m = 1.14 \times 10^{-6}$ g

5 (a) (i) 94; (ii) 142; (iii) 235

(b) Binding energy per nucleon values in MeV from graph are U: 7.4, Rb: 8.6, Cs: 8.4, so total binding energy in MeV for U: 1739, Rb: 808, Cs: 1193, giving total energy release as 262 MeV.

(c) (i) Graph shows two symmetrical peaks with smooth trough between; relative yield zero at nucleon numbers of about 80 and 160; trough at 0.01% (approx. zero) at 120; maximum yield at about 6%
(ii) Rb and Cs marked on graph close to each peak

2.3 Nuclear physics – 2

1 (a) (i) Number of nuclei decaying per second in the source; count rate without source present
(ii) distance of detector from source or dimensions of source or detector window or efficiency of detector or rate of emission v. detection, e.g. dead time correction; and effect on count rate for chosen suggestion
(b) (i) Take lns of both sides and appreciate that $\ln e^{-\lambda t} = -\lambda t$ and $\ln C/C_o = \ln C - \ln C_o$
(ii) gradient = 0.056 h^{-1}; $T = \ln 2/\lambda$ = $\ln 2$/gradient = $\ln 2/0.056$ h; T = 12.4 h
(c) Mass change; charge change; range; speed of emission; monoenergetic v. range of speeds; alpha emitted from only high-mass nuclei; number of particles involved in the decay

2 (a) (i) p, 94; n, 145
(ii) p, 92; n, 143
(b) $\lambda = 0.693/T = 0.693/24000 \times 3.2 \times 10^7 = 9 \times 10^{-13}\ s^{-1}$
(c) (i) $n = P/\varepsilon$; $=2.5/8.2 \times 10^{-13} = 3.0(48) \times 10^{12}$
(ii) $A = \lambda N$; giving $N = 3 \times 10^{12}/9 \times 10^{-13} = 3.3 \times 10^{24}$
(iii) $m = (N/N_A).M = (3.3 \times 10^{24}/6.02 \times 10^{23}) \times 0.239$; $= 1.3(4)$ kg
or $m = AuN = 239 \times 1.66 \times 10^{-27} \times 3.3 \times 10^{24}$
(d) Advantage: higher energy per particle or shorter half-life so smaller mass required; disadvantage: power does not remain 'constant' for long period; safety alternatives: short half-life means fewer disposal or storage problems; higher energy per particle needs more shielding

3 (a) (i) In units of 10^{10} 2.0, 1.0, 0.5, 0.25;
(b) (ii) $(65/600) \times 2.5 \times 10^{10} = 2.7 \times 10^{10}$
(iii) 3000 years
(c) (i) No living organism, no calibration, no carbon
(ii) low count rate, no carbon-14
(iii) too little difference in count rate

4 (a) Alphas have nucleon number of 4 and proton number of 2 so 8 alphas are needed to balance nucleon number or 5 alphas are needed to balance proton number, i.e. one equation number can be balanced, but not both together using the same number of alpha decays.
(b) Number of lead-206 nuclei increases; the rate of increase slows down as uranium-238 decreases; number of lead-206 equals the number of uranium-238 after one half-life and is three times the number of uranium-238 after two half-lives because uranium-238 has halved twice
(c) (i) Curve starts at 0,0; curves exponentially up to pass through 5,1 and 10,3.
(ii) number of lead-206 = $N_0 - N$; number of uranium-238 = $N = N_0 e^{-\lambda t}$; substitute into equation for R and simplify
(iii) $\ln(R + 1) = \lambda t$ so $t = \ln(1.81)/4.8 \times 10^{-18}$ $= 1.2 \times 10^{17}$ s

5 (a) (i) Mixture of free ions and electrons, i.e. charged matter in a state of dynamic equilibrium;
(ii) at high enough temperature for electrons to have enough energy to be free and not recombine with ions.
(b) (i) Nuclei have enough energy to overcome their mutual repulsion, i.e. the Coulomb barrier;
(ii) high enough density or pressure so that the nuclei are closer together increasing the probability of nuclei combining.
(c) (i) Because carbon is regenerated at the end
(ii) $4\,^1_1H \rightarrow \,^4_2He + 2\,^0_1e + 2\,^0_0\nu$
(iii) energy release = $4 \times 7.1 \times 10^6 \times 1.6 \times 10^{-19}$ $= 4.5 \times 10^{-12}$ J;
binding energy involves ^4_2He being fused of protons and neutrons; protons have initial k.e. so energy release is greater; electrons or positrons are generated using some mass-energy
(d) Total power = $4.5 \times 10^{-12} \times 8 \times 10^{37} = 3.6 \times 10^{26}$ W

2.4 Medical imaging

1 (a) Main attenuation process with diagnostic X-rays is p.e. effect, which depends strongly on proton number (proportional to Z^3); hence differential absorption
(b) (i) Fluorescent crystals in screen absorb X-rays; energy re-emitted as visible light onto film; film more sensitive to light than X-rays so greater blackening;
(ii) much lower dose required than without.
(c) (i) Where tissues have similar *Z*, there is little difference in X-ray absorption; contrast media are used to enhance difference.
(ii) use of for example barium in digestive tract with higher *Z* than surrounding tissue will absorb X-rays more than tissue and provide density variation (i.e. contrast) on film.

2 (a) Energy absorbed by the volume of tissue.

(b) Bone has a higher proton number compared to soft tissue, so bone has a higher attenuation, that is, absorbs more.

(c) Values of first three cells (in a row) calculated as 20,10,10
values of last three cells (in a row) calculated as 10,20,20
values of middle cells calculated as 20,20,10, so cell Y is made up of soft tissue.

3 (a) (i) 1.64×10^{-13} J;
(ii) each ray has energy 8.2×10^{-14} J, that is 0.51 MeV

(b) 1.2×10^{20} Hz

(c) For a path difference of 0.30 m then time difference is 0.5×10^{-9} s and conclusion could be dubious; can only resolve to nearest 7 cm.

4 (a) Piezoelectric crystal deforms when a p.d. is applied across it; crystal oscillates when an alternating p.d. is applied; if this frequency matches the resonance frequency of the crystal, ultrasound is generated. Ultrasound in turn causes crystal to resonate; causing alternating voltage across it. Pulsing is needed as reflected signal needs to be compared to initial signal. With a continuous a.c. signal, comparison is not possible. Backing material damps the crystal vibration after a.c. pulse ends so that the crystal is ready to receive the reflected signal.

(b) (i) 7.0×10^{-6} s; (ii) 0.0112 m;
(iii) 5.6×10^{-3} m; (iv) 7.7×10^{-3} m

(c) e.g. monitoring fetal growth, as ultrasound is not ionising but X-rays are.

5 (a) It is non-invasive; no damage at low energy levels to tissue; rapid result achieved; differences in acoustic impedances between tissues allows echoes to be produced at interfaces.

(b) Echoes give indication of depth of reflecting object; echo is not received when the interface is not perpendicular to the incident sound beam; echo can be confused from a moving object; interpretation difficulties

(c) 2D B-scan: transducer moves across body and rocks so body viewed from many points; composite image built up to give 2D cross-section. Brightness indicates measure of echo strength. Chance of finding perpendicular surface increased so object not missed unlike A-scan; brightness of image indicates size of image since echoes are from many points.
Real-time B-scan: uses array of transducers operated rapidly in succession; picture of each scan appears on screen; each individual picture of poor quality but sequence improves overall quality. Surface still needs to be perpendicular to the beam but movement shown in sequence of pictures; brightness and multiple reflections indicate size of object.

(d) Resolution (measures smallest detail) depends on λ and so is better as λ decreases; hence best resolution at high frequencies.
Attenuation (energy loss) by scattering or absorption of sound by molecules as beam passes through tissue increases as frequency rises; hence better penetration at low frequencies – so must compromise and choose frequency to match requirement of particular application.

2.5 Modelling the universe

1 (a) A is going away and B is coming towards Earth, Doppler shift

(b) (i) 7.5×10^4 s, 20.9 h;
(ii) $F = mv^2/r = 3750$ N;
(iii) $GMm/r^2 = 3750$ giving $M = 6 \times 10^{26}$ kg

(c) Rearrange $mv^2/r = GMm/r^2$ to $v^2 = GM/r$

(d) Velocity is proportional to $r^{-0.5}$ so $4 \times r$ decreases v by a factor of $4^{0.5} = 2$.

2 (a) (i) GM/r^2; (iii) 1.1×10^9 N kg^{-1}
(b) (i) 3.1×10^6 m s^{-1}; (ii) 9.6×10^8 m s^{-2}

(c) To keep a particle on the surface, the magnitude of the field strength must equal or exceed the magnitude of the centripetal acceleration. This is the case for the star considered.

3 (a) Collapse under gravity with gravitational potential energy becoming kinetic energy; increasing random kinetic energy means increasing temperature until fusion reactions can start, i.e. protons with sufficient random k.e. to overcome Coulomb repulsion.

(b) (i) Primordial He formed in big bang;
(ii) first stars would have contained virtually no elements heavier than He; also, solar He abundance is greater than primordial.

4 (a) Newtonian gravity; spherical universe; uniform density

(b) $\rho_0 = 4.58 \times 10^{-27}$ kg m^{-3} = 2.7 H atoms m^{-3}

(c) Open: $\rho < \rho_0$ will continue to expand forever;
flat: $\rho = \rho_0$ will just continue to expand forever;
closed: $\rho > \rho_0$ will expand and then contract back to a big crunch.

5 (a) 6.3×10^{14} J

(b) 6.2×10^{11} kg s^{-1}

(c) (i) 3.2×10^{17} s = 1×10^{10} y
(ii) e.g. Sun is 100% H at start of main sequence lifetime; has a constant power output; constant temperature

6 (a) Corresponds to $T = 3$ K; blackbody spectrum; uniform or isotropic; shows ripples.
(b) Early universe very hot; matter and radiation in equilibrium; atoms form, matter and radiation decoupled, universe becomes transparent; radiation has stretched with the universe
(c) (i) Homogeneous: the same everywhere, uniform; isotropic: looks the same in every direction;
(ii) cosmic microwave background radiation is highly uniform, so the universe must be uniform too.

7 (a) Infinite universe; each line of sight ends on a star (or can argue in terms of shells); so sky bright at night. Big bang model: finite universe expanding, causing radiation from distant stars to be redshifted.
(b) (i) 70 km s^{-1} Mpc^{-1} = 2.3×10^{-18} s^{-1}
(ii) 4.3×10^{17} s
(iii) rate of expansion is non-uniform because of gravity

8 (b) Relative motion between source and observer, i.e. Doppler effect
(c) $v = (\Delta\lambda/\lambda)c = 2.3 \pm 0.1 \times 10^5$ m s^{-1}
(d) (i) period T from graph = 70 ± 3 hours, giving $T = 2.52 \times 10^5$ s
(ii) $v = 2\pi r/T$ gives $r = 9.2 \pm 0.4 \times 10^9$ m

Glossary

a.c. generator A generator that, via the use of slip rings, produces an alternating e.m.f. and so an alternating current.

absorption spectra A spectrum of dark lines across the pattern of spectral colours produced when light passes through a gas and the gas absorbs certain frequencies, depending on the elements in the gas.

acceleration (*a*) The rate of change of velocity, measured in metres per second squared (ms^{-2}), a vector quantity

acceleration of free fall (*g*) The acceleration of a body falling under gravity. On Earth it has the value of 9.81 m s^{-2}.

acoustic impedance (*Z*) The property of a material that determines the intensity of ultrasound refracted at a boundary with another material. As given by $Z = \rho c$, measured in kg m^{-2} s^{-1}.

activity (*A*) The number of radioactive decays per unit time. Measured in becquerels (Bq).

alpha particle A particle comprising 2 protons and 2 neutrons ejected from the nucleus during radioactive decay.

alternating current Electric current that reverses its direction with a constant frequency. For example the UK mains electricity supply is a.c. with a frequency of 50 Hz.

ammeter A device used to measure electric current, connected in series with the components.

amount of substance SI quantity, measured in moles (mol).

ampere SI unit for electric current, e.g. 4 A.

amplitude, oscillations (x_o) The maximum displacement from the rest or equilibrium position, measured in metres (m).

amplitude, waves (x_o) The maximum displacement of a wave from its mean (or rest) position, measured in metres (m).

angular momentum A property of an object that depends on its angular velocity.

annihilation The process when a particle and antiparticle interact and their combined mass is coverted to energy via $E = mc^2$.

antiparticle A particle of antimatter that has the same rest mass but, if charged, the equal and opposite charge to its corresponding particle. For example the positron is the antiparticle of the electron.

area (*A*) A physical quantity representing the size of a surface, measured in metres squared (m^2).

astronomical unit (AU) The average distance from the Earth to the Sun. 1 AU = 1.496×10^{11} m.

atom The smallest part of a specific element. It comprises protons, neutrons in the nucleus orbited by electrons.

attenuation coefficient (μ) A constant used to calculate the intensity of X-rays as they pass through a material. $I = I_o e^{-\mu x}$.

average speed A measure of the total distance travelled in a unit time.

Avogadro constant (N_A) A constant giving the number of particles in 1 mol of a substance. $N_A = 6.022 \times 10^{23}$ mol^{-1}.

back e.m.f. *see* induced e.m.f.

baryon A particle consisting of three quarks (e.g. a proton or neutron).

baryon number A property of baryons and quarks that is conserved in particle interactions.

becquerel Unit of activity, e.g. 10,000 Bq. 1 Bq is 1 radioactive decay per second.

beta decay The radioactive decay that causes emission of a beta particle and an antineutrino from the nucleus when a neutron breaks down into a proton under the influence of the weak nuclear force.

beta particle A high-speed electron emitted from the nucleus during beta decay.

big bang theory The theory that the universe was created out of nothing from a single point. The universe was once much smaller, hotter and denser. It expanded from this state into the universe we see today.

binary stars Two stars in orbit around their common centre of gravity.

binding energy The energy required to separate an atom into its component parts.

binding energy per nucleon The average energy required to remove a nucleon from the nucleus.

black hole The remains of the core of a very large star after it has gone supernova. It has an infinite density and a gravitational field strength so great that even light cannot escape.

Boltzmann constant (*k*) A constant used when dealing with gases relating the temperature of the gas to the average kinetic energy of the particles in the gas. It can be thought of as the gas constant for a single molecule. $k = 1.3807 \times 10^{-23}$ J K^{-1}.

bottom Type of quark.

Boyle's law The volume of a fixed mass of gas is inversely proportional to pressure exerted on it, provided temperature remains constant.

Brownian motion The random movement of small particles (e.g. pollen or smoke particles) when suspended in a liquid or gas.

capacitance (*C*) The charge stored per unit potential difference, as given by $C = Q/V$. Measured in farads (F).

capacitor An electrical component designed to store charge.

capacitor discharge Connecting a charged capacitor across a resistor and so enabling the charge to flow from one plate to another. The charge remaining decays exponentially, $Q = Q_o e^{-t/CR}$.

Celsius *see* degree Celsius.

centre of gravity The point at which the entire weight of an object can be considered to act.

centre of mass *see* centre of gravity (N.B. although there is a technical difference it is not required at this level).

centripetal acceleration (*a*) The acceleration of a body moving in a circle with constant speed acting towards the centre of the circle. Given by $a = v^2/r$, measured in ms^{-2}.

centripetal force The resultant force on an object, acting towards the centre of the circle causing it to move in a circular path. Given by $F = mv^2/r$, measured in N.

chain reaction One reaction causing another, which causes another, etc. For example a nuclear chain reaction in a nuclear reactor or nuclear weapon.

charge *see* electric charge.

charm Type of quark.

circular motion When an object travels along a circular path, either in a complete circle or as part of a curve with constant radius.

closed universe The situation if the mean density of the universe is greater than the critical density. The universe will collapse back into a single point ('big crunch').

cloud chamber A device used to detect a charged particle by the formation of small clouds along trails of ions.

collimation Focussing an electromagnetic wave (e.g. X-rays) to provide a parallel beam.

comet A body comprising mainly ice and rock in orbit around a star. These orbits are usually highly elliptical.

components of a vector The results from resolving a single vector into horizontal and vertical parts.

Compton effect The effect whereby X-rays deflected off particles have a longer wavelength than their initial wavelength.

computerised axial tomography (CAT) A process using X-rays in 3D and computers in order to produce an image of a slice through the body.

conductor A material with a high number density of conduction electrons and therefore a low resistance.

conservation of charge Physical law stating charge is conserved in all interactions; it cannot be created or destroyed.

conservation of energy Physical law stating energy cannot be created or destroyed, just transformed from one form into another or transferred from one place to another. This is the situation in any closed system.

conservation of momentum Physical law stating that in the absence of external forces the total momentum of a system remains constant.

conventional current A model used to describe the movement of charge in circuit. Conventional current travels from + to − .

cosmological principle On a large scale the universe is uniform (i.e. the universe is the same in all directions and of uniform density, provided a large enough volume is considered).

coulomb Unit of electric charge (C), e.g. 1.6×10^{-19} C. 1 C = 1 A × 1 s.

Coulomb's law The force between two charges is proportional to the product of the charges and inversely proportional to the square of the distance between the charges.

couple Two forces acting on an object that are equal and opposite to each other but not in the same straight line.

critical damping The damping of an oscillating system when the forces cause the system to return to the equilibrium position without oscillating (e.g. a pendulum through thick treacle).

critical density of the universe (ρ_c) The average density of the universe above which the universe will collapse (closed universe) and below which the universe will expand forever (open universe). $\rho_c = 9.5 \times 10^{-27}$ kg m^{-3}.

current *see* electric current.

damped oscillations Oscillations in which the kinetic energy is converted into other forms and so the amplitude of the oscillation reduces.

de Broglie equation An equation expressing the wavelength of a particle as a ratio of Planck's constant and the particle's momentum, *mv*.

decay constant (λ) The probability of radioactive decay. Given by $\lambda = A/N$, measured in s^{-1}.

degree Celsius Unit for temperature, e.g. 100 °C (not the SI unit; see kelvin).

density (ρ) The mass per unit volume, measured in kilograms per cubic metre (kg m^{-3}). A scalar quantity.

diffraction Spreading of a wave after it passes around an obstacle or through a gap.

displacement (*s* or *x*) The distance travelled in a particular direction, measured in metres (m), e.g. 3 m. A vector quantity.

displacement, s.h.m. The displacement of a body

undergoing s.h.m from the rest or equilibrium position. Given by $x = x_o \sin(2\pi ft)$ or $x = x_o \sin(2\pi ft)$. Measured in metres (m).

displacement–time graph A motion graph showing displacement against time for a given body.

distance (*d*) How far one position is from another, measured in metres (m), e.g. 12 m. A scalar quantity.

Doppler effect The change in wavelength caused by the relative motion between the wave source and an observer.

down Type of quark.

driving force A force applied at regular intervals in order to keep an object oscillating.

driving frequency The frequency of the driving force applied to an oscillating object.

dynamo A device that converts kinetic energy into electrical energy.

efficiency The ratio of useful output energy to total input energy.

Einstein's mass/energy equation Equation linking energy, mass and the speed of light in a vacuum. $E = mc^2$.

elastic collision (perfectly) In a perfectly elastic collision kinetic energy and momentum are conserved.

elastic potential energy The energy stored in a stretched or compressed object (for example a spring), measured in joules (J), a scalar quantity.

electric charge (*Q* or *q*) = current × time Measured in coulombs (C), a scalar quantity.

electric current (*I*) A flow of charge. A vector quantity, measured in amperes (A).

electric field A region of space where a charged particle experiences a force. It goes from + to – .

electric field strength (*E*) Force per unit positive charge, given by $E = F/q$, measured in $N\ C^{-1}$.

electromagnetic induction The process of inducing an e.m.f. using a magnetic field and a changing flux linkage.

electromagnetic wave A self-propagating transverse wave that does not require a medium to travel through.

electromotive force (e.m.f.) The electrical energy transferred per unit charge when one form of energy is converted into electrical energy, measured in volts (V).

electron Negatively charged sub-atomic particle with a charge of 1.6×10^{-19} C. Conduction electrons travel around circuits creating an electric current. A lepton.

electron diffraction The process of diffracting an electron through a gap (usually between atoms in a crystal structure, for example graphite). An example of wave–particle duality.

electron flow The movement of electrons (usually around a circuit), from – to +.

electronvolt One electronvolt is the energy change of an electron when it moves through a potential difference of one volt. Its value is 1.6×10^{-19} J.

emission spectrum A pattern of colours of light emitted by a substance with specific wavelengths.

endoscope A coated bundle of optic fibres inserted into the body to provide an image of the internal organs without the need for invasive surgery.

energy (*E*) The stored ability to do work, measured in joules (J). A scalar quantity.

energy levels One of the specific energies an electron can have when in an atom.

equations of motion The equations used to describe displacement, acceleration, initial velocity, final velocity and time when a body undergoes a constant acceleration.

equilibrium The state when zero resultant force acts on an object.

exponential A function that varies as the power of another quantity. For example if $y = a^x$, y varies exponentially with x.

exponential decay At any given time interval there is the same ratio of final value to starting value. For example capacitor discharge and radioactive decay.

farad Unit of capacitance (F). 1 F is 1 C of charge stored per volt.

Faraday's law The magnitude of the induced e.m.f. is equal to the rate of change of flux linkage.

field A region in which a force operates.

fission The process of splitting a large nucleus into two smaller nuclides, often with the emission of several neutrons. This releases energy because of the change in binding energy.

fission products The particles and energy released when a nucleus undergoes fission.

flat universe The situation if the mean density of the universe is equal to the critical density. The galaxies in the universe will slow down but never quite stop. This situation is very unlikely.

Fleming's left-hand rule Used with electric motors and forces acting on moving charges in magnetic fields. It shows the direction of the force on a conductor carrying a current in a magnetic field. Force – thumb, field – first finger, current – second finger, all at right angles to each other.

Fleming's right-hand rule Used with generators and electromagnetic induction. It shows the direction of the induced current when a conductor moves through a magnetic field. Force – thumb, field – first finger, current – second finger, all at right angles to each other.

force (*F*) A push or a pull on an object, measured in newtons (N); a vector quantity.

force constant (*k*) The constant of proportionality in Hooke's law, measured in newtons per metre (N m^{-1}).

forced oscillation When a driving force acts on an object in order to keep it oscillating.

free-body diagram A diagram containing only one body with the forces on that body labelled with arrows.

free fall When an object is accelerating under gravity (i.e. at 9.81 m s^{-2} on Earth).

free oscillations When an object oscillates without a driving force acting to keep it oscillating. Objects undergoing free oscillations vibrate at their natural frequency.

frequency (*f*) The number of oscillations per unit time, measured in hertz (Hz), e.g. 50 Hz.

fundamental particle A particle that cannot be broken down into smaller components (e.g. leptons).

fusion The process of two nuclei joining together and releasing energy from a change in binding energy.

***g*, acceleration of free fall** The acceleration of a body under gravity, 9.81 m s^{-2} on Earth.

galaxy A large collection of stars orbiting its own centre of gravity.

gamma camera A detector of gamma photons emitted from a patient given a radioactive tracer. This is used to produce a real-time image of the path of the tracer through the body.

gamma rays A form of electromagnetic wave with wavelengths between 10^{-16} m and 10^{-9} m. Used in cancer treatment. Emitted from the nucleus during radioactive decay.

Geiger tube A device used to measure radioactive decay by ionisation of the gas inside the tube.

geostationary orbit An orbit of the Earth made by a satellite that has the same time period as the rotation of the Earth (i.e. 24 hours) and is in the equatorial plane.

gradient of a graph The change in *y*-axis over the change in the *x*-axis (rise over step).

gravitational constant (*G*) Constant of proportionality used in Newton's law of gravitation. $G = 6.673 \times 10^{-11}$ m^3 kg^{-1} s^{-2}.

gravitational field A region in which a gravitational force acts on mass.

gravitational field strength (*g*) The gravitational field strength at any point is the force acting per unit mass at that point. Measured in N kg^{-1}. On the surface of the Earth $g = 9.81$ N kg^{-1}.

gravitational force The force due to a gravitational field acting on an object's mass.

gravitational potential energy The energy stored in an object (the work an object can do) by virtue of the object being in a gravitational field. Measured in joules (J); a scalar quantity.

hadron A particle consisting of quarks (i.e. baryons and mesons).

half-life The average time taken for the activity of a radioactive source to decrease to one half of its original value.

half-value thickness The distance in a medium over which X-ray intensity is attenuated to half its original value.

harmonics Whole-number multiples of the fundamental frequency of a stationary wave.

heat capacity *see* specific heat capacity.

heavy damping The damping of an oscillating system by large forces (e.g. a pendulum through water).

homogeneous Of uniform density.

Hubble constant (*H_o*) The constant of proportionality used in Hubble's Law. $H_o = 2.3 \times 10^{-18}$ s^{-1}.

Hubble's law The speed of recession of a galaxy is directly proportional to its distance from the Earth.

ideal gas A gas that has internal energy only in the form of random kinetic energy.

ideal gas equation The equation linking pressure of a gas (*p*), volume of a gas (*V*), molar gas constant (*R*), number of moles of gas (*n*) and temperature (*T*). $pV = nRT$.

ideal gas temperature (*T*) Proportional to the volume of a fixed mass of an ideal gas at constant pressure. Measured in K.

impedance matching The process of matching up materials with similar acoustic impedances to allow good transmission of ultrasound through the materials. For example the use of gel with ultrasound scanning.

impulse The product of the force acting on a body and the time it is acting, given by $impulse = F\Delta t$. It can also be considered to be the change in momentum of a body. Measured in N s or kg m s^{-1}.

induced e.m.f. The e.m.f. produced by electromagnetic induction.

inelastic collision A collision where momentum is conserved but kinetic energy is not.

infrared A form of electromagnetic wave with wavelengths between 7.4×10^{-7} m and 10^{-3} m. Used in remote controls.

insulator A material with a small number density of conduction electrons and therefore a very high resistance.

intensity The energy incident per square metre of a surface per second, measured in watts per metre squared (W m^{-2}).

interference The addition of two or more waves (superposition) that results in a new wave pattern.

internal energy The sum of all the kinetic and potential energies of molecules within a substance.

inverse square law A type of law that obeys $y \propto 1/x^2$. For example Newton's law of gravitation and Coulomb's law.

ion A particle that has a charge due to loss or gain of an electron.

ionisation The process of adding or removing an electron from an atom. NB ionisation by radioactive particles only ever involves removal of electrons.

isotopes Nuclides with the same number of protons but different numbers of neutrons.

isotropic The same in all directions.

joule Unit of energy (J), e.g. 1200 J. 1 J is the work done when a force of 1 N moves its point of application 1 m in the direction of the force.

kelvin SI unit of temperature (K), e.g. 373 K.

Kepler's third law The period of a planet orbiting the sun squared is proportional to the mean radius of its orbit cubed. $T^2 \propto r^3$.

kilowatt Unit of power (kW), e.g. 3.5 kW. 1 kW = 1000 W.

kilowatt-hour Unit of energy (kWh), e.g. 3 kWh. Used by electricity companies when charging for electricity. 1 kWh = 1000 W for 3600 s = 3.6 MJ.

kinetic energy The work an object can do by virtue of its speed, measured in joules (J). A scalar quantity.

kinetic model of a gas The model used to explain properties of gases (pressure, volume, etc.) in terms of the movement and interaction of gas particles.

Kirchhoff's first law The sum of the currents entering any junction is always equal to the sum of the currents leaving the junction (a form of conservation of charge).

Kirchhoff's second law The sum of the e.m.f.s is equal to the sum of the p.d.s in a closed loop (a form of conservation of energy).

Larmor frequency (f_L) The frequency of precession of a proton in a magnetic field. Given by $4.25 \times 10^{-7} \times B$.

latent heat of fusion *see* specific latent heat of fusion.

latent heat of vaporisation *see* specific latent heat of vaporisation.

Lenz's law The direction of any induced current is in a direction that opposes the flux change that causes it.

lepton A fundamental particle. For example an electron or a neutrino.

lepton number A property of leptons that is conserved in interactions.

light damping The damping of an oscillating system by small forces (e.g. a pendulum through air).

light year The distance light travels in a year through a vacuum. 1 ly = 9.461×10^{15} m.

line spectrum A spectrum produced by a material that contains only certain frequencies, owing to electron transitions between energy levels.

linear momentum (p) The product of an object's mass and velocity, given by $p = mv$. Measured in kg ms^{-1}; a vector quantity.

longitudinal wave A wave in which the oscillations are parallel to the direction of wave propagation, e.g. sound.

magnetic field A region of space where a magnetic pole experiences a force. It goes from N to S.

magnetic field strength An alternative name for magnetic flux density.

magnetic flux (ϕ) The product of magnetic flux density and the area at right angles to the flux. Given by $\phi = BA \cos \theta$, measured in weber (Wb).

magnetic flux density (B) A measure of the strength of the magnetic field as given by $B = F/ILsin\theta$. Measured in tesla (T).

magnetic flux linkage ($N\phi$) The product of the magnetic flux and the number of turns on the coil it passes through. Given by magnetic flux linkage = $N\phi$, often measured in weber turns.

magnetic moment A magnetic property caused by a charged particle spinning.

magnetic resonance imaging (MRI) The use of powerful magnetic fields and the spin of hydrogen atoms within the body to produce a detailed image of the internal organs.

main sequence star A star in the main phase of its life.

mass (m) SI quantity, measured in kilograms (kg), e.g. 70 kg. A scalar quantity.

mass spectrometer A device using magnetic fields to sort charged particles by their mass (often used in conjunction with a velocity selector).

mean density of the universe The average density of the universe.

meson A short-lived particle comprised of a quark and anti-quark pair.

meteorite A fragment of rock (or occasionally metal such as iron) that has entered the Earth's atmosphere from space and has landed on the ground.

microwaves A form of electromagnetic wave with

wavelengths between 10^{-4} m and 10^{-1} m. Used in mobile phones.

molar gas constant (*R*) A constant used when dealing with gases. $R = 8.31$ J mol^{-1} K^{-1}.

mole Amount of any substance containing 6.02×10^{23} particles.

molecular ordering A description of the arrangement of molecules within a substance.

molecular spacing A measure of the average separation between molecules in a substance.

molecule The smallest part of a specific chemical compound.

moment of a force The turning effect due to a single force, calculated from the force multiplied by the perpendicular distance from a given point, measured in newton metres (Nm), e.g. 4 Nm. A vector quantity.

momentum *see* linear momentum.

monochromatic light Light waves with a single frequency (or wavelength).

moon A body orbiting a planet.

natural frequency (f_n or f_o) The frequency of the free oscillations of a system (the natural frequency of a pendulum of certain length is the frequency at which the pendulum will swing once released).

nebulae A huge collection of mainly hydrogen gas forming a cloud-like structure in space.

neutrino A fundamental particle (lepton) with a very small mass and no charge.

neutron A component of a nucleus. It comprises 3 quarks (1 up and 2 down) and has no charge.

neutron star The remains of the core of a large star after it has undergone a supernova. It is incredibly dense and is composed mainly of neutrons. Also known as a pulsar.

nuclear reactor A device that enables the energy released in nuclear fission to convert water to steam to turn turbines.

nucleon A particle in the nucleus; a proton or neutron.

nucleon number The number of neutrons added to the number of protons inside a certain nucleus. An alternative name for mass number.

nucleus The centre of an atom containing protons and neutrons.

nuclide A nucleus with a particular number of protons and neutrons.

newton Unit of force (N), e.g. 4000 N. 1 N is the force which gives a mass of 1 kg an acceleration of 1 ms^{-2}.

Newton's first law One of Newton's three laws of motion. An object will remain at rest or continue travelling at a constant velocity unless acted upon by a force.

Newton's law of gravitation The gravitational force of attraction between two bodies is directly proportional to the product of their masses and inversely proportional to the square of the distance between their centres of mass.

Newton's second law One of Newton's three laws of motion. The rate of change of the momentum of an object is directly proportional to the resultant force acting upon it and the change in the momentum is in the same direction as the force. Often written as $F = \Delta p/\Delta t$.

Newton's third law One of Newton's three laws of motion. When body A exerts a force on body B, body B exerts an equal and opposite force on body A.

ohm Unit of resistance (Ω), e.g. 24 Ω. 1 Ω = 1 VA^{-1}.

Ohm's law The electric current through a conductor is proportional to the potential difference across it, provided physical conditions, such as temperature, remain constant.

Olbers' paradox A paradox dealing with the finite or infinite nature of the universe. With an infinite numbers of stars in an infinite universe, no matter what direction you look you will always see a star along your line of sight. Therefore the night sky will be as bright as the day sky.

open universe The situation if the mean density of the universe is less than the critical density. The universe will continue to expand.

pair production The process of creating a particle–antiparticle pair from a high-energy photon. For example X-ray → electron + positron.

parallel circuits A type of circuit where the components are connected in two or more branches and therefore providing more than one path for the electric current.

parsec A unit of distance originating from triangulation methods applied to space. 1 Pc = 3.086×10^{16} m.

period (*T*) The time taken for one complete pattern of oscillation, measured in seconds (s).

perpendicular At right angles (90° or π/2 rad) to.

phase difference, oscillations (ϕ) A measure of the relationship between the pattern of vibration at two points. Two points that have the same pattern of vibration are in phase (0 phase difference). Two points that have exactly the opposite pattern of vibration are out of phase (2π phase difference). Measured in rad.

phase difference, waves (ϕ) The difference by which one wave leads or lags behind an other. For example in phase waves are in step with each other. In waves that are completely out of phase one wave is half a wavelength in front of the other. Measured in radians (rad).

phase of a substance Indicates whether a substance is a solid, a liquid or a gas.

photoelectric effect The emission of electrons from the surface of material when electromagnetic radiation is incident on the surface.

photon A quantum of electromagnetic radiation. For example a photon of light is often described as a particle of light.

piezoelectric effect The change in volume of certain crystals when a p.d. is applied across them. Alternatively the production of an e.m.f. when certain crystals are placed under stress.

pion An example of a meson containing a quark and antiquark. Limited to up and down quarks.

Planck constant (*h*) Constant used in quantum physics; 6.63×10^{-34} Js.

planet A large, approximately spherical body, orbiting a star.

plasma A state in which protons and electrons are not bound to one another because the temperature is too high.

positron emission tomography The use of gamma photons produced when positrons annihilate with electrons inside the body to map out active areas within the body.

potential difference (p.d.) The electrical energy transferred per unit charge when electrical energy is converted into some other form of energy.

potential divider A type of circuit containing two components designed to divide up the p.d. in proportion to the resistances of the components.

potential energy A form of stored energy (see gravitational potential energy, elastic potential energy and spread 1.3.3).

potential gradient The rate at which the potential difference changes with distance. For a uniform electric field; E = potential gradient = V/d. Measured in V m^{-1}.

power (*P*) The rate of doing work, measured in watts (W), a scalar quantity.

precession The movement of a spinning object caused by the effect of a torque leading to a change in the direction of its axis of rotation.

pressure (*p*) Force per unit area, measured in pascals (Pa), e.g. 100 000 Pa. 1 Pa = 1 Nm^{-1}. A scalar quantity.

principle of moments For a body in rotational equilibrium the sum of the clockwise moments equals the sum of the anti-clockwise moments.

progressive wave A wave that travels from one place to another.

proton A component of a nucleus. It comprises 3 quarks (2 up and 1 down) and has a charge of 1.6×10^{-19} C.

proton number The number of protons inside a certain nucleus. Also known as the atomic number.

pulsar *see* neutron star.

pulse repetition frequency Number of ultrasound pulses per second in ultrasound imaging.

quantum A discrete, indivisible quantity.

quark A component of hadrons, possibly a fundamental particle. There are six types of quark; up, down, strange, charm, top and bottom.

quasar Very distant objects with a very large brightness. Possibly galaxies with black holes at their centre.

radian (rad) Unit of angle or phase difference (rad), e.g. 3π rad. One radian is the angle subtended at the center of a circle by an arc of circumference that is equal in length to the radius of the circle. $2\pi = 360°$.

radio waves A form of electromagnetic wave with wavelengths between 10^{-1} m $\rightarrow 10^{4}$ m. Used in telecommunications.

radioactive decay The breakdown of a radioactive nuclide causing the emission of an alpha particle, beta particle or gamma photon from the nucleus.

radioactivity The process of the decay of a radioactive nuclide.

random Radioactive decay is random. It is not possible to predict which radioactive nuclides will decay or when they will decay.

red giant A star in the later stages of its life that has nearly exhausted the hydrogen in its core. It therefore begins to fuse helium, cools and expands.

redshift The apparent increase in wavelength caused when luminous objects (e.g. stars) move away from the observer. An example of the Doppler effect.

resistance (*R*) A property of a component that regulates the electric current through it. Measured in ohms (Ω), e.g. 24 Ω.

resolution of vectors Splitting a vector into horizontal and vertical components (used to aid vector arithmetic).

resonance When the driving frequency is equal to the natural frequency of an oscillating system. This causes a dramatic increase in the amplitude of the oscillations.

resultant force The overall force when two or more forces are combined.

resultant velocity The overall velocity when combining two or more velocities.

scalar A physical property with magnitude (size) but not direction. For example, speed, distance, pressure, potential difference, etc.

scattering The deflection of charged particles off other charged particles (e.g. alpha particles and the nucleus of gold atoms).

series circuit A type of circuit where the components are connected end to end and therefore provide only one path for the electric current.

simple harmonic motion (S.H.M.) When the acceleration *a* of an object is proportional to its displacement *x* and the acceleration is in the opposite direction to the displacement. $a \propto -x$.

slow neutrons Neutrons that have been slowed by the use of a moderator in a nuclear reactor.

specific heat capacity The energy required to raise the temperature of 1 kg of a substance by 1 K. Measured in $J\ kg^{-1}\ K^{-1}$.

specific latent heat of fusion The energy required to change the state of 1 kg of a substance at its melting point from solid to liquid. Measured in $J\ kg^{-1}$.

specific latent heat of vaporisation The energy required to change the state of 1 kg of a substance at its boiling point from liquid to gas. Measured in $J\ kg^{-1}$.

spectral line A line relating to a specific frequency either missing from an absorption spectrum or present in an emission spectrum.

spectrum A series of waves with a range of frequencies; for example, visible spectrum and electromagnetic spectrum.

speed (s) The distance travelled per unit time, measured in metres per second ($m\ s^{-1}$), e.g. 12 $m\ s^{-1}$. A scalar quantity.

spin A property of a particle related to its angular momentum.

spontaneous Radioactive decay is spontaneous. Changing physical conditions (e.g. temperature or pressure) will not cause or prevent the decay of a radioactive nucleus.

standing wave An alternative name for a stationary wave.

star A large body in space emitting heat and light from nuclear fusion within its core.

state of a substance Indicates whether a substance is a solid, a liquid or a gas.

stationary wave A wave formed by the interference of two waves travelling in opposite directions.

strange Type of quark.

strangeness The property of some quarks that is conserved in the strong interaction but not in weak interactions.

strong interaction Interactions involving the strong nuclear force.

strong nuclear force The force between nucleons that holds the nucleus together. All particles that contain quarks can interact via the strong nuclear force.

Sun The name given to our nearest star.

supernova A huge explosion caused when a large star collapses in on itself.

superposition The principle that states that when two or more waves of the same type exist at the same place the resultant wave will be found by adding the displacements of each individual wave.

temperature (T or θ) SI quantity, measured in Kelvin (K), e.g. 273 K. Also measured in Celsius (°C).

tensile force Usually two equal and opposite forces acting on a wire in order to stretch it. When both forces have the value T, the tensile force is also T, not $2T$.

tesla Unit of magnetic flux density (T), e.g. 2 T. 1 T is the magnetic flux density that will produce a force of 1 N on 1 m of wire carrying a current of 1 A perpendicular to the direction of the magnetic field.

thermal equilibrium The condition whereby two objects are at the same temperature and so there is no net thermal energy transfer between them.

threshold frequency The lowest frequency of electromagnetic radiation that will result in the emission of photoelectrons from a specified metal surface.

thrust A type of force due to an engine.

time constant (*CR*) The time taken for the charge remaining on a capacitor to fall to 1/e of its original value. It can be found using the expression *CR*, measured in seconds (s).

time interval (*t*) SI quantity, measured in seconds (s), e.g. 60 s. A scalar quantity.

time period, circular motion (*T*) The time taken for one complete revolution, measured in seconds (s).

time period, wave (*T*) The time taken for one complete wave to pass a given point, measured in seconds (s).

top Type of quark.

torque The turning effect due to a couple, measured in newton metres (Nm).

tracer A radioactive nuclide either ingested by, or injected into, a patient that emits gamma photons to be detected by a gamma camera.

transducer A device that converts a non-electrical signal (e.g. sound) into an electrical signal. For example a microphone.

transformer efficiency The ratio of the energy input of a transformer to its energy output.

transformer, step-down A device that has a greater number of wire turns on the input side than the output side and so reduces the e.m.f. and increases the electric current on the output side.

transformer, step-up A device that has a greater number of wire turns on the output side than the input side and so increases the e.m.f. and reduces the electric current on the output side.

transmutation The change of a nuclide by changing the number of protons and/or neutrons.

transverse wave A wave where the oscillations are perpendicular to the direction of wave propagation, e.g. water waves, electromagnetic waves.

triangle of forces If three forces acting at a point can be represented by the sides of a triangle, the forces are in equilibrium.

turning forces One or more forces that if unbalanced will cause a rotation.

turns ratio The ratio of turns of wire on the input side to the output side of a transformer. This equals the ratio of the input e.m.f. to the output e.m.f.

ultrasound Sound waves above the audible range of human hearing (i.e. greater than 20 000 Hz).

ultraviolet A form of electromagnetic wave with wavelengths between 10^{-9} m and 3.7×10^{-7} m. Causes sun tanning.

unified atomic mass unit Unit of mass (u), equal to 1/12 the mass of an atom of the nuclide $^{12}_{6}C$.

universe All the space, matter and energy that exists (i.e. everything that physically exists).

up Type of quark.

vector A physical quantity that has both magnitude (size) and direction. For example, velocity, force, acceleration, electric current.

velocity (*v*) The displacement per unit time, measured in metres per second (m s^{-1}), e.g. 330 m s^{-1}. A vector quantity.

velocity selector A device using electric and magnetic fields to select a specific velocity of charged particles.

velocity–time graph A motion graph showing velocity against time for a given body.

volt Unit of potential difference and e.m.f. (V), e.g. 230 V. 1 V = 1 J C^{-1}.

voltmeter Device used to measure the p.d. across a component. It is connected in parallel across a component.

volume (*V*) A physical quantity representing how much 3D space an object occupies, measured in metres cubed (m^3).

watt Unit of power (*W*), e.g. 60 W. 1 W = 1 J s^{-1}.

wave A series of vibrations that transfer energy from one place to another.

wavelength (λ) The smallest distance between one point on a wave and the identical point on the next wave (e.g. the distance from one peak to the next peak), measured in metres (m).

wave–particle duality The theory that states all objects can exhibit both wave and particle properties.

weak interaction Interactions involving the weak nuclear force.

weak nuclear force The force that is responsible for beta decay. It occurs between leptons and during hadron decay.

weber Unit of magnetic flux (Wb), e.g. 4 Wb. 1 Wb is the flux when a magnetic flux density of 1 T passes through an area of 1 m^2 at right angles.

weight (*w*) The gravitational force on a body, measured in newtons.

white dwarf The end product of low mass stars when the outer layers have dispersed into space.

work (*W*) The product of force and the distance moved in the direction of the force; it can also be considered as the energy converted from one form into another, measured in joules (J). A scalar quantity.

work function energy (ϕ) The minimum energy required to release an electron from a material, measured in joules (J).

X-rays A form of electromagnetic wave with wavelengths between 10^{-12} m and 10^{-7} m. Used in X-ray photography.

Young's double slit An experiment to demonstrate the wave nature of light via superposition and interference.

Data sheets

The data, formulae and relationships relevant to each unit will be printed as an insert to the examination paper.

Data

Values are given to three significant figures, except where more are useful.

speed of light in a vacuum	c	3.00×10^{8} m s^{-1}
permittivity of free space	ε_0	8.85×10^{-12} C^2 N^{-1} m^{-2} (F m^{-1})
elementary charge	e	1.60×10^{-19} C
Planck constant	h	6.63×10^{-34} J s
gravitational constant	G	6.67×10^{-11} N m^2 kg^{-2}
Avogadro constant	N_A	6.02×10^{23} mol^{-1}
molar gas constant	R	8.31 J mol^{-1} K^{-1}
Boltzmann constant	k	1.38×10^{-23} J K^{-1}
electron rest mass	m_e	9.11×10^{-31} kg
proton rest mass	m_p	1.673×10^{-27} kg
neutron rest mass	m_n	1.675×10^{-27} kg
alpha particle rest mass	m_α	6.646×10^{-27} kg
acceleration of free fall	g	9.81 m s^{-2}

Conversion factors

unified atomic mass unit	1 u = 1.661×10^{-27} kg
electronvolt	1 eV = 1.60×10^{-19} J
	1 day = 8.64×10^{4} s
	1 year ≈ 3.16×10^{7} s
	1 light year ≈ 9.5×10^{15} m

Mathematical equations

arc length = $r\theta$
circumference of circle = $2\pi r$
area of circle = πr^2
curved surface area of cylinder = $2\pi rh$
volume of cylinder = $\pi r^2 h$
surface area of sphere = $4\pi r^2$
volume of sphere = $\frac{4}{3}\pi r^3$
Pythagoras' theorem: $a^2 = b^2 + c^2$
For small angle $\theta \Rightarrow \sin\theta \approx \tan\theta \approx \theta$ and $\cos\theta \approx 1$
$\lg(AB) = \lg(A) + \lg(B)$
$\lg\left(\frac{A}{B}\right) = \lg(A) - \lg(B)$
$\ln(x^n) = n\ln(x)$
$\ln(e^{kx}) = kx$

Formulae and relationships

Unit G481 – Mechanics

$F_x = F\cos\theta$
$F_y = F\sin\theta$
$a = \dfrac{\Delta v}{\Delta t}$
$v = u + at$
$s = \frac{1}{2}(u + v)t$
$s = ut + \frac{1}{2}at^2$
$s = vt - \frac{1}{2}at^2$
$v^2 = u^2 + 2as$
$F = ma$
$W = mg$
moment $= Fx$
torque $= Fd$
$\rho = M/V$
$p = F/A$
$W = Fx\cos\theta$
$E_k = \frac{1}{2}mv^2$
$E_p = mgh$
efficiency $= \dfrac{\text{useful energy output}}{\text{total energy input}} \times 100\%$
$F = kx$
$E = \frac{1}{2}Fx = \frac{1}{2}kx^2$
stress $= \dfrac{F}{A}$
strain $= \dfrac{x}{L}$
Young modulus $= \dfrac{\text{stress}}{\text{strain}}$

Unit G482 – Electrons, waves and photons

$\Delta Q = I\Delta t$
$I = Anev$
$W = VQ$
$V = IR$
$R = R_1 + R_2 + R_3 + \ldots$ in series
$\dfrac{1}{R} = \dfrac{1}{R_1} + \dfrac{1}{R_2} + \dfrac{1}{R_3} + \ldots$ in parallel
$R = \dfrac{\rho l}{A}$
$P = VI = I^2R = \dfrac{V^2}{R}$
$W = VIt$
e.m.f. $= V + Ir$

$V_{out} = \dfrac{R_2}{R_1 + R_2} \times V_{in}$
$v = f\lambda$
$\lambda = \dfrac{ax}{D}$
$d \sin \theta = n\lambda$
$E = hf = \dfrac{hc}{\lambda}$
$hf = \phi + KE_{max}$
$\lambda = \dfrac{h}{mv}$
$R = R_1 + R_2 + \ldots$
$1/R = 1/R_1 + 1/R_2 + \ldots$

Unit G484 – The Newtonian World

$F = \dfrac{\Delta p}{\Delta t}$
$v = \dfrac{2\pi r}{T}$
$a = \dfrac{v^2}{r}$
$F = \dfrac{mv^2}{r}$
$F = \dfrac{GMm}{r^2}$
$g = \dfrac{F}{m}$
$g = \dfrac{GM}{r^2}$
$T^2 = \left(\dfrac{4\pi^2}{GM}\right) r^3$
$f = \dfrac{1}{T}$
$\omega = \dfrac{2\pi}{T} = 2\pi f$
$a = -(2\pi f)^2 x$
$x = A \cos(2\pi ft)x$
$v_{max} = (2\pi f)A$
$E = mc\Delta\theta$
$pV = NkT$
$pV = nRT$
$E = \dfrac{3}{2} kT$

Unit G485 – Fields, Particles and Frontiers of Physics

$E = \frac{F}{Q}$
$F = \frac{Qq}{4\pi\varepsilon_0 r^2}$
$E = \frac{Q}{4\pi\varepsilon_0 r^2}$
$F = \frac{V}{d}$
$F = BIL \sin\theta$
$F = BQv$
$\phi = BA \cos\theta$
induced e.m.f. $= -$ rate of change of magnetic flux linkage
$\frac{V_s}{V_p} = \frac{n_s}{n_p}$
$Q = VC$
$W = \frac{1}{2}QV \quad W = \frac{1}{2}CV^2$
time constant $= CR$
$x = x_0 e^{-\frac{t}{CR}}$
$C = C_1 + C_2 + C_3$
$\frac{1}{C} = \frac{1}{C_1} + \frac{1}{C_2} + \frac{1}{C_3}$
$A = \lambda N$
$A = A_0 e^{-\lambda t}$
$N = N_0 e^{-\lambda t}$
$\lambda t_{1/2} = 0.693$
$\Delta E = \Delta mc^2$
$I = I_0 e^{-\mu x}$
$Z = \rho c$
$\frac{I_r}{I_0} = \frac{(Z_2 - Z_1)^2}{(Z_2 - Z_1)^2}$
$\frac{\Delta\lambda}{\lambda} \approx \frac{v}{c}$
age of universe $\approx \frac{1}{H_0}$
$\rho_0 = \frac{3H_0^2}{8_\pi G}$

Index

Your Exam Café CD-ROM

In the back of this book you will find an Exam Café CD-ROM. This CD contains advice on study skills, Interactive questions to test your learning, a link to our unique partnership with New Scientist, and many more useful features. Load it onto your computer to take a closer look.

Amongst the files on the CD are PDF files, for which you will need the Adobe Reader program, and editable Microsoft Word documents for you to alter and print off if you wish.

Minimum system requirements:

- Windows 2000, XP Pro or Vista
- Internet Explorer 6 or Firefox 2.0
- Flash Player 8 or higher plug-in
- Pentium III 900 MHz with 256 Mb RAM

To run your Exam Café CD, insert it into the CD drive of your computer. It should start automatically; if not, please go to My Computer (Computer on Vista), click on the CD drive and double-click on 'start.html'.

If you have difficulties running the CD, or if your copy is not there, please contact the helpdesk number given below.

Software support

For further software support between the hours of 8.30–5.00 (Mon-Fri), please contact:
Tel: 01865 888108
Fax: 01865 314091
Email: software.enquiries@pearson.com